SYSTEMS AND TRANSFORMS WITH APPLICATIONS IN OPTICS

McGRAW-HILL SERIES IN SYSTEMS SCIENCE

editorial consultants

A. V. Balakrishnan
George Dantzig
Lotfi Zadeh

Systems and Transforms with Applications in Optics

Athanasios Papoulis

Professor of Electrical Engineering
Polytechnic Institute of Brooklyn

McGraw-Hill Book Company

New York   St. Louis   San Francisco   Toronto   London   Sydney

SYSTEMS AND TRANSFORMS
WITH APPLICATIONS IN OPTICS

Library of Congress Catalog Card Number 68-25659

48457

1234567890MAMM7543210698

PREFACE

In recent years, a trend has been developing toward greater interaction between electrical engineering and optics. This is so not only because optical devices are used extensively in signal processing, storage, pattern recognition, and other areas, but also because the underlying theory is closely related to the theory of systems, transforms, and stochastic processes. In fact, whereas in system analysis the Fourier integral is an auxiliary concept, in diffraction theory it represents a physical quantity; whereas only a limited class of electrical signals need be treated as stochastic processes, optical waves are inherently random. The following list illustrates the striking parallels between these two disciplines.

Fresnel diffraction: output of a filter with quadratic phase
Fraunhofer field: Fourier transform
Lens: linear FM generator
Focal plane field: Fourier transform
Contrast improvement: filtering

Apodization: pulse shaping
Coherence: autocorrelation
Michelson interferometer: correlometer consisting of a delay line and an
   adder
Fabry-Perot interferometer: narrow-band filter

Motivated by such observations, I decided to develop a course in the
general area of systems and optics. In the early planning stages of the
course, two approaches seemed attractive: (1) descriptive coverage of a
large number of applications, or (2) extension of signal theory to two
dimensions and space coordinates followed by analytical discussion of
selected applications. As is apparent from this book, I chose the second
approach. This choice reflects my conviction that in education the
primary objective is not the exhaustive coverage of terminal topics but
rather the systematic analysis of all steps from first principles to repre-
sentative illustrations.

The material in this book is essentially self-contained. Part 1 deals
with the general theory of systems and transforms in one and two dimensions. The early notions of the one-dimensional case are covered only
lightly; greater emphasis is placed on more sophisticated concepts, some
of which are new. The two-dimensional case includes singularity functions, systems, Hankel transforms viewed as Fourier transforms, sampling
expansions, asymptotic expansions, and stochastic processes. Part 2 is
devoted to optical applications related to the material in Part 1. Diffraction theory is based entirely on Kirchhoff's formula, thin lenses are
interpreted as transparencies with quadratically varying phase, and the
study of coherence is an extension of the second-order theory of random
signals. To avoid any prerequisites from electromagnetic theory, I considered only the scalar theory of light. The required background from
the theory of stochastic processes is given in Chapter 8.

In exploring the relationship between systems and optics, I had the
following objectives in mind: To make available to our students an
important area and to present it in a language with which they are
familiar; to introduce into optics a point of view that simplifies and
unifies a number of apparently unrelated topics; and to point out certain
analogies that facilitate the transfer of knowledge from one field to the
other. As an interesting example of such analogies, I mention the pulse
compression technique used in radar. This rather recent idea is equivalent to the old principle of concentration of light by a lens.

I should like to emphasize that my aim here is not to formulate a
general mathematical theory but rather to develop certain analytical
techniques and to show their relevance in a large number of applications.
For this reason, I derive various results only formally, often ignoring

mathematical subtleties.   This is apparent in the sections on singularity functions and asymptotic expansions, and in the proofs of various theorems in Fourier analysis.

Most topics covered in the book have been treated elsewhere; however, the approach is distinctly different.   Related references are listed in the Bibliography and in several footnotes.   Any omissions are due to my ignorance.   The book "Principles of Optics" by Born and Wolf deserves special mention.

In the planning and execution of this project I enjoyed the complete understanding of the then department head (at the Polytechnic Institute of Brooklyn), Rudy Drenick.   It is my pleasure to express to him my appreciation.   I also thank my colleagues Leonard Bergstein and Lawrence Levey for their helpful suggestions and critical comments.

Athanasios Papoulis

CONTENTS

1
SYSTEMS AND TRANSFORMS IN DIFFRACTION THEORY

In Part 1 of this book we develop the basic concepts of systems and transforms in one variable, and we extend the investigation to two dimensions. In the selection of topics we were influenced by optical applications. The treatment is self-contained; however, the emphasis is placed not on detailed discussion of early concepts, but on an integrated development of a variety of applications, some of them new. Some familiarity with the elementary theory of one-dimensional systems and transforms is, therefore, desirable.

In the first chapter, we outline certain areas of optics in which the notions of systems, Fourier transforms, and stochastic signals are used extensively. Since this material is included mainly for motivation, most theorems are presented briefly, often without proof. All results of this chapter will be reestablished in Part 2.

1. FOURIER TRANSFORMS IN OPTICS

Consider a monochromatic plane wave

$$v^i(x,y,z,t) = f(x,y)e^{-j\omega(t-z/c)} \tag{1-1}$$

propagating in the z direction with velocity† **c**.   If an opaque screen with an aperture S is placed on the $z = 0$ plane (Fig. 1-1), then from geometric optics one would deduce that the space $z > 0$ is divided into a "visible" cylindrical region, where the field is given by (1-1), and a "dark" region, where the field is zero.   This notion of a beam of light is an approximation that is valid only near the aperture, and the object of diffraction theory is to determine more accurately the diffracted field

$$v(x,y,z,t) = g(x,y,z)e^{-j\omega t} \tag{1-2}$$

at large distances.‡   It can be shown that the field $g(x_0,y_0,z_0)$ at a point $P:(x_0,y_0,z_0)$ of the right space is given by

$$g(x_0,y_0,z_0) \simeq A \iint_S f(x,y)e^{jkr}\, dx\, dy \qquad k = \frac{\omega}{c} \tag{1-3}$$

where $f(x,y)$ is the function in (1-1) specifying the incident wave v^i, and

$$r = \sqrt{(x - x_0)^2 + (y - y_0)^2 + z_0{}^2} \tag{1-4}$$

is the distance from P to the point of integration $(x,y,0)$.   The coefficient A is a slowly varying function of the coordinates of P.   At the end of the

† The boldface letter **c** will be used to denote the velocity of light.
‡ A. Marechal and M. Françon, "Diffraction," Paris, 1960.

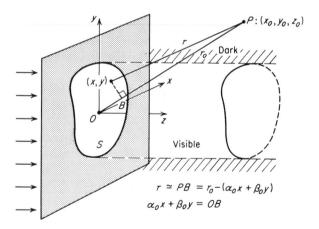

$$r \simeq PB = r_0 - (\alpha_0 x + \beta_0 y)$$
$$\alpha_0 x + \beta_0 y = OB$$

Fig. 1-1

section we trace briefly the steps from first principles to the approximate relationship (1-3).

FRAUNHOFER APPROXIMATION

With r_o the distance from the origin to the point P and

$$\alpha_o = \frac{x_o}{r_o} \qquad \beta_o = \frac{y_o}{r_o}$$

the directional cosines of the line OP, we see from Fig. 1-1 that if r_o is large compared with the dimensions of S [see (1-17)], then

$$r \simeq r_o - (\alpha_o x + \beta_o y) \tag{1-5}$$

and (1-3) yields

$$g(x_o, y_o, z_o) = A e^{jkr_o} \iint\limits_S f(x,y) e^{-jk(\alpha_o x + \beta_o y)} \, dx \, dy \tag{1-6}$$

This result can be expressed in terms of the two-dimensional Fourier transform

$$F(u,v) = \iint\limits_{-\infty}^{\infty} f(x,y) e^{-j(ux+vy)} \, dx \, dy \tag{1-7}$$

of the function $f(x,y)$. Since $f(x,y) = 0$ for (x,y) not in S, (1-6) takes the form

$$g(x_o, y_o, z_o) = A e^{jkr_o} F(k\alpha_o, k\beta_o) \tag{1-8}$$

Thus, on the surface of a sphere centered at the origin, the *amplitude*† of the diffraction field is proportional to the Fourier transform of the aperture function $f(x,y)$.

On the plane $z = z_o$ this is not the case because r_o is no longer constant. However, in a small-angle region $\alpha_o = x_o/r_o \simeq x_o/z_o$, $\beta_o = y_o/r_o \simeq y_o/z_o$, and

$$|g(x_o, y_o, z_o)| = \left| AF\left(\frac{kx_o}{z_o}, \frac{ky_o}{z_o}\right) \right| \tag{1-9}$$

Example 1-1 From (1-9) it follows that if S is a square with sides $2a$ and $2b$, and $f(x,y) = 1$, then [see Chap. 3, (4-30)]

$$|g(x_o, y_o, z_o)| = \left| \frac{4A \, \sin \, (kax_o/z_o) \, \sin \, (kby_o/z_o)}{(kx_o/z_o)(ky_o/z_o)} \right| \tag{1-10}$$

† In the following, the term *amplitude* will mean the function $g(x,y,z)$ in (1-2) (the expression *complex amplitude* is also used). The quantity $|g|^2$ will be referred to as the *intensity* of v.

Hankel transforms

We now assume that S is a circle and $f(x,y)$ has circular symmetry:

$$f(x,y) = f(r) \qquad r = \sqrt{x^2 + y^2}$$

It can be shown that [see Chap. 5, (1-4)] in this case, $F(u,v)$ also has circular symmetry, that is,

$$F(u,v) = F(w) \qquad w = \sqrt{u^2 + v^2}$$

and it is given by

$$F(w) = 2\pi \int_0^a rf(r)J_o(wr)\,dr \qquad (1\text{-}11)$$

where $J_o(x)$ is the Bessel function of order zero, and a is the radius of S. The function $\tilde{f}(w) = F(w)/2\pi$ is the Hankel transform of $f(r)$. Thus [see (1-8)],

$$g(x_o,y_o,z_o) = Ae^{jkr_o}F\left(k\,\frac{\sqrt{x_o{}^2 + y_o{}^2}}{z_o}\right) \qquad (1\text{-}12)$$

Example 1-2   If the incident wave is uniform, then $f(r) = 1$; hence [see Chap. 5, (1-20)],

$$F(w) = 2\pi \int_0^a rJ_o(rw)\,dr = \frac{2\pi aJ_1(aw)}{w}$$

where $J_1(x)$ is the Bessel function of order one.   Inserting into (1-12), we obtain the familiar Airy pattern (Fig. 1-2).

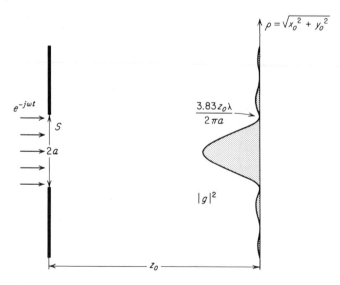

Fig. 1-2

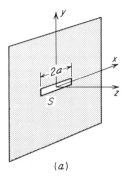 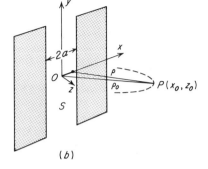

(a) (b)

Fig. 1-3

One-dimensional transforms

The Fraunhofer diffraction reduces to the one-dimensional Fourier transform in the following two cases.

Slit apertures If the aperture S is a narrow slit along the x axis of length $2a$ (Fig. 1-3a), then, with

$$f(x) = f(x,0)$$

the incoming wave along the slit and

$$F(u) = \int_{-a}^{a} f(x)e^{-jux}\,dx$$

its Fourier transform, the diffraction field is proportional to $F(k\alpha_o)$ on the surface of a sphere of radius $r_o \gg a$.

Two-dimensional signals We now assume that the incoming wave is independent of y, that is,

$$f(x,y) = f(x)$$

and that the aperture S is an infinite strip along the y axis of width $2a$ (Fig. 1-3b). We can no longer use (1-3) to determine the resulting diffraction field because this formula is based on the assumption that the dimensions of S are small compared with r_o. In our case, the field $g(x,z)$ is independent of y and it can be determined from the two-dimensional analog of (1-3). With

$$\rho = \sqrt{(x - x_o)^2 + z_o^2} \tag{1-13}$$

the distance from the point P to the point $(x,0)$, it can be shown, as in

(1-3), that

$$g(x_o, z_o) = B \int_{-a}^{a} f(x) e^{jk\rho} \, dx \tag{1-14}$$

Introducing the approximation

$$\rho \simeq \rho_o - \alpha_o x \qquad \rho_o = \sqrt{x_o^2 + y_o^2} \qquad \alpha_o = \frac{x_o}{\rho_o}$$

we conclude from (1-14) that

$$g(x_o, z_o) = B e^{jk\rho_o} \int_{-a}^{a} f(x) e^{-jk\alpha_o x} \, dx = B e^{jk\rho_o} F(k\alpha_o) \tag{1-15}$$

Thus, on the surface of a *cylinder*, $g(x_o, z_o)$ is proportional to the Fourier transform of $f(x)$.

Example 1-3   If the incoming wave is uniform, then $f(x) = 1$, and (1-15) yields

$$|g(x_o, z_o)| = \left| \frac{2B \sin (kax_o/z_o)}{kx_o/z_o} \right|$$

Comments

1. If the aperture S is covered with a thin film, then the far field is again given by (1-6), provided that $f(x,y)$ is replaced by the product

$$f(x,y) T(x,y)$$

where $T(x,y)$ is the transmission function characteristic of the film.

2. It can be shown that if a self-luminous two-dimensional object is placed on the $z = 0$ plane and its amplitude (surface source density) equals

$$f(x,y) e^{-j\omega t}$$

then the resulting far field is proportional to $F(k\alpha_o, k\beta_o)$, as in (1-8).

3. As we see from the first two examples, the far field takes significant values only in the cone

$$\frac{\sqrt{x_o^2 + y_o^2}}{z_o} \le \frac{\lambda}{a} \tag{1-16}$$

where $\lambda = 2\pi c/\omega$ is the wavelength of the incoming signal, and a is the radius of the smallest circle enclosing S (Fig. 1-4).   The above somewhat arbitrary condition gives only the order of magnitude of the angle of the "visible cone."   Thus, if

$$a = 10^{-3} \, \text{m} \qquad \text{and} \qquad \lambda = 6 \times 10^{-7} \, \text{m}$$

then this angle is about 2 minutes.   In general, there is no simple relationship between the extent of a function and its Fourier transform. However, from the uncertainty principle (Chap. 6, Sec. 3) it follows that

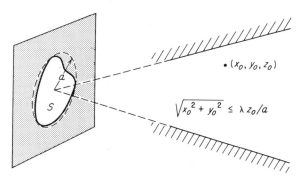

Fig. 1-4

the visible region contains in any case the cone (1-16), and if $f(x,y)$ varies rapidly, it might be considerably broader.

4. It can be shown (Chap. 9, Sec. 3) that the error in (1-6) due to the approximation (1-5) is negligible for

$$z_o > \frac{100a^2}{\lambda} \tag{1-17}$$

Thus, if

$$a = 10^{-3} \text{ m} \qquad \text{and} \qquad \lambda = 5 \times 10^{-7} \text{ m}$$

then the Fraunhofer approximation certainly holds for $z_o > 200$ m.

KIRCHHOFF'S FORMULA AND KIRCHHOFF'S APPROXIMATION

We shall now justify the diffraction integrals (1-3) and (1-14). Suppose that a function $g(x,y,z)$ satisfies the homogeneous wave equation

$$\frac{\partial^2 g}{\partial x^2} + \frac{\partial^2 g}{\partial y^2} + \frac{\partial^2 g}{\partial z^2} + k^2 g = 0 \tag{1-18}$$

everywhere in the region $z \geq 0$. It can be shown that if $z_o > 0$, then with r as in (1-4),

$$g(x_o, y_o, z_o) = \frac{1}{4\pi} \iint\limits_{-\infty}^{\infty} \left[g \frac{\partial}{\partial z}\left(\frac{e^{jkr}}{r}\right) - \frac{e^{jkr}}{r} \frac{\partial g}{\partial z} \right] dx \, dy \tag{1-19}$$

(provided that g satisfies certain general conditions at infinity). This remarkable formula, expressing $g(x_o, y_o, z_o)$ in terms of g and its normal derivative $\partial g/\partial z$ on the plane $z = 0$, shows that all information needed to determine the propagation of an optical wave is contained on a plane separating the sources from the point of observation. It is a special case of Kirchhoff's formula, which is discussed in Chap. 9, Sec. 1.

To apply the above to the diffraction problem, we observe that since there are no sources in the region $z \geq 0$, the diffracted field (1-2) satisfies the wave equation (1-18); hence, it is given by the integral (1-19). The boundary values g and $\partial g/\partial z$ are, of course, not known; therefore (1-19) cannot be used directly. However, for optical signals, it is reasonable to assume that at the opening S of the screen, the perturbed field v equals the incident field v^i [see (1-1)], that is,

$$g(x,y,0) = f(x,y) \qquad \frac{\partial g}{\partial z}(x,y,0) = jkf(x,y) \qquad (x,y) \in S \qquad (1\text{-}20)$$

and at the dark side of the screen it equals zero. Inserting into (1-19), we thus conclude that

$$g(x_o,y_o,z_o) = \frac{1}{4\pi} \iint\limits_{S} f(x,y)e^{jkr}\left[\left(-\frac{1}{r^2} + \frac{jk}{r}\right)\frac{\partial r}{\partial z} - \frac{jk}{r}\right] dx\, dy \qquad (1\text{-}21)$$

If we assume that z_o is large compared with the dimensions of S, then the terms in the bracket can be approximated by constants

$$r \simeq r_o = \sqrt{x_o{}^2 + y_o{}^2 + z_o{}^2} \qquad \frac{\partial r}{\partial z} = -\frac{z_o}{r} \simeq -\frac{z_o}{r_o}$$

and with

$$A = \frac{1}{4\pi}\left[\left(\frac{1}{r_o{}^2} - \frac{jk}{r_o}\right)\frac{z_o}{r_o} - \frac{jk}{r_o}\right] \simeq -\frac{jk(1 + z_o/r_o)}{4\pi r_o} \qquad (1\text{-}22)$$

(1-3) follows. The last approximation resulted because r_o is large compared with the wavelength $\lambda = 2\pi/k$.

For two-dimensional signals, (1-19) reduces to [see Chap. 9, (1-17)]

$$g(x_o,z_o) = \frac{e^{j\pi/4}}{\sqrt{8\pi k}} \int_{-\infty}^{\infty}\left[g\frac{\partial}{\partial z}\left(\frac{e^{jk\rho}}{\sqrt{\rho}}\right) - \frac{e^{jk\rho}}{\sqrt{\rho}}\frac{\partial g}{\partial z}\right] dx \qquad (1\text{-}23)$$

Introducing Kirchhoff's approximation, we obtain, as in (1-21),

$$g(x_o,z_o) = \frac{e^{j\pi/4}}{\sqrt{8\pi k}} \int_{-a}^{a} f(x)e^{jk\rho}\left[\left(-\frac{1}{2\sqrt{\rho^3}} + \frac{jk}{\sqrt{\rho}}\right)\frac{\partial \rho}{\partial z} - \frac{jk}{\sqrt{\rho}}\right] dx \qquad (1\text{-}24)$$

If $z_o \gg a$, then the bracket is approximately constant, and with

$$B = \frac{e^{j\pi/4}}{\sqrt{8\pi k}}\left[\left(\frac{1}{2\sqrt{\rho_o{}^3}} - \frac{jk}{\sqrt{\rho_o}}\right)\frac{z_o}{\rho_o} - \frac{jk}{\sqrt{\rho_o}}\right] \simeq \frac{e^{-j\pi/4}}{2\sqrt{\lambda \rho_o}}\left(1 + \frac{z_o}{\rho_o}\right) \qquad (1\text{-}25)$$

(1-14) follows.

2. FRESNEL DIFFRACTION AND THIN LENSES

We shall now examine the diffraction field for points closer to the aperture. To simplify the notations, we consider only two-dimensional signals. Retaining the first two terms in the expansion of ρ into powers of x, we have, replacing x by ξ and x_o by x,

$$\rho = \sqrt{z_o{}^2 + (x - \xi)^2} \simeq z_o + \frac{(x - \xi)^2}{2z_o} \qquad x, \xi \ll z_o \tag{2-1}$$

and (1-14) yields the Fresnel approximation

$$g(x,z_o) = Be^{jkz_o} \int_{-a}^{a} f(\xi) e^{jk(x-\xi)^2/2z_o}\, d\xi \tag{2-2}$$

Assuming that $f(x) = 0$ for $|x| > a$, we can write the above as a convolution

$$g(x,z_o) = Cf(x) * e^{j\alpha x^2} \qquad \alpha = \frac{k}{2z_o} \tag{2-3}$$

where

$$|C| = |B| = \frac{1}{\sqrt{\lambda z_o}}$$

as we see from (1-25) with $z_o/\rho_o \simeq 1$.

The fundamental relationship (2-3) expresses the diffracted field $g(x,z_o)$ as the output of a system with input $f(x)$ and impulse response $e^{j\alpha x^2}$ (see Chap. 11, Sec. 2).

THIN LENSES

By a two-dimensional lens we shall mean a substance of refractive index n, infinite in the y direction and bounded by two cylindrical surfaces whose cross sections are circles with radii r_1 and r_2 (Fig. 2-1).   If there are no

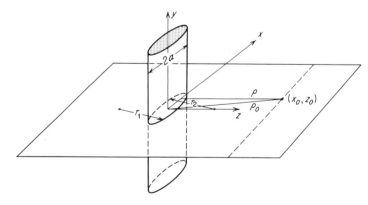

Fig. 2-1

light sources in the homogeneous region $z > 0$, then the field $g(x,z_o)$ can be expressed in terms of its values $g(x,0)$ on the $z = 0$ plane, as in (1-23). To account for the effect of the lens, it therefore suffices to determine the change in the incident wave as it passes through it. If the field on the $z = 0^-$ plane (to the left of the lens) equals $r(x)$, then it can be shown that on the $z = 0^+$ plane it is given by the product

$$r(x)e^{-jkx^2/2\mathbf{f}} \tag{2-4}$$

where† $\mathbf{f}$ is the focal length of the lens given by

$$\frac{1}{\mathbf{f}} = (n-1)\left(\frac{1}{r_1} + \frac{1}{r_2}\right)$$

Thus, the lens is equivalent to a transparency with transmission function

$$T(x) = e^{-j\beta x^2} \qquad \beta = \frac{k}{2\mathbf{f}} \tag{2-5}$$

This is true only for x in the interval $(-a,a)$ covered by the lens; however, this restriction can be ignored by assuming that $r(x) = 0$ for $|x| > a$.

The field $g(x,z_o)$ to the right of the lens can be found from (2-3) if the aperture function $f(x)$ is replaced by (2-4). Hence,

$$g(x,z_o) = C[r(x)e^{-j\beta x^2}] * e^{j\alpha x^2} \tag{2-6}$$

Focal plane

If $z_o = \mathbf{f}$, then $\alpha = \beta$, and (2-6) yields

$$g(x,\mathbf{f}) = C\int_{-\infty}^{\infty} r(\xi)e^{-j\beta\xi^2}e^{j\beta(x-\xi)^2}\,d\xi = Ce^{j\beta x^2}\int_{-\infty}^{\infty} r(\xi)e^{-j2\beta x\xi}\,d\xi \tag{2-7}$$

With $R(u)$ the Fourier transform of $r(x)$, we conclude that

$$g(x,\mathbf{f}) = Ce^{j\beta x^2}R(2\beta x) \qquad 2\beta = \frac{k}{\mathbf{f}} \tag{2-8}$$

Therefore,

$$|g(x,\mathbf{f})|^2 = \frac{1}{\lambda\mathbf{f}}\left|R\left(\frac{kx}{\mathbf{f}}\right)\right|^2 \tag{2-9}$$

Thus on the focal plane $z_o = \mathbf{f}$, the intensity of the diffraction field is proportional to the Fourier spectrum of the incident wave.

It is of interest to note that, off the focal plane, (2-6) equals the Fresnel image of a lensless aperture of suitable size.

Example 2-1   If the incoming wave is uniform, then

$$r(x) = \begin{cases} 1 & |x| < a \\ 0 & |x| > a \end{cases}$$

† The boldface letter $\mathbf{f}$ will be used to denote the focal length of a lens.

and (2-9) yields

$$|g(x,\mathbf{f})|^2 = \frac{4}{\lambda \mathbf{f}} \frac{\sin^2 (kax/\mathbf{f})}{(kx/\mathbf{f})^2}$$

As we see from (1-15), the Fraunhofer field on the surface of a cylinder is proportional to $F(k\alpha_o)$. Since the term $e^{jk\rho_o}$ is rapidly varying, the above is not true on a plane $z = z_o$. With

$$\rho_o = \sqrt{z_o{}^2 + x^2} \simeq z_o + \frac{x^2}{2z_o}$$

we see that on this plane, the field is proportional to

$$e^{jkx^2/2z_o} F\left(\frac{kx}{z_o}\right)$$

If, therefore, the plane is covered with a lens of focal length $\mathbf{f} = z_o$ (Fig. 2-2), then at its right the field will equal

$$e^{-jx^2/2\mathbf{f}} e^{jkx^2/2z_o} F\left(\frac{kx}{z_o}\right) = F\left(\frac{kx}{z_o}\right)$$

within a constant factor. This justifies, in a sense, the statement that a lens transforms cylindrical waves into plane waves.

Image formation

The preceding notions can be used to derive the familiar theorems of geometric optics. As an illustration, we shall determine the image of a plane object.

Suppose that the object $f(x)$ is located at a distance z_s from a lens L of focal length $\mathbf{f}$. Omitting the constant C, we see from (2-3) that the incident field on the lens equals

$$r(x) = f(x) * e^{j\alpha x^2} \qquad \alpha = \frac{k}{2z_s} \qquad (2\text{-}10)$$

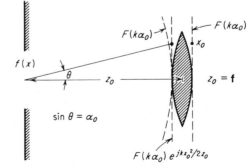

Fig. 2-2

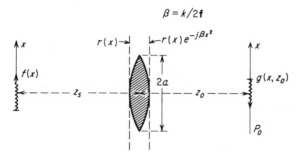

Fig. 2-3

Inserting the above into (2-6), we conclude that the field on a plane P_o (Fig. 2-3)—at a distance z_o from the lens—is given by

$$g(x,z_o) = \{[f(x) * e^{j\alpha x^2}]e^{-j\beta x^2}\} * e^{j\gamma x^2} \tag{2-11}$$

where

$$\beta = \frac{k}{2\mathbf{f}} \qquad \gamma = \frac{k}{2z_o}$$

If z_o is such that

$$\frac{1}{z_s} + \frac{1}{z_o} = \frac{1}{\mathbf{f}}$$

(image plane), then $\alpha + \gamma = \beta$, and (2-11) yields [see Chap. 6, (4-17)]

$$g(x,z_o) = e^{j\gamma\beta x^2/\alpha} f\left(-\frac{\gamma x}{\alpha}\right)$$

Hence,

$$|g(x,z_o)| = \left| f\left(-\frac{z_s x}{z_o}\right) \right| \tag{2-12}$$

Thus, the object is reversed and magnified by a factor z_o/z_s. The above is an approximation based on the assumption that the field $r(x)$ takes significant values only in the region $(-a,a)$ of the lens. The effect of finite lens size is investigated in Chap. 11, Sec. 2.

Fourier planes

Suppose that the field on the left focal plane P_l of a lens (Fig. 2-4) is $f(x)$. We shall determine the field on the right focal plane P_r. This field is given by (2-11), where now

$$\alpha = \beta = \gamma = \frac{k}{2\mathbf{f}}$$

Since (see Chap. 11, Sec. 2)

$$\{[f(x) * e^{j\beta x^2}]e^{-j\beta x^2}\} * e^{j\beta x^2} = \sqrt{\frac{\pi}{\beta}}\, e^{j\pi/4}F(2\beta x) \tag{2-13}$$

where $F(u)$ is the Fourier transform of $f(x)$, we conclude, taking into account the constant C [see (2-3)], that

$$g(x) = AF\left(\frac{2\pi x}{\lambda \mathbf{f}}\right) \qquad |A| = \frac{1}{\sqrt{\lambda \mathbf{f}}} \tag{2-14}$$

Thus, the amplitude $g(x)$ of the field on the plane P_r is proportional to the Fourier transform of the amplitude $f(x)$ of the field on the plane P_l.

ELECTROOPTICAL ANALOGIES

The system interpretation (2-3) of the diffracted field leads to simple analogies between optical and electrical devices. Such analogies can be used to solve a number of problems in signal analysis. Examples are given in Table 2-1. The results, based on (2-3) and (2-4), will be established in subsequent chapters.

We note from (2-3), omitting incidental terms, that the propagation from a plane to another corresponds to the process of passing a signal $f(t)$ through a filter with impulse response

$$e^{j\alpha t^2}$$

Since the Fourier transform of the above equals [see Chap. 3, (1-31)]

$$e^{-j\omega^2/4\alpha}$$

this filter has constant amplitude and quadratic phase.

The system analog of a lens is a signal generator

$$s(t) = e^{-j\beta t^2}$$

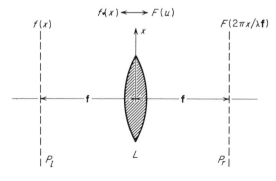

Fig. 2-4

Table 2-1   Electrooptical analogies

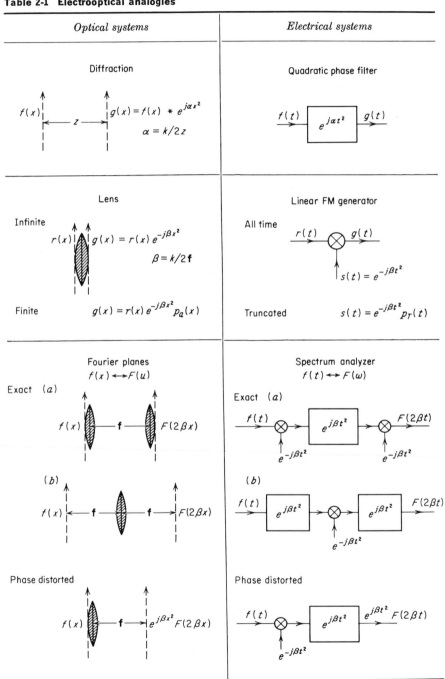

Table 2-1 Electrooptical analogies (Continued)

Optical systems	Electrical systems

Light concentration

Pulse compression

$e^{-j\beta t^2} p_T(t)$

$e^{j\beta t^2}$

$\pi/\beta T$

Image formation

Time scaling

Phase distorted

$$\varphi(x) \mid \longleftarrow z_s \longrightarrow \mid \longleftarrow z_0 \longrightarrow \mid \; e^{j\frac{z_s x^2}{z_0 f}} \varphi\left(-\frac{z_s x}{z_0}\right)$$

$$\frac{1}{z_s} + \frac{1}{z_0} = \frac{1}{f}$$

Phase distorted

$$f(t) \quad e^{j\alpha t^2} \quad e^{-j\beta t^2} \quad e^{j\gamma t^2} \quad e^{j\beta\gamma t^2/\alpha} f(-\gamma t/\alpha)$$

$$\alpha + \gamma = \beta$$

Exact

$$\varphi(x) \mid \leftarrow f_1 \rightarrow \mid \leftarrow f_1 + f_2 \rightarrow \mid \leftarrow f_2 \rightarrow \mid \varphi(-f_1 x/f_2)$$

Exact

$$f(t) \quad e^{j\alpha t^2} \quad e^{-j\alpha t^2} \quad e^{j\frac{\alpha\beta t^2}{\alpha+\beta}} \quad e^{-j\beta t^2} \quad e^{j\beta t^2} \quad f(-\beta t/\alpha)$$

Image formation with finite lens (approximate)

$$G(u) = F(u) p_a(\beta u)$$

$$\varphi(x) \mid \longleftarrow \Phi(u) \mid \longleftarrow 2f \longrightarrow \mid \longleftarrow 2f \longrightarrow \mid \; g(x) \longleftrightarrow G(u)$$

Filtering (approximate)

$F(\omega)$

$G(\omega)$

$0 \qquad \omega$

$0 \quad \beta t_1 \quad \beta t_2 \quad \omega$

$$f(t) \quad e^{j\beta t^2/2} \quad e^{-j\beta t^2} \quad G \quad e^{j\beta t^2/2} \quad g(-t)$$

G: gate opening at t_1
closing at t_2

whose frequency varies linearly with time (linear FM).   If the finite size of the lens is taken into account, then its transmission function equals

$$e^{-j\beta x^2} p_a(x) \qquad p_a(x) = \begin{cases} 1 & |x| < a \\ 0 & |x| > a \end{cases}$$

and the corresponding signal generator is given by

$$e^{-j\beta t^2} p_T(t)$$

3. NONHARMONIC SIGNALS AND COHERENCE

In the preceding section we exhibited the Fourier transform of a function $f(x)$ as a physical quantity, namely, the amplitude of the diffracted field generated by an aperture function $f(x)$.   The independent variables were *space coordinates*, and we assumed that the various signals were harmonic in time, as in (1-2).   In this section we study nonharmonic waves, which are classified into two categories according to the nature of their time dependence.

FINITE ENERGY SIGNALS

Suppose that the aperture of Fig. 3-1 is illuminated by a plane wave of the form

$$v^i(x,y,z,t) = f(x,y)\varphi\left(t - \frac{z}{c}\right) \tag{3-1}$$

where $\varphi(t)$ is a square-integrable function.   In order to determine the diffracted field $v(x,y,z,t)$, it is convenient to introduce the Fourier transform $\Phi(\omega)$ of the *time signal* $\varphi(t)$.   This function permits us to express $\varphi(t)$ as a superposition of exponentials

$$\varphi(t) = \frac{1}{2\pi} \int_{-\infty}^{\infty} \Phi(-\omega) e^{-j\omega t} \, d\omega \tag{3-2}$$

(inversion formula) and to reduce our problem to the harmonic case.

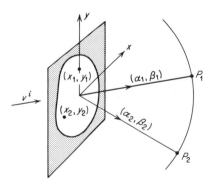

Fig. 3-1

The constant A in Kirchhoff's formula (1-3) is proportional to $\omega = k/\mathbf{c}$ [see (1-22)]. Therefore, for nonharmonic signals, this formula takes the form [see also Chap. 9, (2-6)]

$$v(x_o,y_o,z_o,t) \; \propto \; \iint_S f(x,y)\varphi'\left(t - \frac{r}{\mathbf{c}}\right) dx \, dy \tag{3-3}\dagger$$

This is a linear expression in $\varphi(t)$. Hence, superposition holds. From (1-8) and (3-2) it thus follows that in the Fraunhofer region, the field v is given by

$$v(x_o,y_o,z_o,t) \; \propto \; \int_{-\infty}^{\infty} \omega\Phi(-\omega)F\left(\frac{\omega\alpha_o}{\mathbf{c}}, \frac{\omega\beta_o}{\mathbf{c}}\right) e^{-j\omega(t-r_o/\mathbf{c})} \, d\omega \tag{3-4}$$

The Fresnel region can be treated similarly.

RANDOM SIGNALS

The waves emitted by optical sources are never harmonic in time. Even if they are ideally monochromatic [see Chap. 8, (4-48)], their phase is a complicated function that can be described only in an average sense. For such functions, the quantity of interest is not the instantaneous value of the field v, but its average intensity

$$E\{|v(P,t)|^2\} \; = \; \lim_{T\to\infty} \frac{1}{2T} \int_{-T}^{T} |v(P,t)|^2 \, dt \tag{3-5}$$

We assume that the incoming wave is a random signal $f(x, y, t - z/\mathbf{c})$. It is not enough to know the average intensity of the aperture function $f(x,y,t)$ to determine the average intensity of the diffracted field v. The quantity

$$\Gamma(x_1,y_1;x_2,y_2;\tau) \; = \; \lim_{T\to\infty} \frac{1}{2T} \int_{-T}^{T} f(x_1, y_1, t+\tau)f^*(x_2,y_2,t) \, dt \tag{3-6}$$

must also be given. This quantity is known as the *coherence function* of the signal $f(x,y,t)$.

The Fourier transform of Γ with respect to τ is the *power spectrum* of $f(x,y,t)$. If the τ dependence of Γ is harmonic, i.e.,

$$\Gamma(x_1,y_1;x_2,y_2;\tau) \; = \; \Gamma(x_1,y_1;x_2,y_2)e^{-j\omega\tau} \tag{3-7}$$

then we say that the optical signal $f(x,y,t)$ is *monochromatic*. We shall consider here mainly monochromatic signals.

It can be seen that the resulting diffraction field $v(P,t)$ is also monochromatic. Thus, its coherence function is of the form

$$\Gamma_{vv}(\alpha_1,\beta_1;\alpha_2,\beta_2)e^{-j\omega\tau}$$

---

† The expression $a(P) \propto b(P)$ will mean that $a(P) = kb(P)$, where the factor k is independent of P.

This is the time average of the product

$$v(P_1, t + \tau)v^*(P_2, t)$$

where P_1 and P_2 are two points on a sphere with directional cosines α_1, β_1, and α_2, β_2, respectively (Fig. 3-1). We shall determine Γ_{vv} in the Fraunhofer region for two special but important cases.

Complete incoherence   We say that the aperture function is completely incoherent (in space), if its coherence function is zero for $(x_1,y_1) \neq (x_2,y_2)$. In this case, Γ is of the form

$$\Gamma(x_1,y_1;x_2,y_2) = q(x_1,y_1)\delta(x_1 - x_2)\delta(y_1 - y_2) \tag{3-8}$$

where δ is the impulse function. With $Q(u,v)$ the Fourier transform of $q(x,y)$, it can be shown that [see Chap. 10, (4-14)] the coherence function of the far field v is given by

$$\Gamma_{vv}(\alpha_1,\beta_1;\alpha_2,\beta_2) \propto Q[k(\alpha_1 - \alpha_2),k(\beta_1 - \beta_2)] \tag{3-9}$$

where $k = \omega/\mathsf{c}$. In particular, its average intensity

$$E\{|v(P,t)|^2\} = \Gamma_{vv}(\alpha,\beta;\alpha,\beta) \propto Q(0,0) = \iint_S q(x,y)\,dx\,dy \tag{3-10}$$

is constant on the surface of a sphere.

Complete coherence   The aperture function f is said to be completely coherent if Γ is of the form

$$\Gamma(x_1,y_1;x_2,y_2) = p(x_1,y_1)p^*(x_2,y_2) \tag{3-11}$$

With $P(u,v)$ the Fourier transform of $p(x,y)$, it can be shown that [see Chap. 10, (4-19)]

$$\Gamma_{vv}(\alpha_1,\beta_1;\alpha_2,\beta_2) \propto P(k\alpha_1,k\beta_1)P^*(k\alpha_2,k\beta_2) \tag{3-12}$$

In particular,

$$E\{|v(P,t)|^2\} \propto |P(k\alpha,k\beta)|^2 \tag{3-13}$$

Comments

1. The preceding results hold also if the aperture is replaced by a two-dimensional self-luminous object with surface density $f(x,y,t)$.
2. If a signal is harmonic, as in (1-2), then it is monochromatic; however, the converse is not necessarily true [see Chap. 8, (4-49)].
3. If a signal is completely incoherent, then its average intensity $\Gamma(x,y;x,y)$ is infinite. Nevertheless, the function $q(x,y)$ in (3-8) is often referred to as the average intensity of the signal [see also Chap. 8, (3-11)].

4. A completely coherent object is equivalent to a deterministic object in the following sense. If the object is a harmonically varying signal with amplitude the function $p(x,y)$ in (3-11), then the intensity of its far field is proportional to $|P(k\alpha,k\beta)|^2$, as in (3-13) [see (1-8)].

5. A coherent object (aperture) is "visible" only in a small region; an incoherent object is visible everywhere. Indeed, if the dimensions of the object are large compared with the wavelength λ, then the function $P(k\alpha,k\beta)$ takes significant values only if the directional cosines α and β are small [see, for example, (1-10)]. Hence, the same is true for the average intensity (3-13) of the field v. If, however, the object is incoherent, then the average intensity of its far field is constant. In fact, if the function Γ_{vv} in (3-9) is known for every (α_2,β_2) near an arbitrary point (α_1,β_1), then $Q(u,v)$ and, hence, the average intensity $q(x,y)$ of the object can be determined.

6. Suppose that a coherent (or deterministic) source emitting total power P produces a certain field at a point in its visible region. From the preceding comment it follows that to obtain the same field with an incoherent source, the total power of this source must be vastly greater than P.

7. As we noted, the power spectrum of a signal f is the Fourier transform of its coherence function Γ with respect to τ. In general, there is no connection between the bandwidth of this spectrum and the degree of the spacial coherence of f. A signal can be monochromatic and completely incoherent, or wide-band and coherent. However, it can be shown that if an optical source consists of a number of elementary monochromatic oscillators, then its degree of coherence is large if its power spectrum is narrow.

4. SYSTEMS IN OPTICS

Consider the optical arrangement of Fig. 4-1. On the "object" plane P_s we place a light source of amplitude

$$f(x,y)e^{-j\omega t}$$

and we observe the resulting field

$$g(x,y)e^{-j\omega t}$$

on the "image" plane P_o. This arrangement can thus be viewed as a process of assigning to a given function $f(x,y)$ another function $g(x,y)$. In other words, it is a system (transformation) with input the object $f(x,y)$ and output the image $g(x,y)$. If the optical medium is linear, then g is a linear function of f; hence, the system is linear [o1].†

† The notation [o1] signifies reference o1 at the end of the book.

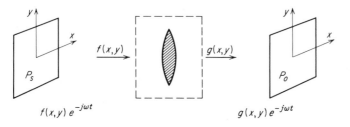

Fig. 4-1

Suppose that a point source

$$\delta(x - \xi)\delta(y - \eta)$$

is placed at the point (ξ,η) of the object plane. The resulting image

$$h(x,y;\xi,\eta)$$

is known as the *point spread*, or point impulse response, of the system. From the linearity of the system it follows that if h is known, then the image g of any object f can be determined. Applying superposition, we conclude that

$$g(x,y) = \iint_S f(\xi,\eta)h(x,y;\xi,\eta)\,d\xi\,d\eta \qquad (4\text{-}1)$$

where the integration extends over the region S of the object.

Suppose now that we form the object $f(x - x_o, y - y_o)$, which results from translating $f(x,y)$ on its plane. If the new image is

$$g(x - x_o, y - y_o) \qquad (4\text{-}2)$$

then we say that the system is *shift-invariant*. Real systems are not shift-invariant. However, if we consider only small displacements, then (4-2) is a reasonable approximation, provided that the coordinates in the image plane are suitably scaled to account for possible magnification. In the following, we shall consider only linear shift-invariant systems.

With

$$h(x,y) = h(x,y;0,0)$$

as the image of a point $\delta(x)\delta(y)$ at the origin, it follows from (4-2) that

$$h(x,y;\xi,\eta) = h(x - \xi, y - \eta) \qquad (4\text{-}3)$$

Inserting into (4-1), we thus express the image as a convolution

$$g(x,y) = \iint_S f(\xi,\eta)h(x - \xi, y - \eta)\,d\xi\,d\eta = f(x,y) ** h(x,y) \qquad (4\text{-}4)$$

of the object $f(x,y)$ with the point spread $h(x,y)$.

If $h(x,y) = \delta(x)\delta(y)$, then $g = f$, and the optical system is *perfect*. We say that the system is *ideal* (or *diffraction-limited*) if the spread of h is due to the fact that the lenses are of finite size.

If the functions f and h are circularly symmetrical, then g is also circularly symmetrical, and it is given by

$$g(r) = f(r) ** h(r) \qquad r = \sqrt{x^2 + y^2} \tag{4-5}$$

where the convolution is with respect to x and y.

Suppose finally that the system consists of cylindrical lenses, and the object $f(x,y) = f(x)$ is independent of y. In this case, the image $g(x)$ is given by the one-dimensional convolution

$$g(x) = \int_{-\infty}^{\infty} f(\xi)h(x - \xi) \, d\xi = f(x) * h(x) \tag{4-6}$$

where $h(x)$ is the image of the line $\delta(x)$.

Transforms With $F(u,v)$, $H(u,v)$, and $G(u,v)$ the Fourier transforms of $f(x,y)$, $h(x,y)$, and $g(x,y)$, respectively, it follows from (4-4) that

$$G(u,v) = F(u,v)H(u,v) \tag{4-7}$$

A similar relationship holds for the one-dimensional case.

For circularly symmetrical signals the above functions become Hankel transforms [see (1-11)], and (4-7) takes the form

$$\bar{g}(w) = 2\pi\bar{f}(w)\bar{h}(w) \tag{4-8}$$

In the study of general systems, Fourier transforms do not represent physical signals. They are auxiliary quantities introduced to reduce convolution to a mere multiplication. However, for optical systems, the function $G(u,v)$ equals the amplitude of the field at the exit pupil.

NONHARMONIC SIGNALS AND COHERENCE

To simplify notations, we shall consider here only one-dimensional systems. The impulse response h was defined as the image of

$$\delta(x)e^{-j\omega t}$$

This function depends, in general, not only on x but also on the frequency ω:

$$h(x;\omega)$$

If it is known for every ω, then the image of a nonharmonic object can be determined by superposition.

Suppose that the amplitude of the object equals

$$f(x)\varphi(t) \tag{4-9}$$

where $\varphi(t)$ is a signal, as in (3-1), with Fourier transform $\Phi(\omega)$. Expressing $\varphi(t)$ in terms of $\Phi(\omega)$ [see (3-2)] and inserting into (4-6), we conclude from the linearity of the system that the image of our object is given by

$$g(x) = \frac{1}{2\pi} \int_{-\infty}^{\infty} \Phi(-\omega)e^{-j\omega t}[f(x) * h(x;\omega)] \, d\omega \tag{4-10}$$

where the convolution in the above bracket is with respect to x, as in (4-6).

If $\Phi(\omega)$ is zero outside the interval $(\omega_o - \omega_c, \omega_o + \omega_c)$, then it suffices to know $h(x;\omega)$ in this interval to determine $g(x)$. If ω_c is sufficiently small, then $h(x;\omega)$ is approximately constant, and (4-10) yields

$$g(x) = [f(x) * h(x;\omega_o)]\varphi(t) \tag{4-11}$$

because the bracket in (4-10) can be taken outside the integral.

Random signals

We now assume that the amplitude of the object is a random signal $f(x,t)$ with coherence function

$$\Gamma_{ff}(x_1,x_2;\tau) = \lim_{T \to \infty} \frac{1}{2T} \int_{-T}^{T} f(x_1, t + \tau)f^*(x_2,t) \, dt \tag{4-12}$$

To determine the coherence function

$$\Gamma_{gg}(x_1,x_2;\tau)$$

of the image $g(x,t)$, we form the cross-coherence function

$$\Gamma_{fg}(x_1,x_2;\tau) = \lim_{T \to \infty} \frac{1}{2T} \int_{-T}^{T} f(x_1, t + \tau)g^*(x_2,t) \, dt \tag{4-13}$$

where x_1 is a point in the object plane P_s, and x_2 is a point in the image plane P_o.

Our analysis will be based on the following two basic theorems (see Chap. 10, Sec. 3).

A. If the quantity $\Gamma_{ff}(x_1, x_2; t_1 - t_2)$, considered as a function of x_2, t_2 (with x_1, t_1 as parameters), is viewed as the amplitude of an object, then the image of this object will equal the quantity $\Gamma_{fg}(x_1, x_2; t_1 - t_2)$, which is also considered as a function of x_2, t_2.

B. If the quantity $\Gamma_{fg}(x_1, x_2; t_1 - t_2)$, considered as a function of x_1, t_1 (with x_2, t_2 as parameters), is viewed as the amplitude of an object, then the image of this object will equal the quantity $\Gamma_{gg}(x_1, x_2; t_1 - t_2)$, which is also considered as a function of x_1, t_1.

We shall consider a monochromatic object first:

$$\Gamma_{ff}(x_1,x_2;\tau) = \Gamma_{ff}(x_1,x_2)e^{-j\omega\tau} \tag{4-14}$$

From the preceding theorem it follows that the functions Γ_{fg} and Γ_{gg} are of the form

$$\Gamma_{fg}(x_1,x_2;\tau) = \Gamma_{fg}(x_1,x_2)e^{-j\omega\tau}$$
$$\Gamma_{gg}(x_1,x_2;\tau) = \Gamma_{gg}(x_1,x_2)e^{-j\omega\tau}$$

because the image of a harmonic object is harmonic. Since

$$e^{-j\omega\tau} = e^{j\omega t_2}e^{-j\omega t_1}$$

the t_2 dependence of Γ_{ff} is proportional to $e^{j\omega t_2} = e^{-j(-\omega)t_2}$. Denoting by $h(x;\omega)$ the point spread of the system, we see from Theorem A that Γ_{fg} is obtained by convolving Γ_{ff} with $h(x_2;-\omega)$, where the convolution is with respect to x_2. Since the image of a real object is real, it follows that

$$h(x_2;-\omega) = h^*(x_2;\omega) = h^*(x)$$

(omitting the ω dependence of h). Hence [see (4-6)],

$$\Gamma_{fg}(x_1,x_2) = \Gamma_{ff}(x_1,x_2) * h^*(x_2) = \int_{-\infty}^{\infty} \Gamma_{ff}(x_1,\xi_2)h^*(x_2 - \xi_2)\,d\xi_2 \tag{4-15}$$

Reasoning similarly, we conclude from Theorem B that

$$\Gamma_{gg}(x_1,x_2) = \Gamma_{fg}(x_1,x_2) * h(x_1) \tag{4-16}$$

where the convolution is with respect to x_1. Combining (4-16) and (4-15), we can thus express Γ_{gg} in terms of Γ_{ff}.

We shall now apply the above to two extreme cases.

Incoherent object If [see (3-8)]

$$\Gamma_{ff}(x_1,x_2) = q(x_1)\delta(x_1 - x_2) \tag{4-17}$$

then (4-15) and (4-16) yield

$$\Gamma_{fg}(x_1,x_2) = q(x_1)h^*(x_2 - x_1) \tag{4-18}$$
$$\Gamma_{gg}(x_1,x_2) = [q(x_1)h^*(x_2 - x_1)] * h(x_1) \tag{4-19}$$

With $x_1 = x_2 = x$, it follows from (4-19) that the average intensity of the image $g(x,t)$ is given by

$$E\{|g(x,t)|^2\} = \Gamma_{gg}(x,x) = \int_{-\infty}^{\infty} q(x - \xi)|h(\xi)|^2\,d\xi = q(x) * |h(x)|^2 \tag{4-20}$$

This relationship shows that if an object is incoherent and monochromatic, then the average intensity of its image equals the amplitude of the output of a new system with point spread $|h(x)|^2$ and input

$$q(x)e^{-j\omega t}$$

Coherent object   If [see (3-11)]

$$\Gamma_{ff}(x_1,x_2) \; = \; p(x_1)p^*(x_2) \tag{4-21}$$

then (4-15) and (4-16) yield

$$\Gamma_{fg}(x_1,x_2) \; = \; p(x_1)[p^*(x_2) * h^*(x_2)] \tag{4-22}$$

$$\Gamma_{gg}(x_1,x_2) \; = \; [p(x_1) * h(x_1)][p^*(x_2) * h^*(x_2)] \tag{4-23}$$

In particular,

$$E\{|g(x,t)|^2\} \; = \; |p(x) * h(x)|^2 \; = \; \left| \int_{-\infty}^{\infty} p(x - \xi)h(\xi) \, d\xi \right|^2 \tag{4-24}$$

We finally observe that if the object is not monochromatic, then the preceding theorem shows that the coherence functions Γ_{fg} and Γ_{gg} can be computed as in the deterministic case [see (4-10)].

part one

SYSTEMS AND TRANSFORMS

2
CONVOLUTION;
SINGULARITIES;
SYSTEMS

In this book, a linear system (operator) is interpreted to be a convolution of a fixed function h (impulse response), with an arbitrary signal f of a given class (input). The properties of such systems are discussed and used to introduce the Fourier integrals as eigenvalues of linear operators. As a preparation, the one- and two-dimensional singularity functions are developed. These functions are used extensively in subsequent chapters.

1. CONVOLUTION

Given two signals $f(t)$ and $h(t)$, we form the function

$$g(t) = \int_{-\infty}^{\infty} f(\tau)h(t-\tau)\,d\tau = \int_{-\infty}^{\infty} f(t-\tau)h(\tau)\,d\tau$$

$$= \int_{-\infty}^{\infty} f\left(\frac{t}{2}-\tau\right) h\left(\frac{t}{2}+\tau\right) d\tau = \int_{-\infty}^{\infty} f\left(\frac{t}{2}+\tau\right) h\left(\frac{t}{2}-\tau\right) d\tau$$

$$(1\text{-}1)$$

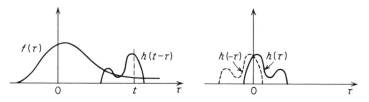

Fig. 1-1

This function is also written in the form

$$g(t) = f(t) * h(t) \tag{1-2}$$

and it is known as the convolution of $f(t)$ and $h(t)$.   The above operation is obviously commutative and associative.   Hence, the expression

$$f_1(t) * f_2(t) * \cdots * f_n(t)$$

is well defined.

The evaluation of $g(t)$ is often facilitated by the following construction.   We form the function $h(-\tau)$ and shift it to the right by t, as in Fig. 1-1.   The area of the product $f(\tau)h(t - \tau)$ yields $g(t)$, as in the first integral in (1-1).   The other integrals lead to similar constructions.

From the above it follows easily that if $f(t)$ and $h(t)$ are zero outside the intervals (a_1,b_1) and (a_2,b_2), respectively (see Fig. 1-2), then $g(t)$ equals zero outside the interval $(a_1 + a_2, b_1 + b_2)$.

We also see that if

$$p_a(t) = \begin{cases} 1 & |t| < a \\ 0 & |t| > a \end{cases} \tag{1-3}$$

is a pulse as in Fig. 1-3, then

$$g(t) = \frac{1}{2a} p_a(t) * f(t) = \frac{1}{2a} \int_{t-a}^{t+a} f(\tau) \, d\tau \tag{1-4}$$

Thus, $g(t)$ is the "moving average" of $f(t)$.

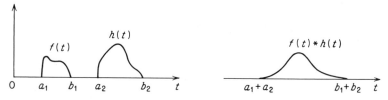

Fig. 1-2

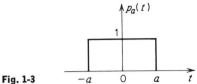

Fig. 1-3

Causal functions   A function will be called causal if it equals zero for $t < 0$.   For causal functions, the convolution takes the following form:
If $h(t) = 0$ for $t < 0$, then

$$f(t) * h(t) = \int_{-\infty}^{t} f(\tau)h(t - \tau)\, d\tau = \int_{0}^{\infty} f(t - \tau)h(\tau)\, d\tau \qquad (1\text{-}5)$$

In particular, with $U(t)$ the unit step function (Fig. 2-1),

$$f(t) * U(t) = \int_{-\infty}^{t} f(\tau)\, d\tau \qquad (1\text{-}6)$$

If $f(t) = 0$ and $h(t) = 0$ for $t < 0$, then

$$f(t) * h(t) = \int_{0}^{t} f(\tau)h(t - \tau)\, d\tau = \int_{0}^{t} f(t - \tau)h(\tau)\, d\tau \qquad (1\text{-}7)$$

Example 1-1

a. If $f(t)$ and $h(t)$ are two pulses, then $f(t) * h(t)$ is given by a trapezoid, as in Fig. 1-4.
b. If $f(t)$ is a pulse train (Fig. 1-5), then $f(t) * f(t)$ consists of triangles.

Example 1-2   With $f(t) = p_{\frac{1}{2}}(t)$ a pulse and $f_1(t) = f_2(t) = \cdots = f_n(t) = f(t)$, the convolution

$$g(t) = f_1(t) * \cdots * f_n(t)$$

is a triangle for $n = 2$, consists of three parabolic pieces for $n = 3$, and is a combination of four cubic curves for $n = 4$ (Fig. 1-6).

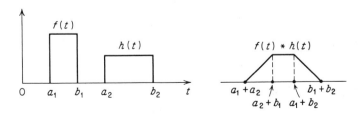

Fig. 1-4

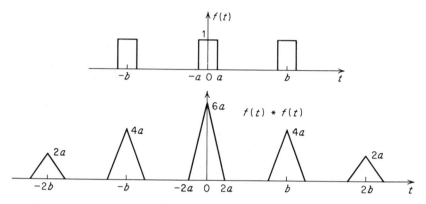

Fig. 1-5

We finally remark that

$$\int_{-\infty}^{\infty} g(t)\, dt = \int_{-\infty}^{\infty} f(t)\, dt \int_{-\infty}^{\infty} h(t)\, dt \qquad (1\text{-}8)$$

This follows readily if both sides of (1-1) are integrated.

Moment expansion

The determination of the convolution $g(t)$ is in principle simple. However, for its numerical evaluation, one needs to compute an infinite integral for every t. In subsequent sections we shall discuss methods for simplifying this operation. In the following we express $g(t)$ in terms of the derivatives of one of the functions $f(t)$ and $h(t)$ and the moments of the other.

If $f(t)$ is of short duration,

$$f(t) = 0 \qquad \text{for } |t| > \epsilon \qquad (1\text{-}9)$$

in the sense that $h(t)$ does not vary appreciably in an interval of length 2ϵ (Fig. 1-7), then $h(t-\tau) \simeq h(t)$ for $|\tau| < \epsilon$ and

$$g(t) = \int_{-\epsilon}^{\epsilon} f(\tau) h(t-\tau)\, d\tau \simeq h(t) \int_{-\epsilon}^{\epsilon} f(\tau)\, d\tau$$

This is the beginning of a series expansion [p2].

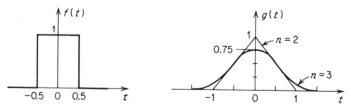

Fig. 1-6

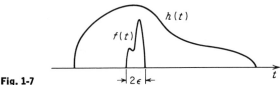

Fig. 1-7

We define the moments m_n of $f(t)$ by

$$m_n = \int_{-\infty}^{\infty} t^n f(t)\, dt \tag{1-10}$$

and with

$$h(t - \tau) = h(t) - \tau h'(t) + \cdots + (-1)^n \tau^n h^{(n)}(t) + \cdots \tag{1-11}$$

we obtain, inserting into (1-1),

$$g(t) = h(t) \int_{-\infty}^{\infty} f(\tau)\, d\tau - h'(t) \int_{-\infty}^{\infty} \tau f(\tau)\, d\tau + \cdots$$

Thus,

$$g(t) = m_0 h(t) - m_1 h'(t) + \cdots + (-1)^n \frac{m_n}{n!} h^{(n)}(t) + \cdots \tag{1-12}$$

If $f(t)$ is even, then $m_{2n+1} = 0$, and the above yields

$$g(t) = m_0 h(t) + \frac{m_2}{2} h''(t) + \cdots \tag{1-13}$$

Clearly, the role of $f(t)$ and $h(t)$ can be interchanged in the evaluation of $g(t)$.

The above expansion is of value only if it converges rapidly. This is the case if $f(t) = 0$ for $|t| > \epsilon$ and $h(\tau)$ is smooth in the interval $(t - \epsilon, t + \epsilon)$ so that only a small number of terms is needed in (1-11) for $|\tau| < \epsilon$.

Example 1-3 Suppose that (Fig. 1-8)

$$f(t) = A p_\epsilon(t) \qquad h(t) = e^{-t^2}$$

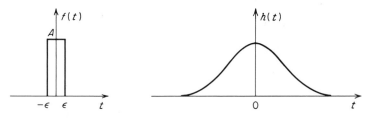

Fig. 1-8

We then have

$$m_0 = 2A\epsilon \qquad m_2 = \tfrac{2}{3}A\epsilon^3 \qquad \frac{d^2 e^{-t^2}}{dt^2} = (4t^2 - 2)e^{-t^2}$$

Hence, retaining only two terms in (1-13), we have

$$g(t) \simeq Ae^{-t^2} \left[2\epsilon + \frac{2\epsilon^3}{3}(4t^2 - 2) \right]$$

TWO-DIMENSIONAL SIGNALS AND CONVOLUTION

By a two-dimensional signal we shall mean a function $f(x,y)$ of two variables. The area of the intersection of the surface $z = f(x,y)$ by an x plane

$$\varphi(x) = \int_{-\infty}^{\infty} f(x,y) \, dy \tag{1-14}$$

we shall call the x *profile* of $f(x,y)$. The function $f(x,y)$ will often be interpreted as surface mass density in the sense that $f(x,y) \, dx \, dy$ equals the mass in the rectangle of Fig. 1-9. With this interpretation, $\varphi(x) \, dx$ equals the mass in the strip $(x, x + dx)$.

We say that $f(x,y)$ has *circular symmetry* if

$$f(x,y) = f(r) \qquad r = \sqrt{x^2 + y^2} \tag{1-15}$$

that is, if the mass density at a point depends only on its distance from the origin.

Given a region A in the plane, we define the *zero-one function* $p_A(x,y)$ associated with A by:

$$p_A(x,y) = \begin{cases} 1 & (x,y) \in A \\ 0 & (x,y) \notin A \end{cases} \tag{1-16}$$

Example 1-4 With C a circle of radius a, we have

$$p_C(x,y) = p_a(r)$$

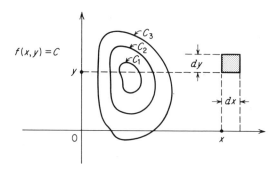

Fig. 1-9

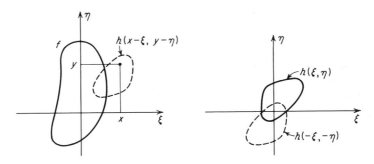

Fig. 1-10

where $p_a(r)$ is a pulse as in (1-3). The corresponding x profile $\varphi(x)$ is given by

$$\varphi(x) = \int_{-\infty}^{\infty} p_a(\sqrt{x^2 + y^2}) \, dy = \int_{-\sqrt{a^2-x^2}}^{\sqrt{a^2-x^2}} dy = 2\sqrt{a^2 - x^2}$$

for $|x| < a$, and it equals zero for $|x| > a$.

Convolution

Given two functions $f(x,y)$ and $h(x,y)$, we define their (double) convolution $g(x,y)$ by

$$g(x,y) = \iint_{-\infty}^{\infty} f(\xi,\eta)h(x - \xi, y - \eta) \, d\xi \, d\eta$$

$$= \iint_{-\infty}^{\infty} f(x - \xi, y - \eta)h(\xi,\eta) \, d\xi \, d\eta \quad (1\text{-}17)$$

This operation will be written in the form

$$g(x,y) = f(x,y) ** h(x,y) \tag{1-18}$$

and it is obviously commutative and associative.

To evaluate $g(x,y)$ at a specific point (x,y), we form the function $h(-\xi, -\eta)$ and translate it by (x,y), as in Fig. 1-10. The volume of the product $f(\xi,\eta)h(x - \xi, y - \eta)$ equals $g(x,y)$.

If $p_A(x,y)$ and $p_B(x,y)$ are the zero-one functions associated with the regions A and B, respectively, then their convolution $g(x,y)$ is found by forming the region B_1 symmetrical with B with respect to the origin and the region B_2, which results from B_1 by an (x,y) translation. The area of the intersection of A and B_2 equals $g(x,y)$.

Example 1-5 With A and B two squares, the convolution

$$g(x,y) = p_A(x,y) ** p_B(x,y)$$

is shown in Fig. 1-11b by its contour lines $g(x,y) = C = $ constant. In Fig. 1-11c we show the curves $g(x,x)$ and $g(x,0)$.

Given $f(r)$ and $h(r)$, we form the two-dimensional signals

$$f(\sqrt{x^2 + y^2}) \qquad \text{and} \qquad h(\sqrt{x^2 + y^2})$$

It is easy to see that their convolution $g(x,y)$ has circular symmetry. Thus, with $r = \sqrt{x^2 + y^2}$

$$g(r) = f(r) ** h(r)$$
$$= \iint_{-\infty}^{\infty} f(\sqrt{\xi^2 + \eta^2}) h[\sqrt{(x - \xi)^2 + (y - \eta)^2}] \, d\xi \, d\eta \quad (1\text{-}19)$$

In polar coordinates

$$\xi = \rho \cos \theta \qquad \eta = \rho \sin \theta$$

the above takes the form (elaborate)

$$f(r) ** h(r) = \int_0^{\infty} \rho f(\rho) \int_{-\pi}^{\pi} h(\sqrt{r^2 + \rho^2 - 2r\rho \cos \theta}) \, d\theta \, d\rho \quad (1\text{-}20)$$

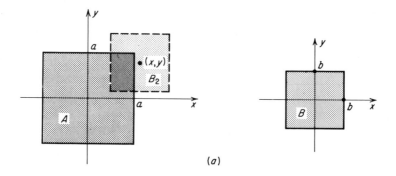

(a)

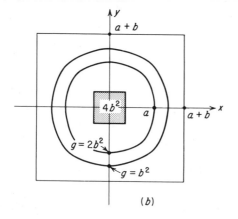

(b)

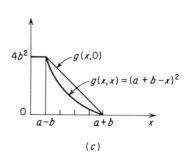

(c)

Fig. 1-11

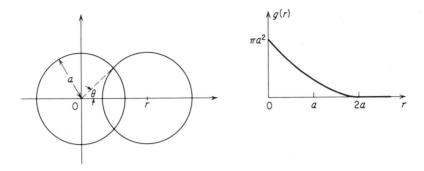

Fig. 1-12

Example 1-6 With $p_a(r)$ as in (1-3), $p_a(r) \ast\ast p_a(r)$ is the area A of the region common to the two circles of Fig. 1-12. With θ as in the figure, we have

$$\cos\theta = \frac{r}{2a} \qquad A = (2\theta - \sin 2\theta)a^2$$

Hence, for $r < 2a$

$$g(r) = p_a(r) \ast\ast p_a(r) = \left(2\cos^{-1}\frac{r}{2a} - \frac{r}{a}\sqrt{1 - \frac{r^2}{4a^2}}\right)a^2$$

For $r > 2a$ the two circles do not intersect; hence, $g(r) = 0$.

Moment expansion The convolution of two functions $f(x,y)$ and $h(x,y)$ can be expressed as a series in terms of the joint moments

$$m_{kr} = \int\!\!\!\int_{-\infty}^{\infty} x^k y^r f(x,y)\,dx\,dy \qquad\qquad (1\text{-}21)$$

of $f(x,y)$ and the derivatives of $h(x,y)$. Inserting the expansion

$$h(x - \xi, y - \eta) = h(x,y) - \xi\frac{\partial h(x,y)}{\partial x} - \eta\frac{\partial h(x,y)}{\partial y} + \cdots$$

into (1-17), we find

$$f \ast\ast h = m_{00}h - \left(m_{10}\frac{\partial h}{\partial x} + m_{01}\frac{\partial h}{\partial y}\right) + \left(\frac{m_{20}}{2}\frac{\partial^2 h}{\partial x^2} + m_{11}\frac{\partial^2 h}{\partial x\,\partial y}\right.$$
$$\left. + \frac{m_{02}}{2}\frac{\partial^2 h}{\partial y^2}\right) - \cdots \quad (1\text{-}22)$$

where all functions are evaluated at (x,y).

2. SINGULARITY FUNCTIONS

The Dirac function $\delta(t)$ will be a central tool in our analysis. In this section we develop certain of its properties, basing the discussion on the fundamental relationship

$$\int_{-\infty}^{\infty} f(t)\delta(t)\, dt = f(0) \tag{2-1}$$

which is valid for any function $f(t)$ continuous at $t = 0$.

The above does not make sense if $\delta(t)$ is an ordinary function. It is meaningful only if the delta function is interpreted as a functional, i.e., as a process of assigning to the function $f(t)$ the number $f(0)$ [l3, m3, p2, z2]. The integral notation is used merely as a convenient way of describing the properties of this functional (linearity, shifting, change of variables, etc.). We can thus treat $\delta(t)$ as an ordinary function obeying all formal rules of integration, provided that all our conclusions are based on (2-1) and not on any point properties of $\delta(t)$. As an illustration, we shall derive a number of properties of the impulse function.

If $f(t)$ is continuous at t, then

$$\int_{-\infty}^{\infty} f(\tau)\delta(\tau - t)\, d\tau = \int_{-\infty}^{\infty} f(t + x)\delta(x)\, dx = f(t) \tag{2-2}$$

The above expresses a function $f(t)$ as a linear combination of impulses $f(\tau)\delta(\tau - t)\, d\tau$, and it is very important in the study of linear systems (operators).

If $\varphi(t)$ is continuous at $t = a$, then

$$\varphi(t)\delta(t - a) = \varphi(a)\delta(t - a) \tag{2-3}$$

because

$$\int_{-\infty}^{\infty} f(t)\varphi(t)\delta(t - a)\, dt = f(a)\varphi(a) = \int_{-\infty}^{\infty} f(t)\varphi(a)\delta(t - a)\, dt$$

With

$$f(t) = \begin{cases} g(t) & b < t < c \\ 0 & t < b \text{ or } t > c \end{cases}$$

we conclude, inserting into (2-2), that

$$\int_{b}^{c} g(\tau)\delta(\tau - t_o)\, d\tau = \begin{cases} g(t_o) & c < t_o < b \\ 0 & \text{elsewhere} \end{cases} \tag{2-4}$$

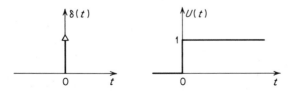

Fig. 2-1

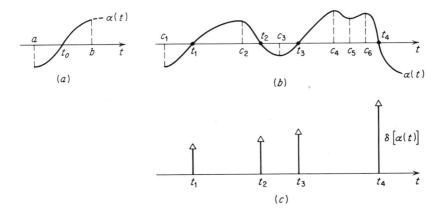

Fig. 2-2

If $t_o = a$ or b, then the above integral is undefined. With $b = -\infty$, $c = t$, $t_o = 0$, we also have

$$\int_{-\infty}^{t} \delta(\tau)\, d\tau = \begin{cases} 1 & t > 0 \\ 0 & t < 0 \end{cases} = U(t)$$

where $U(t)$ is the unit step function (Fig. 2-1).

Differentiating, we conclude that

$$\delta(t) = \frac{dU(t)}{dt} \tag{2-5}$$

This has meaning if both sides are used as integrands in integrals of the form of (2-1).

More generally, suppose that the function $\alpha(t)$ is monotone increasing in the interval (a,b), crossing the t axis at the point t_o of this interval (Fig. 2-2a):

$$\alpha(a) < \alpha(t_o) = 0 < \alpha(b)$$

Clearly, the equation $\alpha(t) = x$ has a single-valued inverse $t(x)$ such that $t(0) = t_o$. With a formal change of variables, we conclude, from (2-4), that

$$\int_{a}^{b} f(t)\delta[\alpha(t)]\, dt = \int_{\alpha(a)}^{\alpha(b)} \frac{f[t(x)]}{\alpha'[t(x)]}\, \delta(x)\, dx = \frac{f[t(0)]}{\alpha'[t(0)]} = \frac{f(t_o)}{\alpha'(t_o)} \tag{2-6}$$

If $\alpha(t)$ is monotone decreasing, then the sign of the result is reversed. Thus, for both cases, the above integral equals $f(t_o)|\alpha'(t_o)|^{-1}$. If $f(t)$ does not intersect the t axis in the interval (a,b), then the integral equals zero.

Suppose now that the equation $\alpha(t) = 0$ has a finite or countably infinite number of zeros t_n on the entire t axis (Fig. 2-2b), that is,

$$\alpha(t_n) = 0$$

and that at these points, $\alpha(t)$ has a continuous derivative $\alpha'(t_n) \neq 0$. We shall show that

$$\delta[\alpha(t)] = \sum_n \frac{\delta(t - t_n)}{|\alpha'(t_n)|} \tag{2-7}$$

In other words, $\delta[\alpha(t)]$ equals a sequence of impulses (Fig. 2-2c) at $t = t_n$ of area $|\alpha'(t_n)|^{-1}$.

To prove (2-7), we divide the t axis into intervals (c_i, c_{i+1}) such that $\alpha(t)$ varies monotonically for $c_i < t < c_{i+1}$. If we express the integral of $f(t)\delta[\alpha(t)]$ from $-\infty$ to ∞ as the sum of integrals in the intervals (c_i, c_{i+1}), we can easily derive (2-7) from (2-6).

With $\alpha(t) = at$, we see from (2-7) that

$$\delta(at) = \frac{\delta(t)}{|a|} \qquad \text{hence} \qquad \delta(-t) = \delta(t) \tag{2-8}$$

Example 2-1

a. If $\alpha(t) = t^2 - 1$, then $t_1 = 1$, $t_2 = -1$, and $\alpha'(t) = 2t$. Hence,

$$\delta(t^2 - 1) = \tfrac{1}{2}\delta(t - 1) + \tfrac{1}{2}\delta(t + 1)$$

b. If $\alpha(t) = \sin t$, then $t_n = n\pi$, $\alpha'(t_n) = \cos n\pi = (-1)^n$. Hence,

$$\delta(\sin t) = \sum_{n=-\infty}^{\infty} \delta(t - n\pi)$$

We finally remark that

$$\delta(t - a) * \delta(t - b) = \delta[t - (a + b)] \tag{2-9}$$

This can be established by showing that each side of (2-9), multiplied by $f(t)$ and integrated from $-\infty$ to ∞, yields $f(a + b)$ (elaborate).

Example 2-2

a. With $f(t) = \delta(t + 1) + \delta(t) + \delta(t - 1)$ (Fig. 2-3) we easily conclude, from (2-9), that

$$f(t) * f(t) = \delta(t + 2) + 2\delta(t + 1) + 3\delta(t) + 2\delta(t - 1) + \delta(t - 2)$$

b. Similarly,

$$\sum_{n=-N}^{N} \delta(t - nT) * \sum_{n=-N}^{N} \delta(t - nT) = \sum_{n=-2N}^{2N} (2N + 1 - |n|)\delta(t - nT)$$

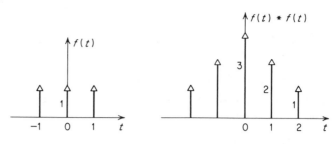

Fig. 2-3

The delta function as a limit Given a family of ordinary functions $k_\alpha(t)$ such that

$$\lim_{\alpha \to \alpha_o} \int_{-\infty}^{\infty} f(t)k_\alpha(t)\, dt = f(0) \tag{2-10}$$

$\delta(t)$ can be written as a limit [13, p2]

$$\delta(t) = \lim k_\alpha(t) \qquad \alpha \to \alpha_o \tag{2-11}$$

in the sense that the number $f(0)$ that $\delta(t)$ assigns to $f(t)$ equals the limit of the integral in (2-10). As examples, we mention the functions $\sqrt{\pi/\alpha}\, e^{-\alpha t^2}$ and $p_\alpha(t)/2\alpha$ (Fig. 2-4), tending to $\delta(t)$ for $\alpha \to 0$.

Of particular interest is the limit

$$\delta(t) = \lim_{\alpha \to \infty} \frac{\sin \alpha t}{\pi t} \tag{2-12}$$

resulting from the basic relationship

$$\lim_{\alpha \to \infty} \int_{-\infty}^{\infty} f(t)\, \frac{\sin \alpha t}{\pi t}\, dt = f(0) \tag{2-13}$$

A consequence of (2-12) is the important identity

$$\frac{1}{2\pi} \int_{-\infty}^{\infty} e^{jwt}\, dw = \delta(t) \tag{2-14}$$

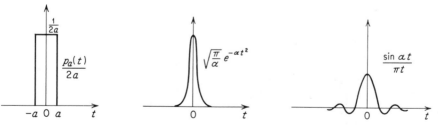

Fig. 2-4

Indeed,

$$\frac{1}{2\pi} \int_{-\infty}^{\infty} e^{jwt} \, dw = \lim_{\alpha \to \infty} \frac{1}{2\pi} \int_{-\alpha}^{\alpha} e^{jwt} \, dw = \lim_{\alpha \to \infty} \frac{\sin \alpha t}{\pi t}$$

TWO-DIMENSIONAL SINGULARITIES

In the xy plane, the product $\delta(x)\delta(y)$ will be interpreted as a unity point mass, in the sense

$$\iint_{-\infty}^{\infty} f(\xi,\eta)\delta(x - \xi)\delta(y - \eta) \, d\xi \, d\eta = f(x,y) \tag{2-15}$$

With $f(x,y) = p_A(x,y)$ as the zero-one function associated with region A [see (1-16)] we obtain, inserting into (2-15),

$$\iint_A \delta(x - a)\delta(y - b) \, dx \, dy = p_A(a,b) \tag{2-16}$$

for every (a,b) not on the boundary of A.

Line masses

The function $\varphi(y)\delta(x - a)$ will be interpreted as a line mass on the line $x = a$, of density $\varphi(y)$. This follows from

$$\iint_{-\infty}^{\infty} f(x,y)\varphi(y)\delta(x - a) \, dx \, dy = \int_{-\infty}^{\infty} f(a,y)\varphi(y) \, dy \tag{2-17}$$

For example, $\delta(x)$ is a line mass of unit density on the y axis, and with $p_a(y)$ a pulse [see (1-3)], $p_a(y)\delta(x)$ is a line segment as in Fig. 2-5.

We note that

$$f(x,y) ** \delta(x) = \iint_{-\infty}^{\infty} f(\xi,\eta)\delta(x - \xi) \, d\xi \, d\eta = \int_{-\infty}^{\infty} f(x,\eta) \, d\eta \tag{2-18}$$

is the x profile $\varphi(x)$ of $f(x,y)$, as defined in (1-14).

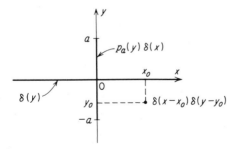

Fig. 2-5

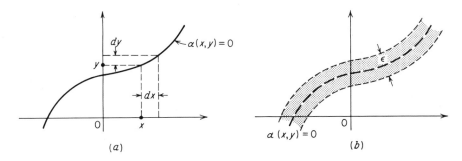

Fig. 2-6

We shall now show that $\delta[\alpha(x,y)]$ is a line mass on the curve $\alpha(x,y) = 0$, with density $\lambda(x,y)$ given by

$$\lambda(x,y) = \frac{1}{\sqrt{\alpha_x{}^2 + \alpha_y{}^2}} \qquad \text{where} \qquad \alpha_x = \frac{\partial\alpha(x,y)}{\partial x}, \; \alpha_y = \frac{\partial\alpha(x,y)}{\partial y}$$

(2-19)

The mass in a vertical strip $(x, x + dx)$ (Fig. 2-6a) equals

$$dm = \frac{dx}{|\alpha_x|}$$

This follows from (2-7). The length of the curve $\alpha(x,y) = 0$ contained in that strip equals

$$ds = \sqrt{(dx)^2 + (dy)^2} = dx\sqrt{1 + \left(\frac{\alpha_y}{\alpha_x}\right)^2}$$

and (2-19) follows because $\lambda = dm/ds$.

A line mass can be approximated by a surface mass on a strip of thickness ϵ (Fig. 2-6b), whose axis is the curve $\alpha(x,y) = 0$ and whose surface density is λ/ϵ.

Example 2-3 On the xy plane, $\delta(r - a)$ is a line mass on the circle

$$\alpha(x,y) = \sqrt{x^2 + y^2} - a = 0$$

Since

$$\alpha_x{}^2 + \alpha_y{}^2 = \frac{x^2}{x^2 + y^2} + \frac{y^2}{x^2 + y^2} = 1$$

its density equals one. The total mass is $2\pi a$.

Product of line masses As we noted, the product $\delta(x - a)\delta(y - b)$ of the line masses $\delta(x - a)$ and $\delta(y - b)$ is a point mass at the intersection

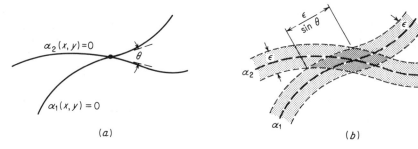

Fig. 2-7

(a,b) of the lines $x = a$ and $y = b$. This can be generalized.† Consider the line masses $\delta[\alpha_1(x,y)]$ and $\delta[\alpha_2(x,y)]$. We shall show that if the two lines intersect at a point (x_o,y_o)

$$\alpha_1(x_o,y_o) = 0 \qquad \alpha_2(x_o,y_o) = 0$$

then the product $\delta[\alpha_1(x,y)]\delta[\alpha_2(x,y)]$ equals a point mass m located at (x_o,y_o) and such that

$$m = \frac{\lambda_1\lambda_2}{\sin\theta} \tag{2-20}$$

In the above, λ_1 and λ_2 are the respective densities of the two line masses at (x_o,y_o), and θ is their intersection angle (Fig. 2-7a). This can be proved by showing that the integral of $f(x,y)\delta[\alpha_1(x,y)]\delta[\alpha_2(x,y)]$ over the whole plane equals $mf(x_o,y_o)$. We shall give a simple justification using the approximation of the two line masses by strips, as in Fig. 2-7b. The intersection of these strips is a rhombus R with sides $\epsilon/\sin\theta$ and area $\epsilon^2/\sin\theta$. The surface density of the product equals zero everywhere except in R, where it equals $\lambda_1\lambda_2/\epsilon^2$. Therefore, the total mass in R is $\lambda_1\lambda_2/\sin\theta$. With $\epsilon \to 0$, we thus obtain (2-20).

If the two lines intersect at several points (x_i,y_i)

$$\alpha_1(x_i,y_i) = 0 \qquad \alpha_2(x_i,y_i) = 0 \tag{2-21}$$

then the product $\delta[\alpha_1(x,y)]\delta[\alpha_2(x,y)]$ equals the point masses at all intersection points. With θ_i the intersection angle at (x_i,y_i), it is known that

$$\sin\theta_i = \frac{|\alpha_{1x}\alpha_{2y} - \alpha_{1y}\alpha_{2x}|}{\sqrt{\alpha_{1x}^2 + \alpha_{1y}^2}\sqrt{\alpha_{2x}^2 + \alpha_{2y}^2}} \tag{2-22}$$

where all partial derivatives are evaluated at (x_i,y_i). From (2-19) to

† A. Papoulis, *J. Opt. Soc. Am.*, vol. 57, pp. 207–213, February, 1967.

(2-21) it follows that

$$\delta[\alpha_1(x,y)]\delta[\alpha_2(x,y)] = \sum_i \frac{\delta(x - x_i)\delta(y - y_i)}{|\alpha_{1x}\alpha_{2y} - \alpha_{1y}\alpha_{2x}|} \tag{2-23}$$

Example 2-4 For $|x_o| < a$, the product

$$\delta(r - a)\delta(x - x_o) \qquad r = \sqrt{x^2 + y^2}$$

equals two point masses m_i at the intersections of the circle $r = a$ with the line $x = x_o$.
The intersection angle is given by (Fig. 2-8a)

$$\sin\theta = \sqrt{1 - \left(\frac{x_o}{a}\right)^2}$$

Hence

$$m_1 = m_2 = \frac{a}{\sqrt{a^2 - x^2}}$$

For $|x_o| > a$, the product is zero. From the above it follows that

$$\varphi(x_o) = \iint\limits_{-\infty}^{\infty} \delta(r - a)\delta(x - x_o)\,dx\,dy = \frac{2ap_a(x_o)}{\sqrt{a^2 - x_o{}^2}}$$

This is the x profile of $\delta(r - a)$ [see (2-18)], and is shown in Fig. 2-8b.

Example 2-5 We shall evaluate the double convolution

$$f(r) = \delta(r - a) ** \delta(r - b)$$

$$= \iint\limits_{-\infty}^{\infty} \delta(\sqrt{\xi^2 + \eta^2} - a)\delta[\sqrt{(x - \xi)^2 + (y - \eta)^2} - b]\,d\xi\,d\eta$$

The factors in the above integral are two circular masses with $\lambda_1 = \lambda_2 = 1$, which are
centered at 0 and r, respectively (Fig. 2-9a). If $a - b < r < a + b$, then the circles

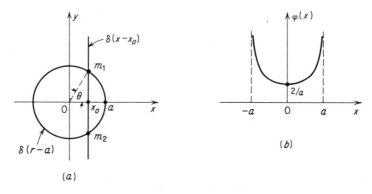

(a)

(b)

Fig. 2-8

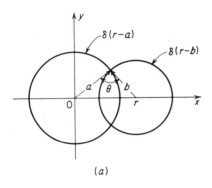

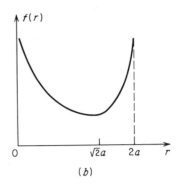

(a)   (b)

Fig. 2-9

intersect at two points at an angle θ such that

$$ab \sin \theta = 2A$$

where A is the area of the triangle with sides a, b, r.   Therefore,

$$f(r) = \frac{2}{\sin \theta} = \frac{ab}{A} \qquad a - b < r < a + b$$

If $r > a + b$ or $r < a - b$, the circles do not intersect.   Hence, $f(r) = 0$.
    If $a = b$, then the above yields the function

$$f(r) = \frac{4a^2}{r \sqrt{4a^2 - r^2}} \qquad r < 2a$$

as shown in Fig. 2-9b.

3. SYSTEMS

We are given a collection of elements f forming a set S_1.   We assume
that arithmetic operations are defined in this set, for example, the sum
$f_1 + f_2$ of two elements f_1 and f_2 or the multiplication af of an element f
by a number a.   We do not elaborate, however, since the properties of
these operations will be evident for the specific cases that we shall soon
consider.

    To every element f of S_1 we assign, according to some rule, an ele-
ment g of another set S_2

$$g = T(f) \tag{3-1}$$

This rule we call a system, and the elements f and g are its input and output (responses) respectively (Fig. 3-1).   Thus, a system is a mapping (or
transformation or operator) of the input set S_1 into the output set S_2.
The sets S_1 and S_2 may be identical.

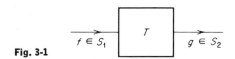

Fig. 3-1

If the elements of S_1 and S_2 are time functions $f(t)$ and $g(t)$, then the system is continuous one-dimensional. If they are functions $f(x,y)$ and $g(x,y)$ of two variables, then it is two-dimensional. If they are sequences of numbers $f(n)$ and $g(n)$, then we have a discrete system. The elements f and g could be vectors (multiinput, multioutput systems) or scalars.

Systems in cascade We are given two systems T^1 and T^2 with respective input and output sets S_1^1, S_1^2 and S_2^1, S_2^2. We say that these systems are in cascade, forming a new system T (Fig. 3-2), if the output of T^1 is input to T^2. With r the output of T^2, we thus have

$$r = T(f) = T^2[T^1(f)] \tag{3-2}$$

For this operation to be meaningful, the output set S_2^1 of system T^1 must be part of the input set S_1^2 of system T^2. For example, if the input to T^2 is the family of all positive functions, it cannot be connected to a system whose output contains functions with negative values.

Linear systems In general, the output of a system must be specified for any input. Thus, since f and af are two separate elements, their outputs do not have to be related. However, if the system is linear, its description is simplified considerably. We say that a system is linear (L) if, with a_1 and a_2 two arbitrary numbers,

$$L[a_1f_1 + a_2f_2] = a_1L[f_1] + a_2L[f_2] \tag{3-3}$$

for any f_1 and f_2 in S_1. Thus, if the outputs to f_1 and f_2 are known, then the output to $a_1f_1 + a_2f_2$ is specified.

In our discussion, we shall consider only continuous linear systems with scalar inputs and outputs.

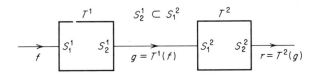

Fig. 3-2

ONE–DIMENSIONAL SYSTEMS

A one-dimensional continuous system is described by a rule of assigning a function $g(t)$ of a class S_2 to a function $f(t)$ of a class S_1 of real or complex functions:

$$g(t) = T[f(t)] \tag{3-4}$$

This rule could be a differential or integral equation, a table, or some other specification. For example, $g(t) = f'(t)$ or $g(t) = f^2(t)$.

In the above interpretation of a system, the elements $f(t)$ are functions specified for every t from $-\infty$ to ∞. Thus, in general, the value $g(t_1)$ of $g(t)$ for $t = t_1$ is determined only if $f(t)$ is known *for every* t. In some cases, this is not necessary. For example, for *memoryless* systems, $g(t)$ is a function

$$g(t) = g[f(t),t] \tag{3-5}$$

of the number $f(t)$ and the time t.

For physical systems, the output $g(t_1)$ depends on the values of $f(t)$ only for $t \leq t_1$. In our language, this means that if two functions $f_1(t)$ and $f_2(t)$ are such that

$$f_1(t) = f_2(t) \qquad \text{for any } t < t_1$$

then with $g_1(t)$ and $g_2(t)$ their respective outputs,

$$g_1(t) = g_2(t) \qquad \text{for } t < t_1$$

A system with the above property will be called *causal.*

Linear systems

Suppose now that the system is linear:

$$L[a_1 f_1(t) + a_2 f_2(t)] = a_1 L[f_1(t)] + a_2 L[f_2(t)] \tag{3-6}$$

$$\text{If} \qquad f(t) \equiv 0 \qquad \text{then} \qquad g(t) \equiv 0 \tag{3-7}$$

because $f(t) = 2f(t)$; hence

$$g(t) = L[f(t)] = L[2f(t)] = 2g(t)$$

If the system is causal and $f(t) = 0$ for $t < t_1$, then $g(t) = 0$ for $t < t_1$. Indeed, since the functions $f(t)$ and 0 are equal for $t < t_1$, it follows from the definition of causality that their responses will be equal for $t < t_1$.

Impulse response
Suppose that the input equals $\delta(t - t_1)$, where t_1 is a parameter. The resulting output

$$h(t;t_1) = L[\delta(t - t_1)] \tag{3-8}$$

is a function of t and the parameter t_1, and it is known as the *impulse response* of the system.

We shall show that the response $g(t)$ to an arbitrary input $f(t)$ can be determined in terms of $f(t)$ and $h(t;t_1)$. Indeed, expressing $f(t)$ as a linear combination of impulses [see (2-2)] we have

$$g(t) = L[f(t)] = L\left[\int_{-\infty}^{\infty} f(\tau)\delta(t - \tau)\, d\tau\right] = \int_{-\infty}^{\infty} f(\tau)L[\delta(t - \tau)]\, d\tau$$

The last equality resulted by writing the integral as a limit of a sum and using (3-6). From the above and (3-8), we thus obtain the fundamental relationship

$$g(t) = \int_{-\infty}^{\infty} f(\tau)h(t;\tau)\, d\tau \tag{3-9}$$

If the system is causal, then

$$h(t;t_1) = 0 \qquad \text{for } t < t_1 \tag{3-10}$$

This follows from the preceding discussion and the fact that $\delta(t - t_1) = 0$ for $t < t_1$. For causal systems, (3-9) takes the form

$$g(t) = \int_{-\infty}^{t} f(\tau)h(t;\tau)\, d\tau \tag{3-11}$$

Linear memoryless systems If a system is memoryless, then for a specific t, $g(t)$ depends only on $f(t)$ and t. If the system is linear also, then it is easy to show that $g(t)$ is a homogeneous linear function of $f(t)$; that is,

$$g(t) = L[f(t)] = a(t)f(t) \tag{3-12}$$

The system is thus specified by the "gain" $a(t)$.

Comment The definition of linearity as given in (3-6) seems to be restrictive if "the initial conditions of the system are not zero," but this is only partially true. Suppose that one is interested in the behavior of a causal system L after a certain time t_o. If

$$g_1(t) = L[f_1(t)] \qquad g_2(t) = L[f_2(t)] \qquad g(t) = L[f(t)]$$

and $f(t) = f_1(t) + f_2(t)$ for $t \geq t_o$ only, it does not of course follow that $g(t) = g_1(t) + g_2(t)$ for $t \geq t_o$ because in our definition of linearity we dealt with signals specified for all t. By writing (3-11) in the form

$$g(t) = \int_{-\infty}^{t_o} f(\tau)h(t;\tau)\, d\tau + \int_{t_o}^{t} f(\tau)h(t;\tau)\, d\tau \qquad t \geq t_o \tag{3-13}$$

one sees that the second integral depends linearly on the input $f(t)$ specified for $t \geq t_o$. The contribution of the first integral is often called "response due to the initial conditions." This separation is of value primarily in the study of "finite-order systems." Terminally, this means that for any $f(t)$

$$\int_{-\infty}^{t_o} f(\tau)h(t;\tau)\, d\tau = a_1\varphi_1(t;t_o) + \cdots + a_n\varphi_n(t;t_o) \qquad t > t_o \quad (3\text{-}14)$$

where $\varphi_1, \ldots, \varphi_n$ are time functions characteristic of the system and independent of the input. The coefficients $a_1, \ldots, a_n$ depend, of course, on $f(t)$. Thus, the "past" of the input is accounted for by the n numbers a_k (initial conditions, or state variables). Such systems can be described by ordinary differential equations and will not be considered further [z1].

The preceding comment holds only if the "initial conditions" are due only to the input prior to $t = t_o$ as in (3-14) (a fact related to the notion of controllability). This is implicit in our definition of a linear system [see also (3-7)].

Shift-invariant systems   We say that a system is shift-invariant (or time-invariant if the independent variable is time) if a shift in the input results in an equal shift in the output:

$$\text{If} \qquad L[f(t)] = g(t) \qquad \text{then} \qquad L[f(t - t_o)] = g(t - t_o) \qquad (3\text{-}15)$$

for any $f(t)$ in S_1 and for any t_o.

If a system is shift-invariant and memoryless, then $g(t) = g[f(t)]$ is a function only of $f(t)$, for example, $f^2(t)$. If a system is linear, shift-invariant, and memoryless, then

$$g(t) = af(t)$$

where a is a constant.

The impulse response $h(t;t_1)$ of a linear shift-invariant system can be determined in terms of the function

$$h(t;0) = h(t)$$

Indeed, since $h(t;t_1)$ is the response to $\delta(t - t_1)$, we conclude from (3-15) that

$$h(t;t_1) = h(t - t_1;0) = h(t - t_1) \qquad (3\text{-}16)$$

Inserting into (3-9), we conclude that the response to an arbitrary input $f(t)$ is given by the convolution integral

$$g(t) = \int_{-\infty}^{\infty} f(\tau)h(t - \tau)\, d\tau = \int_{-\infty}^{\infty} f(t - \tau)h(\tau)\, d\tau \qquad (3\text{-}17)$$

The system is thus determined in terms of the single function $h(t)$.

Conversely, if we are given a function $h(t)$, we can conceive of a system whose output to $f(t)$ is the function $f(t) * h(t)$. Thus, a linear time-invariant system is equivalent to a convolution of a fixed function $h(t)$ with a function $f(t)$ of a certain class.

The response $h(t)$ to the singularity function $\delta(t)$ can be determined as a limit. With $k_n(t)$ a sequence of ordinary functions tending to $\delta(t)$ [see (2-11)], that is,

$$\delta(t) = \lim k_n(t) \qquad n \to \infty$$

and

$$h_n(t) = L[k_n(t)]$$

their response, $h(t)$, is given by the limit

$$h(t) = \lim h_n(t) \qquad n \to \infty \tag{3-18}$$

The system function Suppose that the input to a system (linear shift-invariant) is an exponential

$$f(t) = e^{j\omega t} \tag{3-19}$$

The corresponding response is given by [see (3-17)]

$$g(t) = \int_{-\infty}^{\infty} h(\tau)e^{j\omega(t-\tau)} \, d\tau = e^{j\omega t} \int_{-\infty}^{\infty} h(\tau)e^{-j\omega\tau} \, d\tau$$

The last integral is a function of ω

$$H(\omega) = \int_{-\infty}^{\infty} h(\tau)e^{-j\omega\tau} \, d\tau \tag{3-20}$$

and it is known as the *system function*. The above integral is of course the Fourier transform of $h(t)$ and will be studied in the next chapter.

We thus reach the important conclusion that

$$\text{If} \qquad f(t) = e^{j\omega t} \qquad \text{then} \qquad g(t) = H(\omega)e^{j\omega t} \tag{3-21}$$

or, equivalently,

$$L[e^{j\omega t}] = H(\omega)e^{j\omega t} \tag{3-22}$$

This relationship shows that the exponential $e^{j\omega t}$ is an eigenfunction of our system (linear shift-invariant operator) for any ω. The corresponding eigenvalue is the Fourier transform $H(\omega)$ of the impulse response $h(t)$.

Inversion formula Using the identity (2-14), we shall express $h(t)$ in terms of $H(\omega)$. From the linearity of the system we have

$$h(t) = L[\delta(t)] = L\left[\frac{1}{2\pi}\int_{-\infty}^{\infty} e^{j\omega t} \, d\omega\right] = \frac{1}{2\pi}\int_{-\infty}^{\infty} L[e^{j\omega t}] \, d\omega$$

Hence [see (3-22)]

$$h(t) = \frac{1}{2\pi} \int_{-\infty}^{\infty} H(\omega) e^{j\omega t} \, d\omega \qquad (3\text{-}23)$$

Example 3-1   If

$$f(t) = \sum_n \alpha_n e^{jn\omega_0 t} \qquad (3\text{-}24)$$

then [see (3-22) and (3-6)]

$$g(t) = \sum_n \alpha_n L[e^{jn\omega_0 t}] = \sum_n \alpha_n H(n\omega_0) e^{jn\omega_0 t} \qquad (3\text{-}25)$$

From the above we see that the response to a periodic function is also periodic.

Real systems   The impulse response $h(t)$ of an arbitrary system may be real or complex. If $h(t)$ is real, then we say that the system is real. In this case

$$\operatorname{Re} g(t) = [\operatorname{Re} f(t)] * h(t) = L[\operatorname{Re} f(t)] \qquad (3\text{-}26)$$

as we see from (3-17).   With

$$H(\omega) = R(\omega) + jX(\omega) = A(\omega) e^{j\varphi(\omega)}$$

we conclude that for real systems the response to cos ωt is given by

$$L[\cos \omega t] = \operatorname{Re} H(\omega) e^{j\omega t} = A(\omega) \cos [\omega t + \varphi(\omega)]$$
$$= R(\omega) \cos \omega t - X(\omega) \sin \omega t \qquad (3\text{-}27)$$

This follows from (3-26) and (3-22).

Systems in cascade   Consider two linear systems L_1 and L_2 with impulse responses $h_1(t)$, $h_2(t)$ and system functions $H_1(\omega)$, $H_2(\omega)$, respectively. If these systems are connected in cascade (Fig. 3-3), a new system results with impulse response $h(t)$ and system function $H(\omega)$.   Clearly, $h(t)$ is the output of L_2 when the input to L_1 is $\delta(t)$.   Since the resulting input to L_2 equals $h_1(t)$, we conclude from (3-17) that

$$h(t) = \int_{-\infty}^{\infty} h_1(\tau) h_2(t - \tau) \, d\tau = h_1(t) * h_2(t) \qquad (3\text{-}28)$$

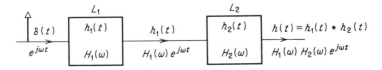

Fig. 3-3

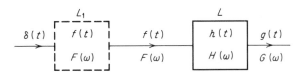

Fig. 3-4

We shall now show that

$$H(\omega) = H_1(\omega)H_2(\omega) \tag{3-29}$$

Indeed, if the input to L_1 is $e^{j\omega t}$, then its output, i.e., the input to L_2, equals $H_1(\omega)e^{j\omega t}$. Therefore, the output to L_2 equals

$$L_2[H_1(\omega)e^{j\omega t}] = H_1(\omega)L_2[e^{j\omega t}] = H_1(\omega)H_2(\omega)e^{j\omega t}$$

and (3-29) follows.

Convolution theorem   Using (3-29), we shall show that the Fourier transforms

$$F(\omega) = \int_{-\infty}^{\infty} f(t)e^{-j\omega t}\,dt \qquad G(\omega) = \int_{-\infty}^{\infty} g(t)e^{-j\omega t}\,dt$$

of the input $f(t)$ and the output $g(t)$ of a given system L are related by

$$G(\omega) = F(\omega)H(\omega) \tag{3-30}$$

where $H(\omega)$ is the system function.

For this purpose, we construct a system L_1 with impulse response $f(t)$, and we connect it with L in cascade (Fig. 3-4).   The impulse response of the combined system equals $g(t)$, and (3-30) follows from (3-29).

TWO-DIMENSIONAL SYSTEMS

A two-dimensional system results from assigning to a function $f(x,y)$ of a class S_1 another function $g(x,y)$ of a class S_2 [see (3-1)].   The preceding discussion can be readily extended to two-dimensional systems.   We shall consider only linear systems, i.e., systems satisfying (3-3).

Point spread   Suppose that the input to the system is a point mass $\delta(x - x_1)\delta(y - y_1)$ at the point (x_1,y_1).   The resulting output will be a function of x, y and the parameters x_1, y_1

$$L[\delta(x - x_1)\delta(y - y_1)] = h(x,y;x_1,y_1) \tag{3-31}$$

This function is known as *point-impulse response* or *point spread*.   Since an arbitrary function $f(x,y)$ can be expressed as the sum (integral) of point masses [see (2-15)]

$$f(x,y) = \iint\limits_{-\infty}^{\infty} f(\xi,\eta)\delta(x - \xi)\delta(y - \eta)\, d\xi\, d\eta$$

we conclude from the linearity of the system that

$$L[f(x,y)] = \iint\limits_{-\infty}^{\infty} f(\xi,\eta)L[\delta(x - \xi)\delta(y - \eta)]\, d\xi\, d\eta$$

Hence, the resulting output is given by

$$g(x,y) = \iint\limits_{-\infty}^{\infty} f(\xi,\eta)h(x,y;\xi,\eta)\, d\xi\, d\eta \qquad (3\text{-}32)$$

The system is thus determined in terms of the two-parameter family of functions $h(x,y;x_1,y_1)$.

Shift-invariant systems A system is called shift-invariant if a displacement of the input results in an equal displacement of the output:

If $L[f(x,y)] = g(x,y)$ then
$$L[f(x - x_o, y - y_o)] = g(x - x_o, y - y_o) \qquad (3\text{-}33)$$

From the above it follows, as in (3-16), that

$$h(x,y;x_1,y_1) = h(x - x_1, y - y_1; 0, 0)$$

The system is thus determined in terms of the response

$$h(x,y;0,0) = h(x,y) = L[\delta(x)\delta(y)] \qquad (3\text{-}34)$$

to the point mass $\delta(x)\delta(y)$ at the origin.

Inserting into (3-32), we obtain the response $g(x,y)$ as a double convolution of the input $f(x,y)$ with the point spread $h(x,y)$:

$$g(x,y) = \iint\limits_{-\infty}^{\infty} f(\xi,\eta)h(x - \xi, y - \eta)\, d\xi\, d\eta = f(x,y) ** h(x,y) \qquad (3\text{-}35)$$

Special cases   If

$$h(x,y) = h(x)$$

is independent of y, then

$$g(x,y) = \int_{-\infty}^{\infty} h(x - \xi) \int_{-\infty}^{\infty} f(\xi,\eta)\, d\eta\, d\xi = g(x)$$

is also independent of y.   With

$$\varphi(x) = \int_{-\infty}^{\infty} f(x,y)\, dy$$

the x profile of the input, we thus have

$$g(x) = \int_{-\infty}^{\infty} h(x - \xi)\varphi(\xi) \, d\xi = h(x) * \varphi(x) \tag{3-36}$$

If

$$h(x,y) = \delta(x)$$

then

$$g(x,y) = \delta(x) * \varphi(x) = \varphi(x) \tag{3-37}$$

Thus, if the point spread of a system equals the line mass $\delta(x)$, then its response to $f(x,y)$ equals the x profile $\varphi(x)$ of $f(x,y)$.

Example 3-2 If $f(x,y) = \sum_i \delta(x - x_i)\delta(y - y_i)$ is a sum of point masses, then

$$g(x,y) = \sum_i h(x - x_i, y - y_i)$$

is the sum of the displacements of $h(x,y)$ as in Fig. 3-5.

The system function Suppose that

$$f(x,y) = e^{j(ux+vy)} \tag{3-38}$$

Inserting into (3-35), we obtain [see also (1-17)]

$$g(x,y) = \iint_{-\infty}^{\infty} h(\xi,\eta)e^{j[u(x-\xi)+v(y-\eta)]} \, d\xi \, d\eta$$

With

$$H(u,v) = \iint_{-\infty}^{\infty} h(\xi,\eta)e^{-j(u\xi+v\eta)} \, d\xi \, d\eta \tag{3-39}$$

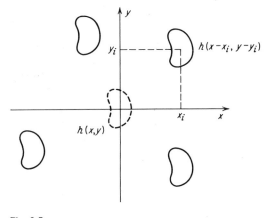

Fig. 3-5

we thus have

$$g(x,y) = L[e^{j(ux+vy)}] = H(u,v)e^{j(ux+vy)} \tag{3-40}$$

The function $H(u,v)$ is the two-dimensional Fourier transform of $h(x,y)$, and it is known as the system function.

Example 3-3   If $f(x,y) = e^{jux}$, then

$$g(x,y) = H(u,0)e^{jux}$$

as we see from (3-40) with $v = 0$.

We shall now express $h(x,y)$ in terms of $H(u,v)$.   From the identity [see (2-14)]

$$\delta(x)\delta(y) = \frac{1}{4\pi^2} \iint\limits_{-\infty}^{\infty} e^{j(ux+vy)} \, du \, dv \tag{3-41}$$

and the linearity of the system, it follows that

$$L[\delta(x)\delta(y)] = \frac{1}{4\pi^2} \iint\limits_{-\infty}^{\infty} L[e^{j(ux+vy)}] \, du \, dv$$

Hence [see (3-34) and (3-40)],

$$h(x,y) = \frac{1}{4\pi^2} \iint\limits_{-\infty}^{\infty} H(u,v)e^{j(ux+vy)} \, du \, dv \tag{3-42}$$

This is the inversion formula for two-dimensional Fourier transforms.

Line spread   The response of a system to a line mass $\delta(x)$ along the $x = 0$ axis is known as line-impulse response or *line spread*.   Denoting it by s_{10}, we see from (3-35) that it is a function only of x, and it is given by

$$L[\delta(x)] = s_{10}(x) = \int_{-\infty}^{\infty} h(x,y) \, dy \tag{3-43}$$

Thus, $s_{10}(x)$ equals the x profile of $h(x,y)$.

We shall now determine the response

$$s_{\alpha\beta}(x,y) = L[\delta(\alpha x + \beta y)] \qquad \alpha^2 + \beta^2 = 1 \tag{3-44}$$

to a line mass of unit density [see (2-19)] on the line $\alpha x + \beta y = 0$.   For this purpose, we form the function

$$s_{\alpha\beta}(z) = \frac{1}{|\alpha\beta|} \int_{-\infty}^{\infty} h\left(\frac{z-\tau}{\alpha}, \frac{\tau}{\beta}\right) d\tau = \frac{1}{|\alpha|} \int_{-\infty}^{\infty} h\left(\frac{z-\beta y}{\alpha}, y\right) dy \tag{3-45}$$

It is easy to see that $s_{\alpha\beta}(z) \, dz$ equals the mass in the strip of Fig. 3-6

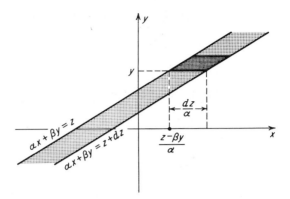

Fig. 3-6

bounded by the lines $\alpha x + \beta y = z$ and $\alpha x + \beta y = z + dz$. Furthermore

$$s_{\alpha\beta}(x,y) = h(x,y) ** \delta(\alpha x + \beta y) = s_{\alpha\beta}(\alpha x + \beta y) \tag{3-46}$$

(elaborate). Thus, $s_{\alpha\beta}(x,y)$ is constant along the line $\alpha x + \beta y = z$. We observe that if $s_{\alpha\beta}(x,y)$ is known for any α, then $h(x,y)$ can be determined. This is established in Chap. 3, Sec. 4, in terms of Fourier transforms [see Chap. 3, (4-27)].

SYSTEMS WITH CIRCULAR SYMMETRY

We say that a system has circular symmetry if

$$h(x,y) = h(r) \qquad r = \sqrt{x^2 + y^2} \tag{3-47}$$

In Chap. 5, Sec. 1, we show that the corresponding system function is the Hankel transform $2\pi\bar{h}(w)$ of $2\pi h(r)$, where $w = \sqrt{u^2 + v^2}$.

If $f(x,y) = f(r)$, then the corresponding response $g(x,y)$ also has circular symmetry, and it is given by [see (1-19)]

$$g(r) = f(r) ** h(r) \tag{3-48}$$

It is easy to show that, because of the symmetry of $h(x,y)$, the generalized line spread $s_{\alpha\beta}(z)$ is independent of α and β; hence,

$$s_{\alpha\beta}(x) = s_{10}(x) = s(x) = \int_{-\infty}^{\infty} h(r)\, dy \tag{3-49}$$

Conversely, if the line spread $s_{\alpha\beta}(z)$ of a two-dimensional system is independent of α and β, then the system has circular symmetry. This follows from Chap. 3, (4-27).

Example 3-4 Suppose that the point spread is a circular mass

$$h(r) = \delta(r - a)$$

The corresponding line spread is given by [see Example 2-4]

$$s(x) = \int_{-\infty}^{\infty} \delta(r - a)\, dy = \begin{cases} \dfrac{2a}{\sqrt{a^2 - x^2}} & |x| < a \\ 0 & |x| > a \end{cases} \tag{3-50}$$

Point spread from line spread

We shall now determine the point spread $h(r)$ in terms of the line spread[†] $s(x)$. For this purpose, we form the function

$$q(x) = \int_{-\infty}^{\infty} s(r)\, dy \qquad r = \sqrt{x^2 + y^2} \tag{3-51}$$

and we maintain that

$$2\pi r h(r) = -\frac{dq(r)}{dr} \qquad \text{for } r > 0 \tag{3-52}$$

Proof The proof will be based on the fact that $h(r)U(r)$ can be expressed as a linear combination of impulses

$$h(r) = \int_{-\infty}^{\infty} h(a)\delta(r - a)\, da \qquad r > 0 \tag{3-53}$$

Since the integral equation (3-49) is linear, it follows from (3-53) that it suffices to establish (3-52) for

$$h(r) = \delta(r - a)$$

only. The line spread of $\delta(r - a)$ is given by (3-50), and the correspond-

[†] E. W. Marchand, *J. Opt. Soc.*, vol. 9, p. 915, 1964.

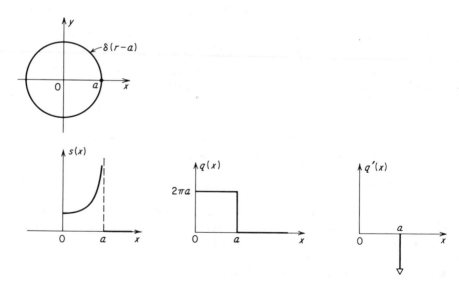

Fig. 3-7

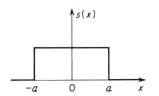 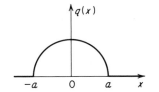

Fig. 3-8

ing $q(x)$ by

$$q(x) = \int_{-(a^2-x^2)^{1/2}}^{(a^2-x^2)^{1/2}} \frac{2a \, dy}{\sqrt{a^2 - r^2}} = 2\pi a \qquad \text{for } |x| < a$$

For $|x| > a$, $q(x) = 0$ (Fig. 3-7).   Hence [see (2-3)]

$$\frac{dq(x)}{dx} = 2\pi a \delta(x - a) = -2\pi x \delta(x - a)$$

and (3-52) follows (for another proof see Prob. 2-10).

Example 3-5   Suppose that the line spread $s(x)$ is given by (Fig. 3-8)

$$s(x) = \begin{cases} 1 & |x| < a \\ 0 & |x| < a \end{cases}$$

We shall determine the corresponding point spread $h(r)$.   From Example 1-4 we have

$$q(x) = \sqrt{a^2 - x^2}$$

for $|x| < a$ and zero for $|x| > a$.   Hence,

$$h(r) = -\frac{1}{2\pi r} \frac{dq(r)}{dr} = \frac{1}{\pi \sqrt{a^2 - r^2}}$$

for $r < a$ and $h(r) = 0$ for $r > a$.

Example 3-6   If (Fig. 3-9)

$$s(x) = \begin{cases} 2\sqrt{a^2 - x^2} & |x| < a \\ 0 & |x| > a \end{cases}$$

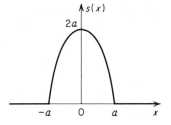 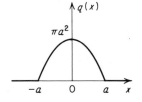 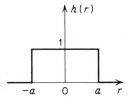

Fig. 3-9

then

$$q(x) = 2 \int_{-(a^2-x^2)^{1/2}}^{(a^2-x^2)^{1/2}} \sqrt{a^2 - r^2} \, dy = \begin{cases} \pi(a^2 - x^2) & |x| < a \\ 0 & |x| > a \end{cases}$$

Hence

$$h(r) = \begin{cases} 1 & r < a \\ 0 & r > a \end{cases}$$

We finally remark that $h(r)$ can be obtained from $s(x)$ with the help of transforms. As we show in Chap. 5, Sec. 2, the Fourier transform of $s(x)$ equals the Hankel transform of $2\pi h(r)$.

Response in terms of line spread   We are given a circularly symmetrical system with point spread $h(r)$ and input $f(r)$. Using (3-52), we shall express its response

$$g(r) = f(r) ** h(r) \tag{3-54}$$

in terms of the line spread [see (2-18)]

$$s(x) = h(r) ** \delta(x)$$

For this purpose, we form the x profiles $\varphi_f(x)$ and $\varphi_g(x)$ of $f(r)$ and $g(r)$, respectively:

$$\varphi_f(x) = f(r) ** \delta(x) \qquad \varphi_g(x) = g(r) ** \delta(x) \tag{3-55}$$

We maintain that

$$\varphi_g(x) = \varphi_f(x) * s(x) \tag{3-56}$$

Proof   If, in (3-36), we change the functions $\varphi(x)$ and $h(x)$ to $\varphi_f(x)$ and $s(x)$, we obtain

$$f(r) ** s(x) = \varphi_f(x) * s(x) \tag{3-57}$$

(elaborate).   From the above and the associative property of convolution it follows that

$$\varphi_g(x) = f(r) ** h(r) ** \delta(x) = f(r) ** s(x) = \varphi_f(x) * s(x)$$

and (3-56) results.

We have, thus, expressed the x profile $\varphi_g(x)$ of $g(r)$ in terms of $\varphi_f(x)$ and $s(x)$.   To complete the determination of $g(r)$, we form the function

$$q_g(x) = \int_{-\infty}^{\infty} \varphi_g(r) \, dy$$

From (3-52) it then follows that

$$g(r) = -\frac{1}{2\pi r} \frac{dq_g(r)}{dr}$$

Eigenfunctions We shall now determine a point spread $h(r)$ with the property that it is proportional to its line spread. In other words, we shall find the eigenfunctions $h(r)$ of the integral equation

$$s(x) = \int_{-\infty}^{\infty} h(\sqrt{x^2 + y^2})\, dy = \lambda h(x) \tag{3-58}$$

We maintain that for any λ

$$h(r) = Ae^{-\alpha r^2} \tag{3-59}$$

where A is an arbitrary constant, and $\alpha = \pi/\lambda^2$.

Proof Since $s(x) = \lambda h(x)$, it follows from (3-51) and (3-58) that

$$q(x) = \int_{-\infty}^{\infty} s(\sqrt{x^2 + y^2})\, dy = \lambda \int_{-\infty}^{\infty} h(\sqrt{x^2 + y^2})\, dy = \lambda^2 h(x)$$

Hence [see (3-52)]

$$2\pi r h(r) = -\lambda^2 \frac{dh(r)}{dr}$$

Solving, we obtain (3-59).

Application Suppose that a function $h(x,y)$ is of the form $h_1(x)h_2(y)$ and that it has circular symmetry:

$$h(x,y) = h_1(x)h_2(y) \qquad h(x,y) = h(r) \qquad r = \sqrt{x^2 + y^2}$$

We shall show that†

$$h(r) = Ae^{-\alpha r^2}$$

Indeed, if the area of $h_2(x)$ equals β, then

$$s(x) = \int_{-\infty}^{\infty} h(x,y)\, dy = h_1(x) \int_{-\infty}^{\infty} h_2(y)\, dy = \beta h_1(x)$$

Furthermore,

$$h(x) = h(x,0) = h_1(x)h_2(0)$$

Hence, $s(x) = \beta h(x)/h_2(0)$. With $\lambda = \beta/h_2(0)$, we thus conclude that $s(x)$ satisfies (3-58); therefore, $h(r)$ is given by (3-59).

PROBLEMS

2-1. Show that if $g(t) = f(t) * h(t)$, then

$$f(t + a) * h(t + a) = g(t + 2a) \qquad f(at) * h(at) = \frac{g(at)}{|a|}$$

† For an application in probability theory see A. Papoulis, *IEEE Trans. Inform. Theory*, vol. IT-14, January, 1968.

2-2. Show that

$$e^{-\alpha t^2} * e^{-\beta t^2} = \sqrt{\frac{\pi\gamma}{\alpha\beta}}\, e^{-\gamma t^2} \qquad \text{where} \qquad \frac{1}{\gamma} = \frac{1}{\alpha} + \frac{1}{\beta}$$

2-3. Show that

$$e^{j\alpha t^2} * e^{-j\alpha t^2} = \frac{\pi}{|\alpha|}\, \delta(t)$$

2-4. Show that

$$\int_{-1}^{1} \delta(x - \alpha t)\, dt = \begin{cases} \dfrac{1}{\alpha} & |x| < \alpha \\ 0 & |x| > \alpha \end{cases} \qquad \int_{-\infty}^{\infty} \delta(x - y^3)\, dy = \frac{1}{3\sqrt[3]{x^2}}$$

2-5. Show that

(a) $\qquad \delta[(t - 1)(t - 2)] = \delta(t - 1) + \delta(t - 2)$

(b) $\qquad$ If $\quad f(t) \sin t \equiv 0 \quad$ then $\quad f(t) = \displaystyle\sum_{n=-\infty}^{\infty} c_n \delta(t - n\pi)$

2-6. With θ as in Fig. P2-6 and $r = \sqrt{x^2 + y^2}$, show that

$$p_a(r) ** \delta(r - b) = \begin{cases} 2\pi & r < a - b \\ 2b\theta & a - b < r < a + b \\ 0 & r > a + b \end{cases}$$

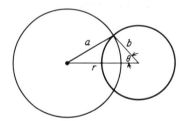

Fig. P2-6

2-7. The system function of a real system equals $R(\omega) + jX(\omega)$. Show that if the input is $2\cos^2 at$, then the resulting response equals $R(0) + R(2a)\cos 2at$.

2-8. Show that if the impulse response of a linear system L is real and even, then $\cos at$ is an eigenfunction of L; that is, $L(\cos at) = \varphi(a)\cos at$.

2-9. The response $g(x,y)$ of a system to $f(x,y) = \delta(x)$ equals $s(x)$ (line spread). With $S(u)$ the Fourier transform of $s(x)$, show that

$$\text{If} \qquad f(x,y) = e^{ju_o x} \qquad \text{then} \qquad g(x,y) = S(u_o)e^{ju_o x}$$

2-10. Show that if

$$s(x) = \int_{-\infty}^{\infty} h(r)\, dy \qquad q(x) = \int_{-\infty}^{\infty} s(r)\, dy \qquad r = \sqrt{x^2 + y^2}$$

then

(a) $\qquad q(x) = 2\pi \displaystyle\int_{0}^{\infty} yh(r)\, dy \qquad$ hence $\qquad h(x) = -\dfrac{1}{2\pi x}\dfrac{dq(x)}{dx}$

(b) $\qquad h(x) = -\dfrac{1}{\pi}\displaystyle\int_{x}^{\infty} \dfrac{s'(r)}{\sqrt{r^2 - x^2}}\, dr$

3
FOURIER TRANSFORMS

The basic properties of Fourier integrals are presented with some elaboration on energy theorems and Hilbert transforms. Examples include Bessel functions and Fresnel integrals. The analysis is extended to two-dimensional signals.

1. ONE–DIMENSIONAL SIGNALS

Given a function $f(t)$ real or complex, we form the integral†

$$F(\omega) = \int_{-\infty}^{\infty} f(t)e^{-j\omega t}\, dt \tag{1-1}$$

If this integral exists for every real ω, it defines the Fourier transform $F(\omega)$ of the signal $f(t)$. A sufficient condition for the existence of $F(\omega)$ is the absolute integrability of $f(t)$.

† In this book, all improper integrals will be interpreted as Cauchy principle values [p2].

The function $f(t)$ can be recovered from $F(\omega)$ by the *inversion formula*

$$f(t) = \frac{1}{2\pi} \int_{-\infty}^{\infty} F(\omega)e^{j\omega t}\, d\omega \tag{1-2}$$

The above holds at every continuity point of $f(t)$. If $f(t)$ is discontinuous at $t = t_o$, then the integral (1-2) equals the average of $f(t_o{}^+)$ and $f(t_o{}^-)$ [p2]. If, therefore, we assume that

$$f(t) = \frac{f(t^+) + f(t^-)}{2} \tag{1-3}$$

then (1-2) will hold for every t.

The inversion formula was formally derived in Chap. 2, (3-23), with the help of the integral representation in Chap. 2, (2-14), of the delta function. We shall repeat the proof using the identity [see Chap. 2, (2-12)]

$$\delta(t - \tau) = \lim_{a\to\infty} \frac{\sin a(t - \tau)}{\pi(t - \tau)} \tag{1-4}$$

Integrating (1-1) from $-a$ to a and changing the order of integration, we find

$$\int_{-a}^{a} F(\omega)e^{j\omega t}\, d\omega = \int_{-\infty}^{\infty} f(\tau) \int_{-a}^{a} e^{j\omega(t-\tau)}\, d\omega\, d\tau = 2 \int_{-\infty}^{\infty} f(\tau) \frac{\sin a(t - \tau)}{t - \tau}\, d\tau$$

From the above and (1-4) it follows with $a \to \infty$ that

$$\int_{-\infty}^{\infty} F(\omega)e^{j\omega t}\, d\omega = 2\pi \int_{-\infty}^{\infty} f(\tau)\delta(t - \tau)\, d\tau = 2\pi f(t)$$

and (1-2) results.

We shall use the notation

$$f(t) \leftrightarrow F(\omega)$$

to indicate that the functions $f(t)$ and $F(\omega)$ are related by (1-1) and (1-2). If $f(t)$ is *real*, then its transform

$$F(\omega) = R(\omega) + jX(\omega) = A(\omega)e^{j\varphi(\omega)}$$

has the property that

$$\begin{array}{ll} R(-\omega) = R(\omega) & X(-\omega) = -X(\omega) \\ A(-\omega) = A(\omega) & \varphi(-\omega) = -\varphi(\omega) \end{array} \tag{1-5}$$

as it is easy to see. Furthermore,

$$f(t) = \frac{1}{2\pi} \int_{-\infty}^{\infty} A(\omega)e^{j[\omega t+\varphi(\omega)]}\, d\omega = \frac{1}{\pi} \operatorname{Re} \int_{0}^{\infty} A(\omega)e^{[\omega t+\varphi(\omega)]}\, d\omega \tag{1-6}$$

In Sec. 3 we show that the imaginary part of the last integral is the Hilbert transform of $f(t)$.

If $f(t)$ is real and even, then $F(\omega)$ is real, and it is given by

$$F(\omega) = 2 \operatorname{Re} \int_0^\infty f(t) e^{-j\omega t}\, dt \qquad (1\text{-}7)$$

Example 1-1 The function

$$f(t) = e^{-\alpha|t|} \qquad \alpha > 0$$

is real and even. Hence

$$F(\omega) = 2 \operatorname{Re} \int_0^\infty e^{-\alpha t} e^{-j\omega t}\, dt = \operatorname{Re} \frac{2}{\alpha + j\omega} = \frac{2\alpha}{\alpha^2 + \omega^2}$$

We observe that if a function $f(t)$ is expressed as an integral of the form (1-2), then the integrand $F(\omega)$ is its Fourier transform. This is illustrated in the next example.

Example 1-2 The properties of the Bessel functions are discussed in Chap. 5. In the following, we derive their Fourier transforms using the integral representation

$$J_{2n}(t) = \frac{1}{\pi} \int_{-\pi/2}^{\pi/2} \cos 2n\theta e^{jt \sin\theta}\, d\theta$$

$$J_{2n+1}(t) = \frac{-j}{\pi} \int_{-\pi/2}^{\pi/2} \sin (2n+1)\theta e^{jt \sin\theta}\, d\theta \qquad (1\text{-}8)$$

which results readily from Chap. 5, (5-5).

Consider first the function

$$J_0(t) = \frac{1}{\pi} \int_{-\pi/2}^{\pi/2} e^{jt \sin\theta}\, d\theta \qquad (1\text{-}9)$$

With

$$\omega = \sin \theta \qquad d\omega = \cos\theta\, d\theta = \sqrt{1 - \omega^2}\, d\theta$$

(1-9) yields

$$J_0(t) = \frac{1}{\pi} \int_{-1}^{1} \frac{e^{j\omega t}}{\sqrt{1 - \omega^2}}\, d\omega$$

This integral is of the form of (1-2), where $F(\omega) = 2(1 - \omega^2)^{-\frac{1}{2}}$ for $|\omega| < 1$ and zero for $|\omega| > 1$. Therefore,

$$J_0(t) \leftrightarrow \begin{cases} \dfrac{2}{\sqrt{1 - \omega^2}} & |\omega| < 1 \\ 0 & |\omega| < 1 \end{cases} \qquad (1\text{-}10)$$

From the above and from the evenness of $J_0(t)$ we conclude that

$$\int_{-\infty}^{\infty} J_0(t) e^{-j\omega t}\, dt = 2 \int_0^\infty J_0(t) \cos \omega t\, dt = \begin{cases} \dfrac{2}{\sqrt{1 - \omega^2}} & |\omega| < 1 \\ 0 & |\omega| > 1 \end{cases} \qquad (1\text{-}11)$$

The general case can be developed similarly. With $C_n(\omega)$ and $S_n(\omega)$, the Tchebycheff cosine and sine polynomials, defined by

$$C_n(\omega) = \cos n\theta \qquad S_n(\omega) = \sin n\theta \qquad \sin \theta = \omega$$

we maintain that

$$J_{2n}(t) \leftrightarrow \frac{2C_{2n}(\omega)p_1(\omega)}{\sqrt{1 - \omega^2}} \qquad p_1(\omega) = \begin{cases} 1 & |\omega| < 1 \\ 0 & |\omega| > 1 \end{cases} \qquad (1\text{-}12)$$

$$J_{2n+1}(t) \leftrightarrow \frac{-2jS_{2n+1}(\omega)p_1(\omega)}{\sqrt{1 - \omega^2}} \qquad\qquad\qquad\qquad (1\text{-}13)$$

Indeed, with $\omega = \sin \theta$, we have

$$J_{2n}(t) = \frac{2}{2\pi} \int_{-1}^{1} \frac{C_{2n}(\omega)}{\sqrt{1 - \omega^2}} e^{j\omega t} \, d\omega$$

as it is easy to see, and (1-12) results.   The proof of (1-13) is identical.

Example 1-3   We shall show that the transform of the sign function equals $2/j\omega$:

$$\operatorname{sgn} t = \begin{cases} 1 & t > 0 \\ -1 & t < 0 \end{cases} \leftrightarrow \frac{2}{j\omega} \qquad\qquad (1\text{-}14)$$

The inverse transform of $2/j\omega$ is given by

$$\frac{1}{2\pi} \int_{-\infty}^{\infty} \frac{2}{j\omega} e^{j\omega t} \, d\omega = \int_{-\infty}^{\infty} \frac{\sin \omega t}{\pi t} \, d\omega$$

The last integral equals one for $t > 0$ as it is well known, and (1-14) follows.

THEOREMS AND EXAMPLES

In Table 1-1 we list a number of simple theorems [p2] that can be readily derived from (1-1) or (1-2).   It is assumed that all functions involved have Fourier transforms.   The examples of Table 1-2 are discussed in the text.

Example 1-4 (Interference)   Consider the functions $f(t)$ and $F(\omega)$ of Fig. 1-1.   With t_o a given constant, we have

$$f(t + t_o) + f(t - t_o) \leftrightarrow F(\omega)(e^{j\omega t_o} + e^{-j\omega t_o}) = 2F(\omega) \cos \omega t_o$$

Clearly, $F(\omega) \cos \omega t_o$ equals zero for

$$\omega t_o = (n + \tfrac{1}{2})\pi$$

Thus, the distance between consecutive zeros equals

$$\frac{\pi}{t_o}$$

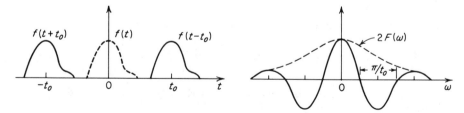

Fig. 1-1

Table 1-1 Fourier transform theorems

$f(t) = \dfrac{1}{2\pi} \displaystyle\int_{-\infty}^{\infty} F(\omega)e^{j\omega t}\, d\omega$	$F(\omega) = \displaystyle\int_{-\infty}^{\infty} f(t)e^{-j\omega t}\, dt$
$f(at)$	$\dfrac{1}{\lvert a \rvert} F\left(\dfrac{\omega}{a}\right)$
$f^*(t)$	$F^*(-\omega)$
$F(t)$	$2\pi f(-\omega)$
$f(t - t_o)$	$F(\omega)e^{-jt_o\omega}$
$f(t)e^{j\omega_o t}$	$F(\omega - \omega_o)$
$f(t)\cos \omega_o t$	$\dfrac{1}{2}[F(\omega + \omega_o) + F(\omega - \omega_o)]$
$f(t)\sin \omega_o t$	$\dfrac{j}{2}[F(\omega + \omega_o) - F(\omega - \omega_o)]$
$\dfrac{d^n f(t)}{dt^n}$	$(j\omega)^n F(\omega)$
$(-jt)^n f(t)$	$\dfrac{d^n F(\omega)}{d\omega^n}$
$m_n = \displaystyle\int_{-\infty}^{\infty} t^n f(t)\, dt$	$F(\omega) = \displaystyle\sum_{n=0}^{\infty} \dfrac{m_n}{n!}(-j\omega)^n$
$\displaystyle\int_{-\infty}^{\infty} f_1(\tau)f_2(t - \tau)\, d\tau$	$F_1(\omega)F_2(\omega)$
$\displaystyle\int_{-\infty}^{\infty} f(t + \tau)f^*(\tau)\, d\tau$	$\lvert F(\omega) \rvert^2$
$\displaystyle\int_{-\infty}^{\infty} \lvert f(t) \rvert^2\, dt = \dfrac{1}{2\pi} \displaystyle\int_{-\infty}^{\infty} \lvert F(\omega) \rvert^2\, d\omega$	
$f(t) + j\hat{f}(t)$	$2F(\omega)U(\omega)$
$\hat{f}(t)$	$-j\,\text{sgn}\,\omega F(\omega)$
$\displaystyle\sum_{n=-\infty}^{\infty} f(t + nT) = \dfrac{1}{T} \displaystyle\sum_{n=-\infty}^{\infty} F\left(\dfrac{2\pi n}{T}\right)e^{j2\pi nt/T}$	

Table 1-2 Examples of Fourier transforms

$$f(t) = \frac{1}{2\pi} \int_{-\infty}^{\infty} F(\omega) e^{j\omega t}\, d\omega \qquad\qquad F(\omega) = \int_{-\infty}^{\infty} f(t) e^{-j\omega t}\, dt$$

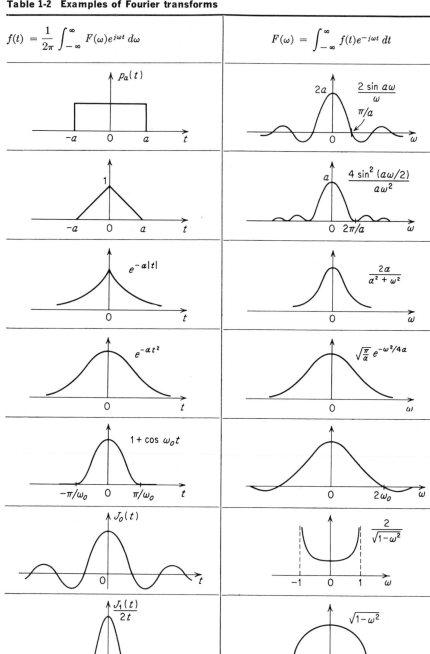

Table 1-2 Examples of Fourier transforms (continued)

$f(t) = \dfrac{1}{2\pi}\displaystyle\int_{-\infty}^{\infty} F(\omega)e^{j\omega t}\,d\omega$	$F(\omega) = \displaystyle\int_{-\infty}^{\infty} f(t)e^{-j\omega t}\,dt$
$e^{-\alpha t}U(t)$	$\dfrac{1}{\alpha + j\omega}$
$\dfrac{j}{\pi t}$	$\operatorname{sgn}\omega$
$t^{\alpha}U(t) \qquad \alpha > -1$	$\dfrac{\Gamma(\alpha + 1)}{|\omega|^{\alpha+1}}\; e^{\pm \frac{j\pi(\alpha+1)}{2}} \qquad \begin{array}{l} -\ \text{if } \omega > 0 \\ +\ \text{if } \omega < 0 \end{array}$
$t^{n}e^{-\alpha t}U(t) \qquad \alpha > 0$	$\dfrac{n!}{(\alpha + j\omega)^{n+1}}$
$J_{n}(t)$	$\begin{cases} \dfrac{2\cos\,(n\arcsin\omega)}{\sqrt{1-\omega^2}} & n \text{ even } |\omega| < 1 \\[2ex] \dfrac{-2j\sin\,(n\arcsin\omega)}{\sqrt{1-\omega^2}} & n \text{ odd } |\omega| < 1 \\[2ex] 0 & |\omega| > 1 \end{cases}$
$\dfrac{J_{n}(t)}{t^{n}}$	$\begin{array}{ll} \dfrac{2(1-\omega^2)^{n-\frac{1}{2}}}{1\cdot 3\cdot 5\,\cdots\,(2n-1)} & |\omega| < 1 \\[2ex] 0 & |\omega| > 1 \end{array}$
$e^{j\alpha t^{2}}$	$\sqrt{\dfrac{\pi}{\alpha}}\; e^{j\pi/4}e^{-j\omega^2/4\alpha}$
$\cos \alpha t^{2}$	$\sqrt{\dfrac{\pi}{\alpha}}\,\cos\left(\dfrac{\omega^2}{4\alpha} - \dfrac{\pi}{4}\right)$
$\sin \alpha t^{2}$	$-\sqrt{\dfrac{\pi}{\alpha}}\,\sin\left(\dfrac{\omega^2}{4\alpha} - \dfrac{\pi}{4}\right)$
$e^{j\alpha t^{2}} \qquad 0 < t < T$	$\sqrt{\dfrac{\pi}{2\alpha}}\; e^{-j\omega^2/4\alpha}\left[\mathbf{F}\left(\sqrt{\alpha}\,T - \dfrac{\omega}{2\sqrt{\alpha}}\right) + \mathbf{F}\left(\dfrac{\omega}{2\sqrt{\alpha}}\right)\right]$
$0 \qquad \text{otherwise}$	$\mathbf{F}(x) = \sqrt{\dfrac{2}{\pi}}\displaystyle\int_{0}^{x} e^{jy^2}\,dy$

Therefore, by measuring this distance, we can determine the constant t_o. This principle is used in interferometers.

Example 1-5 (Poisson's integral formula)   We shall determine the Fourier transform $F_n(\omega)$ of the function

$$R_n(t) = \frac{J_n(t)}{t^n} \tag{1-15}$$

For this purpose, we shall use the recursion formula (5-19), Chap. 5:

$$R_n''(t) + R_n(t) = (2n + 1)R_{n+1}(t) \tag{1-16}$$

Since

$$R_n''(t) \leftrightarrow -\omega^2 F_n(\omega)$$

we conclude, taking the transforms of both sides of (1-16), that

$$(1 - \omega^2)F_n(\omega) = (2n + 1)F_{n+1}(\omega) \qquad n = 0, 1, \ldots \tag{1-17}$$

Hence,

$$F_n(\omega) = \frac{1 - \omega^2}{2n - 1}F_{n-1}(\omega) = \cdots = \frac{(1 - \omega^2)^n F_o(\omega)}{(2n - 1)(2n - 3) \cdots 3.1} \tag{1-18}$$

as we see by repeated application of (1-17). But [see (1-10)]

$$R_o(t) = J_o(t) \leftrightarrow \frac{2p_1(\omega)}{\sqrt{1 - \omega^2}} = F_o(\omega)$$

Therefore,

$$F_n(\omega) = \frac{2(1 - \omega^2)^{n-1/2}}{1.3 \cdots (2n - 3)(2n - 1)} \qquad \text{for } |\omega| < 1 \tag{1-19}$$

and equals zero for $|\omega| > 1$.

With $n = 1$, the pair

$$\frac{J_1(t)}{t} \leftrightarrow \begin{cases} 2\sqrt{1 - \omega^2} & |\omega| < 1 \\ 0 & |\omega| > 1 \end{cases} \tag{1-20}$$

results.

As an application of (1-19) we shall give a simple proof of Poisson's integral formula

$$J_n(t) = \frac{t^n}{1.3 \cdots (2n - 1)} \frac{1}{\pi} \int_{-\pi/2}^{\pi/2} \cos(t \cos \theta) \sin^{2n} \theta \, d\theta \tag{1-21}$$

Applying (1-2) to the even function $F_n(\omega)$, we have

$$\frac{J_n(t)}{t^n} = \frac{1}{2\pi} \int_{-1}^{1} \frac{2(1 - \omega^2)^{n-1/2}}{1.3 \cdots (2n - 1)} \cos \omega t \, d\omega$$

and (1-21) follows with $\omega = \cos \theta$.

THE GAMMA FUNCTION

The gamma function $\Gamma(\alpha)$ is defined by the integral

$$\Gamma(\alpha) = \int_0^\infty x^{\alpha-1}e^{-x} \, dx \qquad \alpha > 0 \tag{1-22}$$

and it satisfies the relationship

$$\Gamma(\alpha + 1) = \alpha\Gamma(\alpha) \tag{1-23}$$

which results readily from the definition. The integral converges only for $\alpha > 0$; however, the definition of $\Gamma(\alpha)$ can be extended to negative noninteger values of α by means of (1-23). Since $\Gamma(1) = 1$, it follows from (1-23) that if $\alpha = n$ is an integer, then

$$\Gamma(n + 1) = n\Gamma(n) = n(n - 1) \cdots \Gamma(1) = n! \tag{1-24}$$

The value of $\Gamma(\alpha)$ for $\alpha = \tfrac{1}{2}$ can be derived from the well-known integral

$$\int_{-\infty}^{\infty} e^{-v^2}\, dy = \sqrt{\pi} \tag{1-25}$$

Indeed, with $x = y^2$, we have

$$\Gamma(\tfrac{1}{2}) = \int_{0}^{\infty} x^{-\frac{1}{2}}e^{-x}\, dx = 2\int_{0}^{\infty} e^{-v^2}\, dy = \sqrt{\pi} \tag{1-26}$$

With $x = pt$, it follows from (1-22) that

$$\int_{0}^{\infty} t^{\alpha}e^{-pt}\, dt = \frac{\Gamma(\alpha + 1)}{p^{\alpha+1}} \qquad \alpha > -1 \tag{1-27}$$

for $p > 0$. It can be shown that (1-27) also holds for complex $p = \sigma + j\omega$, provided that $\sigma \geq 0$. Hence,

$$t^{\alpha}e^{-\sigma t}U(t) \leftrightarrow \frac{\Gamma(\alpha + 1)}{(\sigma + j\omega)^{\alpha+1}} \tag{1-28}$$

With $p = j\omega$, (1-27) yields

$$\int_{0}^{\infty} t^{\alpha}e^{-j\omega t}\, dt = \frac{\Gamma(\alpha + 1)}{(j\omega)^{\alpha+1}} \qquad \alpha > -1 \tag{1-29}$$

This relationship will be used extensively.

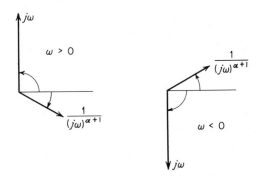

Fig. 1-2

Comment If α is not an integer, then $(j\omega)^\alpha$ is multivalued. For the validity of (1-29), the angle of $j\omega$ must equal $\pi/2$ for $\omega > 0$ and $-\pi/2$ for $\omega < 0$ (Fig. 1-2). This follows from the analyticity of the integral (1-27) in the region Re $p \geq 0$ (see Sec. 3).

From (1-29) we thus obtain the pair

$$t^\alpha U(t) \leftrightarrow \frac{\Gamma(\alpha + 1)}{|\omega|^{\alpha+1}} e^{\mp j\pi(\alpha+1)/2} \tag{1-30}$$

where the minus sign holds for $\omega > 0$ and the plus sign for $\omega < 0$.

Example 1-6   Using (1-29) we shall show that

$$e^{j\alpha t^2} \leftrightarrow \sqrt{\frac{\pi}{\alpha}}\, e^{-j\omega^2/4\alpha} e^{j\pi/4} \tag{1-31}$$

Since

$$\alpha t^2 - \omega t = \alpha \left(t - \frac{\omega}{2\alpha} \right)^2 - \frac{\omega^2}{4\alpha}$$

we have, with $\sqrt{\alpha}\, t - \omega/2\sqrt{\alpha} = y$,

$$\int_{-\infty}^{\infty} e^{j\alpha t^2} e^{-j\omega t}\, dt = e^{-j\omega^2/4\alpha} \int_{-\infty}^{\infty} e^{j\alpha(t-\omega/2\alpha)^2}\, dt = \frac{1}{\sqrt{\alpha}} e^{-j\omega^2/4\alpha} \int_{-\infty}^{\infty} e^{jy^2}\, dy$$

But

$$\int_{-\infty}^{\infty} e^{jy^2}\, dy = 2 \int_0^{\infty} e^{jy^2}\, dy = \int_0^{\infty} x^{-1/2} e^{jx}\, dx = \sqrt{\pi}\, e^{j\pi/4} \tag{1-32}$$

and (1-31) follows. The last equality, above, resulted from setting $\omega = -1$ and $\alpha = -\frac{1}{2}$ in (1-29).

It can be shown (Prob. 3-8) that (1-31) also holds for $\alpha = j\beta$. From this and the shifting theorem (Table 1-1) it follows that

$$e^{-\beta(t-\eta)^2} \leftrightarrow \sqrt{\frac{\pi}{\beta}}\, e^{-j\eta\omega - \omega^2/4\beta} \tag{1-33}$$

FRESNEL INTEGRALS

The Fresnel cosine and sine integrals are defined by

$$C(\tau) = \int_0^{\tau} \cos \frac{\pi}{2} y^2\, dy \qquad S(\tau) = \int_0^{\tau} \sin \frac{\pi}{2} y^2\, dy \tag{1-34}$$

These functions and their derivatives

$$\frac{dC(\tau)}{d\tau} = \cos \frac{\pi}{2} \tau^2 \qquad \frac{dS(\tau)}{d\tau} = \sin \frac{\pi}{2} \tau^2$$

are shown in Fig. 1-3. Their extrema, $\tau_m{}^c$ and $\tau_m{}^s$, coincide with the zero crossings of $\cos(\pi\tau^2/2)$ and $\sin(\pi\tau^2/2)$. Thus

$$\tau_{max}^c = \sqrt{4n+1} \qquad \tau_{min}^c = \sqrt{4n+3} \qquad n = 0, 1, 2, \ldots$$
$$\tau_{max}^s = \sqrt{4n+2} \qquad \tau_{min}^s = \sqrt{4n}$$

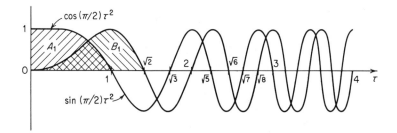

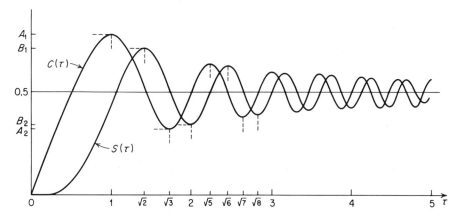

Fig. 1-3

We find it convenient to introduce also the complex function

$$\mathbf{F}(x) = \sqrt{\frac{2}{\pi}} \int_0^x e^{jy^2}\, dy \qquad\qquad (1\text{-}35)$$

It is easy to see that

$$\mathbf{F}(x) = C\left(x\sqrt{\frac{2}{\pi}}\right) + jS\left(x\sqrt{\frac{2}{\pi}}\right) \qquad\qquad (1\text{-}36)$$

From (1-32) it follows that

$$\mathbf{F}(\infty) = \frac{1}{\sqrt{2}}\, e^{j\pi/4} \qquad \text{hence} \qquad C(\infty) = S(\infty) = \tfrac{1}{2} \qquad (1\text{-}37)$$

Cornu spiral   If $\mathbf{F}(x)$ is plotted in the complex plane as the real parameter x takes values from 0 to ∞, the curve of Fig. 1-4, known as the Cornu spiral [b1, j1], results.   From

$$\frac{d\mathbf{F}(x)}{dx} = \sqrt{\frac{2}{\pi}}\, e^{jx^2}$$

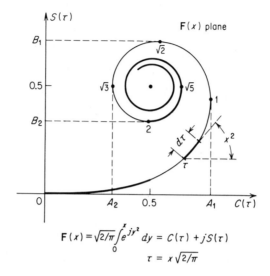

$$F(x) = \sqrt{2/\pi} \int_0^x e^{jy^2}\, dy = C(\tau) + jS(\tau)$$

$$\tau = x\sqrt{2/\pi}$$

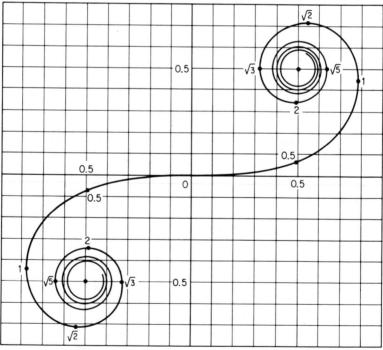

Fig. 1-4

it follows that for $dx > 0$, the amplitude and phase of the increment $d\mathbf{F}$ are given by

$$|d\mathbf{F}| = \sqrt{\frac{2}{\pi}}\, dx \qquad \theta_{d\mathbf{F}} = x^2$$

Hence,

$$\int_0^x |d\mathbf{F}(x)|\, dx = \sqrt{\frac{2}{\pi}}\, x$$

Thus, the length of the spiral from the origin to the point $\mathbf{F}(x)$ equals $x\sqrt{2/\pi}$.

Series expansions Expanding the exponential in (1-35) and integrating the resulting series termwise, we obtain

$$\mathbf{F}(x) = \sqrt{\frac{2}{\pi}}\left(x + j\frac{x^3}{3} + \frac{j^2}{2!}\frac{x^5}{5} + \cdots + \frac{j^n}{n!}\frac{x^{2n+1}}{2n+1} + \cdots\right)$$

(1-38)

From the above and (1-36) it follows that

$$\sqrt{\frac{\pi}{2}}\, C\left(x\sqrt{\frac{2}{\pi}}\right) = x - \frac{x^5}{2!5} + \cdots + \frac{(-1)^n}{(2n)!}\frac{x^{4n+1}}{4n+1} + \cdots$$

(1-39)

$$\sqrt{\frac{\pi}{2}}\, S\left(x\sqrt{\frac{2}{\pi}}\right) = \frac{x^3}{3} - \frac{x^7}{3!7} + \cdots + \frac{(-1)^n}{(2n+1)!}\frac{x^{4n+3}}{4n+3} + \cdots$$

(1-40)

Large x In Chap. 7, Sec. 3, we show that $\mathbf{F}(x)$ can be expanded into a series in powers of $1/x$:

$$\mathbf{F}(x) = \frac{1}{\sqrt{2}}\, e^{j\pi/4} + \frac{1}{jx\sqrt{2\pi}}\, e^{jx^2} + \cdots$$

(1-41)

This can also be derived from (1-35) by integration by parts. From the real and imaginary parts of (1-41), the expansions

$$C(\tau) = \tfrac{1}{2} - \frac{1}{\pi\tau}\sin\left(\frac{\pi}{2}\tau^2\right) + \cdots$$

(1-42)

$$S(\tau) = \tfrac{1}{2} - \frac{1}{\pi\tau}\cos\left(\frac{\pi}{2}\tau^2\right) + \cdots$$

(1-43)

easily result.

If $\mathbf{F}(x)$ is approximated by only two terms of the series (1-38) or (1-41), the resulting error is less than 0.01 for x in the heavy parts of the Cornu spiral of Fig. 1-4.

Example 1-7   We shall determine the Fourier transform $F(\omega)$ of the function

$$f(t) = \begin{cases} e^{j\alpha t^2} & 0 < t < T \\ 0 & \text{otherwise} \end{cases}$$

Reasoning as in Example 1-6, we find

$$F(\omega) = \int_0^T e^{j\alpha t^2} e^{-j\omega t}\, dt = e^{-j\omega^2/4\alpha} \int_0^T e^{j\alpha(t-\omega/2\alpha)^2}\, dt$$

$$= \frac{1}{\sqrt{\alpha}} e^{-j\omega^2/4\alpha} \int_{-\omega/2\sqrt{\alpha}}^{\sqrt{\alpha}\,T-\omega/2\sqrt{\alpha}} e^{jv^2}\, dy$$

Hence

$$F(\omega) = \sqrt{\frac{\pi}{2\alpha}}\left[\mathsf{F}\left(\sqrt{\alpha}\,T - \frac{\omega}{2\sqrt{\alpha}}\right) + \mathsf{F}\left(\frac{\omega}{2\sqrt{\alpha}}\right)\right] e^{-j\omega^2/4\alpha} \tag{1-44}$$

as we see from (1-35) and the fact that $\mathsf{F}(-x) = -\mathsf{F}(x)$.

With $T = \infty$, (1-44) yields the pair

$$e^{j\alpha t^2} U(t) \leftrightarrow \sqrt{\frac{\pi}{2\alpha}}\left[\frac{1+j}{2} + \mathsf{F}\left(\frac{\omega}{2\sqrt{\alpha}}\right)\right] e^{-j\omega^2/4\alpha}$$

2. CONVOLUTION; ENERGY; MOMENTS

Given two signals $f_1(t)$ and $f_2(t)$ with transforms $F_1(\omega)$ and $F_2(\omega)$, we form their convolution

$$f(t) = f_1(t) * f_2(t) \tag{2-1}$$

As we have shown in Chap. 2, (3-30), its transform $F(\omega)$ is such that

$$F(\omega) = F_1(\omega)F_2(\omega) \tag{2-2}$$

We give below a direct justification of this important theorem.   Taking the transform of $f_1(t) * f_2(t)$ and interchanging the order of integration, we obtain, with $t - \tau = x$,

$$\int_{-\infty}^{\infty} e^{-j\omega t}\left[\int_{-\infty}^{\infty} f_1(\tau)f_2(t - \tau)\, d\tau\right] dt$$

$$= \int_{-\infty}^{\infty} f_1(\tau) \int_{-\infty}^{\infty} e^{-j\omega t} f_2(t - \tau)\, dt\, d\tau$$

$$= \int_{-\infty}^{\infty} f_1(\tau) e^{-j\omega\tau} \int_{-\infty}^{\infty} e^{-j\omega x} f_2(x)\, dx\, d\tau = F_1(\omega)F_2(\omega)$$

and (2-2) follows.

Expressing $f(t)$ in terms of its transform, as in (1-2), we can write (2-2) in the form

$$\int_{-\infty}^{\infty} f_1(\tau)f_2(t - \tau)\, d\tau = \frac{1}{2\pi}\int_{-\infty}^{\infty} F_1(\omega)F_2(\omega)e^{j\omega t}\, d\omega \tag{2-3}$$

By a similar argument one can derive the frequency convolution

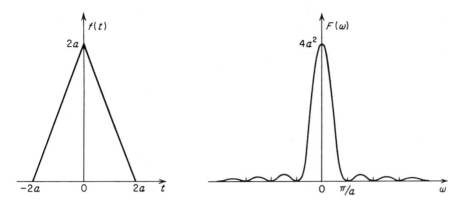

Fig. 2-1

theorem

$$f_1(t)f_2(t) \leftrightarrow \frac{1}{2\pi} F_1(\omega) * F_2(\omega) \tag{2-4}$$

Example 2-1   Since

$$p_a(t) \leftrightarrow \frac{2 \sin a\omega}{\omega}$$

and the convolution of a pulse with itself is a triangle, as in Fig. 2-1 (see Example 1-2, Chap. 2), we conclude from (2-2) that

$$\text{If} \quad f(t) = \begin{cases} 2a - |t| & |t| < 2a \\ 0 & |t| > 2a \end{cases} \quad \text{then} \quad F(\omega) = \frac{4 \sin^2 a\omega}{\omega^2} \tag{2-5}$$

Parseval's formula

From (2-3) we have, with $t = 0$,

$$\int_{-\infty}^{\infty} f_1(\tau)f_2(-\tau) \, d\tau = \frac{1}{2\pi} \int_{-\infty}^{\infty} F_1(\omega)F_2(\omega) \, d\omega \tag{2-6}$$

Introducing the function $G(\omega) = F_2^*(\omega)$, we see from Table 1-1 that its inverse $g(t)$ is such that $f_2(t) = g^*(-t)$. Dropping the subscript of $f_1(t)$, we thus have, from (2-6),

$$\int_{-\infty}^{\infty} f(t)g^*(t) \, dt = \frac{1}{2\pi} \int_{-\infty}^{\infty} F(\omega)G^*(\omega) \, d\omega \tag{2-7}$$

Finally, with $f(t) = g(t)$, the energy theorem

$$\int_{-\infty}^{\infty} |f(t)|^2 \, dt = \frac{1}{2\pi} \int_{-\infty}^{\infty} |F(\omega)|^2 \, d\omega \tag{2-8}$$

results.

Example 2-2 The energy theorem can be used to simplify the evaluation of certain integrals. Thus from the pair [see (1-28)]

$$te^{-\sigma t}U(t) \leftrightarrow \frac{1}{(\sigma + j\omega)^2}$$

and (2-8) it follows that

$$\frac{1}{2\pi} \int_{-\infty}^{\infty} \frac{d\omega}{(\sigma^2 + \omega^2)^2} = \int_{0}^{\infty} t^2 e^{-2\sigma t}\, dt = \frac{1}{4\sigma^3}$$

Example 2-3 If $F(\omega)$ is the transform of $f(t)$, then

$$f(t + a) - f(t) \leftrightarrow F(\omega)(e^{ja\omega} - 1)$$

But

$$|e^{ja\omega} - 1|^2 = 2 - 2\cos a\omega$$

Applying (2-8), we thus obtain

$$\int_{-\infty}^{\infty} |f(t + a) - f(t)|^2\, dt = \frac{1}{2\pi} \int_{-\infty}^{\infty} 2|F(\omega)|^2(1 - \cos a\omega)\, d\omega \tag{2-9}$$

Example 2-4 (Ambiguity and correlation) Given a signal $f(t)$ and a parameter τ, we denote by $\chi(\omega,\tau)$ the Fourier transform of the product $f(t + \tau)f^*(t)$ with respect to t:

$$f(t + \tau)f^*(t) \leftrightarrow \chi(\omega,\tau)$$

Thus [w3],

$$\chi(\omega,\tau) = \int_{-\infty}^{\infty} f(t + \tau)f^*(t)e^{-j\omega t}\, dt \tag{2-10}$$

With $F(\omega)$ the transform of $f(t)$, we have (Table 1-1)

$$f(t + \tau) \leftrightarrow e^{j\omega\tau}F(\omega) \qquad f^*(t) \leftrightarrow F^*(-\omega)$$

From the above and the frequency convolution theorem (2-4) it follows that

$$\chi(\omega,\tau) = \frac{1}{2\pi} e^{j\omega\tau}F(\omega) * F^*(-\omega) = \frac{1}{2\pi} \int_{-\infty}^{\infty} F(y)F^*(y - \omega)e^{jy\tau}\, dy \tag{2-11}$$

We now define the correlation $\rho(\tau)$ of the signal $f(t)$ by [p2]

$$\rho(\tau) = \chi(0,\tau) = \int_{-\infty}^{\infty} f(t + \tau)f^*(t)\, dt \tag{2-12}$$

From (2-11) we obtain, with $\omega = 0$,

$$\rho(\tau) = \frac{1}{2\pi} \int_{-\infty}^{\infty} |F(y)|^2 e^{jy\tau}\, dy \tag{2-13}$$

Hence

$$\rho(\tau) \leftrightarrow |F(\omega)|^2 \qquad \rho(t) = f(t) * f^*(-t) \tag{2-14}$$

From (2-13) we see that

$$|\rho(\tau)| \le \frac{1}{2\pi} \int_{-\infty}^{\infty} |F(y)|^2\, dy = \rho(0) = \int_{-\infty}^{\infty} |f(t)|^2\, dt \tag{2-15}$$

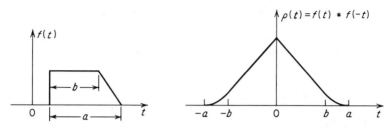

Fig. 2-2

From (2-9) and (2-13) it follows that

$$\int_{-\infty}^{\infty} |f(t+\tau) \pm f(t)|^2 \, dt = 2 \, \mathrm{Re} \, [\rho(0) \pm \rho(\tau)] \qquad (2\text{-}16)$$

Since $|F(\omega)|^2$ is real, it follows that

$$\rho(-\tau) = \rho^*(\tau)$$

If $f(t)$ is real, then $\rho(\tau)$ is real and even.

In Fig. 2-2 we have shown a signal $f(t)$ and its correlation $\rho(\tau)$.

MOMENT THEOREM

The moments m_n of a function $f(t)$ are defined by

$$m_n = \int_{-\infty}^{\infty} t^n f(t) \, dt \qquad (2\text{-}17)$$

We find it convenient to introduce also the mean

$$\eta = \frac{m_1}{m_0} \qquad (2\text{-}18)$$

and the variance

$$\sigma^2 = \frac{m_2}{m_0} - \eta^2 = \frac{1}{m_0} \int_{-\infty}^{\infty} (t-\eta)^2 f(t) \, dt \qquad (2\text{-}19)$$

of $f(t)$. If $f(t)$ is interpreted as mass density on the t axis, then η is its center of gravity and σ its radius of gyration.

These quantities will now be related to the derivatives of $F(\omega)$ at the origin. Expanding the exponential in (1-1) and integrating termwise, we obtain [p2]

$$F(\omega) = \int_{-\infty}^{\infty} f(t)[1 - j\omega t + (j\omega t)^2 + \cdots] \, dt = \sum_{n=0}^{\infty} \frac{(-j\omega)^n}{n!} m_n$$

From the above it follows that

$$(-j)^n m_n = \frac{d^n F(0)}{d\omega^n} \qquad (2\text{-}20)$$

If the signal $f(t)$ is real and $m_0 \geq 0$, then with $F(\omega) = A(\omega)e^{j\varphi(\omega)}$ we have

$$A(-\omega) = A(\omega) \qquad \varphi(-\omega) = -\varphi(\omega)$$

It then follows that

$$A'(0) = \varphi(0) = \varphi''(0) = 0$$

and (2-20) yields, after some easy computations,

$$m_0 = F(0) = A(0) \qquad \eta = -\varphi'(0) \qquad \sigma^2 = -\frac{A''(0)}{A(0)} \tag{2-21}$$

Thus, the mean η of $f(t)$ equals the slope of the *phase lag* $-\varphi(\omega)$ at the origin, and its variance σ^2 equals the curvature of $A(\omega)/A(0)$.

Convolution

Suppose now that

$$f(t) = f_1(t) * f_2(t)$$

From (2-2) we conclude that $F(0) = F_1(0)F_2(0)$. Therefore,

$$\int_{-\infty}^{\infty} f(t)\, dt = \int_{-\infty}^{\infty} f_1(t)\, dt \int_{-\infty}^{\infty} f_2(t)\, dt \tag{2-22}$$

Since $F(\omega) = F_1(\omega)F_2(\omega)$, it follows from (2-21), after some thought, that the mean and variance of the above functions are related by

$$\eta = \eta_1 + \eta_2 \qquad \sigma^2 = \sigma_1^2 + \sigma_2^2 \tag{2-23}$$

Central limit theorem   The evaluation of the convolution

$$f(t) = f_1(t) * \cdots * f_n(t)$$

of a large number of functions is numerically involved.   The preceding relationships permit the easy determination of the area

$$\int_{-\infty}^{\infty} f(t)\, dt = A(0) = A_1(0) \cdots A_n(0) \tag{2-24}$$

of $f(t)$, as well as its mean η and variance σ^2,

$$\eta = \eta_1 + \cdots + \eta_n \qquad \sigma^2 = \sigma_1^2 + \cdots + \sigma_n^2 \tag{2-25}$$

in terms of the corresponding quantities of the functions $f_1(t), \ldots, f_n(t)$.

If these functions are nonnegative, that is,

$$f_i(t) \geq 0$$

then under general conditions, their convolution $f(t)$ is approximately equal to a normal curve with area $A(0)$, mean η, and variance σ^2:

$$f(t) \simeq \frac{A(0)}{\sigma \sqrt{2\pi}} e^{-(t-\eta)^2/2\sigma^2} \qquad (2\text{-}26)$$

provided n is sufficiently large (equality for $n \to \infty$). This remarkable result, known as the central limit theorem, is used extensively in probability theory [p1, u1]. The theorem can be phrased in the frequency domain. Since [see (1-33)]

$$\frac{1}{\sigma \sqrt{2\pi}} e^{-(t-\eta)^2/2\sigma^2} \leftrightarrow e^{-j\eta\omega-(\omega^2\sigma^2/2)}$$

we conclude from (2-26) that

$$F(\omega) = F_1(\omega) \cdots F_n(\omega) \simeq A(0)e^{-j\eta\omega-(\omega^2\sigma^2/2)} \qquad (2\text{-}27)$$

Thus, the product of functions with positive inverse transforms (such functions are called positive-definite) approaches a normal curve.

Example 2-5 Suppose that the functions $f_i(t)$ equal a pulse, and $n = 3$

$$f_i(t) = p_T(t) \qquad i = 1, 2, 3$$

As we have shown in Example 1-2, Chap. 2, their convolution $f(t)$ consists of three

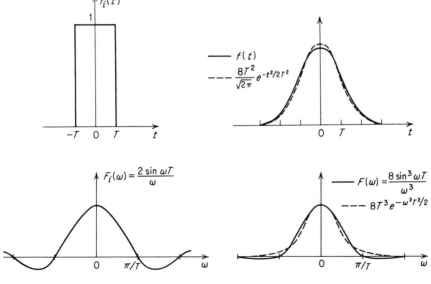

Fig. 2-3

parabolic pieces as in Fig. 2-3.   Since

$$A_i(0) = \int_{-T}^{T} dt = 2T \qquad \eta_i = 0 \qquad \sigma_i{}^2 = \frac{1}{2T} \int_{-T}^{T} t^2 \, dt = \frac{T^2}{3}$$

we conclude from (2-24) and (2-25) that

$$A(0) = 8T^3 \qquad \eta = 0 \qquad \sigma^2 = T^2$$

Inserting into (2-26), we obtain the approximation (Fig. 2-3)

$$f(t) \simeq \frac{8T^2}{\sqrt{2\pi}} e^{-t^2/2T^2}$$

Since

$$f_i(t) = p_T(t) \leftrightarrow \frac{2 \sin \omega T}{\omega} = F_i(\omega)$$

we have $F(\omega) = 8 \sin^3 \omega T / \omega^3$, and (2-27) yields

$$8 \frac{\sin^3 \omega T}{\omega^3} \simeq 8T^3 e^{-\omega^2 T^2/2}$$

Example 2-6   Four identical systems with impulse response $h_i(t)$ are connected in cascade, as in Fig. 2-4, forming a new system with impulse response

$$h(t) = h_1(t) * \cdot \cdot \cdot * h_4(t)$$

We shall assume that

$$h_i(t) = e^{-\alpha t} U(t) \leftrightarrow H_i(\omega) = \frac{1}{\alpha + j\omega} \qquad i = 1, \ldots , 4$$

It then follows from (2-2) and (1-28) that

$$h(t) = \frac{1}{3!} t^3 e^{-\alpha t} U(t) \leftrightarrow H(\omega) = \frac{1}{(\alpha + j\omega)^4}$$

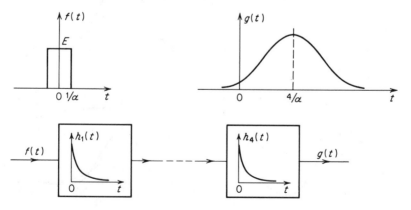

Fig. 2-4

Clearly

$$H_i(0) = \frac{1}{\alpha} \qquad \eta_i = \alpha \int_0^\infty t e^{-\alpha t}\, dt = \frac{1}{\alpha} \qquad \sigma_i^2 = \alpha \int_0^\infty \left(t - \frac{1}{\alpha}\right)^2 e^{-\alpha t}\, dt = \frac{1}{\alpha^2}$$

Hence [see (2-24) and (2-25)],

$$H(0) = \frac{1}{\alpha^4} \qquad \eta = \frac{4}{\alpha} \qquad \sigma^2 = \frac{4}{\alpha^2}$$

Inserting into (2-26) and (2-28), we obtain the approximations

$$t^3 e^{-\alpha t} U(t) \simeq \frac{3}{\alpha^3 \sqrt{2\pi}} e^{-(\alpha t - 4)^2/8}$$

$$\frac{1}{(\alpha + j\omega)^4} \simeq \frac{1}{\alpha^4} e^{-j4\omega/\alpha} e^{-2\omega^2/\alpha^2}$$

Suppose now that the input to this system is a pulse

$$f(t) = \begin{cases} E & |t| < 1/\alpha \\ 0 & |t| > 1/\alpha \end{cases}$$

It is easy to see that the area of this pulse equals $2E/\alpha$, its mean is zero, and its variance $1/3\alpha^2$. Therefore, the response $g(t)$ is approximately a normal curve with area, mean, and variance

$$\frac{2E}{\alpha^5} \qquad \frac{4}{\alpha} \qquad \frac{4}{\alpha^2} + \frac{1}{3\alpha^2}$$

respectively.

3. ANALYTICITY OF $F(\omega)$ AND HILBERT TRANSFORMS

We shall now investigate the analytic properties of the Fourier transform $F(\omega)$ of an absolutely integrable function $f(t)$. Following the usual practice, we set $p = j\omega$, forming thus the "Laplace transform"

$$F_o(p) = F\left(\frac{p}{j}\right) \tag{3-1}$$

of $f(t)$. If $f(t)$ is zero outside the interval (a,b),

$$f(t) = 0 \qquad \text{for } t < a \text{ or } t > b \tag{3-2}$$

then $F_o(p)$ is given by

$$F_o(p) = \int_a^b f(t) e^{-pt}\, dt \tag{3-3}$$

where the constants a and b may be infinite.

Theorem

1. If the limits a and b are finite, then $F_o(p)$ is an analytic function of p in the entire complex plane, and its derivative is obtained by differenti-

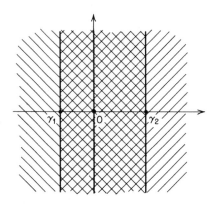

Fig. 3-1

ating (3-3) under the integral sign

$$\frac{dF_o(p)}{dp} = \int_a^b (-t)f(t)e^{-pt}\, dt \tag{3-4}$$

Unless $f(t)$ is identically zero, $p = \infty$ is a singular point of $F_o(p)$.

2. If a is finite and $b = \infty$, then $F_o(p)$ is analytic in the region

$$\text{Re } p > \gamma_1 \qquad \gamma_1 \leq 0 \tag{3-5}$$

including the right plane $\text{Re } p \geq 0$ (Fig. 3-1).

If $a \geq 0$, then $F_o(p)$ tends to zero for $p \to \infty$ in the region $\text{Re } p \geq 0$:

$$F_o(p) \to 0 \qquad \text{for } p \to \infty,\ \text{Re } p \geq 0 \tag{3-6}$$

3. If $a = -\infty$ and b is finite, then $F_o(p)$ is analytic in the region

$$\text{Re } p < \gamma_2 \qquad \gamma_2 \geq 0 \tag{3-7}$$

If $b \leq 0$, then

$$F_o(p) \to 0 \qquad \text{for } p \to \infty,\ \text{Re } p \leq 0 \tag{3-8}$$

4. If $a = -\infty$ and $b = +\infty$, then $F_o(p)$ is analytic in the strip

$$\gamma_1 < \text{Re } p < \gamma_2 \qquad \gamma_1 \leq 0 \leq \gamma_2 \tag{3-9}$$

Furthermore,

$$F_o(j\omega) \to 0 \qquad \text{for } |\omega| \to \infty$$

We give below the proof of part 1 of this basic theorem [d1, w2]. Part 2 follows by a limiting argument; however, the details will not be given. Part 3 is a consequence of 2, with p replaced by $-p$. Finally, part 4 results by writing $F_o(p)$ as a sum of two integrals in the intervals $(-\infty, 0)$ and $(0, \infty)$ and using 2 and 3.

Proof We form the integral

$$I(\epsilon) = \frac{F_o(p + \epsilon) - F_o(p)}{\epsilon} + \int_a^b tf(t)e^{-pt}\,dt$$

$$= \int_a^b \left[\frac{e^{-(p+\epsilon)t} - e^{-pt}}{\epsilon} + t\right]f(t)\,dt$$

It is easy to see that for $a \le t \le b$

$$\left|\frac{e^{-(p+\epsilon)t} - e^{-pt}}{\epsilon} + t\right| = \left|e^{-pt}\epsilon t^2\left(\frac{1}{2!} - \frac{\epsilon t}{3!} + \frac{\epsilon^2 t^2}{4!} - \cdots\right)\right|$$

$$\le |\epsilon|c^2 e^{c|p|}e^{c|\epsilon|}$$

where c is the larger of the two numbers $|a|$ and $|b|$. Hence

$$|I(\epsilon)| \le |\epsilon|c^2 e^{c|\epsilon|+c|p|}\int_a^b |f(t)|\,dt \xrightarrow[\epsilon\to 0]{} 0$$

and (3-4) follows.

The four cases of the preceding theorem are illustrated in the following examples:

1. $p_a(t) \leftrightarrow \dfrac{e^{pa} - e^{-pa}}{p}$ analytic for every p

2. $e^{-\alpha t}U(t) \leftrightarrow \dfrac{1}{p + \alpha}$ analytic in the half-plane Re $p > -\alpha$

3. $e^{\alpha t}U(-t) \leftrightarrow \dfrac{1}{\alpha - p}$ analytic in the half-plane Re $p < \alpha$

4. $e^{-\alpha|t|} \leftrightarrow \dfrac{2\alpha}{\alpha^2 - p^2}$ analytic in the strip $-\alpha < $ Re $p < \alpha$

HILBERT TRANSFORMS

Consider a *real* function $f(t)$ with Fourier transform $F(\omega)$. The integral

$$z(t) = \frac{1}{\pi}\int_0^\infty F(\omega)e^{j\omega t}\,d\omega \tag{3-10}$$

is known as the *analytic signal* associated with $f(t)$. The above integral is of the form (3-3) with $a = 0$, $b = \infty$. Interchanging jt with $-p$, we conclude from part 2 of the preceding theorem that $z(t)$ is an analytic function of t for every t in the upper half of the complex t plane.

Clearly [see (1-6)], the real part of $z(t)$ equals $f(t)$. Its imaginary part, denoted by $\hat{f}(t)$, is called the *Hilbert transform* of $f(t)$:

$$z(t) = f(t) + j\hat{f}(t) \qquad f(t) = \text{Re } z(t) \tag{3-11}$$

With $Z(\omega)$ and $\hat{F}(\omega)$ the Fourier transforms of $z(t)$ and $\hat{f}(t)$, respec-

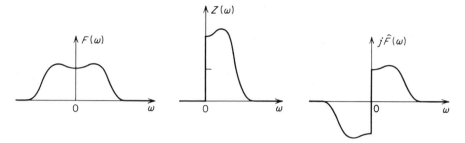

Fig. 3-2

tively, we see from (3-10) that

$$Z(\omega) = 2F(\omega)U(\omega) = \begin{cases} 2F(\omega) & \omega > 0 \\ 0 & \omega < 0 \end{cases} \tag{3-12}$$

and since $Z(\omega) = F(\omega) + j\hat{F}(\omega)$, it follows that

$$\hat{F}(\omega) = -jF(\omega) \operatorname{sgn} \omega = \begin{cases} -jF(\omega) & \omega > 0 \\ jF(\omega) & \omega < 0 \end{cases} \tag{3-13}$$

The above functions are shown in Fig. 3-2, where it is assumed for simplicity that $F(\omega)$ is real. We note that $|F(\omega)| = |\hat{F}(\omega)|$; hence,

$$\int_{-\infty}^{\infty} f^2(t)\, dt = \int_{-\infty}^{\infty} \hat{f}^2(t)\, dt \tag{3-14}$$

If $f(t)$ is even, then $F(\omega)$ is real; hence, $\hat{f}(t)$ is odd, and it is given by

$$\hat{f}(t) = \frac{1}{\pi} \int_0^{\infty} F(\omega) \sin \omega t\, d\omega \tag{3-15}$$

as we see from (3-11).

The function $\hat{f}(t)$ can be expressed in terms of $f(t)$. Since [see (1-14)]

$$\frac{1}{\pi t} \leftrightarrow -j \operatorname{sgn} \omega$$

we conclude from (3-13) and the convolution theorem that

$$\hat{f}(t) = f(t) * \frac{1}{\pi t} = \int_{-\infty}^{\infty} \frac{f(\tau)}{\pi(t - \tau)}\, d\tau \tag{3-16}$$

From (3-13) it also follows that $\hat{f}(t)$ is the output of the *quadrature filter*

$$H(\omega) = \begin{cases} -j & \omega > 0 \\ j & \omega < 0 \end{cases} \tag{3-17}$$

shown in Fig. 3-3.

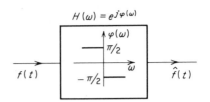

Fig. 3-3

We finally remark that

$$\int_{-\infty}^{\infty} f_1(t + \tau)f_2(\tau)\, d\tau = \int_{-\infty}^{\infty} \hat{f}_1(t + \tau)\hat{f}_2(\tau)\, d\tau \qquad (3\text{-}18)$$

Indeed, the left side above equals $f_1(t) * f_2(-t)$, and its Fourier transform is given by

$$F_1(\omega)F_2(-\omega)$$

Similarly, the transform of the right side equals [see (3-13)]

$$\hat{F}_1(\omega)\hat{F}_2(-\omega) = -jF_1(\omega)\,\text{sgn}\,\omega(-j)F_2(-\omega)\,\text{sgn}\,(-\omega) = F_1(\omega)F_2(-\omega)$$

because $\text{sgn}\,(-\omega) = -\,\text{sgn}\,\omega$, and (3-18) follows. Equation (3-14) is a special case of (3-18).

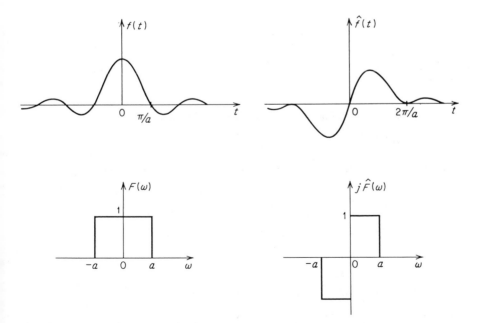

Fig. 3-4

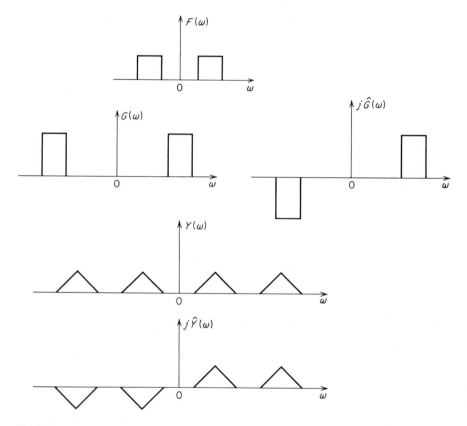

Fig. 3-5

Example 3-1   We shall find the Hilbert transform of the even function

$$f(t) = \frac{\sin at}{\pi t}$$

The Fourier transform of $f(t)$ is a pulse, as in Fig. 3-4. Hence [see (3-15)],

$$\hat{f}(t) = \frac{1}{\pi} \int_0^a \sin \omega t \, d\omega = \frac{1 - \cos at}{\pi t}$$

Example 3-2   From the transform pair

$$J_o(t) \leftrightarrow \frac{2 p_1(\omega)}{\sqrt{1 - \omega^2}}$$

it follows that the Hilbert transform of the Bessel function is given by

$$\hat{J}_o(t) = \frac{2}{\pi} \int_0^1 \frac{\sin \omega t}{\sqrt{1 - \omega^2}} \, d\omega = \frac{2}{\pi} \int_0^{\pi/2} \sin \left(t \sin \theta \right) d\theta = H_o(t) \tag{3-19}$$

as we see from (3-15), with $\omega = \sin \theta$. $H_o(t)$ is known as the *Struve function*. It can be shown that

$$H_o(t) = \sum_{n=0}^{\infty} \frac{(-1)^n (t/2)^{2n+1}}{\Gamma^2(n + \tfrac{3}{2})} \tag{3-20}$$

Example 3-3[†] We are given two signals $f(t)$ and $g(t)$ with nonoverlapping transforms $F(\omega)$ and $G(\omega)$, that is,

$$F(\omega)G(\omega) = 0$$

such that $G(\omega)$ occupies the higher frequencies, as in Fig. 3-5. With

$$y(t) = f(t)g(t)$$

we maintain that

$$\hat{y}(t) = f(t)\hat{g}(t) \tag{3-21}$$

It suffices to show that the transforms of both sides of (3-21) are equal. Clearly [see (2-4)],

$$Y(\omega) = \frac{1}{2\pi} F(\omega) * G(\omega)$$

The transform $Y(\omega)$ is shown in Fig. 3-5. Reversing its sign for $\omega < 0$, we obtain $j\hat{Y}(\omega)$. This function equals the convolution of $F(\omega)$ with $j\hat{G}(\omega)$, and (3-21) follows.

Modulation

Consider a function $f(t)$ and its analytic signal $z(t)$. With ω_o a given constant, we form the function

$$z_l(t) = z(t)e^{-j\omega_o t} = p(t) + jq(t) \tag{3-22}$$

From the above and (3-11) it follows that

$$f(t) = \mathrm{Re}\, z(t) = \mathrm{Re}\, z_l(t)e^{j\omega_o t}$$

Hence,

$$f(t) = p(t) \cos \omega_o t - q(t) \sin \omega_o t \tag{3-23}$$

† E. Bedrosian, *Proc. IEEE*, vol. 51, May, 1963, pp. 868–869.

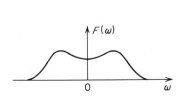 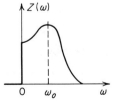 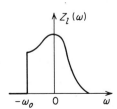

Fig. 3-6

Thus an *arbitrary* function $f(t)$ can be written in the form of (3-23).

The Fourier transform

$$Z_l(\omega) = Z(\omega + \omega_o) \tag{3-24}$$

of $z_l(t)$ is obtained by shifting $Z(\omega)$ to the left, as in Fig. 3-6.

The functions $p(t)$ and $q(t)$ are the *in-phase* and *quadrature* components of $f(t)$ with respect to ω_o. Their transforms are determined in Prob. 3-10.

Symmetry   We now assume that the amplitude of $Z(\omega)$ is symmetrical and that its phase is antisymmetrical about the point a (Fig. 3-7):

$$Z(a + \omega) = Z^*(a - \omega) \tag{3-25}$$

From the above and (3-24) we see that if $\omega_o = a$, then

$$Z_l(-\omega) = Z_l^*(\omega) \tag{3-26}$$

Hence, $z_l(t) = p_a(t)$ is real, and (3-23) yields

$$f(t) = p_a(t) \cos \omega_o t \tag{3-27}$$

If $\omega_o = a + b$, then, with $p_a(t)$ as in (3-27),

$$z_l(t) = p_a(t)e^{-jbt} = p_a(t)(\cos bt - j \sin bt)$$

as it is easy to see.

Example 3-4   Using the above, we shall determine the inverse transform of the function $F(\omega)$ shown in Fig. 3-7. The corresponding $Z(\omega)$ satisfies (3-25). With $\omega_o = a$, $Z_l(\omega)$ is a triangle; therefore [see (2-5) and (3-27)]

$$z_l(t) = \frac{2 \sin^2 (ct/2)}{\pi c t^2} \qquad f(t) = \frac{2 \sin^2 (ct/2)}{\pi c t^2} \cos at$$

Single side band   Consider the signal

$$f(t) = 2p(t) \cos \omega_o t$$

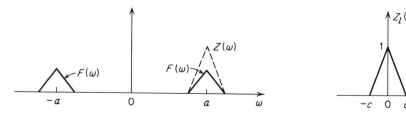

Fig. 3-7

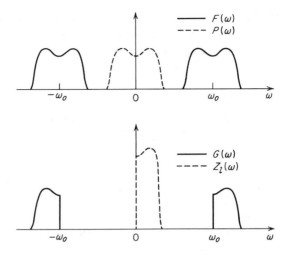

Fig. 3-8

With $P(\omega)$ the transform of $p(t)$, we have

$$F(\omega) = P(\omega - \omega_o) + P(\omega + \omega_o)$$

If we eliminate the components of $F(\omega)$ in the interval $(-\omega_o, \omega_o)$, the function $G(\omega)$ of Fig. 3-8 results. We shall show that its inverse transform $g(t)$ is given by

$$g(t) = p(t) \cos \omega_o t - \hat{p}(t) \sin \omega_o t \qquad (3\text{-}28)$$

Proof With $Z(\omega) = 2G(\omega)U(\omega)$ and $Z_l(\omega)$ as in (3-24), we see from Fig. 3-8 that

$$Z_l(\omega) = 2P(\omega)U(\omega)$$

Therefore, the inverse transform $z_l(t)$ of $Z_l(\omega)$ is the analytic signal associated with $p(t)$

$$z_l(t) = p(t) + j\hat{p}(t)$$

and (3-28) follows from (3-23).

4. TWO–DIMENSIONAL SIGNALS

Given a function of two variables $f(x,y)$, we form the integral

$$F(u,v) = \iint\limits_{-\infty}^{\infty} f(x,y)e^{-j(ux+vy)} \, dx \, dy \qquad (4\text{-}1)$$

This integral defines the two-dimensional Fourier transform $F(u,v)$ of $f(x,y)$. As we shall presently show, by viewing $F(u,v)$ as a succession of two one-dimensional transforms, we can derive all theorems of this section from the corresponding theorems of Sec. 1. Indeed, with

$$\Gamma(u,y) = \int_{-\infty}^{\infty} f(x,y)e^{-jux}\,dx \tag{4-2}$$

the transform of $f(x,y)$ with respect to x, we see from (4-1) that $F(u,v)$ is the transform $\Gamma(u,y)$ with respect to y:

$$F(u,v) = \int_{-\infty}^{\infty} \Gamma(u,y)e^{-jvy}\,dy \tag{4-3}$$

Thus,

$$f(x,y) \leftrightarrow \Gamma(u,y) \leftrightarrow F(u,v) \tag{4-4}$$

From the one-dimensional inversion formula (1-2) we have

$$f(x,y) = \frac{1}{2\pi}\int_{-\infty}^{\infty} \Gamma(u,y)e^{jux}\,du \qquad \Gamma(u,y) = \frac{1}{2\pi}\int_{-\infty}^{\infty} F(u,v)e^{jvy}\,dv$$

The above relationships yield the following result.

Inversion formula

$$f(x,y) = \frac{1}{4\pi^2}\iint_{-\infty}^{\infty} F(u,v)e^{j(ux+vy)}\,du\,dv \tag{4-5}$$

The pair of functions $f(x,y)$ and $F(u,v)$, related by (4-1) and (4-5), will be denoted by

$$f(x,y) \Leftrightarrow F(u,v) \tag{4-6}$$

THEOREMS

The following theorems can be easily derived either directly from the definition or from (4-4) and the theorems in Table 1-1.

$$f^*(x,y) \Leftrightarrow F^*(-u,-v) \tag{4-7}$$

$$F(x,y) \Leftrightarrow 4\pi^2 f(-u,-v) \tag{4-8}$$

$$f(x - x_o, y - y_o) \Leftrightarrow F(u,v)e^{-j(ux_o+vy_o)} \tag{4-9}$$

$$f(x,y)e^{j(u_o x+v_o y)} \Leftrightarrow F(u - u_o, v - v_o) \tag{4-10}$$

$$f(ax,by) \Leftrightarrow \frac{1}{|ab|}F\left(\frac{u}{a}, \frac{u}{b}\right) \tag{4-11}$$

More generally,

$$f(a_1 x + b_1 y, a_2 x + b_2 y) \Leftrightarrow \frac{1}{|a_1 b_2 - a_2 b_1|}F(A_1 u + A_2 v, B_1 u + B_2 v) \tag{4-12}$$

where

$$\begin{bmatrix} A_1 & B_1 \\ A_2 & B_2 \end{bmatrix} = \begin{bmatrix} a_1 & b_1 \\ a_2 & b_2 \end{bmatrix}^{-1}$$

This follows readily if in the Fourier transform

$$\int\limits_{-\infty}^{\infty}\int f(a_1x + b_1y, a_2x + b_2y)e^{-j(ux+vy)}\, dx\, dy$$

we introduce the transformations $a_1x + b_1y = \xi$, $a_2x + b_2y = \eta$.

Differentiating (4-1) or (4-5) under the integral sign, we find

$$\frac{\partial f(x,y)}{dx} \Leftrightarrow juF(u,v) \tag{4-13}$$

$$\frac{\partial^2 f(x,y)}{\partial x^2} + \frac{\partial^2 f(x,y)}{\partial y^2} \Leftrightarrow -(u^2 + v^2)F(u,v) \tag{4-14}$$

$$xf(x,y) \Leftrightarrow j\frac{\partial F(u,v)}{\partial u} \qquad xyf(x,y) \Leftrightarrow -\frac{\partial^2 F(u,v)}{\partial u\, \partial v} \tag{4-15}$$

Suppose now that $f(x,y)$ is real. In this case, $F^*(u,v) = F(-u,-v)$. If $f(x,y) = f(-x,-y)$, then $F(u,v)$ is real and $F(u,v) = F(-u,-v)$. If $f(x,y) = f(-x,y)$, then $F^*(u,v) = F(u,-v) = F(-u,-v)$.

Finally, if $f(x,y) = f(-x,y) = f(x,-y) = f(-x,-y)$, then $F(u,v)$ is real and $F(u,v) = F(-u,v) = F(u,-v) = F(-u,-v)$.

With

$$f_1(x) \leftrightarrow F_1(u) \qquad f_2(y) \leftrightarrow F_2(v)$$

the one-dimensional transforms of the functions $f_1(x)$ and $f_2(y)$, it follows easily from (4-1) that

$$f_1(x)f_2(y) \Leftrightarrow F_1(u)F_2(v) \tag{4-16}$$

If we introduce the polar coordinates

$$x = r\cos\theta \qquad y = r\sin\theta \qquad u = w\cos\varphi \qquad v = w\sin\varphi$$

then $f(x,y)$ and $F(u,v)$ become $f_o(r,\theta)$ and $F_o(w,\varphi)$, respectively. We then have

$$f_o(ar, \theta + \theta_o) \overset{x,y}{\underset{u,v}{\Leftrightarrow}} \frac{1}{a^2}F_o\left(\frac{w}{a}, \varphi + \theta_o\right) \tag{4-17}$$

as it is easy to see from (4-12). Thus, if $f(x,y)$ is rotated by an angle θ_o, its transform $F(u,v)$ is rotated by the same angle.

Convolution theorem and Parseval's formula

Given two functions $f_1(x,y)$ and $f_2(x,y)$ with respective transforms $F_1(u,v)$ and $F_2(u,v)$, we shall show that the transform $F(u,v)$ of their double convolution $f(x,y)$ [see Chap. 2, (1-17)] equals $F_1(u,v)F_2(u,v)$

$$f_1(x,y) ** f_2(x,y) \leftrightarrow F_1(u,v)F_2(u,v) \qquad (4\text{-}18)$$

Indeed, with $\Gamma_1(u,y)$, $\Gamma_2(u,y)$, and $\Gamma(u,y)$ the transforms of $f_1(x,y)$, $f_2(x,y)$, and $f(x,y)$ with respect to x, we conclude by repeated application of (2-2) that

$$\int_{-\infty}^{\infty} f_1(\xi,\eta)f_2(x-\xi, y-\eta)\, d\xi \overset{x}{\leftrightarrow} \Gamma_1(u,\eta)\Gamma_2(u, y-\eta)$$

Hence

$$\iint_{-\infty}^{\infty} f_1(\xi,\eta)f_2(x-\xi, y-\eta)\, d\xi\, d\eta \overset{x}{\leftrightarrow} \int_{-\infty}^{\infty} \Gamma_1(u,\eta)\Gamma_2(u, y-\eta)\, d\eta$$

$$\overset{y}{\leftrightarrow} F_1(u,v)F_2(u,v)$$

and (4-18) follows.

With $f_1(x,y) = f(x,y)$, $f_2(x,y) = g^*(-x,-y)$, we obtain from (4-18), as in (2-7), Parseval's formula

$$\iint_{-\infty}^{\infty} f(x,y)g^*(x,y)\, dx\, dy = \frac{1}{4\pi^2} \iint_{-\infty}^{\infty} F(u,v)G^*(u,v)\, du\, dv \qquad (4\text{-}19)$$

Finally, with $f(x,y) = g(x,y)$, the above yields

$$\iint_{-\infty}^{\infty} |f(x,y)|^2\, dx\, dy = \frac{1}{4\pi^2} \iint_{-\infty}^{\infty} |F(u,v)|^2\, du\, dv \qquad (4\text{-}20)$$

Example 4-1   From the pair (see Prob. 3-8)

$$e^{-\alpha t^2} \leftrightarrow \sqrt{\frac{\pi}{\alpha}}\, e^{-\omega^2/4\alpha} \qquad (4\text{-}21)$$

and (4-16) we conclude that

$$e^{-\alpha(x^2+y^2)} \leftrightarrow \frac{\pi}{\alpha}\, e^{-(u^2+v^2)/4\alpha} \qquad (4\text{-}22)$$

Line spread

Consider a signal $h(x,y)$ with transform $H(u,v)$.   From (4-1) we see that

$$H(u,0) = \int_{-\infty}^{\infty} e^{-jux} \int_{-\infty}^{\infty} h(x,y)\, dy\, dx \qquad (4\text{-}23)$$

With $s(x)$ the x profile of $h(x,y)$ (line spread) and $S(\omega)$ its Fourier transform, that is,

$$s(x) = \int_{-\infty}^{\infty} h(x,y)\, dy \leftrightarrow S(\omega) \qquad (4\text{-}24)$$

we see from (4-23) that

$$S(\omega) = H(\omega, 0) \tag{4-25}$$

This result can be generalized. With

$$s_{\alpha\beta}(x) = \frac{1}{|\alpha\beta|} \int_{-\infty}^{\infty} h\left(\frac{x-y}{\alpha}, \frac{y}{\beta}\right) dy \qquad \alpha^2 + \beta^2 = 1 \tag{4-26}$$

[generalized point spread as in Chap. 2, (3-45)] and

$$s_{\alpha\beta}(x) \leftrightarrow S_{\alpha\beta}(\omega)$$

its Fourier transform, we maintain that

$$S_{\alpha\beta}(\omega) = H(\alpha\omega, \beta\omega) \tag{4-27}$$

Indeed, from (4-12) we have (elaborate)

$$\frac{1}{|\alpha\beta|} h\left(\frac{x-y}{\alpha}, \frac{y}{\beta}\right) \Leftrightarrow H(\alpha u, \beta u + \beta v)$$

But $s_{\alpha\beta}(x)$ is the x profile of the left side above; hence [see (4-25)], its transform is obtained by setting $u = \omega$ and $v = 0$ in $H(\alpha u, \beta u + \beta v)$. The result is (4-27).

If $S_{\alpha\beta}(\omega)$ is known for every α and β, then $H(u,v)$ can be determined from (4-27) with

$$\omega = \sqrt{u^2 + v^2} \qquad \alpha = \frac{u}{\omega} \qquad \beta = \frac{v}{\omega}$$

Zero-one functions We shall now determine the transform $F(u,v)$ of the zero-one function

$$p_A(x,y) = \begin{cases} 1 & (x,y) \in A \\ 0 & (x,y) \notin A \end{cases}$$

associated with region A of Fig. 4-1. We assume that any vertical line

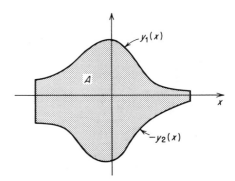

Fig. 4-1

intersects the boundary of A at no more than two points. Denoting by $y_1(x)$ and $-y_2(x)$ the upper and lower boundaries of A, we conclude from (4-1) that

$$F(u,v) = \int_{-\infty}^{\infty} e^{-jux} \int_{-y_2(x)}^{y_1(x)} e^{-jvy}\, dy\, dx \tag{4-28}$$

With

$$y(x) = \tfrac{1}{2}[y_1(x) + y_2(x)] \leftrightarrow Y(u)$$

we note that

$$F(u,0) = \int_{-\infty}^{\infty} e^{-jux}[y_1(x) + y_2(x)]\, dx = 2Y(u) \tag{4-29}$$

Example 4-2 Suppose that A is a rectangle, as in Fig. 4-2. Clearly, $y_1(x) = y_2(x) = b$ for $|x| < a$ and equals zero otherwise. Hence

$$F(u,v) = \int_{-a}^{a} e^{-jux} \int_{-b}^{b} e^{-jvy}\, dy\, dx = \frac{4 \sin au \sin bv}{uv} \tag{4-30}$$

With $a = b$, the transform of the square B results. Rotating this square by $\theta_o = \pi/4$, we obtain the rhombus C. Its transform is given by

$$F_1(u,v) = \frac{8 \sin\,[a(u + v)/\sqrt{2}]\, \sin\,[a(u - v)/\sqrt{2}]}{(u + v)(u - v)}$$

This follows by setting $a = b$ in (4-30) and rotating by $\pi/4$ [see (4-17) or (4-12)].

Example 4-3 If A is a circle of radius a (Fig. 4-3a), then

$$y_1(x) = y_2(x) = y(x) = \begin{cases} \sqrt{a^2 - x^2} & |x| < a \\ 0 & |x| > a \end{cases}$$

Therefore [see (4-29)], with $x = a \sin \theta$

$$F(u,0) = 2 \int_{-a}^{a} \sqrt{a^2 - x^2}\, e^{-jux}\, dx = 2 \int_{-\pi/2}^{\pi/2} a^2 \cos^2 \theta e^{-jau \sin \theta}\, d\theta$$

From the above and Prob. 5-11 it follows that

$$F(u,0) = \frac{2\pi a J_1(au)}{u}$$

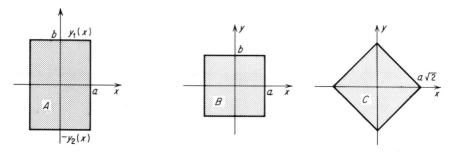

Fig. 4-2

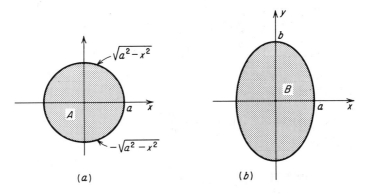

Fig. 4-3

where $J_1(x)$ is the Bessel function of order one. Since $p_A(x,y)$ has circular symmetry, $F(u,v)$ must also have circular symmetry; hence

$$F(u,v) = \frac{2\pi a J_1(a \sqrt{u^2 + v^2})}{\sqrt{u^2 + v^2}} \qquad (4\text{-}31)$$

This important result is reestablished in Chap. 5, (1-20).

With B the ellipse of Fig. 4-3b, it is easy to see that

$$p_B(x,y) = p_A\left(x, \frac{y}{c}\right) \qquad \text{where} \qquad c = \frac{b}{a}$$

Therefore the transform of $p_B(x,y)$ is given by

$$F_1(u,v) = \frac{2\pi c a J_1(a \sqrt{u^2 + c^2 v^2})}{\sqrt{u^2 + c^2 v^2}} = \frac{2\pi a b J_1(\sqrt{a^2 u^2 + b^2 v^2})}{\sqrt{a^2 u^2 + b^2 v^2}}$$

This follows from (4-11) and (4-31).

We now assume that the boundary of A is symmetrical about the x axis (Fig. 4-4). With

$$y_1(x) = y_2(x) = y(x)$$

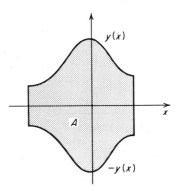

Fig. 4-4

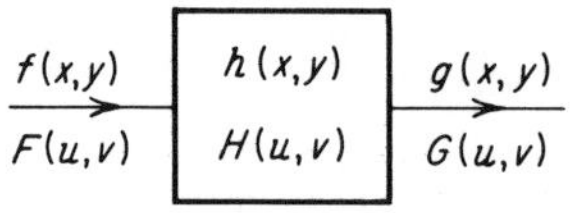

Fig. 4-5

(4-28) yields

$$F(u,v) = 2 \int_{-\infty}^{\infty} e^{-jux} \frac{\sin [y(x)v]}{v} \, dx \tag{4-32}$$

Since

$$\frac{\sin [y(x)v]}{v} = y(x) - \frac{v^2}{6} y^3(x) + \cdots$$

the transform $F(u,v)$ can be written as the series

$$F(u,v) = 2Y(u) - \frac{v^2}{3} Y_3(u) + \cdots$$

where $Y_n(u)$ is the transform of $y^n(x)$. This expression simplifies the evaluation of $F(u,v)$ in the vicinity of the u axis.

Systems

Consider a system with input $f(x,y)$, impulse response $h(x,y)$, and output $g(x,y)$ (Fig. 4-5). With $F(u,v)$, $H(u,v)$, and $G(u,v)$ the Fourier transforms of these functions, it follows from Chap. 2, (3-30), and the convolution theorem (4-18) that

$$G(u,v) = F(u,v)H(u,v) \tag{4-33}$$

This result will be used extensively.

PROBLEMS

3-1. Show that

$$\frac{\sin \pi x}{x} p_1(x) \leftrightarrow Si(\omega + \pi) - Si(\omega - \pi)$$

3-2. Find the Fourier transform of the function

$$f(t) = \begin{cases} \displaystyle\sum_{n=-\infty}^{\infty} \alpha_n e^{jn\omega_0 t} & |t| < \dfrac{\pi}{\omega_o} \\ 0 & |t| > \dfrac{\pi}{\omega_o} \end{cases}$$

3-3. Show that

$$\frac{1}{\sqrt{|t|}} \leftrightarrow \frac{\sqrt{2\pi}}{\sqrt{|\omega|}} \qquad \sin \alpha|t| \leftrightarrow \frac{2\alpha}{\alpha^2 - \omega^2}$$

3-4. Consider a system with impulse response $h(t)$ and system function

$$H(\omega) = e^{-j\theta(\omega)} \qquad \theta(\omega) = \begin{cases} \alpha\omega^2 & \omega > 0 \\ -\alpha\omega^2 & \omega < 0 \end{cases}$$

With $C(\tau)$ and $S(\tau)$ the Fresnel cosine and sine integrals, show that

$$h(t) = \frac{1}{\sqrt{2\pi\alpha}} \left[\tfrac{1}{2} + C\left(\frac{t}{\sqrt{2\pi\alpha}}\right) \right] \cos\frac{t^2}{4\alpha} + \frac{1}{\sqrt{2\pi\alpha}} \left[\tfrac{1}{2} + S\left(\frac{t}{\sqrt{2\pi\alpha}}\right) \right] \sin\frac{t^2}{4\alpha}$$

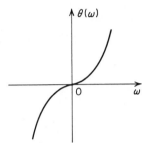

Fig. P3-4

3-5. With $f(t) \leftrightarrow F(\omega)$, $f(t)e^{j\alpha t^2} \leftrightarrow F_1(\omega)$, show that

    (a) $f(t) * e^{j\alpha t^2} = e^{j\alpha t^2} F_1(2\alpha t)$

    (b) $F_1(\omega) = e^{j\pi/4} \sqrt{\dfrac{\pi}{\alpha}} F(\omega) * e^{-j\omega^2/4\alpha}$

3-6. (a) Show that

$$e^{-\alpha|t|}(\cos\alpha|t| + \sin\alpha|t|) \leftrightarrow \frac{8\alpha^3}{\omega^4 + 4\alpha^4}$$

    (b) Using Fourier transforms, show that if $y(x)$ satisfies the equation

$$M\frac{d^4y(x)}{dx^4} + ky(x) = mf(x)$$

for all x, then, with $\alpha = (k/4M)^{1/4}$,

$$y(x) = \frac{m}{8M\alpha^3} e^{-\alpha|x|}(\cos\alpha|x| + \sin\alpha|x|) * f(x)$$

3-7. Show that if

$$f(t) \leftrightarrow A(\omega)e^{j\varphi(\omega)}$$

then

$$\int_{-\infty}^{\infty} t^2|f(t)|^2 \, dt = \frac{1}{2\pi} \int_{-\infty}^{\infty} \left[\left(\frac{dA}{d\omega}\right)^2 + A^2\left(\frac{d\varphi}{d\omega}\right)^2 \right] d\omega$$

3-8. Show that

$$\cos t^2 \leftrightarrow \sqrt{\pi} \cos\left(\frac{\pi - \omega^2}{4}\right) \qquad \sin t^2 \leftrightarrow \sqrt{\pi} \sin\left(\frac{\pi - \omega^2}{4}\right)$$

$$e^{-\alpha t^2} \leftrightarrow \sqrt{\frac{\pi}{\alpha}} e^{-\omega^2/4\alpha}$$

3-9. Show that if $f(t) \leftrightarrow F(\omega)$, then

$$\int_{-a}^{a} |f(t)|^2 \, dt = \frac{1}{2\pi^2} \iint_{-\infty}^{\infty} F(x)F^*(y) \, \frac{\sin a(x-y)}{x-y} \, dx \, dy$$

3-10. Given a real signal $f(t)$ with Fourier transform $F(\omega)$, we form the function $Z_l(\omega)$ (Fig. P3-10) and its in-phase and quadrature components

$$P(\omega) = Z_l(\omega) + Z_l^*(-\omega) \qquad Q(\omega) = -[Z_l(\omega) - Z_l^*(-\omega)]j$$

Show that their inverse transforms $p(t)$ and $q(t)$ are real, and

$$f(t) = p(t) \cos \omega_o t - q(t) \sin \omega_o t$$

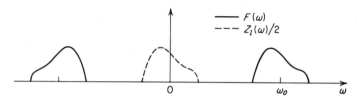

Fig. P3-10

3-11. Consider a real causal signal

$$f(t) = 0 \qquad \text{for } t < 0$$

with Fourier transform $F(\omega) = R(\omega) + jX(\omega)$ and finite energy E.   Show that

(a) If $f(t) = f_e(t) + f_o(t)$ (even and odd parts), then

$$f_e(t) = f_o(t) \operatorname{sgn} t$$

(b) $$f(0^+) = \frac{1}{\pi} \int_{-\infty}^{\infty} R(\omega) \, d\omega$$

(c) $$\frac{\pi E}{2} = \int_{0}^{\infty} R^2(\omega) \, d\omega = \int_{0}^{\infty} X^2(\omega) \, d\omega$$

(d) $$R(\omega) = \hat{X}(\omega) = \frac{1}{\pi} \int_{-\infty}^{\infty} \frac{X(y)}{\omega - y} \, dy$$

(e) For any $\varphi(x)$, $\hat{\hat{\varphi}}(x) = -\varphi(x)$.

(f) From (d) and (e) conclude that

$$X(\omega) = -\hat{R}(\omega) = -\frac{1}{\pi} \int_{-\infty}^{\infty} \frac{R(y)}{\omega - y} \, dy$$

3-12. Show that if $f(x,y) \leftrightarrow F(u,v)$, then

$$\iint_{-\infty}^{\infty} f\left(\frac{x}{2} + \xi, \frac{y}{2} + \eta\right) f^*\left(\frac{x}{2} - \xi, \frac{y}{2} - \eta\right) d\xi \, d\eta \Leftrightarrow |F(u,v)|^2$$

4
FOURIER SERIES AND SAMPLING EXPANSIONS

Transforms of singularity functions are determined and used to derive the properties of Fourier series, Poisson sums, and sampling expansions in one and two variables.

1. TRANSFORMS OF SINGULARITY FUNCTIONS

In this section we shall develop a number of transform pairs involving singularity functions. From Chap. 2, (2-1), we have

$$\int_{-\infty}^{\infty} \delta(t)e^{-j\omega t}\,dt = 1 \tag{1-1}$$

Hence (Fig. 1-1),

$$\delta(t) \leftrightarrow 1 \tag{1-2}$$

and

$$\delta(t - t_o) \leftrightarrow e^{-j\omega t_o} \tag{1-3}$$

$$e^{j\omega_o t} \leftrightarrow 2\pi\delta(\omega - \omega_o) \tag{1-4}$$

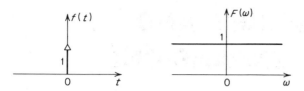

Fig. 1-1

Furthermore,

$$\cos \omega_o t = \frac{e^{j\omega_o t} + e^{-j\omega_o t}}{2} \leftrightarrow \pi[\delta(\omega - \omega_o) + \delta(\omega + \omega_o)] \tag{1-5}$$

$$\sin \omega_o t = \frac{e^{j\omega_o t} - e^{-j\omega_o t}}{2j} \leftrightarrow j\pi[\delta(\omega + \omega_o) - \delta(\omega - \omega_o)] \tag{1-6}$$

Since $\operatorname{sgn} t \leftrightarrow 2/j\omega$ [see Chap. 3, (1-14)], the transform of the unit step function $U(t)$ is given by (Fig. 1-2)

$$U(t) = \tfrac{1}{2}(1 + \operatorname{sgn} t) \leftrightarrow \pi\delta(\omega) + \frac{1}{j\omega} \tag{1-7}$$

From (1-3) we have (Fig. 1-3)

$$\sum_{n=-N}^{N} \delta(t - nT) \leftrightarrow \sum_{n=-N}^{N} e^{-jnT\omega} = \frac{e^{j\omega NT} - e^{-j\omega(N+1)T}}{1 - e^{-j\omega T}}$$

$$= \frac{\sin \omega(N + \tfrac{1}{2})T}{\sin (\omega T/2)} \tag{1-8}$$

Using the above pair, we shall find the transform of the repetition

$$f(t) = \sum_{n=-N}^{N} f_o(t - nT)$$

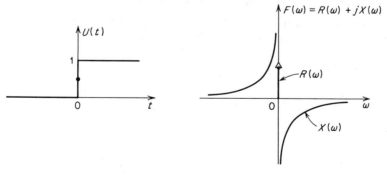

Fig. 1-2

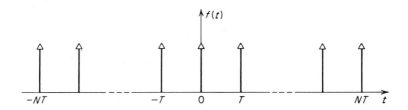

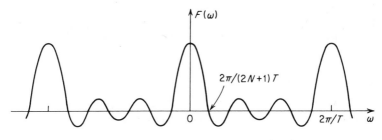

Fig. 1-3

of a signal $f_o(t)$ (Fig. 1-4).   Clearly, $f(t)$ can be written as a convolution of $f_o(t)$ with a pulse train

$$f(t) = f_o(t) * \sum_{n=-N}^{N} \delta(t - nT) \tag{1-9}$$

Therefore, if

$$f_o(t) \leftrightarrow F_o(\omega)$$

then (convolution theorem), the transform of $f(t)$ is given by

$$F(\omega) = F_o(\omega) \frac{\sin (N + \frac{1}{2})\omega T}{\sin (\omega T/2)} \tag{1-10}$$

We note that it is not necessary to assume that $f_o(t)$ is of duration T for the validity of (1-10).

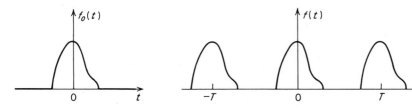

Fig. 1-4

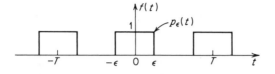

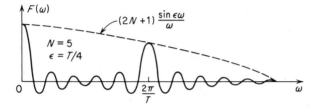

Fig. 1-5

Example 1-1   If $f_o(t) = p_\epsilon(t)$ is a pulse as in Fig. 1-5, then

$$F(\omega) = \frac{2 \sin \epsilon\omega}{\omega} \frac{\sin (N + \frac{1}{2})\omega T}{\sin (\omega T/2)}$$

Example 1-2   Suppose that

$$f(t) = e^{i\theta(t)} \qquad \text{for} \qquad |t| < \frac{(2N + 1)T}{2}$$

and it equals zero elsewhere.   The function $\theta(t)$ is shown in Fig. 1-6.   Clearly, $f(t)$ is of the form of (1-9) with

$$f_o(t) = e^{i(\alpha+\beta t)} \qquad \text{for } |t| < \frac{T}{2}$$

Hence,

$$F_o(\omega) = e^{i\alpha} \int_{-T/2}^{T/2} e^{i\beta t} e^{-i\omega t} \, dt = e^{i\alpha} \frac{2 \sin [(\omega - \beta)T/2]}{\omega - \beta}$$

Therefore,

$$F(\omega) = e^{i\alpha} \frac{2 \sin [(\omega - \beta)T/2]}{\omega - \beta} \frac{\sin (N + \frac{1}{2})\omega T}{\sin (\omega T/2)}$$

The convolution of two pulse trains is given by (see Example 2-2,

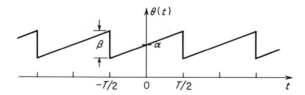

Fig. 1-6

Table 1-1 Transforms of singularity functions

$$f(t) \leftrightarrow F(\omega)$$

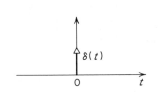

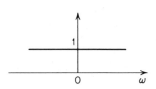

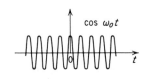

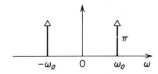

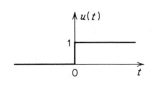

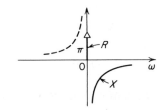

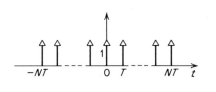

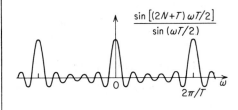

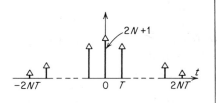

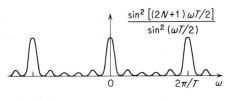

$\delta(x)\delta(y) \Leftrightarrow 1$ $\delta(x) \Leftrightarrow 2\pi\delta(v)$

    $\varphi(x) \Leftrightarrow 2\pi\Phi(u)\delta(v)$ $\varphi(x)\delta(y) \Leftrightarrow \Phi(u)$

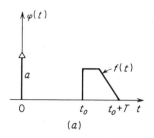

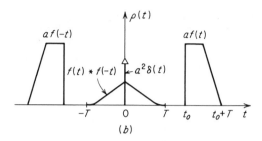

Fig. 1-7

Chap. 2)

$$\sum_{n=-N}^{N} \delta(t - nT) * \sum_{n=-N}^{N} \delta(t - nT)$$

$$= \sum_{n=-2N}^{2N} (2N + 1 - |n|)\delta(t - nT)$$

Hence [see (1-8) and Chap. 3, (2-2)]

$$\sum_{n=-2N}^{2N} (2N + 1 - |n|)\delta(t - nT) \leftrightarrow \frac{\sin^2 \omega(N + \frac{1}{2})T}{\sin^2 (\omega T/2)} \qquad (1\text{-}11)$$

Table 1-1 contains transform pairs involving singularity functions.

The principle of holography   As an application of the use of $\delta(t)$, we shall show how a function $f(t)$ can be recovered from its energy spectrum properly modified.   (See also Sec. 11-1.)   We assume that $f(t)$ is of finite duration T, and select its front at $t = t_o > 0$ (Fig. 1-7a).   Thus

$$f(t) = 0 \qquad \text{for } t < t_o \text{ or } t > t_o + T$$

We now form the signal

$$\varphi(t) = a\delta(t) + f(t)$$

and its transform

$$\Phi(\omega) = a + F(\omega)$$

and we claim that $f(t)$ can be recovered from $|\Phi(\omega)|^2$.   Indeed, with $\rho(t)$ the inverse of $|\Phi(\omega)|^2$ [see Chap. 3, (2-14)], that is,

$$\rho(t) \leftrightarrow |\Phi(\omega)|^2 = \Phi(\omega)\Phi^*(\omega)$$

we have, assuming for simplicity that $f(t)$ is real,

$$\rho(t) = \varphi(t) * \varphi(-t) = [a\delta(t) + f(t)] * [a\delta(-t) + f(-t)]$$
$$= af(t) + af(-t) + a^2\delta(t) + f(t) * f(-t)$$

as in Fig. 1-7b.   If

$$T < t_o$$

then the functions $f(t)$, $f(-t)$ and $f(t) * f(-t)$ do not overlap, and $af(t)$ is the portion of $\rho(t)$ in the interval $(t_o, t_o + T)$.   For $T > t_o$ this is no longer true.   However, if a is sufficiently large, then the interference due to the term $f(t) * f(-t)$ is negligible, and $f(t)$ can again be distinguished in $\rho(t)$.

TWO–DIMENSIONAL SINGULARITIES

We recall that if $f_1(x) \leftrightarrow F_1(u)$, $f_2(y) \leftrightarrow F_2(v)$, then

$$f_1(x)f_2(x) \Leftrightarrow F_1(u)F_2(v) \tag{1-12}$$

From the above and (1-3) it follows that

$$\delta(x - x_o)\delta(y - y_o) \Leftrightarrow e^{-j(ux_o + vy_o)}$$

Consider now a rectangular array of points (Fig. 1-8)

$$s(x,y) = \sum_{m=-M}^{M} \sum_{n=-N}^{N} \delta(x - ma)\delta(y - nb)$$

Since it is a product of a function of x times a function of y, we conclude from (1-12) and (1-8) that

$$S(u,v) = \frac{\sin (M + \frac{1}{2})au}{\sin (au/2)} \frac{\sin (N + \frac{1}{2})bv}{\sin (bv/2)} \tag{1-13}$$

This result can be used to find the transform of the function

$$f(x,y) = \sum_{m=-M}^{M} \sum_{n=-N}^{N} f_o(x - ma, y - nb) = f_o(x,y) ** s(x,y)$$

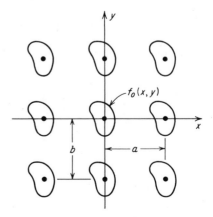

Fig. 1-8

which is shown in Fig. 1-8.   With $F_o(u,v)$ the transform of $f_o(x,y)$, we conclude from (1-13) and the convolution theorem that

$$F(u,v) = F_o(u,v) \frac{\sin (M + \frac{1}{2})au}{\sin (au/2)} \frac{\sin (N + \frac{1}{2})bv}{\sin (bv/2)}$$

We note that $F(u,v) = 0$ on the lines

$$u = \frac{2\pi m}{(2M + 1)a} \qquad v = \frac{2\pi n}{(2N + 1)b}$$

where m and n are integers different from zero.

Line singularities

Consider a function $\varphi(x)$ with one-dimensional Fourier transform $\Phi(u)$:

$$\varphi(x) \leftrightarrow \Phi(u)$$

In the xy plane, the function $f(x,y) = \varphi(x)$ is of the form $f_1(x)f_2(y)$, where $f_1(x) = \varphi(x)$ and $f_2(y) = 1$.   Therefore [see (1-12) and (1-4)],

$$\varphi(x) \Leftrightarrow \Phi(u)2\pi\delta(v) \tag{1-14}$$

Thus, if a function $f(x,y)$ is independent of y, then its two-dimensional transform consists of line masses on the u axis of line density $2\pi\Phi(u)$.
    Similarly,

$$\varphi(y) \Leftrightarrow 2\pi\delta(u)\Phi(v) \tag{1-15}$$

    Reasoning as above, we also have

$$\varphi(x)\delta(y) \Leftrightarrow \Phi(u) \qquad \delta(x)\varphi(y) \Leftrightarrow \Phi(v) \tag{1-16}$$

Hence, if $f(x,y)$ consists of line masses on the x axis, then its transform is independent of v.
    As a special case, we observe that (Fig. 1-9)

$$\delta(x) \Leftrightarrow 2\pi\delta(v) \qquad \delta(y) \Leftrightarrow 2\pi\delta(u) \tag{1-17}$$

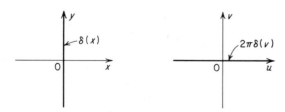

Fig. 1-9

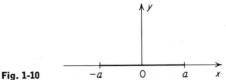

Fig. 1-10

Example 1-3 (Slit) If $f(x,y) = p_a(x)\delta(y)$ is a line mass of unit density on the segment $(-a,a)$ of the x axis (Fig. 1-10), then

$$F(u,v) = \frac{2 \sin au}{u}$$

is independent of v.

We finally remark that if $f(x,y) = \delta[\alpha(x,y)]$ is a line mass on the curve $\alpha(x,y) = 0$ of density $(\alpha_x{}^2 + \alpha_y{}^2)^{-\frac{1}{2}}$ [see Chap. 2, (2-19)], then $F(u,v)$ is given by the line integral

$$\int_C \frac{e^{-j(ux+vy)}}{\sqrt{\alpha_x{}^2 + \alpha_y{}^2}}\, ds$$

along the curve $\alpha(x,y) = 0$.

2. FOURIER SERIES

Suppose that a function $f(t)$ is given by the sum

$$f(t) = \sum_{n=-\infty}^{\infty} \alpha_n e^{jn\omega_o t} \tag{2-1}$$

Its Fourier transform is then a sequence of equidistant impulses [see (1-4)]

$$F(\omega) = \sum_{n=-\infty}^{\infty} 2\pi\alpha_n \delta(\omega - n\omega_o) \tag{2-2}$$

Multiplying both sides of (2-1) by $e^{-jn\omega_o t}$ and integrating from $-T/2$ to $T/2$, we conclude that

$$\alpha_n = \frac{1}{T} \int_{-T/2}^{T/2} f(t) e^{-jn\omega_o t}\, dt \tag{2-3}$$

It is easy to see that the function $f(t)$ is periodic, with period $2\pi/\omega_o$ (Fig. 2-1).   That is,

$$f(t + T) = f(t) \qquad T = \frac{2\pi}{\omega_o} \tag{2-4}$$

because

$$e^{jn\omega_o(t+T)} = e^{jn\omega_o t}$$

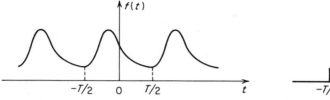

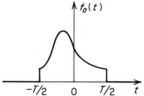

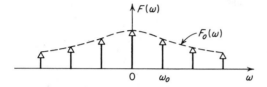

Fig. 2-1

Conversely, if $f(t)$ is periodic, as in (2-4), then, in general, it can be written as a sum of the form (2-1). Conditions for the validity of this fundamental expansion are extensively discussed in the literature. In the following we shall give a formal proof based on the theory of Fourier transforms.

Taking the transforms of both sides of (2-4), we have

$$F(\omega)e^{j\omega T} = F(\omega) \tag{2-5}$$

But this is possible only if $F(\omega) = 0$ when $e^{j\omega T} \neq 1$, that is, when $\omega \neq 2\pi n/T$. Thus,

$$F(\omega) \neq 0 \qquad \text{only if} \qquad \omega = \frac{2\pi n}{T} = n\omega_o \tag{2-6}$$

If $f(t)$ is not identically zero, then the above is true only if $F(\omega)$ consists of impulses at the points $n\omega_o$, that is,

$$F(\omega) = \sum_{n=-\infty}^{\infty} \beta_n \delta(\omega - n\omega_o)$$

and (2-1) follows with $\beta_n = 2\pi\alpha_n$.

We now form the function (Fig. 2-1)

$$f_o(t) = \begin{cases} f(t) & |t| < \dfrac{T}{2} \\[2mm] 0 & |t| > \dfrac{T}{2} \end{cases} \tag{2-7}$$

Its transform $F_o(\omega)$ is given by

$$F_o(\omega) = \int_{-T/2}^{T/2} f(t)e^{-j\omega t}\, dt$$

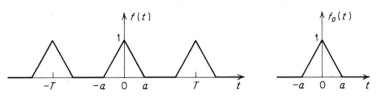

Fig. 2-2

Therefore [see (2-3)],

$$F_o(n\omega_o) = \int_{-T/2}^{T/2} f(t)e^{-jn\omega_o t}\, dt = T\alpha_n \qquad (2\text{-}8)$$

This relationship is used to facilitate the evaluation of α_n.

We note that $f(t)$ can be written as a sum

$$f(t) = \sum_{n=-\infty}^{\infty} f_o(t + nT) \qquad (2\text{-}9)$$

Example 2-1 Suppose that $f(t)$ is a sequence of triangles, as in Fig. 2-2. The function $f_o(t)$ is a single triangle; hence (see Example 2-1, Chap. 3),

$$F_o(\omega) = \frac{4\sin^2{(a\omega/2)}}{a\omega^2}$$

From the above and (2-8) it follows that the Fourier series coefficients of $f(t)$ are given by

$$\alpha_n = \frac{4}{T}\frac{\sin^2{(na\pi/T)}}{a(2n\pi/T)^2} = \frac{T\sin^2{(na\pi/T)}}{an^2\pi^2}$$

Example 2-2 If $f(t)$ is an impulse train (Fig. 2-3), that is,

$$f(t) = \sum_{n=-\infty}^{\infty} \delta(t - nT)$$

then $f_o(t) = \delta(t)$ and $F_o(\omega) = 1$. Therefore, the coefficients of the Fourier series expansion of $f(t)$ are given by $\alpha_n = 1/T$. Thus, the transform of an impulse train is an impulse train. Inserting α_n into (2-1), we obtain the useful identity

$$\sum_{n=-\infty}^{\infty} \delta(t - nT) = \frac{1}{T}\sum_{n=-\infty}^{\infty} e^{jn\omega_o t}$$

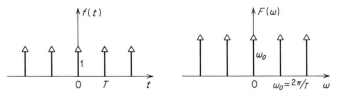

Fig. 2-3

Parseval's formula for Fourier series   We shall show that

$$\frac{1}{T} \int_{-T/2}^{T/2} |f(t)|^2 \, dt = \sum_{n=-\infty}^{\infty} |\alpha_n|^2 \tag{2-10}$$

Indeed, with $f_o(t)$ as in (2-7), we have from (2-2), (2-8), and Parseval's formula [Chap. 3, (2-7)]

$$\int_{-T/2}^{T/2} |f(t)|^2 \, dt = \int_{-\infty}^{\infty} f_o(t) f^*(t) \, dt$$

$$= \frac{1}{2\pi} \int_{-\infty}^{\infty} F_o(\omega) \sum_{n=-\infty}^{\infty} 2\pi \alpha_n^* \delta(\omega - n\omega_o) \, d\omega = \sum_{n=-\infty}^{\infty} F_o(n\omega_o) \alpha_n^*$$

and (2-10) follows.   The above is usually derived from the orthogonality of the functions $e^{jn\omega_o t}$ in the interval $(-T/2, T/2)$.

As a corollary of (2-10), we observe that

$$\frac{1}{2\pi} \int_{-\infty}^{\infty} |F_o(\omega)|^2 \, d\omega = \int_{-T/2}^{T/2} |f_o(t)|^2 \, dt = \frac{1}{T} \sum_{n=-\infty}^{\infty} \left| F_o\left(\frac{2\pi n}{T}\right) \right|^2 \tag{2-11}$$

Thus if a function is time-limited, the area of its energy spectrum can be written as a sum.

Truncated Fourier series and Fejér sums

We shall relate the finite sum

$$f_N(t) = \sum_{n=-N}^{N} \alpha_n e^{jn\omega_o t}$$

to the function $f(t)$.   With $F_N(\omega)$ the transform of $f_N(t)$, we have [see (2-8)]

$$F_N(\omega) = 2\pi \sum_{n=-N}^{N} \alpha_n \delta(\omega - n\omega_o) = \frac{F_o(\omega)}{T} \sum_{n=-N}^{N} 2\pi \delta(\omega - n\omega_o) \tag{2-12}$$

because $F_o(\omega)\delta(\omega - n\omega_o) = F_o(n\omega_o)\delta(\omega - n\omega_o)$.   With $k(t)$ the inverse transform of the last sum, we see from (1-8) that

$$k(t) = \frac{\sin \omega_o(N + \tfrac{1}{2})t}{\sin (\omega_o t/2)} \leftrightarrow 2\pi \sum_{n=-N}^{N} \delta(\omega - n\omega_o) \tag{2-13}$$

Since the inverse $f_o(t)$ of $F_o(\omega)$ is zero for $|t| > T/2$, we conclude from (2-13), (2-12), and the convolution theorem that

$$f_N(t) = \frac{1}{T} \int_{-T/2}^{T/2} f(\tau) k(t - \tau) \, d\tau \tag{2-14}$$

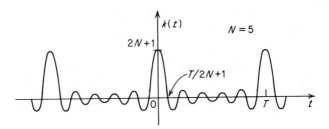

Fig. 2-4

Thus, $f_N(t)$ equals the weighted average of $f(t)$ with the Fourier series kernel $k(t)$ as weight (Fig. 2-4).

Suppose now that we want to approximate $f(t)$ by a trigonometric sum $\varphi_N(t)$:

$$f(t) \simeq \varphi_N(t) = \sum_{n=-N}^{N} \gamma_n e^{jn\omega_o t} \tag{2-15}$$

If $\varphi_N(t)$ is so selected that for a specific N the mean-square error

$$\int_{-T/2}^{T/2} |f(t) - \varphi_N(t)|^2 \, dt$$

is minimum, then (see Prob. 6-3) we must have

$$\gamma_n = \alpha_n \qquad \text{hence} \qquad \varphi_N(t) = f_N(t)$$

If one is interested in minimizing the maximum error $|f(t) - \varphi_N(t)|$, then the above criterion is not satisfactory, particularly in the vicinity of the discontinuity points of $f(t)$.   A better fit can be obtained if

$$\gamma_n = \left(1 - \frac{|n|}{N}\right) \alpha_n$$

that is, if the low frequency components of $f(t)$ are favored linearly [11]. The resulting approximation

$$\varphi_N(t) = \sum_{n=-N}^{N} \left(1 - \frac{|n|}{N}\right) \alpha_n e^{jn\omega_o t} \tag{2-16}$$

is known as a Fejér sum.

We shall now relate $\varphi_N(t)$ to $f(t)$.   From (2-16) and (2-8) we see that the transform $\Phi_N(\omega)$ of $\varphi_N(t)$ is given by

$$\Phi_N(\omega) = 2\pi \sum_{n=-N}^{N} \left(1 - \frac{|n|}{N}\right) \alpha_n \delta(\omega - n\omega_o)$$

$$= \frac{F_o(\omega)}{T} \sum_{n=-N}^{N} 2\pi \left(1 - \frac{|n|}{N}\right) \delta(\omega - n\omega_o)$$

With $k_F(t)$ the inverse transform of the last sum, we see from (1-11), with $2N + 1$ replaced by N, that

$$k_F(t) = \frac{\sin^2(\omega_o N t/2)}{N \sin^2(\omega_o t/2)} \leftrightarrow 2\pi \sum_{n=-N}^{N} \left(1 - \frac{|n|}{N}\right) \delta(\omega - n\omega_o) \qquad (2\text{-}17)$$

From the above we conclude, as in (2-14), that

$$\varphi_N(t) = \frac{1}{T} \int_{-T/2}^{T/2} f(\tau) k_F(t - \tau) \, d\tau \qquad (2\text{-}18)$$

Thus, $\varphi_N(t)$ equals the weighted average of $f(t)$ with the "Fejér kernel" $k_F(t)$ as weight (Fig. 2-5).

Comment The Fejér sum is used not only to improve the approximation to $f(t)$ but also for another reason. Suppose that $f(t) \geq 0$. This is, for example, the case if $f(t)$ is a power spectrum (with t replaced by ω). Since $k(t)$ takes negative values, the resulting sum $f_N(t)$ might be negative. However,

$$k_F(t) \geq 0$$

Therefore $\varphi_N(t) \geq 0$, as we see from (2-18). Thus, by using the Fejér sum, we have retained the positiveness of our signal.

TWO-DIMENSIONAL FOURIER SERIES

A function of two variables $f(x,y)$ is called periodic in x if

$$f(x + a, y) = f(x,y) \qquad (2\text{-}19)$$

for any x and y. Considering $f(x,y)$ as a function of x, with y a parameter, we can expand it into a Fourier series. The coefficients of the

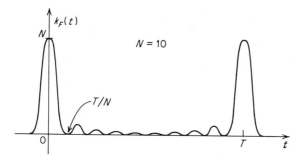

Fig. 2-5

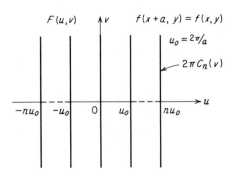

Fig. 2-6

resulting expansion will, of course, depend on y. Thus,

$$f(x,y) = \sum_{n=-\infty}^{\infty} c_n(y)e^{jnu_o x} \qquad u_o = \frac{2\pi}{a} \qquad (2\text{-}20)$$

$$c_n(y) = \frac{1}{a}\int_{-a/2}^{a/2} f(x,y)e^{-jnu_o x}\,dx \qquad (2\text{-}21)$$

With $C_n(v)$ the Fourier transform of $c_n(y)$, that is,

$$c_n(y) \leftrightarrow C_n(v)$$

we conclude, taking transforms of both sides of (2-20), that

$$f(x,y) \Leftrightarrow F(u,v) = 2\pi \sum_{n=-\infty}^{\infty} C_n(v)\delta(u - nu_o) \qquad (2\text{-}22)$$

because

$$e^{jnu_o x} \leftrightarrow 2\pi\delta(u - nu_o)$$

Thus, $F(u,v)$ consists of a line mass (as in Fig. 2-6) along the lines $u = nu_o$ and of line density $2\pi C_n(v)$.

Similarly, if $f(x,y)$ is periodic in y, then $F(u,v)$ consists of line masses on lines parallel to the u axis.

Suppose now that $f(x,y)$ is *doubly periodic*, i.e., that

$$f(x + na, y + mb) = f(x,y) \qquad (2\text{-}23)$$

for any integer m and n and any x and y. Thus, $f(x,y)$ is determined from its values in a rectangle with sides a and b. Clearly, $f(x,y)$ is periodic in x. Hence, it can be expanded into a series (2-20) with coefficients given by (2-21). We observe that

$$c_n(y + b) = \frac{1}{a}\int_{-a/2}^{a/2} f(x, y + b)e^{-jnu_o x}\,dx$$

$$= \frac{1}{a}\int_{-a/2}^{a/2} f(x,y)e^{-jnu_o x}\,dx = c_n(y)$$

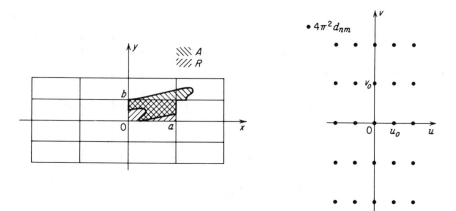

Fig. 2-7

Therefore, the functions $c_n(y)$ are periodic with period b. Expanding them into a Fourier series, we thus have

$$c_n(y) = \sum_{m=-\infty}^{\infty} d_{nm}e^{jmv_oy} \qquad v_o = \frac{2\pi}{b} \tag{2-24}$$

where

$$d_{nm} = \frac{1}{b} \int_{-b/2}^{b/2} c_n(y)e^{-jmv_oy}\,dy \tag{2-25}$$

If we insert (2-24) into (2-20), we obtain the double Fourier series expansion

$$f(x,y) = \sum_{n=-\infty}^{\infty} \sum_{m=-\infty}^{\infty} d_{nm}e^{j(nu_ox+mv_oy)} \tag{2-26}$$

of $f(x,y)$. The coefficients d_{nm} are given by

$$d_{nm} = \frac{1}{ab} \int_0^b \int_0^a f(x,y)e^{-j(nu_ox+mv_oy)}\,dx\,dy \tag{2-27}$$

as we see from (2-25) and (2-21).

From (2-26) and (1-4) we conclude that the transform of $f(x,y)$ is given by

$$F(u,v) = 4\pi^2 \sum_{n=-\infty}^{\infty} \sum_{m=-\infty}^{\infty} d_{nm}\delta(u-nu_o)\delta(v-mv_o) \tag{2-28}$$

Thus, the transform of a doubly periodic function consists of point masses (Fig. 2-7) at the points

$$(nu_o, mv_o) = \left(\frac{2\pi n}{a}, \frac{2\pi m}{b}\right)$$

Comment In (2-27), the domain of integration is a rectangle R with sides a and b. This domain can be modified. Suppose that A is a region (Fig. 2-7) equivalent to R in the sense that if $(x,y) \in R$, then for some integers m and n $(x + na, y + mb) \in A$, and if two points in R are distinct, then their images in A are also distinct. It then follows from the double periodicity of $f(x,y)$ and of the exponential $e^{-j(u_o x + v_o y)}$ that

$$d_{nm} = \frac{1}{ab} \iint\limits_A f(x,y) e^{-j(nu_o x + mv_o y)} \, dx \, dy \tag{2-29}$$

The coefficients d_{nm} can be expressed in terms of the Fourier transform $F_o(u,v)$ of the function

$$f_o(x,y) = \begin{cases} f(x,y) & (x,y) \in A \\ 0 & (x,y) \notin A \end{cases}$$

From (2-29) we easily find, as in (2-8), that

$$d_{nm} = \frac{F_o(nu_o, mv_o)}{ab} \tag{2-30}$$

We note that

$$f(x,y) = \sum_{n=-\infty}^{\infty} \sum_{m=-\infty}^{\infty} f_o(x + na, y + mb) \tag{2-31}$$

Example 2-3 Suppose that

$$f_o(x,y) = \begin{cases} 1 & \sqrt{x^2 + y^2} \leq r_o \\ 0 & \text{otherwise} \end{cases}$$

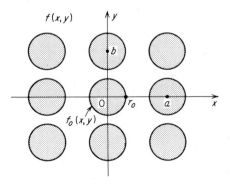

Fig. 2-8

where r_o is less than $a/2$ and $b/2$. From Chap. 3, (4-30), we see that

$$F_o(u,v) = 2\pi r_o \frac{J_1(r_o \sqrt{u^2 + v^2})}{\sqrt{u^2 + v^2}}$$

Forming the periodic repetition $f(x,y)$ of $f_o(x,y)$ (Fig. 2-8), we conclude from (2-30) that the coefficients of the Fourier expansion of $f(x,y)$ are given by

$$d_{nm} = \frac{2\pi r_o J_1[r_o \sqrt{(nu_o)^2 + (mv_o)^2}]}{ab \sqrt{(nu_o)^2 + (mv_o)^2}}$$

Skew-periodic functions

We say that a function $f(x,y)$ is *skew-periodic* if

$$f(x + na_1 + ma_2,\, y + nb_1 + mb_2) = f(x,y) \tag{2-32}$$

for any x and y and any integer m and n. Thus, $f(x,y)$ is determined from its values in the parallelogram $OA_1A_2A_3$ of Fig. 2-9a or in any other "equivalent" region.

The function $f(x,y)$ can be expanded into a double Fourier series with frequencies u_1, v_1, u_2, v_2 defined as follows. On the sides OA_1 and OA_2 of the above parallelogram we locate the points B_1 and B_2 such that

$$\overline{OB_1} = \frac{2\pi}{\overline{OA_1}} \qquad \overline{OB_2} = \frac{2\pi}{\overline{OA_2}}$$

where overbars signify lengths. We then locate the points C_1 and C_2, with the construction shown in Fig. 2-9a, and denote their coordinates by u_1, v_1 and u_2, v_2, respectively:

$$C_1{:}(u_1,v_1) \qquad C_2{:}(u_2,v_2)$$

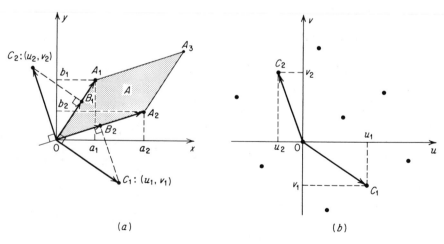

(a)   (b)

Fig. 2-9

It can be shown that

$$f(x,y) = \sum_{n=-\infty}^{\infty} \sum_{m=-\infty}^{\infty} d_{nm} e^{j[(nu_1+mu_2)x+(nv_1+mv_2)y]} \tag{2-33}$$

The coefficients d_{nm} are given by

$$d_{nm} = \frac{1}{\bar{A}} \iint_A f(x,y) e^{-j[(nu_1+mu_2)x+(nv_1+mv_2)y]} \, dx \, dy \tag{2-34}$$

where A is the parallelogram of Fig. 2-9 or any other equivalent region, and $\bar{A}$ is its area. Thus, the Fourier transform of $f(x,y)$ is given by

$$F(u,v) = 4\pi^2 \sum_{n=-\infty}^{\infty} \sum_{m=-\infty}^{\infty} d_{nm} \delta(u - nu_1 - mu_2) \delta(v - nv_1 - mv_2) \tag{2-35}$$

It consists of point masses, as in Fig. 2-9b. Expansion (2-33) or the equivalent (2-35) can be justified either by changing variables or by observing that [see (2-32)]

$$F(u,v) e^{j[(na_1+ma_2)u+(nb_1+mb_2)v]} = F(u,v)$$

This is possible only if $F(u,v)$ consists of point masses at all points u_i, v_i such that the above exponential equals one, i.e., for

$$(na_1 + ma_2)u_i + (nb_1 + mb_2)v_i = 2\pi r$$

and (2-35) follows. The fussy details are omitted. Once (2-33) is established, (2-34) follows from the orthogonality of the exponentials.

POISSON'S SUM FORMULA

Given an arbitrary function $h(t)$ with transform $H(\omega)$

$$h(t) \leftrightarrow H(\omega)$$

we shall show that

$$\sum_{n=-\infty}^{\infty} h(t + nT) = \frac{1}{T} \sum_{n=-\infty}^{\infty} H(n\omega_o) e^{jn\omega_o t} \qquad \omega_o = \frac{2\pi}{T} \tag{2-36}$$

This fundamental relationship is known as Poisson's formula.

Proof   The proof follows easily from the identity (see Example 2-2)

$$\sum_{n=-\infty}^{\infty} \delta(t + nT) = \frac{1}{T} \sum_{n=-\infty}^{\infty} e^{jn\omega_o t} \tag{2-37}$$

Indeed, if the impulse train

$$f(t) = \sum_{n=-\infty}^{\infty} \delta(t + nT)$$

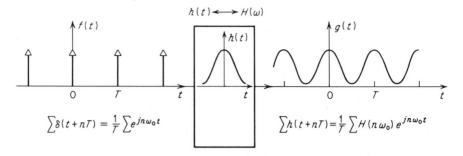

Fig. 2-10

is the input to a linear system (Fig. 2-10) with impulse response $h(t)$, then the output equals

$$g(t) = \sum_{n=-\infty}^{\infty} h(t + nT) \qquad (2\text{-}38)$$

Using the representation of $f(t)$ as a sum of exponentials, as in (2-37), we conclude that

$$g(t) = \frac{1}{T} \sum_{n=-\infty}^{\infty} H(n\omega_o)e^{jn\omega_o t}$$

because the response to $e^{jn\omega_o t}$ equals $H(n\omega_o)e^{jn\omega_o t}$, and (2-36) follows.

Comments   With $t = 0$, we conclude from (2-36) that

$$\sum_{n=-\infty}^{\infty} h(nT) = \frac{1}{T} \sum_{n=-\infty}^{\infty} H(n\omega_o) \qquad (2\text{-}39)$$

If $h(t)$ is discontinuous for $t = nT$, then $h(nT)$ in (2-39) must equal $[h(nT^+) + h(nT^-)]/2$ [see Chap. 3, (1-3)].   Thus if

$$h(t) = 0 \qquad \text{for } t < 0$$

then (2-39) yields

$$\frac{h(0^+)}{2} + \sum_{n=1}^{\infty} h(nT) = \frac{1}{T} \sum_{n=-\infty}^{\infty} H(n\omega_o) \qquad (2\text{-}40)$$

Application   We observe from (2-36) that if

$$H(n\omega_o) = 0 \qquad \text{for } n \neq 0 \qquad (2\text{-}41)$$

then the sum

$$\sum_{n=-\infty}^{\infty} h(t + nT) = \frac{1}{T} H(0) = \frac{1}{T} \int_{-\infty}^{\infty} h(t)\, dt \tag{2-42}$$

is independent of t. Condition (2-41) is also necessary for the above sum to be independent of t.

Special cases

1. If the function $h(t)$ is band-limited by ω_o, that is, if $H(\omega) = 0$ for $|\omega| \geq \omega_o$, then (2-41) holds. Hence, $h(t)$ satisfies (2-42).
2. Given an arbitrary function $\varphi(t)$ with transform $\Phi(\omega)$, we form its "moving average"†

$$h(t) = \frac{1}{T} \int_{t-T/2}^{t+T/2} \varphi(\tau)\, d\tau$$

Since [see Chap. 2, (1-4), and Chap. 3, (2-2)]

$$H(\omega) = \Phi(\omega) \frac{2 \sin (\omega T/2)}{\omega T}$$

if follows that $H(n\omega_o) = 0$ for $n \neq 0$; therefore, $h(t)$ satisfies (2-42).

Two dimensions

Poisson's formula can be readily extended to two-dimensional signals. Given a function $h(x,y)$ with transform $H(u,v)$, one can show that

$$\sum_{n=-\infty}^{\infty} \sum_{m=-\infty}^{\infty} h(x + na,\, y + mb)$$

$$= \frac{1}{ab} \sum_{n=-\infty}^{\infty} \sum_{m=-\infty}^{\infty} H(u + nu_o,\, v + mv_o) e^{j(nu_o x + mv_o y)}$$

where $u_o = 2\pi/a$, $v_o = 2\pi/b$. The proof is similar to the proof of (2-36).

3. THE SAMPLING THEOREM‡

Consider a band-limited signal $f(t)$ with Fourier transform $F(\omega)$:

$$F(\omega) = 0 \qquad \text{for } |\omega| \geq \omega_1 \tag{3-1}$$

$$f(t) = \frac{1}{2\pi} \int_{-\omega_1}^{\omega_1} F(\omega) e^{j\omega t}\, d\omega \tag{3-2}$$

† F. J. Sciré, *Proc. IEEE*, vol. 56, pp. 204–205, February, 1968.
‡ A. Papoulis, *Proc. IEEE*, vol. 54, pp. 947–955, July, 1966.

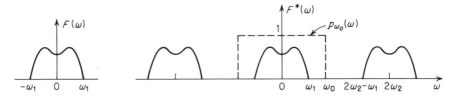

Fig. 3-1

We shall show that $f(t)$ can be determined from its values $f(nT)$ at a sequence of equidistant points $t = nT$, provided that

$$T \leq \frac{\pi}{\omega_1} \tag{3-3}$$

In fact, with $\omega_2 = \pi/T$ and ω_o any number between ω_1 and $2\omega_2 - \omega_1$, that is,

$$\omega_2 = \frac{\pi}{T} \qquad \omega_1 \leq \omega_o \leq 2\omega_2 - \omega_1 \tag{3-4}$$

the given signal can be expressed as a sum

$$f(t) = \sum_{n=-\infty}^{\infty} f(nT) \frac{\sin \omega_o(t - nT)}{\omega_2(t - nT)} \tag{3-5}$$

known as the "sampling expansion" of $f(t)$.

Proof We expand the function $F(\omega)$ into a Fourier series in the interval $(-\omega_2, \omega_2)$:

$$F(\omega) = \sum_{n=-\infty}^{\infty} A_n e^{-jnT\omega} \qquad |\omega| \leq \omega_2 \tag{3-6}$$

where [see (3-1)]

$$A_n = \frac{1}{2\omega_2} \int_{-\omega_2}^{\omega_2} F(\omega)e^{jnT\omega} \, d\omega = \frac{T}{2\pi} \int_{-\omega_1}^{\omega_1} F(\omega)e^{jnT\omega} \, d\omega$$

From the above and (3-2) we conclude that

$$A_n = Tf(nT) \tag{3-7}$$

as in (2-9). The sum in (3-6) is obviously the periodic repetition of $F(\omega)$ (Fig. 3-1). Denoting it by $F^*(\omega)$, we thus have

$$F^*(\omega) = \sum_{n=-\infty}^{\infty} Tf(nT)e^{-jnT\omega} = \sum_{n=-\infty}^{\infty} F\left(\omega + \frac{2\pi n}{T}\right) \tag{3-8}$$

This follows also from Poisson's sum formula (2-36) with the variables

ω and t interchanged.   With $p_{\omega_o}(\omega)$ a pulse, we conclude from the above that

$$F(\omega) = \sum_{n=-\infty}^{\infty} Tf(nT)e^{-jnT\omega}p_{\omega_o}(\omega) = F^*(\omega)p_{\omega_o}(\omega) \tag{3-9}$$

[Note that by $F^*(\omega)$ we do not mean the conjugate of $F(\omega)$.]   Since

$$\frac{\sin \omega_o(t - nT)}{\pi(t - nT)} \leftrightarrow e^{-jnT\omega}p_{\omega_o}(\omega) \tag{3-10}$$

the sampling expansion (3-5) follows from (3-9).

OTHER FORMS OF THE THEOREM

1. The sampling expansion can be written in the form

$$f(t - a) = \sum_{n=-\infty}^{\infty} f(nT - a)\frac{\sin \omega_o(t - nT)}{\omega_2(t - nT)} \tag{3-11}$$

where a is any constant.

Proof   The transform of $f(t - a)$ equals $e^{-ja\omega}F(\omega)$.   This function is zero for $|\omega| \geq \omega_1$; hence (3-5) can be applied to $f(t - a)$.   The result is (3-11).

2. Replacing $t - a$ by t in (3-11), we obtain

$$f(t) = \sum_{n=-\infty}^{\infty} f(nT - a)\frac{\sin \omega_o(t + a - nT)}{\omega_2(t - nT)} \tag{3-12}$$

3. Consider a function $k(t)$ with Fourier transform $K(\omega)$ such that (see Fig. 3-2)

$$K(\omega) = \begin{cases} 1 & -\omega_1 \leq \omega \leq \omega_1 \\ 0 & 2n\omega_2 - \omega_1 \leq \omega \leq 2n\omega_2 + \omega_1, n \neq 0 \\ \text{arbitrary} & \text{elsewhere} \end{cases} \tag{3-13}$$

It is easy to see, as in (3-9), that

$$F(\omega) = F^*(\omega)K(\omega) = \sum_{n=-\infty}^{\infty} Tf(nT)e^{-jnT\omega}K(\omega)$$

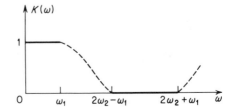

Fig. 3-2

Taking the inverse of both sides, we conclude that

$$f(t) = \sum_{n=-\infty}^{\infty} Tf(nT)k(t - nT) \tag{3-14}$$

This expansion is used to relax the filter requirements in the reconstruction of $f(t)$ from its sampled values by filtering.

Comments

1. In the usual form of the theorem, it is assumed that $\omega_o = \omega_2$. The resulting kernel

$$\frac{\sin \omega_2(t - nT)}{\omega_2(t - nT)}$$

is then zero for $t = mT$, $m \neq n$.

2. Given an arbitrary sequence of numbers a_n, if we form the sum

$$x(t) = \sum_{n=-\infty}^{\infty} a_n \frac{\sin \omega_o(t - nT)}{\omega_2(t - nT)}$$

where $\omega_o \leq \omega_2 = \pi/T$, then $x(t)$ is band-limited by ω_o [see (3-10)].

3. From (3-9) we conclude that

$$F(\omega) = \int_{-\infty}^{\infty} f(t)e^{-j\omega t}\, dt = \sum_{n=-\infty}^{\infty} Tf(nT)e^{-jnT\omega} \qquad |\omega| \leq \frac{\pi}{T} \tag{3-15}$$

Hence

$$F(0) = \int_{-\infty}^{\infty} f(t)\, dt = \sum_{n=-\infty}^{\infty} Tf(nT) \qquad \text{for } T \leq \frac{\pi}{\omega_1} \tag{3-16}$$

We also note that [see (2-10) and (3-9)]

$$\frac{1}{2\pi} \int_{-\omega_1}^{\omega_1} |F(\omega)|^2\, d\omega = \int_{-\infty}^{\infty} f^2(t)\, dt = \sum_{n=-\infty}^{\infty} Tf^2(nT) \qquad \text{for } T \leq \frac{\pi}{\omega_1}$$

4. With

$$f(t) = \frac{\sin \omega_o(t - c)}{\pi(t - c)} \qquad F(0) = p_{\omega_o}(0) = 1$$

(3-16) yields

$$\sum_{n=-\infty}^{\infty} T \frac{\sin \omega_o(nT - c)}{\pi(nT - c)} = 1$$

for any ω_o, c, and $T \leq \pi/\omega_o$.

5. With

$$f(t) = \frac{\sin \omega_1 t}{t} \qquad a = t_1 \qquad t + a = t_2$$

we obtain from (3-12) the identity

$$\sum_{n=-\infty}^{\infty} \frac{\sin \omega_1(t_1 - nT)}{t_1 - nT} \frac{\sin \omega_o(t_2 - nT)}{\omega_2(t_2 - nT)} = \frac{\sin \omega_1(t_1 - t_2)}{t_1 - t_2} \qquad (3\text{-}17)$$

which is valid for $\omega_2 = \pi/T$ and $\omega_1 \leq \omega_o \leq 2\omega_2 - \omega_1$.

6. The sampling theorem can be applied to the function $f^2(t)$ if the sampling rate is sufficiently high. From the frequency convolution theorem [Chap. 3, (2-4)] we have

$$f^2(t) \leftrightarrow \frac{1}{2\pi} F(\omega) * F(\omega)$$

Clearly, if $F(\omega) = 0$ for $|\omega| > \omega_1$, then the function $F(\omega) * F(\omega)$ equals zero for $|\omega| \geq 2\omega_1$. Thus, $f^2(t)$ is band-limited by $2\omega_1$. Applying (3-5) to this function, we obtain

$$f^2(t) = \sum_{n=-\infty}^{\infty} f^2(nT) \frac{\sin \omega_o(t - nT)}{\omega_2(t - nT)} \qquad \omega_2 = \frac{\pi}{T}$$

provided that $2\omega_1 \leq \omega_o \leq 2\omega_2 - 2\omega_1$.

PHYSICAL REGENERATION OF A SIGNAL FROM ITS SAMPLED VALUES

In principle, a band-limited function $f(t)$ can be regenerated by creating a sequence of equidistant impulses (Fig. 3-3), that is,

$$f^*(t) = \sum_{n=-\infty}^{\infty} Tf(nT)\delta(t - nT) \qquad (3\text{-}18)$$

and passing them through a suitable filter. With

$$F^*(\omega) = \sum_{n=-\infty}^{\infty} Tf(nT)e^{-jnT\omega} \qquad (3\text{-}19)$$

as the transform of $f^*(t)$ [see also (3-8)], if the system function $H(\omega)$ of the filter is so selected that

$$F^*(\omega)H(\omega) = F(\omega)e^{-j\omega t_o} \qquad (3\text{-}20)$$

then the resulting output $g(t) = f(t - t_o)$ will equal the signal $f(t)$ delayed by t_o. The delay t_o is introduced to facilitate the design of the filter.

If T is given its largest possible value

$$T = \frac{\pi}{\omega_1}$$

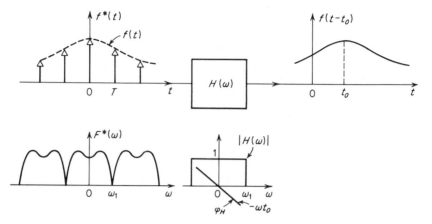

Fig. 3-3

then (3-20) can be satisfied only if the filter is ideal low-pass with (Fig. 3-3)

$$H(\omega) = \begin{cases} e^{-j\omega t_o} & |\omega| < \omega_1 \\ 0 & |\omega| > \omega_1 \end{cases} \tag{3-21}$$

Such a filter is, of course, impossible to realize and difficult to approximate.

The demands on the filter can be considerably relaxed if the sampling rate $1/T$ is increased (Fig. 3-1). For

$$\omega_2 = \frac{\pi}{T} > \omega_1$$

the output of the filter will equal $f(t - t_o)$, provided that (Fig. 3-4)

$$H(\omega) = \begin{cases} e^{-j\omega t_o} & |\omega| < \omega_1 \\ 0 & |\omega| > 2\omega_2 - \omega_1 \\ \text{arbitrary} & \omega_1 < |\omega| < 2\omega_2 - \omega_1 \end{cases} \tag{3-22}$$

By increasing ω_2, we have thus removed the requirement of a sharp cutoff. The existence of a free attenuation interval $(\omega_1, 2\omega_2 - \omega_1)$ facilitates the approximation of $H(\omega)$ by a real filter.

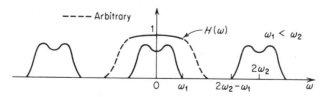

Fig. 3-4

Fig. 3-5

Real pulses Suppose, finally, that we use for the recovery of $f(t)$, not the sequence of impulses $f^*(t)$, but the signal

$$f_o(t) = \sum_{n=-\infty}^{\infty} Tf(nT)h_o(t - nT) \tag{3-23}$$

where $h_o(t)$ is an arbitrary function (Fig. 3-5) selected for convenience of generation. We now seek a filter $H_1(\omega)$ such that if the input is $f_o(t)$, then the output equals $f(t - t_o)$.

Clearly, $f_o(t)$ can be considered as the output of a *hypothetical filter* with input $f^*(t)$ and impulse response $h_o(t)$. With $H_o(\omega)$ the transform of $h_o(t)$, that is,

$$h_o(t) \leftrightarrow H_o(\omega)$$

we easily conclude that if the product $H_o(\omega)H_1(\omega)$ satisfies (3-22), then the output of the two filters $H_o(\omega)$ and $H_1(\omega)$, in cascade with input $f^*(t)$, will equal $f(t - t_o)$. Therefore, the output of $H_1(\omega)$ with input $f_o(t)$ will also equal $f(t - t_o)$. Thus the system function $H_1(\omega)$ must be given by

$$H_1(\omega) = \frac{H(\omega)}{H_o(\omega)} \tag{3-24}$$

where $H(\omega)$ is any function satisfying (3-22).

Example 3-1 Suppose that $h_o(t)$ is a pulse

$$h_o(t) = \frac{1}{2\delta} p_\delta(t) \tag{3-25}$$

as in Fig. 3-6. Since its transform

$$H_o(\omega) = \frac{\sin \delta\omega}{\delta\omega} \tag{3-26}$$

is small for large ω, the presence of $h_o(t)$ causes a reduction in the high-frequency content of the input to $H_1(\omega)$, and so its attenuation requirements can be relaxed. However, since $H_o(\omega)$ is not constant for $|\omega| < \omega_1$, the spectrum of $F(\omega)$ is distorted, and this distortion must be compensated by $H_1(\omega)$.

To satisfy (3-24) we must have

$$H_1(\omega) = \frac{\delta\omega}{\sin \delta\omega} \qquad \text{for } |\omega| < \omega_1 \tag{3-27}$$

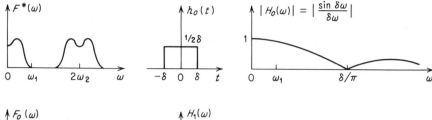

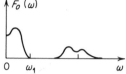 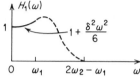

Fig. 3-6

This can be simplified if $\delta\omega_1 \ll 1$. Since

$$\frac{x}{\sin x} \simeq \frac{x}{x - x^3/3!} \simeq 1 + \frac{x^2}{6} \qquad \text{for } x \ll 1$$

(3-27) yields

$$H_1(\omega) \simeq 1 + \frac{(\omega\delta)^2}{6} \qquad \text{for } |\omega| < \omega_1$$

TWO-DIMENSIONAL SIGNALS

We shall extend the sampling theorem to two-dimensional signals.   Consider a function $f(x,y)$ with transform $F(u,v)$ such that

$$F(u,v) = 0 \qquad (u,v) \notin A \tag{3-28}$$

where A is an open region contained in a rectangle R with sides $2a$ and $2b$ (Fig. 3-7).   Thus

$$f(x,y) = \frac{1}{4\pi^2} \iint_A F(u,v)e^{j(ux+vy)} \, du \, dv \tag{3-29}$$

We denote by B a region in R that contains A, i.e.,

$$A \subset B \subset R$$

but is otherwise arbitrary, and denote by $P_B(u,v)$ its zero-one function

$$P_B(u,v) = \begin{cases} 1 & (u,v) \in B \\ 0 & (u,v) \notin B \end{cases} \tag{3-30}$$

With

$$k_B(x,y) = \frac{1}{4\pi^2} \iint_B e^{j(ux+vy)} \, du \, dv \tag{3-31}$$

the inverse transform of $P_B(u,v)$, we maintain that

$$f(x,y) = \sum_{n=-\infty}^{\infty} \sum_{m=-\infty}^{\infty} cdf(nc,md)k_B(x-nc, y-md) \tag{3-32}$$

where

$$c = \frac{\pi}{a} \qquad d = \frac{\pi}{b} \tag{3-33}$$

Proof We expand the function $F(u,v)$ into a Fourier series in the rectangle R [see (2-26)]:

$$F(u,v) = \sum_{n=-\infty}^{\infty} \sum_{m=-\infty}^{\infty} D_{nm}e^{-j(ncu+mdv)} \qquad |u| \le a, |v| \le b \tag{3-34}$$

$$D_{nm} = \frac{1}{4ab} \int_{-b}^{b} \int_{-a}^{a} F(u,v)e^{j(ncu+mdv)} \, du \, dv$$

$$= \frac{cd}{4\pi^2} \iint_A F(u,v)e^{j(ncu+mdv)} \, du \, dv$$

From the above and (3-29) we conclude that

$$D_{nm} = cdf(nc,md) \tag{3-35}$$

Inserting into (3-34), we have [see (3-28) and (3-30)]

$$F(u,v) = \sum_{n=-\infty}^{\infty} \sum_{m=-\infty}^{\infty} cdf(nc,md)e^{-j(ncu+mdv)}P_B(u,v)$$

and the sampling expansion (3-32) follows by taking the inverse transforms of both sides.

Depending on the choice of B, we can have various expansions for

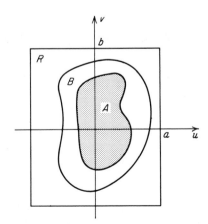

Fig. 3-7

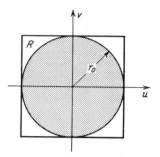

Fig. 3-8

$f(x,y)$. If $B = R$, then [see Chap. 3, (4-30)]

$$k_B(x,y) = \frac{\sin\,ax\,\sin\,by}{\pi x \pi y}$$

Hence,

$$f(x,y) = \sum_{n=-\infty}^{\infty} \sum_{m=-\infty}^{\infty} f(nc,md)\,\frac{\sin\,a(x-nc)\,\sin\,b(y-md)}{a(x-nc)b(y-md)} \qquad (3\text{-}36)$$

If B is a circle of radius r_o, then [see Chap. 3, (4-31)]

$$k_B(x,y) = \frac{r_o}{2\pi}\,\frac{J_1(r_o\sqrt{x^2+y^2})}{\sqrt{x^2+y^2}}$$

With R a square, as in Fig. 3-8, we have with $a = b = r_o$

$$f(x,y) = \frac{\pi}{2}\sum_{n=-\infty}^{\infty} \sum_{m=-\infty}^{\infty} f\left(\frac{n\pi}{r_0},\frac{m\pi}{r_0}\right)\frac{J_1[\sqrt{(r_ox-n\pi)^2+(r_oy-m\pi)^2}]}{\sqrt{(r_ox-n\pi)^2+(r_oy-m\pi)^2}}$$

Most of the remarks of the one-dimensional case hold also for $f(x,y)$. For example, from (3-34) and (3-35) we conclude that

$$F(0,0) = \iint\limits_{-\infty}^{\infty} f(x,y)\,dx\,dy = \sum_{n=-\infty}^{\infty} \sum_{m=-\infty}^{\infty} cdf(nc,md)$$

We finally mention that if the functions $f(x,y)$ and $h(x,y)$ are such that

$$F(u,v) = 0 \qquad H(u,v) = 0 \qquad \text{for } |u| \ge a,\ |v| \ge b$$

then, with $c = \pi/a$, $d = \pi/b$, we have

$$\iint\limits_{-\infty}^{\infty} f(\xi,\eta)h(x-\xi,\,y-\eta)\,d\xi\,d\eta$$

$$= cd\sum_{n=-\infty}^{\infty} \sum_{m=-\infty}^{\infty} f(nc,md)h(x-nc,\,y-md)$$

The proof is similar to the proof of (4-9).

4. EXTENSIONS OF THE SAMPLING THEOREM

Consider a function $f(t)$ with Fourier transform $F(\omega)$ such that

$$F(\omega) = 0 \qquad \text{for } |\omega| \geq \omega_o \tag{4-1}$$

As it is easy to see from (3-11), the sampling theorem can be written in the form

$$f(t + \tau) = \sum_{n = -\infty}^{\infty} f(t + nT) \frac{\sin \omega_o(\tau - nT)}{\omega_o(\tau - nT)} \qquad T = \frac{\pi}{\omega_o} \tag{4-2}$$

In the following we give various extensions of this basic formula.

EXPANSION OF THE OUTPUT OF A LINEAR SYSTEM

If the above signal $f(t)$ is the input to a system $H(\omega)$ (Fig. 4-1), then the resulting output is given by

$$g(t + \tau) = \frac{1}{2\pi} \int_{-\omega_o}^{\omega_o} F(\omega)H(\omega)e^{j\omega(t+\tau)} \, d\omega \tag{4-3}$$

for any t and τ. We shall express $g(t + \tau)$ in terms of the sampled values $f(t + nT)$ of the input.

For this purpose, we expand the function

$$H(\omega)e^{j\omega\tau}$$

into a Fourier series in the interval $(-\omega_o, \omega_o)$:

$$H(\omega)e^{j\omega\tau} = \sum_{n = -\infty}^{\infty} a_n e^{jnT\omega} \qquad |\omega| \leq \omega_o \tag{4-4}$$

where

$$a_n = \frac{1}{2\omega_o} \int_{-\omega_o}^{\omega_o} H(\omega)e^{j\omega\tau}e^{-jnT\omega} \, d\omega \tag{4-5}$$

Inserting (4-4) into (4-3) and using the inversion formula

$$f(t + nT) = \frac{1}{2\pi} \int_{-\omega_o}^{\omega_o} F(\omega)e^{j(t+nT)\omega} \, d\omega$$

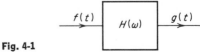

Fig. 4-1

we obtain

$$g(t + \tau) = \sum_{n=-\infty}^{\infty} a_n f(t + nT) \tag{4-6}$$

In this expansion, the coefficients a_n are independent of the input $f(t)$, but they depend on the parameter τ. They can be expressed in terms of the function

$$h_o(t) = \frac{1}{2\pi} \int_{-\omega_o}^{\omega_o} H(\omega) e^{j\omega t} \, d\omega \tag{4-7}$$

Indeed, from (4-5) we see that

$$a_n = T h_o(\tau - nT) \tag{4-8}$$

We remark that if $H(\omega) = 1$, then $g(t) = f(t)$, and (4-6) yields (4-2) as a special case.

Convolution as summation

Suppose that

$$H(\omega) = 0 \qquad \text{for } |\omega| \geq \omega_o$$

With $h(t)$ the inverse transform of $H(\omega)$, it follows from (4-7) that $h(t) = h_o(t)$; hence [see (4-8) and (4-6)],

$$g(t + \tau) = T \sum_{n=-\infty}^{\infty} f(t + nT) h(\tau - nT) \tag{4-9}$$

Thus if two functions $f(t)$ and $h(t)$ are band-limited, then their convolution $g(t)$ can be written as a summation.

Hilbert transforms

As we have shown in Chap. 3, (3-13), the Hilbert transform $f(t)$ can be considered as the output of a system with input $f(t)$, and

$$H(\omega) = -j \operatorname{sgn} \omega$$

Since

$$\frac{1}{2\omega_o} \int_{\omega_o}^{\omega_o} (-j \operatorname{sgn} \omega) e^{j\omega\tau} e^{-jnT\omega} \, d\omega = 2 \frac{\sin^2 [\omega_o(\tau - nT)/2]}{\omega_o(\tau - nT)}$$

it follows from (4-6) that

$$\hat{f}(t + \tau) = 2 \sum_{n=-\infty}^{\infty} \frac{\sin^2 [\omega_o(\tau - nT)/2]}{\omega_o(\tau - nT)} f(t + nT) \tag{4-10}$$

We note that the above can be also deduced from (4-2). Indeed, the Hilbert transform of $\sin \omega_o(\tau - nT)/\omega_o(\tau - nT)$ equals

$$2\frac{\sin^2 [\omega_o(\tau - nT)/2]}{\omega_o(\tau - nT)}$$

(See Example 3-1, Chap. 3.)   Considering (4-2) as a function of τ and taking the Hilbert transform of both sides, we obtain (4-10).

Derivatives

With τ a given parameter, the function

$$g(t) = \sin \omega_o\tau f'(t) - \omega_o \cos \omega_o\tau f(t)$$

is the output of a system with input $f(t)$ and

$$H(\omega) = j\omega \sin \omega_o\tau - \omega_o \cos \omega_o\tau$$

The coefficients a_n of the series expansion of

$$(j\omega \sin \omega_o\tau - \omega_o \cos \omega_o\tau)e^{j\omega\tau}$$

in the interval $(-\omega_o,\omega_o)$ are given by

$$a_n = \frac{(-1)^{n-1} \sin^2 \omega_o\tau}{\omega_o(\tau - nT)^2}$$

Hence,

$$\sin \omega_o\tau f'(t) - \omega_o \cos \omega_o\tau f(t) = \sum_{n=-\infty}^{\infty} \frac{(-1)^{n-1} \sin^2 \omega_o\tau}{\omega_o(\tau - nT)^2} f(t + nT - \tau)$$

$$(4-11)$$

as we see from (4-6) after replacing t by $t - \tau$.   This result can also be derived from (4-2) (elaborate).

With $\tau = T/2$, (4-11) yields

$$f'(t) = \omega_o \sum_{n=-\infty}^{\infty} \frac{(-1)^{n-1}}{(n\pi - \pi/2)^2} f\left(t + nT - \frac{T}{2}\right) \qquad (4-12)$$

S. N. Bernstein's inequality   Suppose that a function $f(t)$ is bounded by a constant M in the interval $(-\infty,\infty)$:

$$|f(t)| \leq M \qquad (4-13)$$

In general, its derivative $f'(t)$ can take arbitrarily large values.   However, if $f(t)$ is band-limited, as in (4-1), then

$$|f'(t)| \leq \omega_o M \qquad (4-14)$$

This nontrivial result, known as Bernstein's inequality, is a special case of the following.†

For any α

$$|\sin \alpha f'(t) - \omega_o \cos \alpha f(t)| \leq \omega_o M \tag{4-15}$$

Proof With $\omega_o \tau = \alpha$, we conclude from (4-11) and (4-13) that

$$|\sin \alpha f'(t) - \omega_o \cos \alpha f(t)| \leq \omega_o M \sum_{n=-\infty}^{\infty} \frac{\sin^2 \alpha}{(\alpha - n\pi)^2} \tag{4-16}$$

But

$$\sum_{n=-\infty}^{\infty} \frac{\sin^2 \alpha}{(\alpha - n\pi)^2} = 1 \tag{4-17}$$

and (4-15) results. The last equality follows from (3-17), with

$$t_1 = t_2 = \frac{\alpha}{\omega_o} \qquad \omega_1 = \omega_o = \omega_2 = \frac{\pi}{T}$$

If $\alpha = \pi/2$, then (4-15) yields (4-14).

We note that if

$$f(t) = M \cos (\omega_o t + \alpha)$$

then the limit $\omega_o M$ in (4-14) is reached for $t = 0$. This is, of course, possible only if we allow $F(\omega)$ to contain an impulse at the end points $\omega = \pm \omega_o$ of the interval $(-\omega_o, \omega_o)$. Otherwise, $\omega_o M$ can only be approached (arbitrarily closely).

Conversely, if the upper limit in (4-15) is reached, then (see Prob. 4-6) $f(t)$ must be of the form

$$f(t) = A e^{j\omega_o t} + B e^{-j\omega_o t}$$

In Chap. 6, Sec. 1, we show that $f'(t)$ is bounded by the energy of $f(t)$.

GENERALIZED SAMPLING THEORY‡

As we have seen, a function $f(t)$ can be expressed in terms of $f(nT)$, provided that T does not exceed π/ω_o. However, if not only $f(nT)$, but also the sampled values of its derivatives or of other linear functionals of $f(t)$ are known, then the sampling interval can be increased. We shall explore this idea, basing the results on the following interesting decomposition theorem.

† N. I. Achieser, "Theory of Approximation" (trans. from the Russian), Frederick Ungar Publishing Co., New York, 1956.
‡ A. Papoulis, New Results in Sampling Theory, *Hawaii Intern. Conf. System Sciences*, January, 1968.

Expansion of a function into a series with periodic coefficients

We are given N functions

$$H_1(\omega), H_2(\omega), \ldots, H_N(\omega)$$

defined for $|\omega| < \omega_o$. With

$$c = \frac{2\omega_o}{N}$$

we assume that these functions are such that

$$\begin{vmatrix} H_1(\omega) & H_2(\omega) & \cdots & H_N(\omega) \\ H_1(\omega + c) & H_2(\omega + c) & \cdots & H_N(\omega + c) \\ \cdots\cdots\cdots\cdots\cdots\cdots\cdots & & & \cdots\cdots\cdots\cdots\cdots \\ H_1[\omega + (N-1)c] & H_2[\omega + (N-1)c] & \cdots & H_N[\omega + (N-1)c] \end{vmatrix} \neq 0 \quad (4\text{-}18)$$

for

$$-\omega_o < \omega < -\omega_o + c$$

but otherwise arbitrary.

Theorem   Any function $\Phi(\omega)$ can be written as a sum

$$\Phi(\omega) = H_1(\omega)\Phi_1(\omega) + \cdots + H_N(\omega)\Phi_N(\omega) \qquad |\omega| \leq \omega_o \qquad (4\text{-}19)$$

where the functions $\Phi_i(\omega)$ are periodic with period c, that is,

$$\Phi_i(\omega + c) = \Phi_i(\omega) \qquad i = 1, \ldots, N \qquad (4\text{-}20)$$

Proof   Consider the system

$$H_1(\omega)\Phi_1(\omega) + \cdots + H_N(\omega)\Phi_N(\omega) = \Phi(\omega)$$

$$H_1(\omega + c)\Phi_1(\omega) + \cdots + H_N(\omega + c)\Phi_N(\omega) = \Phi(\omega + c)$$

$$\cdots\cdots\cdots\cdots\cdots\cdots\cdots\cdots\cdots\cdots\cdots\cdots\cdots\cdots \qquad (4\text{-}21)$$

$$\begin{aligned} H_1[\omega + (N-1)c]\Phi_1(\omega) \\ + \cdots + H_N[\omega + (N-1)c]\Phi_N(\omega) = \Phi[\omega + (N-1)c] \end{aligned}$$

As we see from (4-18), this system can be solved for every ω in the interval $(-\omega_o, -\omega_o + c)$.   We have thus determined the functions $\Phi_i(\omega)$ in this interval.   Using (4-20), we extend their definition everywhere. The functions so constructed are periodic, and, as we see from (4-21), they satisfy (4-19) for every $|\omega| \leq \omega_o$.

System response   Suppose that the band-limited signal $f(t)$ is the input to the N systems of Fig. 4-2.   Denoting by $H_i(\omega)$ the corresponding system functions and by $g_i(t)$ the resulting responses, we have

$$g_i(t) = \frac{1}{2\pi} \int_{-\omega_o}^{\omega_o} F(\omega)H_i(\omega)e^{j\omega t}\,d\omega \qquad i = 1, \ldots, N \qquad (4\text{-}22)$$

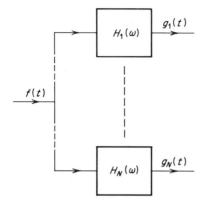

Fig. 4-2

We shall show that the output $g(t)$ of the system of Fig. 4-1 can be expressed in terms of the sampled values $g_i(n\bar{T})$ of the responses $g_i(t)$, where

$$\bar{T} = NT = \frac{N\pi}{\omega_o} = \frac{2\pi}{c} \tag{4-23}$$

For this purpose, we expand the function

$$H(\omega)e^{j\omega\tau}$$

into a series of the form (4-19).   Thus

$$H(\omega)e^{j\omega\tau} = \sum_{i=1}^{N} H_i(\omega)\Phi_i(\omega) \qquad |\omega| \leq \omega_o \tag{4-24}$$

where the functions $\Phi_i(\omega)$ are determined by solving the system

$$\sum_{i=1}^{N} H_i(\omega + kc)\Phi_i(\omega) = H(\omega + kc)e^{j(\omega+kc)\tau} \qquad k = 0, \ldots, N-1 \tag{4-25}$$

for $-\omega_o < \omega < -\omega_o + c$, and using (4-20).

The functions so determined are periodic with period c, and, therefore, they can be expanded into Fourier series of the form

$$\Phi_i(\omega) = \sum_{n=-\infty}^{\infty} a_{ni}e^{jn\bar{T}\omega} \qquad i = 1, \ldots, N \tag{4-26}$$

From the above and (4-24) it follows that

$$H(\omega)e^{j\omega\tau} = H_1(\omega) \sum_{n=-\infty}^{\infty} a_{n1}e^{jn\bar{T}\omega} + \cdots + H_N(\omega) \sum_{n=-\infty}^{\infty} a_{nN}e^{jn\bar{T}\omega} \tag{4-27}$$

Inserting into (4-3), we obtain, with (4-22), our final result

$$g(t + \tau) = \sum_{n=-\infty}^{\infty} [a_{n1}g_1(t + n\bar{T}) + \cdots + a_{nN}g_N(t + n\bar{T})] \quad (4\text{-}28)$$

Comment In the expansion (4-26), the coefficients

$$a_{ni}(\tau) = \frac{1}{c} \int_{-\omega_o}^{-\omega_o+c} \Phi_i(\omega) e^{-jn\bar{T}\omega} \, d\omega$$

are functions of the parameter τ. These functions can be expressed in terms of the average $a_{0i}(\tau)$ of $\Phi_i(\omega)$. Indeed, on the right side of (4-25), $e^{j\omega\tau}$ is a common factor. Furthermore,

$$e^{jkc\tau} = e^{jkc(\tau-n\bar{T})}$$

Therefore,

$$a_{ni}(\tau) = a_{0i}(\tau - n\bar{T})$$

as it is easy to show (elaborate).

APPLICATIONS

The general expansion (4-28) will now be applied to a number of special cases.

Hilbert transforms

We shall express $f(t)$ in terms of its samples $f(2nT)$ and the samples $\hat{f}(2nT)$ of its Hilbert transform $\hat{f}(t)$. For this purpose, we set $N = 2$

$$H(\omega) = 1 \qquad H_1(\omega) = 1 \qquad H_2(\omega) = -j \, \text{sgn} \, \omega$$

It then follows that $c = \omega_o$, $\bar{T} = 2T$, and

$$g(t) = f(t) \qquad g_1(t) = f(t) \qquad g_2(t) = \hat{f}(t)$$

The system (4-25) yields

$$\Phi_1(\omega) - j\Phi_2(\omega) = e^{j\omega\tau} \qquad -\omega_o < \omega < 0$$
$$\Phi_1(\omega) + j\Phi_2(\omega) = e^{j(\omega+\omega_o)\tau}$$

Hence,

$$\Phi_1(\omega) = \frac{1 + e^{j\omega_o\tau}}{2} e^{j\omega\tau} \qquad \Phi_2(\omega) = \frac{1 - e^{j\omega_o\tau}}{2j} e^{j\omega\tau}$$

Expanding these functions into a Fourier series in the interval $(-\omega_o, 0)$ and inserting into (4-28), we obtain

$$f(t + \tau) = \frac{1}{\omega_o} \sum_{n=-\infty}^{\infty} \frac{\sin \omega_o\tau f(t + 2nT) - 2\sin^2 (\omega_o\tau/2)\hat{f}(t + 2nT)}{\tau - 2nT}$$

$$(4\text{-}29)$$

Derivatives

The function $f(t)$ can be determined from the sample values

$$f^{(i)}(n\bar{T}) \qquad i = 0, \ldots, N-1 \qquad \bar{T} = NT$$

of its derivatives.   Indeed, with

$$H(\omega) = 1 \qquad H_i(\omega) = (j\omega)^{i-1} \qquad i = 1, \ldots, N$$

we have

$$g(t) = f(t) \qquad g_i(t) = f^{(i-1)}(t)$$

The system (4-25) takes the form

$$\sum_{i=1}^{N} j(\omega + kc)^{N-1}\Phi_i(\omega) = e^{j(\omega+kc)\tau} \qquad k = 0, \ldots, N-1 \qquad (4\text{-}30)$$

It is easy to see that (see Prob. 4-7) the corresponding determinant (4-18) is different from zero; hence (4-30) can be solved.   Expanding the functions $\Phi_i(\omega)$ so determined into a Fourier series, we thus obtain [see (4-28)]

$$f(t + \tau) = \sum_{n=-\infty}^{\infty} [a_{n1}f(t + n\bar{T}) + \cdots + a_{nN}f^{(N-1)}(t + n\bar{T})] \qquad (4\text{-}31)$$

We shall carry out the details for $N = 2$.   Clearly,

$$c = \omega_o \qquad \bar{T} = 2T$$

and (4-30) yields

$$\Phi_1(\omega) + j\omega\Phi_2(\omega) = e^{j\omega\tau} \qquad -\omega_o < \omega < 0$$
$$\Phi_1(\omega) + j(\omega + \omega_o)\Phi_2(\omega) = e^{j(\omega+\omega_o)\tau}$$

Hence,

$$\Phi_1(\omega) = e^{j\omega\tau}\left[1 - \frac{\omega}{\omega_o}(e^{j\omega_o\tau} - 1)\right] \qquad \Phi_2(\omega) = e^{j\omega\tau}\frac{e^{j\omega_o\tau} - 1}{j\omega_o}$$

Expanding into a Fourier series in the interval $(-\omega_o,0)$ and inserting into (4-31), we obtain

$$f(t + \tau) = \frac{4\sin^2(\omega_o\tau/2)}{\omega_o^2} \sum_{n=-\infty}^{\infty} \left[\frac{f(t + 2nT)}{(\tau - 2nT)^2} + \frac{f'(t + 2nT)}{\tau - 2nT}\right] \qquad (4\text{-}32)$$

Bunched samples

If $f(t)$ is known at the points (Fig. 4-3)

$$\alpha_i + n\bar{T} \qquad i = 1, \ldots, N \qquad \bar{T} = NT$$

Fig. 4-3

then it can be determined for any t.   This follows from (4-28), with

$$H(\omega) = 1 \qquad H_i(\omega) = e^{j\alpha_i\omega} \qquad g(t) = f(t) \qquad g_i(t) = f(t + \alpha_i)$$

We shall carry out the details for $N = 2$, and

$$\alpha_1 = -\alpha_2 = \alpha$$

In this case, the system (4-25) takes the form

$$e^{j\alpha\omega}\Phi_1(\omega) + e^{-j\alpha\omega}\Phi_2(\omega) = e^{j\omega\tau}$$

$$e^{j\alpha(\omega+\omega_o)}\Phi_1(\omega) + e^{-j\alpha(\omega+\omega_o)}\Phi_2(\omega) = e^{j(\omega+\omega_o)\tau}$$

Hence,

$$\Phi_1(\omega) = e^{j\omega(\tau-\alpha)} \frac{e^{j\omega_o\tau} - e^{-j\omega_o\alpha}}{e^{j\omega_o\alpha} - e^{-j\omega_o\alpha}}$$

$$\Phi_2(\omega) = e^{j\omega(\tau+\alpha)} \frac{e^{j\omega_o\alpha} - e^{j\omega_o\tau}}{e^{j\omega_o\alpha} - e^{-j\omega_o\alpha}}$$

and (4-28) yields

$$f(t + \tau) = \frac{\cos \omega_o\alpha - \cos \omega_o\tau}{\omega_o \sin \omega_o\alpha} \sum_{n=-\infty}^{\infty} \left[\frac{f(t + \alpha + 2nT)}{\tau - 2nT - \alpha} - \frac{f(t - \alpha + 2nT)}{\tau - 2nT + \alpha} \right] \quad (4\text{-}33)$$

We conclude with the observation that $f(t)$ can be determined from irregular samples, provided that they are sufficiently dense.   However, the resulting expressions are complicated.†

PROBLEMS

4-1. The pulse train

$$f(t) = \sum_{n=1}^{N} a_n \delta(t - nT)$$

is the input to a linear system with impulse response a triangle, as in Fig. P4-1.
Show that
  (a) The resulting output $g(t)$ is a polygon such that $g(nT) = a_n$.
  (b) The Fourier transform $G(\omega)$ of the polygon $g(t)$ is given by

† R. Paley and N. Wiener, "Fourier Transforms in the Complex Domain," p. 115, American Mathematical Society, New York, 1934.

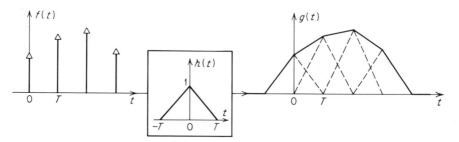

Fig. P4-1

$$G(\omega) = \frac{4 \sin^2 (\omega T/2)}{T\omega^2} \sum_{n=1}^{N} g(nT)e^{-jnT\omega}$$

4-2. With E the energy of $f(r,\theta)$ in the xy plane, show that if

$$f(r,\theta) = \sum_{n=-\infty}^{\infty} a_n(r)e^{jn\theta}$$

then

$$E = 2\pi \sum_{n=-\infty}^{\infty} \int_0^{\infty} r|a_n(r)|^2 \, dr$$

4-3.† The function $f(x,y)$ is skew-periodic, as in (2-32), and the corresponding parallelogram of Fig. 2-9a is a 60° rhombus with sides a.

(a) Show that $u_1 = 2\pi/a$, $v_1 = -2\pi/a \sqrt{3}$, $u_2 = 0$, $v_2 = 4\pi/a \sqrt{3}$.

(b) Show that the coefficients d_{nm} can be obtained by replacing in (2-34) the parallelogram A by the hexagon of Fig. P4-3.

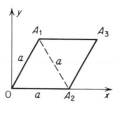

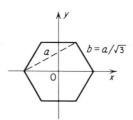

Fig. P4-3

4-4. With

$$f(x,y) \Leftrightarrow F(u,v) \qquad \rho(x,y) \Leftrightarrow |F(u,v)|^2$$

show that if

$$\rho(a,b) = \rho(0,0) \qquad \text{then} \qquad f(x + na, y + mb) = f(x,y)$$

for any integer n and m.

† A. E. Laemmel, The Scanning Process in Picture Transmissions *PIB-MRI Report* R-563-57, *PIB* **491,** 1957.

4-5. With $\omega_o = \pi/T$, show that if $N < aT/2\pi < N + 1$, then

$$\sum_{n=-\infty}^{\infty} \frac{\sin a(t + nT)}{t + nT} = \omega_o \frac{\sin (2N + 1)\omega_o t}{\sin \omega_o t}$$

4-6. The function $f(t)$ is band-limited by ω_o, as in (4-1), and $|f(t)| \leq M$ for every t. Show that if for some $t = t_o$, $f'(t_o) = \omega_o M$, then

$$f(t) = Ae^{j\omega_o t} + Be^{-j\omega_o t} \quad \text{and} \quad |A| + |B| = M$$

4-7. (Vandermond determinant) Show that

$$D = \begin{vmatrix} x_1^{n-1}, & x_1^{n-2}, & \ldots, & 1 \\ x_2^{n-1}, & x_2^{n-2}, & \ldots, & 1 \\ x_n^{n-1}, & x_n^{n-2}, & \ldots, & 1 \end{vmatrix} = \prod_{\substack{i=1,\ldots,n \\ j=i+1,\ldots,n}} (x_i - x_j)$$

Hint: $D = 0$ for $x_i = x_j$.

4-8. The input to a linear system is a function $f(t)$, which is band-limited by ω_o, as in (4-1). Express $f(t)$ in terms of the sampled values $g(n\pi/\omega_o)$ of the output $g(t)$.

4-9. (a) The signal $f(t)$ is band-limited by ω_o. With $z(t)$ its analytic signal, show that

$$z(t) = 2e^{j\omega_o t/2} \sum_{n=-\infty}^{\infty} (-1)^n z(2nT) \frac{\sin (\omega_o t/2)}{\omega_o t - 2n\pi} \qquad T = \frac{\pi}{\omega_o}$$

(b) Show that if $f(t)$ is a bandpass signal, as in Fig. P4-9, then

$$z(t) = e^{j\omega_c t} \sum_{n=-\infty}^{\infty} z(nT)e^{-jn\omega_c T} \frac{\sin \omega_o(t - nT)}{\omega_o(t - nT)} \qquad T = \frac{\pi}{\omega_o}$$

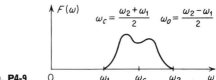

Fig. P4-9

Hint: Apply the sampling expansion to the signal $z(t)e^{-j\omega_c t}$.

4-10. The input to a system $H(\omega)$ is a band-limited signal $f(t)$, and is bounded by M:

$$|f(t)| \leq M \qquad F(\omega) = 0 \qquad \text{for } |\omega| \geq \omega_o$$

With $g(t)$ the resulting response and

$$H(\omega)e^{j\omega t} = \sum_{n=-\infty}^{\infty} a_n(t)e^{jn\pi\omega/\omega_o} \qquad |\omega| \leq \omega_o$$

show that

$$|g(t)| \leq M \sum_{n=-\infty}^{\infty} |a_n(t)|$$

5

HANKEL TRANSFORMS

If a two-dimensional signal has circular symmetry, then its Fourier transform reduces to a Hankel transform. Based on this observation, we develop the theory of Hankel transforms as a special case of the corresponding theory of Fourier transforms. In the last section, we derive the relevant properties of Bessel functions.

1. HANKEL TRANSFORMS AS FOURIER TRANSFORMS OF FUNCTIONS WITH CIRCULAR SYMMETRY

In the following analysis, we shall make frequent use of the Bessel function $J_o(x)$ of order zero, as shown in Fig. 1-1. This function can be defined by the series expansion (5-26), as a solution of a differential equation [see (5-24)], or by the integral

$$J_o(x) = \frac{1}{2\pi} \int_{-\pi}^{\pi} e^{jx \cos (\theta - \alpha)} \, d\theta \tag{1-1}$$

Since $\cos\theta$ is periodic, this integral is independent of α. The equivalence of the various definitions of $J_o(x)$ and other properties of Bessel functions are discussed in Sec. 5.

Given a function $f(r)$ and a real constant w, we form the integral

$$\tilde{f}(w) = \int_0^\infty rf(r)J_o(wr)\,dr \tag{1-2}$$

This integral defines the *Hankel transform* $\tilde{f}(w)$ of $f(r)$ [c1, s4].

The function $\tilde{f}(w)$ can be expressed in terms of the two-dimensional Fourier transform $F(u,v)$ of the function $f(\sqrt{x^2+y^2})$. Indeed, with

$$f(\sqrt{x^2+y^2}) \Leftrightarrow F(u,v) \tag{1-3}$$

we maintain the following.

Theorem $F(u,v)$ has circular symmetry, and it is given by

$$F(u,v) = 2\pi\tilde{f}(\sqrt{u^2+v^2}) \tag{1-4}$$

Proof   With

$$
\begin{array}{lll}
x = r\cos\theta & y = r\sin\theta & r = \sqrt{x^2+y^2} \\
u = w\cos\varphi & v = w\sin\varphi & w = \sqrt{u^2+v^2}
\end{array}
\tag{1-5}
$$

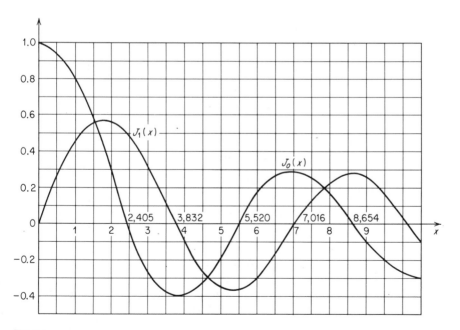

Fig. 1-1

we have

$$ux + vy = wr \cos \theta \cos \varphi + wr \sin \theta \sin \varphi = wr \cos (\theta - \varphi)$$
$$dx \, dy = r \, dr \, d\theta$$

Inserting the transformations (1-5) into the integral (4-1), Chap. 3, which defines $F(u,v)$, we have [see (1-1)]

$$F(u,v) = \int_0^\infty rf(r) \int_{-\pi}^{\pi} e^{-jwr \cos (\theta-\varphi)} \, d\theta \, dr = 2\pi \int_0^\infty rf(r) J_o(wr) \, dr$$
$$= 2\pi \bar{f}(w)$$

and (1-4) follows.

Fundamental observation   By viewing the Hankel transform $\bar{f}(w)$ as a special case of a two-dimensional Fourier transform, we can derive all its properties from the corresponding properties of Fourier transforms (Table 1-1).

Inversion formula   We shall show that

$$f(r) = \int_0^\infty w\bar{f}(w) J_o(rw) \, dw \tag{1-6}$$

Proof   Inserting $F(u,v) = 2\pi\bar{f}(\sqrt{u^2 + v^2})$ into the Fourier inversion formula [Chap. 3, (4-5)] and using (1-5), we obtain

$$f(\sqrt{x^2 + y^2}) = \frac{1}{4\pi^2} \int_0^\infty 2\pi w\bar{f}(w) \int_{-\pi}^{\pi} e^{jrw \cos (\theta-\varphi)} \, d\varphi \, dw$$

and (1-6) follows.   For its validity at points of discontinuity of $f(r)$ we must have

$$f(r) = \frac{f(r^+) + f(r^-)}{2}$$

as in Chap. 3, (1-3).

We shall use the notation

$$f(r) \overset{h}{\leftrightarrow} \bar{f}(w)$$

to indicate that $\bar{f}(w)$ is the Hankel transform of $f(r)$.   We note that

$$f(\sqrt{x^2 + y^2}) \Leftrightarrow 2\pi\bar{f}(\sqrt{u^2 + v^2}) \tag{1-7}$$

PROPERTIES OF HANKEL TRANSFORMS

Symmetry   From the symmetry of (1-2) and (1-6), we conclude that the Hankel transform of $\bar{f}(r)$ must equal $f(w)$:

$$\bar{f}(r) \overset{h}{\leftrightarrow} f(w) \tag{1-8}$$

Scaling From (1-2), we easily conclude that if $a > 0$, then

$$f(ar) \overset{h}{\leftrightarrow} \frac{1}{a^2} \bar{f}\left(\frac{w}{a}\right) \tag{1-9}$$

This also follows from (1-7) and Chap. 3, (4-11).

Differentiation It is easy to see that, with $r = \sqrt{x^2 + y^2}$,

$$\frac{\partial^2 f(\sqrt{x^2 + y^2})}{\partial x^2} + \frac{\partial^2 f(\sqrt{x^2 + y^2})}{\partial y^2} = \frac{1}{r}\frac{d}{dr}\left[r\frac{df(r)}{dr}\right]$$

Hence [see (1-4) and Chap. 3, (4-14)],

$$\frac{1}{r}\frac{d}{dr}\left[r\frac{df(r)}{dr}\right] \Leftrightarrow -(u^2 + v^2)F(u,v) = -2\pi w^2\bar{f}(w)$$

Using again the fact that the two-dimensional Fourier transform of a circularly symmetrical function equals 2π times its Hankel transform, we conclude that

$$\frac{d^2 f(r)}{dr^2} + \frac{1}{r}\frac{df(r)}{dr} \overset{h}{\leftrightarrow} -w^2\bar{f}(w) \tag{1-10}$$

Convolution theorem Given two functions $f_1(r)$ and $f_2(r)$ with Hankel transforms $\bar{f}_1(w)$ and $\bar{f}_2(w)$, we shall determine the inverse Hankel transform of the product $\bar{f}_1(w)\bar{f}_2(w)$. From (1-7) and the convolution theorem [Chap. 3, (4-18)], we have

$$\iint\limits_{-\infty}^{\infty} f_1(\sqrt{\xi^2 + \eta^2})f_2[\sqrt{(x - \xi)^2 + (y - \eta)^2}]\,d\xi\,d\eta \Leftrightarrow 4\pi^2\bar{f}_1(w)\bar{f}_2(w)$$

Hence,

$$f_1(r) ** f_2(r) \overset{h}{\leftrightarrow} 2\pi\bar{f}_1(w)\bar{f}_2(w) \tag{1-11}$$

Thus, to find the inverse Hankel transform of $2\pi\bar{f}_1(w)\bar{f}_2(w)$, we convolve $f_1(\sqrt{x^2 + y^2})$ with $f_2(\sqrt{x^2 + y^2})$, and in the answer we replace $\sqrt{x^2 + y^2}$ by r.

Parseval's formula Introducing the transformations (1-5) into Parseval's formula [Chap. 3, (4-19)], we obtain, with (1-7),

$$\int_0^\infty rf_1(r)f_2^*(r)\int_{-\pi}^\pi d\theta\,dr = \frac{1}{4\pi^2}\int_0^\infty w[2\pi\bar{f}_1(w)][2\pi\bar{f}_2^*(w)]\int_{-\pi}^\pi d\varphi\,dw$$

Hence

$$\int_0^\infty rf_1(r)f_2^*(r)\,dr = \int_0^\infty wf_1(w)\bar{f}_2^*(w)\,dw \tag{1-12}$$

Table 1-1   Hankel transform theorems

$$f(r) = \int_0^\infty w\bar{f}(w)J_o(rw)\,dw \overset{h}{\leftrightarrow} \bar{f}(w) = \int_0^\infty rf(r)J_o(wr)\,dr$$

$$f(\sqrt{x^2+y^2}) \Leftrightarrow 2\pi\bar{f}(\sqrt{u^2+v^2})$$

$\bar{f}(r)$	$f(w)$
$f(\alpha r)$	$\dfrac{1}{\alpha^2}\bar{f}\left(\dfrac{w}{\alpha}\right)$
$f''(r) + \dfrac{1}{r}f'(r)$	$-w^2\bar{f}(w)$
$f_1(r) ** f_2(r)$	$2\pi\bar{f}_1(w)\bar{f}_2(w)$

$$\int_0^\infty r|f(r)|^2\,dr = \int_0^\infty w|\bar{f}(w)|^2\,dw$$

$m_n = \displaystyle\int_0^\infty r^n f(r)\,dr$	$\bar{f}(w) = \displaystyle\sum_{n=0}^\infty \dfrac{(-1)^n m_{2n+1}}{(n!)^2 2^{2n}}\,w^{2n}$

$$\int_{-\infty}^\infty f(\sqrt{x^2+y^2})\,dy \leftrightarrow 2\pi\bar{f}(u)$$

$$\int_0^\infty rf(r)e^{-j\omega r}\,dr = R_1(\omega) + jX_1(\omega)$$

$$\bar{f}(w) = \frac{2}{\pi}\int_0^{\pi/2} R_1(w\cos\theta)\,d\theta \qquad R_1(w) = w\int_0^{\pi/2}\bar{f}'(w\cos\theta)\,d\theta + \bar{f}(0)$$

and with $f_1(r) = f_2(r) = f(r)$

$$\int_0^\infty r|f(r)|^2\,dr = \int_0^\infty w|\bar{f}(w)|^2\,dw \tag{1-13}$$

Moment theorem   The function $\bar{f}(w)$ can be expressed in terms of the moments

$$m_n = \int_0^\infty r^n f(r)\,dr \tag{1-14}$$

of $f(r)$.   Inserting the expansion [see (5-26)]

$$J_o(x) = 1 - \left(\frac{x}{2}\right)^2 + \frac{1}{(2!)^2}\left(\frac{x}{2}\right)^4 - \cdots = \sum_{n=0}^\infty \frac{(-1)^n}{(n!)^2}\left(\frac{x}{2}\right)^{2n}$$

into (1-2) and interchanging the order of integration and summation, we have

$$\bar{f}(w) = \sum_{n=0}^\infty \frac{(-1)^n}{(n!)^2}\left(\frac{w}{2}\right)^{2n}\int_0^\infty r^{2n+1}f(r)\,dr$$

Table 1-2 Examples of Hankel transforms

$$f(r) = \int_0^\infty w\bar{f}(w)J_o(rw)\,dw \overset{h}{\leftrightarrow} \bar{f}(w) = \int_0^\infty rf(r)J_o(wr)\,dr$$

$\dfrac{1}{r}$	$\dfrac{1}{w}$
$\delta(r-a)$	$aJ_o(aw)$
e^{-ar^2}	$\dfrac{1}{2a}\,e^{-w^2/4a}$
e^{jar^2}	$\dfrac{j}{2a}\,e^{-jw^2/4a}$
e^{-ar}	$\dfrac{a}{\sqrt{(a^2+w^2)^3}}$
$\dfrac{e^{-ar}}{r}$	$\dfrac{1}{\sqrt{a^2+w^2}}$
$\dfrac{\sin ar}{r}$	$\begin{cases} \dfrac{1}{\sqrt{w^2-a^2}} & w>a \\ 0 & w<a \end{cases}$
$\dfrac{J_n(r)}{r^n}$	$\begin{cases} \dfrac{(1-w^2)^{n-1}}{2^{n-1}(n-1)!} & w<1 \\ 0 & w>1 \end{cases}$
$\begin{matrix} 1 & 0<r<a \\ 0 & r.>a \end{matrix}\Big\}$	$\dfrac{aJ_1(aw)}{w}$
$\begin{matrix} J_o(br) & 0<r<a \\ 0 & r>a \end{matrix}\Big\}$	$\dfrac{abJ_1(ab)J_o(aw) - awJ_o(ab)J_1(aw)}{b^2-w^2}$
$J_o{}^2(ar)$	$\begin{cases} \dfrac{2}{\pi w\,\sqrt{4a^2-w^2}} & w<2a \\ 0 & w>2a \end{cases}$
$\dfrac{J_o(ar)J_1(ar)}{r}$	$\begin{cases} \dfrac{1}{a\pi}\cos^{-1}\dfrac{w}{2a} & w<2a \\ 0 & w>2a \end{cases}$
$2\pi\,\dfrac{J_1{}^2(ar)}{r^2}$	$\begin{cases} 2\cos^{-1}\dfrac{w}{2a} - \dfrac{w}{a}\sqrt{1-\dfrac{w^2}{4a^2}} & w<2a \\ 0 & w>2a \end{cases}$

Hence,

$$\bar{f}(w) = m_1 - \frac{m_3}{4} w^2 + \frac{m_5}{64} w^4 - \cdots = \sum_{n=0}^{\infty} \frac{(-1)^n m_{2n+1}}{(n!)^2 2^{2n}} w^{2n} \quad (1\text{-}15)$$

EXAMPLES

We give below a number of Hankel transform pairs (see also Table 1-2). They are derived from the relationship between Fourier and Hankel transforms, or from the basic properties of the Bessel functions. These properties are developed in the last section of this chapter.

1. From the Fourier pair [see Chap. 3, (4-22)]

$$e^{-a(x^2+y^2)} \Longleftrightarrow \frac{\pi}{a} e^{-(u^2+v^2)/4a}$$

and (1-7) we have

$$e^{-ar^2} \overset{h}{\leftrightarrow} \frac{1}{2a} e^{-w^2/4a} \qquad a > 0 \tag{1-16}$$

2. Similarly, from Chap. 3, (1-31), it follows that

$$e^{jar^2} \overset{h}{\leftrightarrow} \frac{j}{2a} e^{-jw^2/4a} \tag{1-17}$$

Since $J_o(x)$ is real, we conclude that if

$$f_1 + jf_2 \overset{h}{\leftrightarrow} \bar{f}_1 + j\bar{f}_2$$

then

$$f_1 \overset{h}{\leftrightarrow} \bar{f}_1 \qquad f_2 \overset{h}{\leftrightarrow} \bar{f}_2$$

Applying the above to (1-17), we obtain

$$\cos ar^2 \overset{h}{\leftrightarrow} \frac{1}{2a} \sin \frac{w^2}{4a} \tag{1-18}$$

$$\sin ar^2 \overset{h}{\leftrightarrow} \frac{1}{2a} \cos \frac{w^2}{4a} \tag{1-19}$$

3. An important example is the function

$$p_a(r) = \begin{cases} 1 & |r| < a \\ 0 & |r| > a \end{cases}$$

From the identity [see (5-16)]

$$\int_0^a r J_o(wr) \, dr = \frac{a J_1(aw)}{w}$$

we conclude that

$$p_a(r) \overset{h}{\leftrightarrow} \frac{aJ_1(aw)}{w} \qquad a > 0 \tag{1-20}$$

where $J_1(x)$ is the Bessel function of order one.

4. From Chap. 3, (1-10) and (2-21), it follows that

$$\int_0^\infty J_o(wr)\, dr = \frac{1}{w}$$

Hence,

$$\frac{1}{r} \overset{h}{\leftrightarrow} \frac{1}{w}$$

5. Since

$$\int_0^\infty r\delta(r - a)J_o(wr)\, dr = aJ_o(aw)$$

we have

$$\delta(r - a) \overset{h}{\leftrightarrow} aJ_o(aw) \qquad a > 0 \tag{1-21}$$

and with the symmetry theorem

$$aJ_o(ar) \overset{h}{\leftrightarrow} \delta(w - a) \qquad a > 0 \tag{1-22}$$

6. A less trivial example is the Bessel function $J_o(br)$, which is truncated above $r = a$. Its transform $\bar{f}(w)$ can be determined from the identity [see (5-22)]

$$\int_0^a rJ_o(br)J_o(wr)\, dr = a\, \frac{bJ_1(ab)J_o(aw) - wJ_o(ab)J_1(aw)}{b^2 - w^2}$$

Thus,

$$J_o(br)p_a(r) \overset{h}{\leftrightarrow} \frac{abJ_1(ab)J_o(aw) - awJ_o(ab)J_1(aw)}{b^2 - w^2} \tag{1-23}$$

We remark that for $w = b$ [see (5-23)]

$$\bar{f}(b) = \frac{a^2}{2}\, [J_o{}^2(ab) + J_1{}^2(ab)] \tag{1-23a}$$

For $w \to \infty$, $\bar{f}(w)$ goes to zero as $w^{-3/2}$ if $J_o(ab) \neq 0$, and as $w^{-5/2}$ if $J_o(ab) = 0$ (see Chap. 7, Sec. 4).

7. Using the convolution theorem (1-11), one can derive several useful transform pairs. We shall write this theorem in the form

$$2\pi f_1(r)f_2(r) \overset{h}{\leftrightarrow} \bar{f}_1(w) ** \bar{f}_2(w) \tag{1-24}$$

where the right side is a double convolution in u and v, and $w = \sqrt{u^2 + v^2}$. The next three examples follow from (1-24).

If $f_1(r) = f_2(r) = J_1(ar)/r$, then (1-24) yields [see (1-20)]

$$2\pi \frac{J_1{}^2(ar)}{r^2} \overset{h}{\leftrightarrow} \frac{1}{a^2} p_a(w) ** p_a(w) \tag{1-25}$$

The double convolution of the circle $w = \sqrt{u^2 + v^2} \leq a$ with itself is evaluated in Example 1-6, Chap. 2. Inserting the result in (1-25), we obtain the pair

$$2\pi \frac{J_1{}^2(ar)}{r^2} \overset{h}{\leftrightarrow} \left(2 \cos^{-1} \frac{w}{2a} - \frac{w}{a} \sqrt{1 - \frac{w^2}{4a^2}} \right) p_{2a}(w) \tag{1-26}$$

8. It is easy to show that (Prob. 2-6) the double convolution of a circle $u^2 + v^2 \leq a^2$ with a circular line mass $\delta(w - a)$ is given by

$$p_a(w) ** \delta(w - a) = 2a \cos^{-1} \frac{w}{2a} \tag{1-27}$$

for $w \leq 2a$; it is zero for $w > 2a$. Since

$$J_o(ar) \overset{h}{\leftrightarrow} \frac{1}{a} \delta(w - a) \qquad \frac{J_1(ar)}{r} \overset{h}{\leftrightarrow} \frac{1}{a} p_a(w)$$

we obtain from (1-27) and (1-24)

$$\frac{J_o(ar)J_1(ar)}{r} \overset{h}{\leftrightarrow} \frac{p_{2a}(w)}{a\pi} \cos^{-1} \frac{w}{2a} \tag{1-28}$$

9. In Example 2-5, Chap. 2, we showed that

$$\delta(w - a) ** \delta(w - a) = \frac{4a^2}{w \sqrt{4a^2 - w^2}}$$

for $w < 2a$ and equals zero for $w > 2a$. Applying the above to (1-24) with $f_1(r) = f_2(r) = J_o(ar)$, we conclude that

$$J_o{}^2(ar) \overset{h}{\leftrightarrow} \frac{2p_{2a}(w)}{\pi w \sqrt{4a^2 - w^2}} \tag{1-29}$$

10. We shall use the moment theorem (1-15) to show that

$$e^{-ar} \overset{h}{\leftrightarrow} \frac{a}{\sqrt{(a^2 + w^2)^3}} \tag{1-30}$$

The moments of e^{-r} are

$$m_n = \int_0^\infty r^n e^{-r} \, dr = n!$$

Inserting into (1-15), we conclude that the Hankel transform of e^{-r} is given by

$$\bar{f}(w) = \sum_{n=0}^\infty \frac{(-1)^n (2n + 1)!}{(n!)^2 2^{2n}} w^{2n}$$

The above sum is the expansion of $(1 + w^2)^{-3/2}$, as it is easy to show, and (1-30) follows with (1-9).

11. As an application of the differentiation theorem, we shall show that

$$\frac{e^{-ar}}{r} \overset{h}{\leftrightarrow} \frac{1}{\sqrt{a^2 + w^2}} \tag{1-31}$$

From (1-10) and (1-30) we have

$$\frac{d^2 e^{-r}}{dr^2} + \frac{1}{r}\frac{de^{-r}}{dr} = e^{-r} - \frac{1}{r}e^{-r} \overset{h}{\leftrightarrow} \frac{-w^2}{\sqrt{(1 + w^2)^3}} = \frac{1}{\sqrt{(1 + w^2)^3}}$$
$$- \frac{1}{\sqrt{1 + w^2}}$$

and (1-31) follows from (1-30).

12. As a last example, we shall determine the Hankel transform $\bar{R}_n(w)$ of the function

$$R_n(r) = \frac{J_n(r)}{r^n}$$

This is an important example, and leads to Sonine's integral. The result will be established by induction based on the recursion formula

$$R_n''(r) + \frac{1}{r} R_n'(r) + R_n(r) = 2n R_{n+1}(r)$$

which is proved in Sec. 5 [see (5-20)]. From the above and (1-10) we have

$$(1 - w^2)\bar{R}_n(w) = 2n\bar{R}_{n+1}(w)$$

Hence,

$$\bar{R}_{n+1}(w) = \frac{1 - w^2}{2n}\,\bar{R}_n(w) = \cdots = \frac{(1 - w^2)^n}{2^n n!}\,\bar{R}_1(w)$$

But [see (1-20)]

$$R_1(r) = \frac{J_1(r)}{r} \overset{h}{\leftrightarrow} p_1(w)$$

Therefore,

$$\frac{J_n(r)}{r^n} \overset{h}{\leftrightarrow} \frac{(1 - w^2)^{n-1}}{2^{n-1}(n - 1)!}\,p_1(w) \tag{1-32}$$

Corollaries

Using the preceding Hankel transforms, we shall derive a number of identities involving the Bessel functions. Direct proofs of most of these identities are not simple [w1].

From (1-16)

$$\int_0^\infty re^{-ar^2}J_o(wr)\,dr = \frac{1}{2a}\,e^{-w^2/4a}$$

From (1-20) and the fact that $f(r) = [f(r^+) + f(r^-)]/2$

$$\int_0^\infty J_1(aw)J_o(rw)\,dw = \begin{cases} \dfrac{1}{a} & |r| < a \\[2mm] \dfrac{1}{2a} & |r| = a \\[2mm] 0 & |r| > a \end{cases}$$

Using the Hankel transform pair (1-20) and the fact that $2\pi\bar{f}(\sqrt{u^2 + v^2})$ is the Fourier transform of $f(\sqrt{x^2 + y^2})$, we can derive the Fourier transform of the zero-one function associated with the circle $x^2 + y^2 \leq a^2$:

$$\left.\begin{matrix} 1 & x^2 + y^2 \leq a^2 \\ 0 & \text{otherwise} \end{matrix}\right\} \Leftrightarrow 2\pi a\,\frac{J_1(a\sqrt{u^2 + v^2})}{\sqrt{u^2 + v^2}}$$

From (1-20) and the energy theorem (1-13)

$$\int_0^\infty \frac{J_1{}^2(aw)}{w}\,dw = \frac{1}{a^2}\int_0^a r\,dr = \tfrac{1}{2}$$

This follows also from (1-26) because $\bar{f}(0) = 2\cos^{-1}0 = \pi$.
From (1-22)

$$a\int_0^\infty rJ_o(ar)J_o(wr)\,dr = \delta(w - a)$$

From (1-22) and the differentiation theorem (1-10)

$$\frac{d^2J_o(ar)}{dr^2} + \frac{1}{r}\frac{dJ_o(ar)}{dr} \overset{h}{\leftrightarrow} -\frac{w^2}{a}\,\delta(w - a) = -a\delta(w - a)$$

because $\varphi(w)\delta(w - a) = \varphi(a)\delta(w - a)$. But the inverse Hankel transform of $a\delta(w - a)$ equals $a^2J_o(ar)$; hence,

$$\frac{d^2J_o(ar)}{dr^2} + \frac{1}{r}\frac{dJ_o(ar)}{dr} = -a^2J_o(ar)$$

which is a well-known result [see (5-24)].
From (1-28)

$$\int_0^\infty J_1(ar)J_o(ar)J_o(wr)\,dr = \begin{cases} \dfrac{1}{a\pi}\cos^{-1}\dfrac{w}{2a} & |w| < 2a \\[2mm] 0 & \text{otherwise} \end{cases}$$

We know from Chap. 2, Example 2-5, that the convolution of two

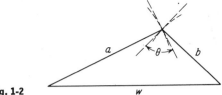

Fig. 1-2

circular line masses is given by

$$\delta(w - a) ** \delta(w - b) = \begin{cases} \dfrac{2}{\sin\theta} & \text{for } |a - b| < w < a + b \\ 0 & \text{otherwise} \end{cases}$$

where θ is the angle of intersection of the circles shown in Fig. 1-2. From the above and the convolution theorem (1-24) it follows that

$$\int_0^\infty rJ_o(ar)J_o(br)J_o(wr)\, dr = \frac{1}{\pi ab \sin\theta} \qquad \text{for } |a - b| < w < a + b$$

From (1-31)

$$\int_0^\infty e^{-ar}J_o(wr)\, dr = \frac{1}{\sqrt{a^2 + w^2}}$$

This relationship shows that the unilateral Laplace transform of $J_o(t)$ equals $(1 + p^2)^{-\frac{1}{2}}$.

From (1-32) and the scaling theorem (1-9)

$$a^n \int_0^\infty r^{1-n}J_n(ar)J_o(wr)\, dr = \frac{(a^2 - w^2)^{n-1}}{2^{n-1}(n - 1)!}\, p_a(w)$$

Sonine's integral   From (1-32) we see that

$$\frac{J_n(r)}{r^n} = \frac{1}{2^{n-1}(n - 1)!} \int_0^1 wJ_o(wr)(1 - w^2)^{n-1}\, dw \tag{1-33}$$

and with

$$w = \sin\theta \qquad 1 - w^2 = \cos^2\theta \qquad dw = \cos\theta\, d\theta$$

we obtain Sonine's integral formula [w1]

$$J_n(r) = \frac{r^n}{2^{n-1}(n - 1)!} \int_0^{\pi/2} J_o(r\sin\theta)\sin\theta\cos^{2n-1}\theta\, d\theta \tag{1-34}$$

HANKEL TRANSFORMS IN SYSTEMS WITH CIRCULAR SYMMETRY

Consider a two-dimensional system with impulse response

$$h(x,y) = h(\sqrt{x^2 + y^2}) = h(r) \qquad r = \sqrt{x^2 + y^2}$$

As we know, if the input $f(x,y)$ is circularly symmetrical, then the output $g(x,y)$ is also circularly symmetrical, and it is given by

$$g(r) = f(r) ** h(r) \tag{1-35}$$

In the analysis of such systems, Hankel transforms enter naturally. Indeed, with

$$f(r) \overset{h}{\leftrightarrow} \bar{f}(w) \qquad h(r) \overset{h}{\leftrightarrow} \bar{h}(w) \qquad g(r) \overset{h}{\leftrightarrow} \bar{g}(w)$$

we see from (1-11) that the convolution (1-35) in the xy plane becomes a mere multiplication:

$$\bar{g}(w) = 2\pi\bar{f}(w)\bar{h}(w) \tag{1-36}$$

System functions as eigenvalues   Suppose that the input to our system is the Bessel function $J_o(ar)$:

$$f(r) = J_o(ar)$$

Since

$$J_o(ar) \overset{h}{\leftrightarrow} \frac{\delta(w - a)}{a}$$

and $\varphi(w)\delta(w - a) = \varphi(a)\delta(w - a)$, we conclude from (1-36) that

$$\bar{g}(w) = \frac{2\pi}{a}\,\delta(w - a)\bar{h}(w) = \frac{2\pi\bar{h}(a)}{a}\,\delta(w - a)$$

Therefore,

$$g(r) = 2\pi\bar{h}(a)J_o(ar)$$

Thus, if a linear two-dimensional system (operator) L has circular symmetry, then

$$L[J_o(a\sqrt{x^2 + y^2})] = 2\pi\bar{h}(a)J_o(a\sqrt{x^2 + y^2})$$

In other words, for any a, the Bessel function $J_o(a\sqrt{x^2 + y^2})$ is an eigenfunction of L, and the corresponding eigenvalue equals $2\pi\bar{h}(a)$.

2. RELATIONSHIP BETWEEN FOURIER AND HANKEL TRANSFORMS

As we know, if $\bar{f}(w)$ is the Hankel transform of $f(r)$, then

$$2\pi\bar{f}(\sqrt{u^2 + v^2}) = F(u,v) \tag{2-1}$$

is the two-dimensional Fourier transform of $f(\sqrt{x^2 + y^2})$. We shall now show that $2\pi\bar{f}(\omega)$ equals the one-dimensional Fourier transform

$$\Phi(\omega) = \int_{-\infty}^{\infty} e^{-j\omega x}\varphi(x)\,dx \tag{2-2}$$

of the profile

$$\varphi(x) = \int_{-\infty}^{\infty} f(\sqrt{x^2 + y^2})\, dy \tag{2-3}$$

Indeed, since [see Chap. 3, (4-25)]

$$\Phi(\omega) = F(\omega, 0)$$

and $F(\omega, 0) = 2\pi \bar{f}(\omega)$, it follows that

$$\varphi(x) \leftrightarrow 2\pi \bar{f}(\omega) \tag{2-4}$$

This result can be used to establish Hankel transform pairs from known Fourier transforms, and conversely, Fourier transforms from Hankel transform pairs.

Example 2-1   If $f(r) = p_a(r)$ is a pulse (Fig. 2-1), then

$$\varphi(x) = \int_{-\sqrt{a^2-x^2}}^{\sqrt{a^2-x^2}} dy = 2\sqrt{a^2 - x^2} \qquad \text{for } |x| < a$$

and

$$\varphi(x) = 0 \qquad \text{for } |x| > a$$

But the Hankel transform of $p_a(r)$ equals $aJ_1(aw)/w$.   Therefore, the Fourier transform of $2\sqrt{a^2 - x^2}$ equals $2\pi aJ_1(a\omega)/\omega$:

$$\sqrt{a^2 - x^2}\, p_a(x) \leftrightarrow \frac{\pi aJ_1(a\omega)}{\omega} \tag{2-5}$$

Example 2-2   We shall now determine the Hankel transform $\bar{f}(w)$ of the function

$$f(r) = \frac{p_a(r)}{\sqrt{a^2 - r^2}}$$

using (2-4).   The corresponding $\varphi(x)$ is given by

$$\varphi(x) = \int_{-\sqrt{a^2-x^2}}^{\sqrt{a^2-x^2}} \frac{dy}{\sqrt{a^2 - (x^2 + y^2)}} = \int_{-\pi/2}^{\pi/2} d\theta = \pi$$

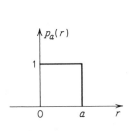

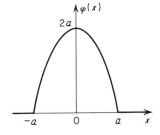

Fig. 2-1

for $|x| < a$; it equals zero for $|x| > a$.   Hence

$$\Phi(\omega) = \int_{-a}^{a} \pi e^{-j\omega x}\, dx = \frac{2\pi \sin a\omega}{\omega} = 2\pi \bar{f}(\omega)$$

We thus obtain the Hankel pair

$$\frac{p_a(r)}{\sqrt{a^2 - r^2}} \overset{h}{\longleftrightarrow} \frac{\sin aw}{w} \tag{2-6}$$

From (2-6) and the Hankel inversion formula (1-6) we deduce the interesting identity

$$\int_0^{\infty} \sin awJ_o(rw)\, dw = \frac{p_a(r)}{\sqrt{a^2 - r^2}} \tag{2-7}$$

Comment   From (2-4) we conclude that if a linear system has circular symmetry, then the Fourier transform of its line spread $s(x)$ equals the Hankel transform of $2\pi h(r)$, where $h(r)$ is its point spread.

INTEGRAL EQUATIONS

We shall now express the Hankel transform $\bar{f}(w)$,

$$f(r) \overset{h}{\longleftrightarrow} \bar{f}(w)$$

of a function $f(r)$ in terms of the Fourier transform of $f(r)$ truncated for $r < 0$.

We denote by

$$F_1(\omega) = \int_0^{\infty} rf(r)e^{-j\omega r}\, dr = R_1(\omega) + jX_1(\omega) \tag{2-8}$$

the Fourier transform of $rf(r)U(r)$.   Assuming that $f(r)$ is real, we have

$$R_1(-\omega) = R_1(\omega) \qquad X_1(-\omega) = -X_1(\omega)$$

We shall show that

$$\bar{f}(w) = \frac{1}{2\pi} \int_{-\pi}^{\pi} F_1(w \cos \theta)\, d\theta = \frac{2}{\pi} \int_0^{\pi/2} R_1(w \cos \theta)\, d\theta \tag{2-9}$$

Proof   Inserting the integral form of the Bessel function $J_o(wr)$ into the definition (1-2), we have

$$\bar{f}(w) = \int_0^{\infty} rf(r) \frac{1}{2\pi} \int_{-\pi}^{\pi} e^{-jwr \cos \theta}\, d\theta\, dr = \frac{1}{2\pi} \int_{-\pi}^{\pi} \int_0^{\infty} rf(r)e^{-jwr \cos \theta}\, dr\, d\theta$$

The last integral equals $F_1(w \cos \theta) = R_1(w \cos \theta) + jX_1(w \cos \theta)$. Since $X_1(\omega)$ is odd, we have

$$X_1[\omega \cos (\pi + \theta)] = -X_1(\omega \cos \theta)$$

Hence the integral of $X_1(\omega \cos \theta)$ in the $(-\pi, \pi)$ interval equals zero, and (2-9) follows.

We shall soon see that the integral equation (2-9) can be solved for $R_1(\omega)$. The result is [see (2-18)]

$$R_1(w) = w \int_0^{\pi/2} \tilde{f}'(w \cos \theta) \, d\theta + \tilde{f}(0) \tag{2-10}$$

Comment If

$$f(r)U(r) \leftrightarrow F(\omega) = R(\omega) + jX(\omega)$$

then (frequency differentiation)

$$F_1(\omega) = jF'(\omega) \qquad R_1(\omega) = -X'(\omega) \qquad X_1(\omega) = R'(\omega)$$

Complex Hankel transforms

To facilitate the inversion of (2-9), we shall introduce the notion of the complex Hankel transform† $\tilde{f}_c(w)$ of $f(r)$ as the conjugate of the analytic signal associated with $\tilde{f}(w)$ (see Chap. 3, Sec. 3)

$$\tilde{f}_c(w) = \tilde{f}(w) - j\hat{\tilde{f}}(w) \tag{2-11}$$

In the above, $\hat{\tilde{f}}(w)$ is the Hilbert transform of $\tilde{f}(w)$, and it is given by

$$\hat{\tilde{f}}(w) = \int_0^\infty rf(r)\hat{J}_o(wr) \, dr \tag{2-12}$$

as we can see from (1-2) and the fact that the Hilbert transform of a sum of several functions equals the sum of their Hilbert transforms. To complete the determination of $\tilde{f}_c(w)$, it suffices, therefore, to find $\hat{J}_o(wr)$. As we know [see Chap. 3, (3-19)], the Hilbert transform $\hat{J}_o(t)$ of $J_o(t)$ is the Struve function $H_o(t)$:

$$\hat{J}_o(t) = H_o(t) = \frac{2}{\pi} \int_0^1 \frac{\sin \omega t}{\sqrt{1 - \omega^2}} \, d\omega = \frac{2}{\pi} \int_0^{\pi/2} \sin(t \cos \theta) \, d\theta \tag{2-13}$$

Hence, the complex Hankel transform of $f(r)$ is given by

$$\tilde{f}_c(w) = \int_0^\infty rf(r)[J_o(wr) - jH_o(wr)] \, dr \tag{2-14}$$

With $\varphi(x)$ as in (2-3), we maintain that

$$\int_0^\infty \varphi(x)e^{-jwx} \, dx = \pi \tilde{f}_c(w) \tag{2-15}$$

Indeed, since the function $\varphi(-\omega) = \varphi(\omega)$ is the Fourier transform of $\tilde{f}(t)$ [see (2-4)], the analytic signal $\tilde{f}_c(-t) = \tilde{f}(t) + j\hat{\tilde{f}}(t)$ associated with $\tilde{f}(t)$ will have as its Fourier transform the function $2\varphi(\omega)U(\omega)$ [see Chap. 3, (3-12)], and (2-15) follows with $\omega = x$, $-t = w$.

† A. Papoulis, *J. Opt. Soc. Am.*, vol. 57, pp. 207–213, February, 1967.

Integral equations   We shall now show that

$$\tilde{f}_c(w) = \frac{2}{\pi} \int_0^{\pi/2} F_1(w \cos \theta) \, d\theta \tag{2-16}$$

where $F_1(\omega)$ is as in (2-8).   For this purpose, we note that [see (2-13)]

$$J_o(x) - j\hat{J}_o(x) = \frac{2}{\pi} \int_0^{\pi/2} e^{-jx \cos \theta} \, d\theta \tag{2-17}$$

Inserting into (2-14) and interchanging the order of integration, we have

$$\tilde{f}_c(w) = \frac{2}{\pi} \int_0^{\pi/2} \int_0^\infty rf(r)e^{-jwr \cos \theta} \, dr \, d\theta$$

and (2-16) follows.   Equation (2-9) is the real part of (2-16).

The function $F_1(w)$ in (2-8) can be expressed in terms of $\tilde{f}_c(w)$ by

$$F_1(w) = w \int_0^{\pi/2} \tilde{f}_c'(w \cos \theta) \, d\theta + \tilde{f}(0) \tag{2-18}$$

where $\tilde{f}_c'(w)$ is the derivative of $\tilde{f}_c(w)$.   Equation (2-10) is the real part of (2-18).

Proof   We shall base the proof of (2-18) on the relationship [see Chap. 2, (3-52)]

$$2\pi x f(x) = -\frac{dq(x)}{dx} \qquad x > 0 \tag{2-19}$$

between $f(r)$ and the profile

$$q(x) = \int_{-\infty}^\infty \varphi(\sqrt{x^2 + y^2}) \, dy \tag{2-20}$$

of $\varphi(r)$.   With $\bar{\varphi}_c(w)$ the complex Hankel transform of $\varphi(r)$ and $\Phi_1(\omega)$ the Fourier transform of $r\varphi(r)U(r)$, we have, differentiating (2-15),

$$\Phi_1(\omega) = \int_0^\infty r\varphi(r)e^{-j\omega r} \, dr = j\pi \tilde{f}_c'(\omega) \tag{2-21}$$

and, with (2-16),

$$\bar{\varphi}_c(w) = \frac{2}{\pi} \int_0^{\pi/2} \Phi_1(w \cos \theta) \, d\theta = 2j \int_0^{\pi/2} \tilde{f}_c'(w \cos \theta) \, d\theta \tag{2-22}$$

Since $q(x)$ is the profile of $\varphi(r)$, it follows from (2-15) that the Fourier transform of $q(x)U(x)$ equals $\pi\bar{\varphi}_c(\omega)$.   Hence,

$$\frac{d[q(x)U(x)]}{dx} \leftrightarrow j\omega\pi\bar{\varphi}_c(\omega)$$

(derivative theorem).   But

$$\frac{d[q(x)U(x)]}{dx} = q'(x)U(x) + q(x)\delta(x)$$

and the Fourier transform of $q(x)\delta(x) = q(0)\delta(x)$ equals $q(0)$; therefore, the Fourier transform of $q'(x)U(x)$ equals $j\omega\pi\bar{\varphi}_c(\omega) - q(0)$. From this and (2-19) it follows that

$$2\pi F_1(\omega) = -j\omega\pi\bar{\varphi}_c(\omega) + q(0) \tag{2-23}$$

where [see (2-4) and (2-20)]

$$q(0) = \int_{-\infty}^{\infty} \varphi(x)\,dx = 2\pi\bar{f}(0) \tag{2-24}$$

Inserting (2-22) and (2-24) into (2-23), we obtain (2-18).

Schlömilch series   As an application of the foregoing, we shall show that a function $x(t)$ can be expanded into a series [w1] of the form

$$x(t) = \frac{a_0}{2} + \sum_{n=1}^{\infty} a_n J_o\left(\frac{n\pi t}{a}\right) \qquad 0 < t < a \tag{2-25}$$

and will evaluate the coefficients a_n.

Consider the function $R_1(\omega)$ in (2-8). This function is even, and hence can be expanded into a cosine series

$$R_1(\omega) = \frac{a_0}{2} + \sum_{n=1}^{\infty} a_n \cos n\omega \qquad |\omega| < \pi \tag{2-26}$$

where

$$a_n = \frac{2}{\pi} \int_0^{\pi} R_1(\omega) \cos n\omega\,d\omega \tag{2-27}$$

Inserting the series (2-26) into (2-9) and interchanging integration and summation, we have, for $|w| < \pi$,

$$\bar{f}(w) = \frac{a_0}{2} + \sum_{n=1}^{\infty} a_n \frac{2}{\pi} \int_0^{\pi/2} \cos(nw \cos\theta)\,d\theta$$

Hence

$$\bar{f}(w) = \frac{a_0}{2} + \sum_{n=1}^{\infty} a_n J_o(nw) \qquad |w| < \pi \tag{2-28}$$

We shall now express a_n in terms of $\bar{f}(w)$. This is easily done by inserting (2-10) into (2-27). For $n \neq 0$, the integration of $\bar{f}(0) \cos n\omega$ in the interval $(0,\pi)$ equals zero; therefore,

$$a_0 = 2\bar{f}(0) + \frac{2}{\pi} \int_0^{\pi} \int_0^{\pi/2} w\bar{f}'(w \cos\theta)\,d\theta\,dw$$

$$a_n = \frac{2}{\pi} \int_0^{\pi} \int_0^{\pi/2} w\bar{f}'(w \cos\theta) \cos n\omega\,d\theta\,dw \tag{2-29}$$

Thus, an arbitrary function $\bar{f}(w)$ can be expanded into the Schlömilch series (2-28) in the interval $(0,\pi)$. This is done by considering it as a Hankel transform. The coefficients a_n are given by (2-29). With $\bar{f}(\pi t/a) = x(t)$, (2-25) results.

3. FOURIER-BESSEL SERIES AND SAMPLING THEOREM

It is known that the Bessel function $J_o(x)$ has infinitely many zeros x_i. This can be deduced, for example, from its asymptotic form

$$J_o(x) \approx \sqrt{\frac{2}{\pi x}} \cos\left(x - \frac{\pi}{4}\right) \qquad x \to \infty$$

(see Chap. 7, Example 2-3). Similarly, for a given a, the equation $J_o(ar) = 0$ has infinitely many roots:

$$\alpha_i = \frac{x_i}{a} \qquad J_o(\alpha_i a) = 0 \qquad i = 1, 2, \ldots \tag{3-1}$$

In the following we shall show that the functions $J_o(\alpha_i r)$ form an orthogonal set in the interval $(0,a)$, and we shall investigate the possibility of expanding an arbitrary function $f(r)$ into a series

$$f(r) = \sum_{i=1}^{\infty} b_i J_o(\alpha_i r) \qquad 0 < r < a \tag{3-2}$$

This series corresponds closely to the sine expansion of a function $f(r)$ in an interval $(0,a)$. Indeed, the Fourier expansion is also based on the orthogonality of the functions $\sin \omega_i r$, where ω_i are the roots of $\sin \omega_i a = 0$.

Since $J_o(\alpha_i a) = 0$, it follows from (5-22) and (5-23), with proper changes in the various parameters, that

$$\int_0^a r J_o(\alpha_i r) J_o(\alpha_j r)\, dr = \begin{cases} \dfrac{a^2}{2} J_1{}^2(\alpha_i a) & i = j \\ 0 & i \neq j \end{cases} \tag{3-3}$$

Thus, the functions $J_o(\alpha_i r)$, $i = 1, 2, \ldots$, form an orthogonal set in the interval $(0,a)$. If we accept the fact that $f(r)$ can be written as a series (3-2), then the coefficients b_n can be readily evaluated. Indeed, multiplying both sides by $r J_o(\alpha_n r)$ and integrating from 0 to a, we find, with (3-3),

$$b_n = \frac{2}{a^2 J_1{}^2(\alpha_n a)} \int_0^a r f(r) J_o(\alpha_n r)\, dr \tag{3-4}$$

To prove the Fourier-Bessel expansion (3-2), one must show that if the numbers b_n in (3-4) are inserted into (3-2), then the sum equals $f(r)$. This can be established, as in the proof of the Fourier series expansion, by forming the partial sum

$$f_N(r) = \sum_{n=1}^{N} b_n J_o(\alpha_n r) \tag{3-5}$$

and showing that it tends to $f(r)$ with $N \to \infty$. Inserting (3-4) into (3-5) and interchanging the order of integration and summation, we have

$$f_N(r) = \int_0^a x f(x) \sum_{n=1}^{N} \frac{2 J_o(\alpha_n r) J_o(\alpha_n x)}{a^2 J_1^2(\alpha_n a)} \, dx \tag{3-6}$$

Thus, $f_N(r)$ is given by the weighted average

$$f_N(r) = \int_0^a x f(x) T_N(r;x) \, dx \tag{3-7}$$

of $x f(x)$, with the Fourier-Bessel kernel

$$T_N(r;x) = \sum_{n=1}^{N} \frac{2 J_o(\alpha_n r) J_o(\alpha_n x)}{a^2 J_1^2(\alpha_n a)} \tag{3-8}$$

corresponding to the kernel

$$k_N(t - \tau) = \frac{\sin\left[(N + \frac{1}{2})(t - \tau)\right]}{T \sin\left[\omega_o(t - \tau)/2\right]}$$

in the theory of Fourier series. One can show that [w1] for $0 < r, x < a$,

$$x T_N(r;x) \to \delta(r - x) \qquad N \to \infty \tag{3-9}$$

from which the expansion (3-2) results. The functions in (3-9) must, of course, be interpreted as distributions, i.e., as integrands in integrals of the form (3-7). The limit holds, provided that both sides operate on

Table 3-1†   Zeros of $J_o(x)$ and corresponding values of $J_1(x)$

n	x_n	$J_1(x_n)$	n	x_n	$J_1(x_n)$
1	2.404826	+0.519147	11	33.775820	+0.137297
2	5.520078	−0.340265	12	36.917098	−0.131325
3	8.653728	+0.271453	13	40.058426	+0.126070
4	11.791534	−0.232460	14	43.199792	−0.121397
5	14.930918	+0.206546	15	46.341188	+0.117211
6	18.071064	−0.187729	16	49.482610	−0.113429
7	21.211637	+0.173266	17	52.624052	+0.109991
8	24.352472	−0.161702	18	55.765511	−0.106848
9	27.493480	+0.152181	19	58.906984	+0.103960
10	30.634606	−0.144166	20	62.048469	−0.101293

† "Royal Society Mathematical Tables," Bessel Functions, Part III, Zeros and Associated Values, Cambridge University Press, London, 1960.

functions satisfying certain general conditions [bounded variation and absolute integrability of $\sqrt{r}\,f(r)$].

The roots $x_n = \alpha_n a$ of $J_o(x)$ and the corresponding values of $J_1(x)$ are shown in Table 3-1 for n up to 20.

Relationship to Hankel transforms   The coefficients b_n can be expressed in terms of the Hankel transform

$$\bar{f}_o(w) = \int_0^a rf(r)J_o(wr)\,dr \qquad (3\text{-}10)$$

of the function

$$f_o(r) = \begin{cases} f(r) & 0 < r < a \\ 0 & r > a \end{cases} \qquad (3\text{-}11)$$

[See also Chap. 4, (2-8).]   From (3-4) we see that

$$b_n = \frac{2\bar{f}_o(\alpha_n)}{a^2 J_1{}^2(\alpha_n a)} \qquad (3\text{-}12)$$

Example 3-1   We shall expand the function

$$f(r) = a^2 - r^2$$

into a Fourier-Bessel series in the interval $(0,a)$.   From (1-32) we have (with a suitable scaling)

$$f_o(r) = (a^2 - r^2)p_a(r) \overset{h}{\leftrightarrow} \frac{2a^2 J_2(aw)}{w^2} = \bar{f}_o(w)$$

Therefore,

$$b_n = \frac{4J_2(\alpha_n a)}{\alpha_n{}^2 J_1{}^2(\alpha_n a)}$$

and

$$a^2 - r^2 = 4 \sum_{n=1}^{\infty} \frac{J_2(\alpha_n a)}{\alpha_n{}^2 J_1{}^2(\alpha_n a)} J_o(\alpha_n r) \qquad 0 < r < a$$

Example 3-2   The Hankel transform $\bar{f}_o(w)$ of the truncated Bessel function

$$f_o(r) = J_o(cr)p_a(r)$$

is given by (1-23).   Since $J_o(\alpha_n a) = 0$, we have

$$\bar{f}_o(\alpha_n) = \frac{\alpha_n a J_o(ac)J_1(\alpha_n a)}{\alpha_n{}^2 - c^2}$$

Therefore,

$$J_o(cr) = \frac{2J_o(ac)}{a} \sum_{n=1}^{\infty} \frac{\alpha_n J_o(\alpha_n r)}{J_1(\alpha_n a)(\alpha_n{}^2 - c^2)} \qquad 0 < r < a$$

Comments   In the Fourier-Bessel expansion (3-2) the sum

$$s(r) = \sum_{n=1}^{\infty} b_n J_o(\alpha_n r) = \sum_{n=1}^{\infty} \frac{2\tilde{f}_o(\alpha_n)}{a^2 J_1{}^2(\alpha_n a)} J_o(\alpha_n r) \tag{3-13}$$

is a function $s(r)$ defined *for every* r.   For $r < a$, $s(r)$ equals the given function $f(r)$.   It is of interest to examine the properties of $s(r)$ for $r > a$. Its Hankel transform $\bar{s}(w)$ is given by

$$\bar{s}(w) = \sum_{n=1}^{\infty} \frac{2\tilde{f}_o(\alpha_n)}{\alpha_n a^2 J_1(\alpha_n a)} \delta(w - \alpha_n) = \tilde{f}_o(w) \sum_{n=1}^{\infty} \frac{2\delta(w - \alpha_n)}{\alpha_n a^2 J_1{}^2(\alpha_n a)} \tag{3-14}$$

This follows from (3-13), (1-22), and the fact that

$$\tilde{f}_o(w)\delta(w - \alpha_n) = \tilde{f}_o(\alpha_n)\delta(w - \alpha_n)$$

Thus, $\bar{s}(w)$ is a sequence of impulses, as in Fig. 3-1.   Since

$$J_o(aw)\delta(w - \alpha_n) = J_o(\alpha_n a)\delta(w - \alpha_n) = 0$$

we conclude that

$$\bar{s}(w)J_o(aw) = 0$$

From the above and the convolution theorem it follows that $s(r)$ satisfies

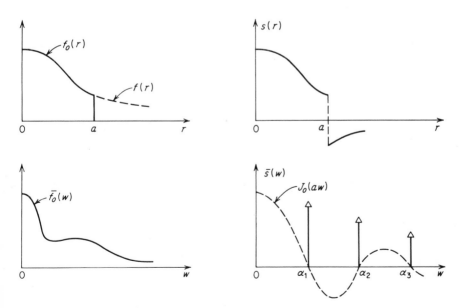

Fig. 3-1

the identity

$$s(r) ** \delta(r - a) \equiv 0 \qquad (3\text{-}15)$$

for every r. In other words, in the xy plane, the average value of $s(\sqrt{x^2 + y^2})$ over the circumference of any circle of radius a equals zero.

Conversely, suppose that a function $s(r)$ can be found such that for $r < a$ it equals $f(r)$ and for $r > a$ it is so defined as to satisfy (3-15). It will then follow that $\bar{s}(w)J_o(aw) = 0$. But this is possible only if $\bar{s}(w)$ consists of impulses at the zeros α_i of $J_o(aw)$:

$$\bar{s}(w) = \sum_{n=1}^{\infty} c_n \delta(w - \alpha_n) \qquad \text{hence} \qquad s(r) = \sum_{n=1}^{\infty} \frac{c_n}{\alpha_n} J_o(\alpha_n r)$$

Thus, $s(r)$ is expressed as a series of Bessel functions, and since $f(r) = s(r)$ for $r < a$, the Fourier-Bessel expansion (3-2) results with $c_n = \alpha_n b_n$. In other words, to prove (3-2) it suffices to show that if a function $f(r)$ is specified only for $0 < r < a$, then for $r > a$ it can be so defined as to satisfy (3-15).

PARSEVAL'S FORMULA

Proceeding as in Chap. 4, (2-10), we shall show that

$$\int_0^a r f^2(r) \, dr = \sum_{n=1}^{\infty} \frac{2\bar{f}_o{}^2(\alpha_n)}{a^2 J_1{}^2(\alpha_n a)} = \frac{a^2}{2} \sum_{n=1}^{\infty} J_1{}^2(\alpha_n a) b_n{}^2 \qquad (3\text{-}16)$$

where $\bar{f}_o(w)$ is the finite Hankel transform (3-10) of $f(r)$. This result can also be proved directly from (3-3).

Proof From (3-13) and (3-11) we have

$$s(r) = \sum_{i=1}^{\infty} b_i J_o(\alpha_i r) \overset{h}{\leftrightarrow} \sum_{i=1}^{\infty} \frac{b_i}{\alpha_i} \delta(w - \alpha_i)$$

$$f_o(r) \overset{h}{\leftrightarrow} \bar{f}_o(w)$$

From the above and Parseval's formula (1-12) it follows that [see Chap. 2, (2-4)]

$$\int_0^{\infty} r f_o(r) s(r) \, dr = \int_0^{\infty} w \bar{f}_o(w) \sum_{i=1}^{\infty} \frac{b_i}{\alpha_i} \delta(w - \alpha_i) \, dw = \sum_{i=1}^{\infty} b_i \bar{f}_o(\alpha_i)$$

And since

$$f_o(r) = s(r) = f(r) \qquad \text{for } r < a \text{ and } f_o(r) = 0 \qquad \text{for } r > a$$

(3-16) results [see (3-12)].

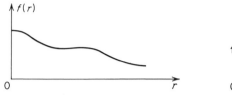 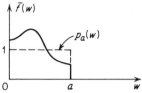

Fig. 3-2

SAMPLING THEOREM

We are given a function $f(r)$ with a band-limited Hankel transform $\bar{f}(w)$ (Fig. 3-2):

$$\bar{f}(w) = 0 \qquad w > a$$

We maintain that $f(r)$ can be recovered from its values $f(\alpha_i)$ where the numbers α_i are defined in (3-1). In fact, we shall show that

$$f(r) = \frac{2}{a} \sum_{n=1}^{\infty} \frac{\alpha_n f(\alpha_n)}{J_1(\alpha_n a)} \frac{J_o(ar)}{\alpha_n^2 - r^2} \tag{3-17}$$

Proof Expanding $\bar{f}(w)$ into a Fourier-Bessel series as in (3-2) and noting that $\bar{f}(w) = 0$ for $w > a$, we have

$$\bar{f}(w) = \frac{2}{a^2} \sum_{n=1}^{\infty} \frac{f(\alpha_n)}{J_1^2(\alpha_n a)} J_o(\alpha_n w) p_a(w) \tag{3-18}$$

where $p_a(w)$ is a pulse. Since $J_o(\alpha_n a) = 0$, we have from (1-23) and the symmetry theorem,

$$\alpha_n a J_1(\alpha_n a) \frac{J_o(ar)}{\alpha_n^2 - r^2} \overset{h}{\leftrightarrow} J_o(\alpha_n w) p_a(w)$$

and the sampling expansion (3-17) follows if we take the inverse transform of (3-18).

4. GENERALIZED HANKEL TRANSFORMS

The Hankel transform $\bar{f}(w)$ of a function $f(r)$ was defined by (1-2). If, in this integral, $J_o(x)$ is replaced by the Bessel function

$$J_n(x) = \frac{1}{2\pi} \int_{-\pi}^{\pi} e^{j(n\alpha - x \sin \alpha)} \, d\alpha \tag{4-1}$$

of order n, the resulting integral

$$\bar{f}_n(w) = \int_0^{\infty} r f(r) J_n(wr) \, dr \tag{4-2}$$

is the Hankel transform of $f(r)$ of order n [s4].

We shall show that $\tilde{f}_n(w)$ can be interpreted as a two-dimensional Fourier transform

$$f(r)e^{jn\theta} \Leftrightarrow 2\pi\tilde{f}_n(w)e^{-jn\varphi} \tag{4-3}$$

where the transform is with respect to the variables x, y and u, v, as specified by

$$\begin{aligned} x &= r\cos\theta & y &= r\sin\theta \\ u &= w\sin\varphi & v &= w\cos\varphi \end{aligned} \tag{4-4}$$

Proof With the above transformations, the Fourier integral (4-1), Chap. 3, yields

$$F(u,v) = \int_0^\infty rf(r) \int_{-\pi}^{\pi} e^{j[n\theta - wr\sin(\theta+\varphi)]}\, d\theta\, dr \tag{4-5}$$

Letting $\theta = \alpha - \varphi$, we conclude from (4-1) and the periodicity of $\sin\alpha$, that

$$\int_{-\pi}^{\pi} e^{j[n\theta - wr\sin(\theta+\varphi)]}\, d\theta = e^{-jn\varphi}\int_{-\pi}^{\pi} e^{j(n\alpha - wr\sin\alpha)}\, d\alpha = 2\pi e^{-jn\varphi}J_n(wr)$$

Inserting into (4-5), we obtain (4-3).

Inversion formula From (4-3), (4-4), and the Fourier inversion formula [Chap. 3, (4-5)], it follows that

$$f(r)e^{jn\theta} = \frac{1}{4\pi^2}\int_0^\infty 2\pi w\tilde{f}_n(w)\int_{-\pi}^{\pi} e^{-j[n\varphi - wr\sin(\theta+\varphi)]}\, d\varphi\, dw$$

Hence,

$$f(r) = \int_0^\infty w\tilde{f}_n(w)J_n(rw)\, dw \tag{4-6}$$

One can similarly derive other properties of Hankel transforms from (4-3). We shall discuss only the derivative theorem.

Differentiation It is easy to show that

$$\left[\frac{\partial}{\partial x^2} + \frac{\partial}{\partial y^2}\right][f(r)e^{jn\theta}] = \left[\frac{d^2f(r)}{dr^2} + \frac{1}{r}\frac{df(r)}{dr} - \frac{n^2}{r^2}f(r)\right]e^{jn\theta}$$

As we see from Chap. 3, (4-14), the Fourier transform of the above function equals $-(u^2 + v^2)F(u,v)$, where $F(u,v) = 2\pi\tilde{f}_n(w)e^{-jn\varphi}$ is the Fourier transform of $f(r)e^{jn\theta}$ in the variables x and y. The right side above is of the form (4-3); hence, its Fourier transform equals $2\pi e^{-jn\varphi}$ times the Hankel transform of order n of the function in brackets.

Therefore

$$\frac{d^2f(r)}{dr^2} + \frac{1}{r}\frac{df(r)}{dr} - \frac{n^2}{r^2}f(r) \overset{h_n}{\longleftrightarrow} -w^2\bar{f}_n(w) \tag{4-7}$$

where h_n means nth-order Hankel transforms.

Arbitrary functions   We know that the analysis of two-dimensional systems with circular symmetry is facilitated with the use of zero-order Hankel transforms, provided that the input also has circular symmetry. We shall soon show that if the input does not have circular symmetry, then Hankel transforms of a general order, suitably defined, must be used.

If an arbitrary signal $f(x,y)$ is considered as a function of the variables r and θ introduced in (4-4), then it can be expanded into a Fourier series in θ.

The coefficients of the resulting expansion will of course be functions of r:

$$f(r\cos\theta, r\sin\theta) = \sum_{n=-\infty}^{\infty} a_n(r)e^{jn\theta} \tag{4-8}$$

With $\bar{a}_{nn}(w)$ the nth-order Hankel transform of $a_n(r)$, the Fourier transform of $a_n(r)e^{jn\theta}$ equals $2\pi\bar{a}_{nn}(w)e^{-jn\varphi}$.   Transforming (4-8) termwise, we thus conclude that

$$\sum_{n=-\infty}^{\infty} a_n(r)e^{jn\theta} \overset{x,y}{\underset{u,v}{\Longleftrightarrow}} 2\pi \sum_{n=-\infty}^{\infty} \bar{a}_{nn}(w)e^{-jn\varphi} \tag{4-9}$$

Thus, with $F(u,v)$ the transform of $f(x,y)$, the functions $2\pi\bar{a}_{nn}(w)$ are the coefficients of the Fourier series expansion of $F(w\sin\varphi, w\cos\varphi)$.

Systems   We now apply the signal $f(x,y)$ given by (4-8) to a circularly symmetrical system with impulse response $h(r)$.   With $\bar{h}_o(w) = \bar{h}(w)$ as the Hankel transform of zero order of $h(r)$, the system function is

$$H(u,v) = 2\pi\bar{h}(w)$$

Using the form (4-9) of the transform of $f(x,y)$, we conclude from Chap. 3, (4-32), that the transform $G(u,v)$ of the output $g(x,y)$ is given by

$$G(u,v) = 4\pi^2 \sum_{n=-\infty}^{\infty} \bar{h}(w)\bar{a}_{nn}(w)e^{-jn\varphi} \tag{4-10}$$

Thus, if the function $G(w\sin\varphi, w\cos\varphi)$ is expanded into a Fourier series in the variable φ, the coefficients of the resulting expansion equal

$4\pi^2 \bar{h}(w) \bar{a}_{nn}(w)$.   With

$$b_{nn}(r) = \int_0^\infty w\bar{h}(w)\bar{a}_{nn}(w)J_n(rw)\ dw \qquad (4\text{-}11)$$

the inverse Hankel transform of order n of the function $\bar{h}(w)\bar{a}_{nn}(w)$, we see from (4-10) and (4-3) that

$$g(x,y) = g(r\cos\theta,\, r\sin\theta) = 2\pi \sum_{n=-\infty}^{\infty} b_{nn}(r)e^{jn\theta} \qquad (4\text{-}12)$$

Hence, the coefficients of the Fourier series expansion of $g(r\cos\theta,\, r\sin\theta)$ equal $2\pi b_{nn}(r)$.

5. PROPERTIES OF BESSEL FUNCTIONS

In this section we shall discuss certain basic properties of the Bessel functions $J_n(x)$. These functions can be defined as solutions of the differential equation (5-24)—by their series expansion (5-28) or in other ways [p4, s4, w1]. For our purposes, it is more convenient to define them as the coefficients of the Fourier expansion of the function

$$a(x,\theta) = e^{jx\sin\theta} \qquad (5\text{-}1)$$

This function is periodic in θ, with period 2π. The coefficients $J_n(x)$ of its Fourier series expansion

$$a(x,\theta) = \sum_{n=-\infty}^{\infty} J_n(x)e^{jn\theta} \qquad (5\text{-}2)$$

depend on x, and are given by

$$J_n(x) = \frac{1}{2\pi}\int_{-\pi}^{\pi} a(x,\theta)e^{-jn\theta}\ d\theta = \frac{1}{2\pi}\int_{-\pi}^{\pi} e^{\pm j(n\theta - x\sin\theta)}\ d\theta \qquad (5\text{-}3)$$

Since

$$a(x,-\theta) = a^*(x,\theta)$$

it follows that $J_n(x)$ is real, and

$$J_n(x) = \frac{1}{2\pi}\int_{-\pi}^{\pi} \cos\,(n\theta - x\sin\theta)\ d\theta \qquad (5\text{-}4)$$

Expanding the cosine, above, we easily conclude that

$$J_{2n}(x) = \frac{1}{\pi}\int_{-\pi/2}^{\pi/2} \cos\,(x\sin\theta)\cos 2n\theta\ d\theta$$

$$J_{2n+1}(x) = \frac{1}{\pi}\int_{-\pi/2}^{\pi/2} \sin\,(x\sin\theta)\sin\,(2n+1)\theta\ d\theta \qquad (5\text{-}5)$$

Hence,

$$J_o(0) = 1 \qquad J_n(0) = 0 \qquad n \neq 0 \tag{5-6}$$

$$J_n(-x) = (-1)^n J_n(x) \qquad J_{-n}(x) = (-1)^n J_n(x) \tag{5-7}$$

Equating real and imaginary parts in (5-2), we find [see (5-7)]

$$\cos (x \sin \theta) = \sum_{n=-\infty}^{\infty} J_n(x) \cos n\theta = J_o(x) + 2 \sum_{n=1}^{\infty} J_{2n}(x) \cos 2n\theta$$

$$\sin (x \sin \theta) = \sum_{n=-\infty}^{\infty} J_n(x) \sin n\theta = 2 \sum_{n=0}^{\infty} J_{2n+1}(x) \sin (2n + 1)\theta \tag{5-8}$$

With $\theta = \pi/2$, (5-8) yields

$$\cos x = J_o(x) + 2 \sum_{n=1}^{\infty} (-1)^n J_{2n}(x)$$

$$\sin x = 2 \sum_{n=0}^{\infty} (-1)^n J_{2n+1}(x) \tag{5-9}$$

Recursion formulas

We shall show that

$$J_{n-1}(x) - J_{n+1}(x) = 2J_n'(x) \tag{5-10}$$

$$J_{n-1}(x) + J_{n+1}(x) = \frac{2n}{x} J_n(x) \tag{5-11}$$

Proof   Differentiation of (5-3) yields

$$J_n'(x) = \frac{1}{2\pi} \int_{-\pi}^{\pi} (-j \sin \theta) e^{j(n\theta - x \sin \theta)} \, d\theta$$

$$= \frac{1}{4\pi} \int_{-\pi}^{\pi} (e^{-j\theta} - e^{j\theta}) e^{j(n\theta - x \sin \theta)} \, d\theta$$

and (5-10) follows.

To prove (5-11), we differentiate (5-2) with respect to θ:

$$\frac{\partial a(x,\theta)}{\partial \theta} = jx \cos \theta \, e^{jx \sin \theta} = \sum_{n=-\infty}^{\infty} jn J_n(x) e^{jn\theta}$$

Hence

$$x \frac{e^{j\theta} + e^{-j\theta}}{2} \sum_{n=-\infty}^{\infty} J_n(x) e^{jn\theta} = \sum_{n=-\infty}^{\infty} n J_n(x) e^{jn\theta}$$

The above holds for every θ; therefore, the coefficients of $e^{jn\theta}$ must be the same for both sides of the identity, and (5-11) follows.

Adding and subtracting (5-10) and (5-11), we have

$$J_{n-1}(x) = \frac{n}{x} J_n(x) + J'_n(x) \tag{5-12}$$

$$J_{n+1}(x) = \frac{n}{x} J_n(x) - J'_n(x) \tag{5-13}$$

Hence,

$$x^n J_{n-1}(x) = \frac{d}{dx} [x^n J_n(x)] \tag{5-14}$$

$$-\frac{J_{n+1}(x)}{x^n} = \frac{d}{dx} \left[\frac{J_n(x)}{x^n} \right] \tag{5-15}$$

In particular,

$$x J_o(x) = \frac{d}{dx} [x J_1(x)] \tag{5-16}$$

$$\frac{d J_o(x)}{dx} = -J_1(x) \tag{5-17}$$

With

$$R_n(x) = \frac{J_n(x)}{x^n} \tag{5-18}$$

we shall show that

$$R''_n(x) + R_n(x) = (2n + 1) R_{n+1}(x) \tag{5-19}$$

Indeed, writing (5-15) in the form

$$x R_{n+1}(x) = -R'_n(x)$$

we obtain, by differentiation,

$$R_{n+1}(x) + x R'_{n+1}(x) = -R''_n(x)$$

But [see (5-15) and (5-11)]

$$x R'_{n+1}(x) = -x^2 R_{n+2}(x) = -2(n + 1) R_{n+1}(x) + R_n(x)$$

and (5-19) follows.   This equation is used for a simple proof of Poisson's formula [Chap. 3, (1-21)].

We also note from (5-19) and (5-15) that

$$R''_n(x) + \frac{1}{x} R'_n(x) + R_n(x) = 2n R_{n+1}(x) \tag{5-20}$$

The above leads to Sonine's integral formula (1-34).

Finite integrals

From (5-12) we have, with $n = 1$,

$$\frac{J_1(x)}{x} = J_o(x) - J'_1(x)$$

Multiplying by $J_1(x) = -J_o'(x)$, we obtain

$$\frac{J_1{}^2(x)}{x} = -J_o(x)J_o'(x) - J_1(x)J_1'(x) = -\frac{1}{2}\frac{d}{dx}[J_o{}^2(x) + J_1{}^2(x)]$$

We now integrate the above from 0 to c. Since $J_o{}^2(0) + J_1{}^2(0) = 1$, the result is

$$2\int_0^c \frac{J_1{}^2(x)}{x}\,dx = 1 - J_o{}^2(c) - J_1{}^2(c) \tag{5-21}$$

We shall now establish the basic relationship [s1]

$$\int_0^c xJ_o(ax)J_o(bx)\,dx = \frac{acJ_1(ac)J_o(bc) - bcJ_1(bc)J_o(ac)}{a^2 - b^2} \tag{5-22}$$

It will then follow with $b \to a$ that

$$\int_0^c xJ_o{}^2(ax)\,dx = \frac{c^2}{2}[J_o{}^2(ac) + J_1{}^2(ac)] \tag{5-23}$$

Proof Scaling of (5-16), multiplication by $J_o(ax)$, and integration yields

$$I = \int_0^c xJ_o(ax)J_o(bx)\,dx = \frac{1}{b}\int_0^c J_o(ax)d[xJ_1(bx)]$$

Integrating by parts, we find, with $J_o'(x) = -J_1(x)$,

$$I = \frac{c}{b}J_o(ac)J_1(bc) + \frac{a}{b}\int_0^c xJ_1(ax)J_1(bx)\,dx$$

Since I is a symmetrical function of a and b, it is also given by

$$I = \frac{c}{a}J_o(bc)J_1(ac) + \frac{b}{a}\int_0^c xJ_1(ax)J_1(bx)\,dx$$

If we eliminate the integral in the last two equations, we obtain (5-22). Since

$$\frac{dJ_o(bc)}{db} = -cJ_1(bc) \qquad \frac{d[bJ_1(bc)]}{db} = bcJ_o(bc)$$

(5-23) follows from (5-22) with $b \to a$.

Differential equations

From (5-1) we have

$$\frac{\partial^2 a(x,\theta)}{\partial\theta^2} = (-x^2\cos^2\theta - jx\sin\theta)a(x,\theta)$$

$$\frac{\partial a(x,\theta)}{\partial x} = j\sin\theta\,a(x,\theta)$$

$$\frac{\partial^2 a(x,\theta)}{\partial x^2} = -\sin^2\theta\,a(x,\theta)$$

Hence,

$$x^2 \frac{\partial^2 a}{\partial x^2} + x \frac{\partial a}{\partial x} + x^2 a + \frac{\partial^2 a}{\partial \theta^2} = 0$$

Inserting (5-2) in the above, we find

$$\sum_{n=-\infty}^{\infty} [x^2 J_n''(x) + x J_n'(x) + (x^2 - n^2) J_n(x)] e^{jn\theta} = 0$$

This is an identity in θ; therefore,

$$x^2 J_n''(x) + x J_n'(x) + (x^2 - n^2) J_n(x) = 0 \tag{5-24}$$

Series expansions

With the transformation

$$e^{j\theta} = z$$

it follows from (5-1) and (5-2) that

$$e^{(x/2)(z-z^{-1})} = \sum_{n=-\infty}^{\infty} z^n J_n(x) \tag{5-25}$$

This relationship will be used to obtain the power-series expansion of $J_n(x)$. Clearly, the series

$$e^{xz/2} = 1 + z \left(\frac{x}{2}\right) + \frac{z^2}{2!} \left(\frac{x}{2}\right)^2 + \cdots + \frac{z^n}{n!} \left(\frac{x}{2}\right)^n + \cdots$$

$$e^{-xz^{-1}/2} = 1 - z^{-1} \left(\frac{x}{2}\right) + \frac{z^{-2}}{2!} \left(\frac{x}{2}\right)^2 + \cdots + (-1)^n \frac{z^{-n}}{n!} \left(\frac{x}{2}\right)^n + \cdots$$

are absolutely convergent. If we multiply them and collect terms, we obtain $J_n(x)$ as the coefficient of z^n. Thus, $J_0(x)$ is the constant term (in z):

$$J_0(x) = 1 - \left(\frac{x}{2}\right)^2 + \frac{1}{(2!)^2} \left(\frac{x}{2}\right)^4 - \cdots = \sum_{n=0}^{\infty} \frac{(-1)^n}{(n!)^2} \left(\frac{x}{2}\right)^{2n} \tag{5-26}$$

Similarly,

$$J_1(x) = \frac{x}{2} - \frac{1}{2!} \left(\frac{x}{2}\right)^3 + \frac{1}{2!3!} \left(\frac{x}{2}\right)^5 - \cdots = \sum_{n=0}^{\infty} \frac{(-1)^n}{n!(n+1)!} \left(\frac{x}{2}\right)^{2n+1} \tag{5-27}$$

and, in general,

$$J_n(x) = \sum_{m=0}^{\infty} \frac{(-1)^m}{m!(m+n)!} \left(\frac{x}{2}\right)^{n+2m} \tag{5-28}$$

Lommel's functions of two variables

We shall define the Lommel functions $U_1(a,w)$ and $U_2(a,w)$ as Hankel transforms:

$$a \cos \frac{a}{2} (1 - r^2)p_1(r) \overset{h}{\leftrightarrow} U_1(a,w)$$

$$p_1(r) = \begin{cases} 1 & r < 1 \\ 0 & r > 1 \end{cases} \qquad (5\text{-}29)$$

$$a \sin \frac{a}{2} (1 - r^2)p_1(r) \overset{h}{\leftrightarrow} U_2(a,w)$$

Thus

$$U_1(a,w) = a \int_0^1 r \cos \frac{a}{2} (1 - r^2)J_o(wr)\, dr$$

$$\qquad (5\text{-}30)$$

$$U_2(a,w) = a \int_0^1 r \sin \frac{a}{2} (1 - r^2)J_o(wr)\, dr$$

Expanding the cosine in (5-30), interchanging summation and integration, and using (1-33), we obtain

$$U_1(a,w) = a \sum_{n=0}^{\infty} \frac{(-1)^n}{(2n)!} \int_0^1 rJ_o(wr) \left(\frac{a}{2}\right)^{2n} (1 - r^2)^{2n}\, dr$$

$$= a \sum_{n=0}^{\infty} \frac{(-1)^n}{(2n)!} \left(\frac{a}{2}\right)^{2n} 2^{2n}(2n)! \frac{J_{2n+1}(w)}{w^{2n+1}}$$

Therefore,

$$U_1(a,w) = \sum_{n=0}^{\infty} (-1)^n \left(\frac{a}{w}\right)^{2n+1} J_{2n+1}(w) \qquad (5\text{-}31)$$

Reasoning similarly, we have

$$U_2(a,w) = a \sum_{n=0}^{\infty} \frac{(-1)^n}{(2n + 1)!} \int_0^1 rJ_o(wr) \left(\frac{a}{2}\right)^{2n+1} (1 - r^2)^{2n+1}\, dr$$

$$= a \sum_{n=0}^{\infty} \frac{(-1)^n}{(2n + 1)!} \left(\frac{a}{2}\right)^{2n+1} 2^{2n+1}(2n + 1)! \frac{J_{2n+2}(w)}{w^{2n+2}}$$

Hence

$$U_2(a,w) = \sum_{n=0}^{\infty} (-1)^n \left(\frac{a}{w}\right)^{2n+2} J_{2n+2}(w) \qquad (5\text{-}32)$$

It is easy to see from (5-30) that

$$U_1(-a,w) = -U_1(a,w) \qquad U_2(-a,w) = U_2(a,w) \qquad (5\text{-}33)$$

From the above and (5-29) it follows that

$$p_1(r)e^{j\frac{a}{2}(1 - r^2)} \overset{h}{\leftrightarrow} \frac{1}{a} [U_1(a,w) + jU_2(a,w)] \qquad (5\text{-}34)$$

Hence,

$$p_1(r)e^{j\frac{a}{2}r^2} \overset{h}{\leftrightarrow} \frac{e^{ja/2}}{a}[U_1(a,w) - jU_2(a,w)] \tag{5-35}$$

We also note that

$$U_1(a,a) = \sum_{n=0}^{\infty} (-1)^n J_{2n+1}(a) = \frac{\sin a}{2}$$

$$\tag{5-36}$$

$$U_2(a,a) = -\sum_{n=1}^{\infty} (-1)^n J_{2n}(a) = \tfrac{1}{2}[J_o(a) - \cos a]$$

This follows from (5-31), (5-32), and (5-9).

PROBLEMS

5-1. Show that

(a) $\dfrac{\sin cr}{r} \overset{h}{\leftrightarrow} \dfrac{p_c(w)}{\sqrt{c^2 - w^2}}$ where $p_c(w) = \begin{cases} 1 & |w| < c \\ 0 & |w| > c \end{cases}$

Hint: Set $a = jc$ in (1-31).

(b) $(c^2 - r^2)p_c(r) \overset{h}{\leftrightarrow} \dfrac{4c}{w^3}J_1(cw) - \dfrac{2c^2}{w^2}J_o(cw)J_2(cw)$

(c) $r^2 e^{-ar^2} \overset{h}{\leftrightarrow} \dfrac{1}{2a^2}\left(1 - \dfrac{w^2}{4a}\right)e^{-w^2/4a}$

(d) $J_o(ar)\dfrac{J_1(br)}{r} \overset{h}{\leftrightarrow} \begin{cases} \dfrac{1}{b} & w < |b - a| \\ \dfrac{\theta}{\pi b} & |b - a| < w < b + a \\ 0 & w > b + a \end{cases}$

where θ is the angle in Fig. P5-1.

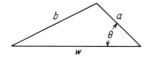

Fig. P5-1

5-2. Show that

$$f(r) ** \delta(r - r_1) = r_1 \int_0^{2\pi} f(\sqrt{r^2 + r_1^2 - 2rr_1 \cos\theta})\,d\theta$$

where $r = \sqrt{x^2 + y^2}$. Using the above, prove that

$$\int_0^{2\pi} J_o(\sqrt{r^2 + r_1^2 - 2rr_1 \cos\theta})\,d\theta = 2\pi J_o(r_1)J_1(r)$$

5-3. Show that if $J_o(x_n) = 0$, then for any a, the average of $J_o(\sqrt{x^2 + y^2})$ over the circle $(x - a)^2 + y^2 = x_n{}^2$ equals zero.

5-4. Using (2-4) and Chap. 2, (3-59), show that if

$$f(x) \leftrightarrow F(u) \qquad f(r) \overset{h}{\leftrightarrow} \bar{f}(w)$$

and $F(u) = k\bar{f}(u)$, then $f(x) = Ae^{-\alpha x^2}$.

5-5. Using the fact that if

$$f(r) \overset{h}{\leftrightarrow} \bar{f}(w)$$

then

$$\int_{-\infty}^{\infty} f(r) \, dy \leftrightarrow 2\pi \bar{f}(w)$$

where $r = \sqrt{x^2 + y^2}$ [see (2-4)], show that

$$\int_{-\infty}^{\infty} \frac{J_1(r)}{r} \, dy = \frac{2 \sin x}{x} \qquad \int_{-\infty}^{\infty} \frac{\sin r}{r} \, dy = \pi J_o(x)$$

Verify Chap. 2, (3-52), for $h(r) = J_1(r)/r$.

5-6. Given a system with point spread $h(r)$ and line spread $s(x)$, we form another system with line spread $s''(x)$. Using (2-4), show that its point spread equals $h''(r) + h'(r)/r$.

5-7. Consider a memoryless system with input $x(t)$ and output $g[x(t)]$. If $x(t) = a \cos \omega t$, then the average

$$\frac{1}{T} \int_{-T/2}^{T/2} g(a \cos \omega t) \, dt = z(a) \qquad T = \frac{2\pi}{\omega}$$

of the output is a function of a. Using (2-10), show that if $g(-x) = g(x)$, then

$$g(x) = z(0) + x \int_0^{\pi/2} z'(x \cos \theta) \, d\theta$$

5-8. (Fourier-Bessel series) Show that

$$2 \sum_{n=1}^{\infty} \frac{J_o(x_n r/a)}{x_n J_1(x_n)} = 1 \qquad 8a^2 \sum_{n=1}^{\infty} \frac{J_1(x_n)}{x_n{}^3} J_o\left(\frac{x_n r}{a}\right) = a^2 - r^2$$

for $|r| < a$, where x_n are the roots of $J_o(x)$.

5-9. Suppose that the Hankel transform of $f(r)$ equals zero for $w > w_o$. With r_i the roots of $J_o(w_o r)$, show that

$$\int_0^{\infty} r f(r) \, dr = \frac{2}{w_o{}^2} \sum_{i=1}^{\infty} \frac{f(r_i)}{J_1{}^2(w_o r_i)}$$

5-10. Show that if

$$a_n(r) \overset{h_n}{\leftrightarrow} \bar{a}_n(w) \qquad b_n(r) \overset{h_n}{\leftrightarrow} \bar{b}_n(w)$$

then

$$\int_0^{\infty} r a_n(r) b_n^*(r) \, dr = \int_0^{\infty} w \bar{a}_n(w) \bar{b}_n^*(w) \, dw$$

5-11. Show that

(a) $\displaystyle\int_0^\infty J_n(x)\,dx = 1 \qquad n \geq 0$

(b) $\displaystyle\int_0^\infty \frac{J_n(x)}{x}\,dx = \frac{1}{n} \qquad n \geq 1$

(c) $\displaystyle J_n{}^2(x) = \frac{1}{\pi}\int_0^\pi J_{2n}(2x\cos\theta)\,d\theta$

(d) $\displaystyle\frac{2}{\pi}\int_{-\pi/2}^{\pi/2} \cos^2\theta\, e^{-jx\sin\theta}\,d\theta = J_o(x) + J_2(x) = \frac{2J_1(x)}{x}$

5-12. Show that

(a) $\displaystyle J_2(x) = J_o(x) - 2J_o''(x) = -J_o(x) - \frac{2}{x}J_o'(x)$

(b) $\displaystyle J_o{}^2(x) + 2\sum_{n=1}^\infty J_n{}^2(x) = 1$

(c) $\displaystyle J_n(x+y) = \sum_{k=-\infty}^\infty J_k(x)J_{n-k}(y)$

5-13. Show that the function $J_o{}^2(x) + J_1{}^2(x)$ is monotone decreasing.

5-14. Show that [see also (5-22)]

$$\int_0^c xJ_n(ax)J_n(bx)\,dx = \frac{c}{a^2 - b^2}\,[aJ_{n+1}(ac)J_n(bc) - bJ_{n+1}(bc)J_n(ac)]$$

5-15. (a) Show that all roots of $J_o(x)$ are simple.
    Hint: Use (5-17) and (5-21).
    (b) Show that for any k, the function $f(x) = xJ_o'(x) + kJ_o(x)$ has a root between any two roots of $J_o(x)$.

5-16. Show that

(a) $\displaystyle |1 - J_o(x)| \leq \frac{x^2}{4}$

(b) If

$$f(r) \overset{h}{\leftrightarrow} \bar{f}(w) \qquad \bar{f}(w) \geq 0 \qquad \text{and} \qquad \bar{f}(w) = 0 \qquad \text{for } w > a$$

then

$$f(0) - f(r) \leq \frac{r^2}{4}\int_0^a w^3\bar{f}(w)\,dw = \frac{r^2}{2}\,|f''(0)| \leq \frac{a^2r^2}{4}f(0)$$

5-17. (Lommel's functions) With

$$U_m(a,w) = \sum_{n=0}^\infty (-1)^n \left(\frac{a}{w}\right)^{2n+m} J_{2n+m}(w)$$

$$V_m(a,w) = \sum_{n=0}^\infty (-1)^n \left(\frac{a}{w}\right)^{-2n-m} J_{-2n-m}(w)$$ (i)

show that

(a) $\displaystyle U_n(a,w) - V_{-n+2}(a,w) = \cos\left(\frac{a}{2} + \frac{w^2}{2a} - \frac{n\pi}{2}\right)$

$$U_{n+1}(a,w) - V_{-n+1}(a,w) = \sin\left(\frac{a}{2} + \frac{w^2}{2a} - \frac{n\pi}{2}\right)$$ (ii)

Hint: Making the substitutions $x = w$, $z = ja/w$ in (5-25), show that

$$e^{j(a/2 + w^2/2a - n\pi/2)} = \sum_{r=-\infty}^{\infty} j^r \left(\frac{a}{w}\right)^{r+n} J_{r+n}(w) \tag{iii}$$

(b) $$U_n(a,w) + U_{n+2}(a,w) = \left(\frac{a}{w}\right)^n J_n(w)$$

$$V_n(a,w) + V_{n+2}(a,w) = \left(\frac{a}{w}\right)^{-n} J_{-n}(w) \tag{iv}$$

(c) $$\left(\frac{\partial^2}{\partial w^2} - \frac{1}{w}\frac{\partial}{\partial w} + \frac{a^2}{w^2}\right) U_n(a,w) = \left(\frac{a}{w}\right)^{n-2} J_n(w)$$

$$\left(\frac{\partial^2}{\partial w^2} - \frac{1}{w}\frac{\partial}{\partial w} + \frac{a^2}{w^2}\right) V_n(a,w) = \left(\frac{a}{w}\right)^{n} J_{-n+2}(w) \tag{v}$$

5-18. (Dini series) With k an arbitrary constant and $\gamma_1, \gamma_2, \ldots$, the positive roots of the equation

$$xJ_1(x) = kJ_0(x)$$

show that if

$$f(r) = \sum_{n=1}^{\infty} c_n J_0(\gamma_n r) \qquad 0 < r < 1$$

then

$$c_n = \frac{2\gamma_n^2}{k^2 + \gamma_n^2} \int_0^1 rf(r)J_0(\gamma_n r)\,dr$$

6

BAND-LIMITED SIGNALS AND UNCERTAINTY PRINCIPLE

In the first two sections of this chapter we introduce a method for evaluating the errors in a variety of numerical approximations. The analysis utilizes the system concept (operator), and is based on bounds of the system response in terms of the energy of the input. In Sec. 3 we discuss the uncertainty principle in Fourier analysis, and we extend it to two dimensions and Hankel transforms. In Sec. 4 we solve the problem of pulse compression, spectral analysis, and real time scaling. The proposed solutions are surprising consequences of corresponding optical phenomena (Chap. 11, Sec. 2). In the last section we develop the generalized uncertainty principle (maximum enclosed energy of band-limited signals). The results are utilized in the apodization problem and in image restoration (Chap. 11, Secs. 4 and 5).

1. LIMITS OF BAND-LIMITED SIGNALS, WITH APPLICATIONS IN NUMERICAL ANALYSIS†

In many areas of engineering and applied sciences, a recurring task is the simplification of various operations by suitable approximations: deriva-

† A. Papoulis, *Proc. IEEE*, vol. 55, pp. 1677–1686, October, 1967.

tives by differences, integrals by sums, infinite series by finite truncations, and others. Such approximations are meaningful only if the resulting errors are small in some sense, and a basic problem in numerical analysis is to establish realistic bounds to these errors. With few exceptions, this problem is difficult, and in most cases it is avoided by using, in truncations for example, a "sufficiently large" number of terms, or, in quadratures, "small enough" intervals. An interval is small, of course, only in comparison with some relevant unit depending on the rate of change of the signals under consideration. It is, therefore, natural to relate the errors to the bandwidths of these signals [see (1-21)]. In this section, we establish simple bounds for errors involving linear functionals of band-limited functions. The assumption of band-limitedness, even though realistic, is restrictive; but, as we shall show, it leads to simple results in a large number of applications.

SCHWARZ' INEQUALITY

In this chapter, we shall extensively use the following inequality:

$$\left| \int_a^b f_1(t) f_2(t) \, dt \right|^2 \leq \int_a^b |f_1(t)|^2 \, dt \int_a^b |f_2(t)|^2 \, dt \tag{1-1}$$

which is valid for any functions, real or complex, that are square-integrable in the interval (a,b). In two dimensions, (1-1) takes the form

$$\left| \iint_R f_1(x,y) f_2(x,y) \, dx \, dy \right|^2 \leq \iint_R |f_1(x,y)|^2 \, dx \, dy \iint_R |f_2(x,y)|^2 \, dx \, dy \tag{1-2}$$

The above relationships hold with the equality sign only if f_1 is proportional to f_2^* (almost) everywhere in the region of integration

$$f_1 \equiv k f_2^* \tag{1-3}$$

Proof We shall prove (1-1); the proof of (1-2) is identical. Denoting by φ the phase angle of the first integral in (1-1), we have

$$\int_a^b f_1 f_2 \, dt = \left| \int_a^b f_1 f_2 \, dt \right| e^{j\varphi} \tag{1-4}$$

With x a real constant, we form the quadratic

$$\begin{aligned}
\int_a^b |f_1 - x e^{j\varphi} f_2^*|^2 \, dt &= \int_a^b |f_1|^2 \, dt \\
&\quad - x \left[e^{-j\varphi} \int_a^b f_1 f_2 \, dt + e^{j\varphi} \int_a^b f_1^* f_2^* \, dt \right] + x^2 \int_a^b |f_2|^2 \, dt \\
&= \int_a^b |f_1|^2 \, dt - 2x \left| \int_a^b f_1 f_2 \, dt \right| + x^2 \int_a^b |f_2|^2 \, dt \geq 0
\end{aligned}$$

The last equality follows from (1-4). The above quadratic is nonnegative for any x; hence, its discriminant must be less than or equal to zero, and (1-1) follows.

If the discriminant equals zero, i.e., if (1-1) holds with the equality sign, then for some $x = x_o$, the quadratic must be zero

$$\int_a^b |f_1 - x_o e^{j\varphi} f_2^*|^2 \, dt = 0$$

and with

$$k = x_o e^{j\varphi}$$

(1-3) results.

MAXIMUM RESPONSE OF LINEAR SYSTEMS

As we show in the applications of this section, the investigation of a variety of numerical operations can be simplified if these operations are viewed as responses of suitably conceived linear systems. The connection between linear systems and numerical operations is not immediately evident. However, once it is recognized, it suggests a unified treatment of a large number of seemingly unrelated problems.

Consider a band-limited signal $f(t)$,

$$f(t) \leftrightarrow F(\omega) \qquad F(\omega) = 0 \qquad \text{for } |\omega| \geq \omega_o \tag{1-5}$$

which has energy E,

$$E = \int_{-\infty}^{\infty} |f(t)|^2 \, dt = \frac{1}{2\pi} \int_{-\omega_o}^{\omega_o} |F(\omega)|^2 \, d\omega \tag{1-6}$$

and a linear system with impulse response $h(t)$ and system function $H(\omega)$:

$$h(t) \leftrightarrow H(\omega)$$

We shall establish a bound for the output

$$g(t) = \frac{1}{2\pi} \int_{-\omega_o}^{\omega_o} F(\omega) H(\omega) e^{j\omega t} \, d\omega \tag{1-7}$$

in terms of the energy E of the input $f(t)$.

Applying Schwarz' inequality to the integral in (1-7), we obtain

$$|g(t)|^2 \leq \frac{1}{4\pi^2} \int_{-\omega_o}^{\omega_o} |F(\omega)|^2 \, d\omega \int_{-\omega_o}^{\omega_o} |H(\omega) e^{j\omega t}|^2 \, d\omega \tag{1-8}$$

Hence,

$$|g(t)|^2 \leq \frac{E}{2\pi} \int_{-\omega_o}^{\omega_o} |H(\omega)|^2 \, d\omega \tag{1-9}$$

Thus, the maximum of $|g(t)|$ is bounded by the mean-square value of $H(\omega)$ in the band of the input.

We now assume that the quantities E, ω_o, and $H(\omega)$ are specified, and we want to find a band-limited signal $f_o(t)$ such that its response $g(t_o)$

at the given time t_o is maximum. For this to be the case, (1-8) must hold with the equality sign for $t = t_o$. As we see from (1-3), this is possible only if the Fourier transform $F_o(\omega)$ of $f_o(t)$ is proportional to the conjugate of

$$H(\omega)e^{j\omega t_o}$$

for every ω in the interval of integration. Since $F_o(\omega)$ is zero for $|\omega| \geq \omega_o$, we thus conclude that

$$F_o(\omega) = AH^*(\omega)e^{-j\omega t_o}p_{\omega_o}(\omega) \tag{1-10}$$

where $p_{\omega_o}(\omega)$ is a pulse (as in Fig. 1-1). The constant A is such as to make the energy of $f_o(t)$ equal E. Since

$$h^*(-t) \leftrightarrow H^*(\omega) \qquad h^*(t_o - t) \leftrightarrow H^*(\omega)e^{j\omega t_o}$$

and

$$\frac{\sin \omega_o t}{\pi t} \leftrightarrow p_{\omega_o}(\omega)$$

it follows from (1-10) and the convolution theorem that

$$f_o(t) = Ah^*(t_o - t) * \frac{\sin \omega_o t}{\pi t} \tag{1-11}$$

The matched filter principle   If no restriction is imposed on the spectrum of the input, then $\omega_o = \infty$. In this case [see (1-10)],

$$F_o(\omega) = AH^*(\omega)e^{-j\omega t_o}$$

Hence, the optimum input is given by (Fig. 1-2), that is,

$$f_o(t) = Ah^*(t_o - t) \tag{1-12}$$

and (1-9) yields

$$|g(t)| \leq E \int_{-\infty}^{\infty} |h(t)|^2 \, dt$$

The above is equivalent to the matched filter principle.

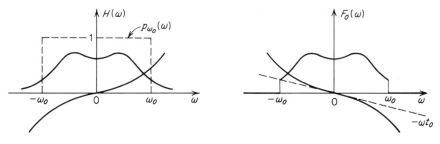

Fig. 1-1

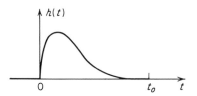
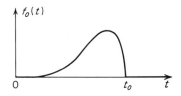

Fig. 1-2

APPLICATIONS

The preceding results will now be applied to a variety of numerical operations involving the band-limited signal $f(t)$.

Signal bounds   If

$$H(\omega) = 1 \qquad \text{then} \qquad f(t) = g(t)$$

In this case, (1-9) yields

$$|f(t)| \leq \sqrt{\frac{E\omega_o}{\pi}} \tag{1-13}$$

Thus, a band-limited function must remain less than $\sqrt{E\omega_o/\pi}$. From (1-11) it follows that this bound is reached for $t = t_o$ only if

$$f(t) = f_o(t) = \sqrt{\frac{E}{\pi\omega_o}} \frac{\sin \omega_o(t - t_o)}{t - t_o} \tag{1-14}$$

We note that

$$|f(t)| \leq |f_o(t_o)| = \sqrt{\frac{E\omega_o}{\pi}} \tag{1-15}$$

Increment bounds   We shall now establish bounds on the variation $f(t + \tau) - f(t)$ of the signal $f(t)$. Clearly, this variation can be considered as the output

$$g(t) = f(t + \tau) - f(t) \tag{1-16}$$

of a system with input $f(t)$ and system function

$$H(\omega) = e^{j\omega\tau} - 1 \tag{1-17}$$

Since

$$|H(\omega)| = 2 \left| \sin \frac{\omega\tau}{2} \right|$$

we have

$$\int_{-\omega_o}^{\omega_o} |H(\omega)|^2 \, d\omega = \frac{4}{\tau} (\omega_o\tau - \sin \omega_o\tau)$$

and (1-9) yields (Fig. 1-3)

$$|f(t + \tau) - f(t)| \leq \sqrt{\frac{2E\omega_o}{\pi}\left(1 - \frac{\sin \omega_o\tau}{\omega_o\tau}\right)} \tag{1-18}$$

The above holds with the equality sign for $t = t_o$ only if [see (1-10)]

$$f(t) = f_o(t) = A[k(t - \tau - t_o) - k(t - t_o)] \tag{1-19}$$

where

$$k(t) = \frac{\sin \omega_o t}{\pi t} \tag{1-20}$$

We note from (1-18) that

$$|f(t + \tau) - f(t)| < \omega_o\tau \sqrt{\frac{E\omega_o}{3\pi}} \tag{1-21}$$

Truncated Taylor series In the following, we shall need the interesting inequality (Prob. 6-2)

$$\left| e^{jx} - \left[1 + jx + \cdots + \frac{(jx)^{n-1}}{(n-1)!}\right]\right| \leq \frac{|x|^n}{n!} \tag{1-22}$$

which is valid for every real x.

Suppose that the function $f(t)$ has derivatives of order up to $n - 1$. If $f(t + \tau)$ is approximated by the first n terms of its Taylor expansion, the error

$$g(t) = f(t + \tau) - \left[f(t) + f'(t)\tau + \cdots + f^{(n-1)}(t)\frac{\tau^{n-1}}{(n-1)!}\right] \tag{1-23}$$

results, and our objective is to bound it.

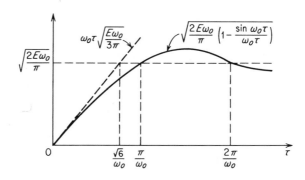

Fig. 1-3

Clearly, $g(t)$ can be considered as the output of a system with input $f(t)$ and system function

$$H(\omega) = e^{j\omega\tau} - \left[1 + j\omega\tau + \cdots + \frac{(j\omega\tau)^{n-1}}{(n-1)!} \right] \tag{1-24}$$

From (1-22) it follows that

$$\int_{-\omega_o}^{\omega_o} |H(\omega)|^2 \, d\omega \leq \frac{\tau^{2n}}{(n!)^2} \int_{-\omega_o}^{\omega_o} \omega^{2n} \, d\omega = \frac{2\omega_o(\omega_o\tau)^{2n}}{(2n+1)(n!)^2}$$

and (1-9) yields

$$|g(t)| \leq \frac{(\omega_o\tau)^n}{n!} \sqrt{\frac{E\omega_o}{\pi(2n+1)}} \tag{1-25}$$

Inequality (1-21) is a special case.

Comment   If $f(t + \tau)$ is approximated by a linear combination of its first n derivatives, the truncated Taylor series is not optimum. Suppose that another set of coefficients is chosen. The resulting error is then given by

$$e(t) = f(t + \tau) - \sum_{i=0}^{n-1} a_i f^{(i)}(t)$$

From the preceding discussion it follows that the maximum value of $|e(t)|$ is minimum if the constants a_i are selected such that they minimize the mean-square error

$$\int_{-\omega_o}^{\omega_o} \left| e^{j\omega\tau} - \sum_{i=0}^{n-1} a_i(j\omega)^i \right|^2 \, d\omega$$

of the approximation of $e^{j\omega\tau}$ by a polynomial (elaborate).

Derivatives   The nth derivative

$$g(t) = \frac{d^n f(t)}{dt^n}$$

of a signal $f(t)$ is the output of a system with input $f(t)$ and system function

$$H(\omega) = (j\omega)^n \tag{1-26}$$

Since

$$\int_{-\omega_o}^{\omega_o} |H(\omega)|^2 \, d\omega = \frac{2\omega_o^{2n+1}}{2n+1}$$

it follows from (1-9) that

$$\left| \frac{d^n f(t)}{dt^n} \right| \le \omega_o{}^n \sqrt{\frac{E\omega_o}{(2n+1)\pi}} \tag{1-27}$$

Equality holds for $t = t_o$ only if

$$f(t) = A \frac{d^n k(t - t_o)}{dt^n}$$

where $k(t)$ is given by (1-20). For $n = 1$, (1-27) yields

$$\left| \frac{df(t)}{dt} \right| \le \omega_o \sqrt{\frac{E\omega_o}{3\pi}} \tag{1-28}$$

This follows also from (1-21) with $\tau \to 0$.

Truncated sampling expansion We shall now bound the truncation error in the sampling expansion [Chap. 4, (4-2)] of a band-limited signal $f(t)$:

$$f(t + \tau) = \sum_{n=-\infty}^{\infty} f(t + nT) \frac{\sin \omega_o(\tau - nT)}{\omega_o(\tau - nT)} \qquad T = \frac{\pi}{\omega_o} \tag{1-29}$$

If, in the above expansion, a finite number of terms is used, then the error

$$e_N(t + \tau) = f(t + \tau) - \sum_{n=-N}^{N} f(t + nT) \frac{\sin \omega_o(\tau - nT)}{\omega_o(\tau - nT)} \tag{1-30}$$

results. This error can be considered as the output of a system with input $f(t)$ and system function

$$H(\omega) = e^{j\omega\tau} - \sum_{n=-N}^{N} e^{jnT\omega} \frac{\sin \omega_o(\tau - nT)}{\omega_o(\tau - nT)} \tag{1-31}$$

Hence [see (1-9)]

$$|e_N(t + \tau)|^2 \le \frac{E}{2\pi} \int_{-\omega_o}^{\omega_o} \left| e^{j\omega\tau} - \sum_{n=-N}^{N} e^{jnT\omega} \frac{\sin \omega_o(\tau - nT)}{\omega_o(\tau - nT)} \right|^2 d\omega \tag{1-32}$$

This result has the following interpretation. If the exponential

$$e^{j\omega\tau}$$

is expanded into a Fourier series in the interval $(-\omega_o, \omega_o)$, then the coefficients of the resulting expansion are given by

$$a_n = \frac{1}{2\omega_o} \int_{-\omega_o}^{\omega_o} e^{j\omega\tau} e^{-jnT\omega} \, d\omega = \frac{\sin \omega_o(\tau - nT)}{\omega_o(\tau - nT)} \tag{1-33}$$

Comparing with (1-31), we conclude that $H(\omega)$ equals the error in the approximation of $e^{j\omega\tau}$ by a truncated Fourier series, and the integral in (1-32) equals the mean-square value of this error. From this observation and Parseval's formula [Chap. 4, (2-10)] it follows that

$$|e_N(t + \tau)|^2 \leq \frac{E\omega_o}{\pi} \sum_{|n|>N} \frac{\sin^2 \omega_o(\tau - nT)}{\omega_o^2(\tau - nT)^2} \tag{1-34}$$

Comment From the preceding discussion we conclude that if a signal $f(t)$ is approximated by a linear combination of its $2N + 1$ values $f(nT)$, then the maximum of the resulting error is minimum if the coefficients of the interpolation formula are given by (1-33).

Optimum slope Suppose that the derivative of $f(t)$ is approximated by a linear combination of $f(t)$ and $f(t - \tau)$. In such an approximation, the error

$$g(t) = \frac{df(t)}{dt} - [af(t) - bf(t - \tau)] \tag{1-35}$$

results, and it is usually assumed that

$$a = b = \frac{1}{\tau} \tag{1-36}$$

We shall determine the maximum of $|g(t)|$ and the values of a and b that minimize this maximum.

As we see from (1-35), the system function yielding $g(t)$ as output is given by

$$H(\omega) = j\omega - a + be^{-j\omega\tau} \tag{1-37}$$

Inserting the integral

$$\int_{-\omega_o}^{\omega_o} |H(\omega)|^2 \, d\omega = \frac{2\omega_o^3}{3} + 2\omega_o(a^2 + b^2) - 4ab \frac{\sin \omega_o\tau}{\tau}$$
$$- \frac{4b}{\tau^2} (\sin \omega_o\tau - \omega_o\tau \cos \omega_o\tau)$$

into (1-9), we find the maximum of $|g(t)|$.

It is easy to see that the above integral is minimum if

$$b = \omega_o \frac{\sin \omega_o\tau - \omega_o \cos \omega_o\tau}{\omega_o^2\tau^2 - \sin^2 \omega_o\tau} = \frac{1}{\tau}\left(1 - \frac{\omega_o^2\tau^2}{20} + \cdots\right)$$
$$a = b \frac{\sin \omega_o\tau}{\omega_o\tau} = \frac{1}{\tau}\left(1 - \frac{13\omega_o^2\tau^2}{60} + \cdots\right)$$

These quantities tend to $1/\tau$ with $\tau \to 0$.

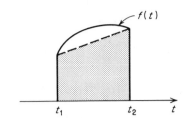

Fig. 1-4

Quadrature Consider, finally, the familiar formula (Fig. 1-4)

$$\int_{t_1}^{t_2} f(t)\, dt \simeq \frac{t_2 - t_1}{2} [f(t_1) + f(t_2)] \tag{1-38}$$

which approximates an integral by the area of a trapezoid. To apply the system concept in the evaluation of the resulting error, we introduce the variables

$$t = \frac{t_2 + t_1}{2} \qquad T = \frac{t_2 - t_1}{2}$$

If an arbitrary factor is inserted in the right side of (1-38), then the error takes the form

$$g(t) = \int_{t-T}^{t+T} f(\tau)\, d\tau - A[f(t + T) + f(t - T)] \tag{1-39}$$

It is easy to see that $g(t)$ is the output of a system with input $f(t)$ and system function

$$H(\omega) = \frac{2 \sin \omega T}{\omega} - A(e^{j\omega T} + e^{-j\omega T})$$

Again, $g(t)$ is bounded by (1-9), where

$$\int_{-\omega_o}^{\omega_o} |H(\omega)|^2 \, d\omega = 4 \int_{-\omega_o}^{\omega_o} \frac{\sin^2 \omega T}{\omega^2} \, d\omega + 4A^2 \int_{-\omega_o}^{\omega_o} \cos^2 \omega T \, d\omega$$
$$- 4A \int_{-\omega_o}^{\omega_o} \frac{\sin 2\omega T}{\omega} \, d\omega$$

This quantity is minimum if

$$A = \frac{2T \int_0^{\omega_o} (\sin 2\omega T / \omega)\, d\omega}{2\omega_o T + \sin 2\omega_o T} = T \left(1 + \frac{\omega_o^2 T^2}{9} + \cdots \right)$$

If T is small, then $A = T$, as in (1-38).

MATCHED FILTER WITH CONSTRAINTS

As a last application of Schwarz' inequality, we shall solve the following problem.

Given two constants E and t_o, and $n + 1$ real functions

$$h(t), \varphi_1(t), \ldots, \varphi_n(t)$$

we form the class C of signals $f(t)$ such that

$$\int_{-\infty}^{\infty} |f(t)|^2 \, dt = E \tag{1-40}$$

$$\int_{-\infty}^{\infty} f(t)\varphi_i(t) \, dt = 0 \qquad i = 1, \ldots, n \tag{1-41}$$

If $f(t)$ is the input to a system with impulse response $h(t)$, then the resulting output is

$$g(t) = \int_{-\infty}^{\infty} f(\tau)h(t - \tau) \, d\tau \tag{1-42}$$

Our problem is to find a function $f_o(t)$ of the class C such that $|g(t_o)|$ is maximum.

Solution   We maintain that the optimum $f_o(t)$ is given by

$$f_o(t) = A[h^*(t_o - t) + \epsilon_1\varphi_1^*(t) + \cdots + \epsilon_n\varphi_n^*(t)] \tag{1-43}$$

where the constants ϵ_i are the solutions of the n equations

$$\int_{-\infty}^{\infty} [h^*(t_o - t) + \epsilon_1\varphi_1^*(t) + \cdots + \epsilon_n\varphi_n^*(t)]\varphi_i(t) \, dt = 0$$

$$i = 1, \ldots, n \tag{1-44}$$

and A is a constant determined from (1-40).

Proof   From (1-41) and (1-42) it follows that

$$g(t_o) = \int_{-\infty}^{\infty} f(t)[h(t_o - t) + \epsilon_1^*\varphi_1(t) + \cdots + \epsilon_n^*\varphi_n(t)] \, dt \tag{1-45}$$

Therefore (Schwarz' inequality),

$$|g(t_o)|^2 \leq E \int_{-\infty}^{\infty} |h(t_o - t) + \epsilon_1^*\varphi_1(t) + \cdots + \epsilon_n^*\varphi_n(t)|^2 \, dt$$

Equality holds only if $f(t)$ is proportional to the conjugate of the bracket in (1-45).   This quantity is a function of the class C [see (1-44)]; hence (1-43) follows.

Comments   The energy of the signal

$$h(t_o - t) + a_1\varphi_1(t) + \cdots + a_n\varphi_n(t)$$

considered as a function of the coefficients a_i is minimum if $a_i = \epsilon_i^*$.

If no integral constraints are imposed on $f(t)$, then $f_o(t)$ equals $h^*(t_o - t)$, as in (1-12).

Specified zero crossings

In many applications (for example, in the problem of eliminating inter-symbol interference), it is desirable to select $f(t)$ such that the response

$g(t)$ crosses the t axis at specified points t_i, that is,

$$g(t_i) = 0 \qquad i = 1, \ldots, n \qquad (1\text{-}46)$$

and $|g(t_o)|$ is maximum. Since

$$g(t_i) = \int_{-\infty}^{\infty} f(t)h(t_i - t)\, dt$$

condition (1-46) is equivalent to the integral constraint (1-41), provided that

$$\varphi_i(t) = h(t_i - t)$$

Hence $f_o(t)$ is again given by (1-43), where the constants ϵ_i are the solutions of

$$\int_{-\infty}^{\infty} [h^*(t_o - t) + \epsilon_1 h^*(t_1 - t) + \cdots$$
$$+ \epsilon_n h^*(t_n - t)]h(t_i - t)\, dt = 0 \quad (1\text{-}47)$$

This expression can be simplified. With

$$\rho(\tau) = \int_{-\infty}^{\infty} h(t + \tau)h^*(t)\, dt = h(\tau) * h^*(-\tau)$$

the autocorrelation of $h(t)$ [see Chap. 3, (2-12)], (1-47) is equivalent to

$$\rho(t_i - t_o) + \epsilon_1 \rho(t_i - t_1) + \cdots + \epsilon_n \rho(t_i - t_n) = 0$$
$$i = 1, \ldots, n \quad (1\text{-}48)$$

A similar solution results if (1-46) is replaced by the vanishing of the derivatives of $g(t)$ at specified points or by any other linear functionals.

Apodization To conclude, we note that other optimization problems can be solved using the preceding method. As an application, we shall present an example that is relevant to the discussion of Chap. 11, Sec. 5.

We want to find a signal $g(t)$ of energy E with band-limited transform

$$G(\omega) = 0 \qquad \text{for } |\omega| > 1 \qquad (1\text{-}49)$$

such that $|g(0)|$ is maximum and subject to the constraints

$$g(\alpha) = 0 \qquad g(-\alpha) = 0 \qquad (1\text{-}50)$$

Solution Consider an ideal low-pass system with cutoff frequency $\omega = 1$ and impulse response

$$h(t) = \frac{\sin t}{\pi t}$$

From assumption (1-49) it follows that if $g(t)$ is the input to this system, the resulting response will equal $g(t)$. Therefore, the desired signal equals

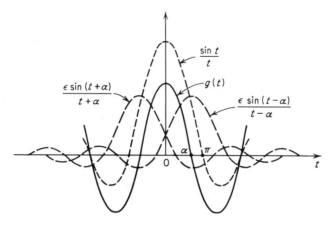

Fig. 1-5

the optimum function $f_o(t)$ of the preceding discussion where

$$t_1 = \alpha \qquad t_2 = -\alpha \qquad t_o = 0$$

and

$$\varphi_1(t) = \frac{\sin (\alpha - t)}{\pi(\alpha - t)} \qquad \varphi_2(t) = \frac{\sin (-\alpha - t)}{\pi(-\alpha - t)}$$

Hence (Fig. 1-5)

$$g(t) = A \left[\frac{\sin t}{t} + \epsilon_1 \frac{\sin (t - \alpha)}{t - \alpha} + \epsilon_2 \frac{\sin (t + \alpha)}{t + \alpha} \right] \tag{1-51}$$

Inserting into (1-50), we conclude that

$$\epsilon_1 = \epsilon_2 = -\frac{\sin \alpha/\alpha}{1 + \sin 2\alpha/2\alpha} \tag{1-52}$$

Vanishing derivatives Suppose now that condition (1-50) is replaced by

$$g''(\gamma) = 0 \qquad g''(-\gamma) = 0 \tag{1-53}$$

Since

$$g''(t) = \int_{-\infty}^{\infty} f(\tau) h''(t - \tau) \, d\tau$$

we conclude from (1-43), with

$$\varphi_1(t) = h''(\gamma - t) \qquad \varphi_2(t) = h''(\gamma + t) \qquad h(t) = \frac{\sin t}{t}$$

that the optimum $g(t)$ is given by

$$g(t) = h(t) - \epsilon[h''(\gamma - t) + h''(\gamma + t)] \tag{1-54}$$

From the above and (1-53) it follows that

$$\epsilon = \frac{h''(\gamma)}{0.2 + h^{(4)}(2\gamma)} \qquad (1\text{-}55)$$

because $h^{(4)}(0) = 0.2$.

2. TWO-DIMENSIONAL SIGNALS

The foregoing analysis can be readily extended to functions of several variables with multidimensional Fourier transforms that are limited in a finite region of space. We shall discuss briefly the two-dimensional case.†

Consider a function $f(x,y)$ with Fourier transform $F(u,v)$:

$$f(x,y) \Leftrightarrow F(u,v)$$

We shall assume that $F(u,v)$ equals zero everywhere except in a finite region R of the uv plane (Fig. 2-1):

$$F(u,v) = 0 \qquad \text{for } (u,v) \text{ not in } R \qquad (2\text{-}1)$$

As in the one-dimensional case, various functionals of $f(x,y)$ will be bounded in terms of its energy:

$$E = \iint\limits_{-\infty}^{\infty} |f(x,y)|^2 \, dx \, dy = \frac{1}{4\pi^2} \iint\limits_{R} |F(u,v)|^2 \, du \, dv \qquad (2\text{-}2)$$

MAXIMUM RESPONSE OF LINEAR SYSTEMS

Consider a two-dimensional system with system function $H(u,v)$. With $f(x,y)$ as input, the resulting output $g(x,y)$ is given by [see Chap. 3, (4-33)]

$$g(x,y) = \frac{1}{4\pi^2} \iint\limits_{R} F(u,v)H(u,v)e^{j(ux+vy)} \, du \, dv \qquad (2\text{-}3)$$

Applying (1-2) to the above integral, we conclude, with (2-2), that

$$|g(x,y)|^2 \le \frac{E}{4\pi^2} \iint\limits_{R} |H(u,v)|^2 \, du \, dv \qquad (2\text{-}4)$$

† A. Papoulis, *J. Opt. Soc. Am.*, vol. 57, pp. 362–366, March, 1967.

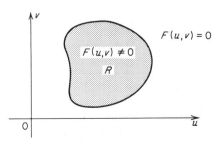

Fig. 2-1

The response $g(x,y)$ reaches its upper limit (2-4) at the point (x_o,y_o) only if the input is a signal $f_o(x,y)$ with transform

$$F_o(u,v) = \begin{cases} AH^*(u,v)e^{-j(ux_o+vy_o)} & (u,v) \text{ in } R \\ 0 & \text{otherwise} \end{cases} \qquad (2\text{-}5)$$

The last two equations are direct extensions of (1-9) and (1-10).

APPLICATIONS

We continue with three applications of (2-4).

Signal bounds   If

$$H(u,v) = 1$$

then

$$f(x,y) = g(x,y)$$

Denoting by R_o the area of the region R, we conclude from (2-4) that

$$|f(x,y)| \leq \frac{\sqrt{ER_o}}{2\pi} \qquad (2\text{-}6)$$

The upper limit is reached at the point (x_o,y_o) only if [see (2-5)]

$$f(x,y) = f_o(x,y) = \frac{1}{2\pi} \sqrt{\frac{E}{R_o}} \iint\limits_{R} e^{j[u(x-x_o)+v(y-y_o)]} \, du \, dv \qquad (2\text{-}7)$$

If the region R is a circle of radius a, then (2-7) yields [see Chap. 3, (4-31)]

$$f_o(x,y) = \sqrt{\frac{E}{\pi}} \frac{J_1[a\sqrt{(x-x_o)^2+(y-y_o)^2}]}{\sqrt{(x-x_o)^2+(y-y_o)^2}}$$

In this case,

$$|f(x,y)| \leq f_o(x_o,y_o) = \frac{a}{2}\sqrt{\frac{E}{\pi}}$$

Increment bounds   The variation

$$g(x,y) = f(x+\alpha,\, y+\beta) - f(x,y)$$

of $f(x,y)$ can be considered as the output of a system with input $f(x,y)$ and system function

$$H(u,v) = e^{j(\alpha u+\beta v)} - 1$$

Since

$$|H(u,v)|^2 = 2 - 2\cos(\alpha u + \beta v)$$

it follows from (2-4) that

$$|f(x + \alpha,\, y + \beta) - f(x,y)|^2 \leq \frac{E}{2\pi^2} \iint\limits_R [1 - \cos(\alpha u + \beta v)]\, du\, dv$$

$$(2\text{-}8)$$

If R is a circle, then (2-8) yields

$$|f(x + \alpha,\, y + \beta) - f(x,y)|^2 \leq \frac{Ea^2}{2\pi} \left[1 - \frac{2J_1(a\sqrt{\alpha^2 + \beta^2})}{a\sqrt{\alpha^2 + \beta^2}} \right] \quad (2\text{-}9)$$

as it is easy to show.

Derivatives   As a last application, we shall bound the derivative

$$g(x,y) = \frac{\partial^{k+r}f(x,y)}{\partial x^k\, \partial y^r}$$

of $f(x,y)$.   With

$$H(u,v) = (ju)^k (jv)^r$$

(2-4) yields

$$\left| \frac{\partial^{k+r}f(x,y)}{\partial x^k\, \partial y^r} \right|^2 \leq \frac{E}{4\pi^2} \iint\limits_R u^{2k} v^{2r}\, du\, dv \qquad (2\text{-}10)$$

HANKEL TRANSFORMS

Consider a signal $f(r)$ with Hankel transform $\bar{f}(w)$:

$$f(r) \overset{h}{\leftrightarrow} \bar{f}(w)$$

We shall say that $f(r)$ is circularly band-limited if

$$\bar{f}(w) = 0 \qquad \text{for } w \geq a \qquad\qquad (2\text{-}11)$$

With

$$E = 2\pi \int_0^\infty r|f(r)|^2\, dr = 2\pi \int_0^a w|\bar{f}(w)|^2\, dw \qquad (2\text{-}12)$$

as the circular energy of $f(r)$, we shall show that

$$|f(r)|^2 \leq \frac{Ea^2}{4\pi} [J_o{}^2(ar) + J_1{}^2(ar)] \qquad (2\text{-}13)$$

and that the upper limit is reached at $r = r_o$ only if

$$f(r) = f_o(r) = Aa\, \frac{r_o J_o(ar) J_1(ar_o) - r J_o(ar_o) J_1(ar)}{r_o{}^2 - r^2} \qquad (2\text{-}14)$$

We note that, unlike (1-13) and (2-6), the limit in (2-13) depends on r (Fig. 2-2).

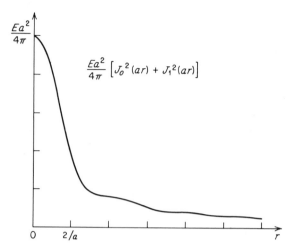

Fig. 2-2

Proof   Applying (1-1) to the Hankel inversion formula

$$f(r) = \int_0^a w\tilde{f}(w)J_o(rw)\,dw \tag{2-15}$$

we conclude, with

$$f_1(w) = \sqrt{w}\,\tilde{f}(w) \qquad f_2(w) = \sqrt{w}\,J_o(rw) \tag{2-16}$$

that

$$|f(r)|^2 \le \int_0^a w|\tilde{f}(w)|^2\,dw \int_0^a wJ_o{}^2(rw)\,dw$$

and (2-13) follows from (2-12) and Chap. 5, (5-23).

The upper limit (2-13) is reached for $r = r_o$ only if $\tilde{f}(w)$ is proportional to $J_o(r_ow)$ [see (1-3) and (2-16)], that is, if

$$\tilde{f}(w) = \tilde{f}_o(w) = \begin{cases} AJ_o(r_ow) & w < a \\ 0 & w > a \end{cases} \tag{2-17}$$

and (2-14) follows [see Chap. 5, (1-23)].

We note that

$$f_o(r_o) = \frac{Ea^2}{4\pi}\,[J_o{}^2(ar_o) + J_1{}^2(ar_o)] \tag{2-18}$$

Increment bounds   We shall need the following inequality for the variation of the Bessel function $J_o(x)$:

$$|J_o(x + y) - J_o(x)| \le \frac{2}{\pi}\,|y| \tag{2-19}$$

This inequality follows from Chap. 5, (1-1), and [see (1-22)]

$$|e^{jx} - 1| \leq x$$

Indeed,

$$|J_o(x + y) - J_o(x)| = \frac{1}{2\pi} \left| \int_{-\pi}^{\pi} e^{jx \cos \theta} (e^{jy \cos \theta} - 1) \, d\theta \right|$$

$$\leq \frac{1}{2\pi} \int_{-\pi}^{\pi} |e^{jy \cos \theta} - 1| \, d\theta \leq \frac{1}{2\pi} \int_{-\pi}^{\pi} |y \cos \theta| \, d\theta = \frac{2}{\pi} |y|$$

Using the above, we shall show that if a function is band-limited as in (2-11), then

$$|f(r + y) - f(r)| \leq \frac{|y|a^2}{\pi} \sqrt{\frac{E}{2\pi}} \tag{2-20}$$

Proof   From (2-15) we have

$$f(r + y) - f(r) = \int_0^a w\tilde{f}(w) \{J_o[(r + y)w] - J_o(rw)\} \, dw$$

Applying Schwarz' inequality to the above, we conclude, with (2-19), that

$$|f(r + y) - f(r)|^2 \leq \int_0^a w|\tilde{f}(w)|^2 \, dw \int_0^a \frac{4}{\pi^2} y^2 w^3 \, dw$$

and (2-20) results.

3. SIGNAL DURATION AND UNCERTAINTY PRINCIPLE

Consider a signal $f(t)$ with Fourier transform $F(\omega)$.   An examination of various transform pairs will reveal that if $f(t)$ is of short duration, then $F(\omega)$ must take significant values over a large (in some sense) segment of the ω axis.   This statement agrees with the scaling theorem

$$f(at) \leftrightarrow \frac{1}{|a|} F\left(\frac{\omega}{a}\right)$$

and the purpose of this section is to investigate its general validity.

UNCERTAINTY PRINCIPLE

We shall show that if the energy of a real or complex signal $f(t)$ equals E, that is,

$$E = \int_{-\infty}^{\infty} |f(t)|^2 \, dt = \frac{1}{2\pi} \int_{-\infty}^{\infty} |F(\omega)|^2 \, d\omega \tag{3-1}$$

then

$$\int_{-\infty}^{\infty} t^2 |f(t)|^2 \, dt \int_{-\infty}^{\infty} \omega^2 |F(\omega)|^2 \, d\omega \geq \frac{\pi}{2} E^2 \tag{3-2}$$

and the equality holds only if

$$f(t) = Ae^{-at^2} \tag{3-3}$$

Proof   If the integral

$$\int_{-\infty}^{\infty} t^2 |f(t)|^2 \, dt$$

is infinite, then (3-2) is trivially true.   We can, therefore, assume that this integral is finite.   From this assumption it follows readily that

$$\sqrt{t}\, f(t) \to 0 \qquad \text{for } |t| \to \infty \tag{3-4}$$

From Schwarz' inequality (1-1) we have, with

$$g(t) = tf(t) \qquad h(t) = \frac{df^*(t)}{dt} \tag{3-5}$$

the following inequality:

$$\left| \int_{-\infty}^{\infty} tf \frac{df^*}{dt} \, dt \right|^2 \le \int_{-\infty}^{\infty} t^2 |f|^2 \, dt \int_{-\infty}^{\infty} \left| \frac{df}{dt} \right|^2 dt \equiv I^2 \tag{3-6}$$

Hence,

$$\left| \int_{-\infty}^{\infty} \left(tf^* \frac{df}{dt} + tf \frac{df^*}{dt} \right) dt \right| \le \left| \int_{-\infty}^{\infty} tf^* \frac{df}{dt} \, dt \right| + \left| \int_{-\infty}^{\infty} tf \frac{df^*}{dt} \, dt \right|$$

$$= 2 \left| \int_{-\infty}^{\infty} tf \frac{df^*}{dt} \, dt \right| \le 2I \tag{3-7}$$

But

$$f^* \frac{df}{dt} + f \frac{df^*}{dt} = \frac{d|f|^2}{dt}$$

Therefore, the first integral in (3-7) equals

$$\int_{-\infty}^{\infty} t \frac{d|f|^2}{dt} \, dt = \int_{-\infty}^{\infty} t \, d|f|^2 = t|f|^2 \Big|_{-\infty}^{\infty} - \int_{-\infty}^{\infty} |f|^2 \, dt = -E$$

as we see, integrating by parts and using (3-4).   From the above, we conclude that

$$E \le 2I \tag{3-8}$$

Since

$$\frac{df(t)}{dt} \leftrightarrow j\omega F(\omega)$$

we have

$$\int_{-\infty}^{\infty} \left| \frac{df}{dt} \right|^2 dt = \frac{1}{2\pi} \int_{-\infty}^{\infty} \omega^2 |F|^2 \, d\omega$$

and (3-2) follows from (3-6) and (3-8).

From (3-5) and (1-3) we see that (3-2) holds with the equality sign if

$$tf(t) = k \frac{df^*(t)}{dt}$$

Integrating, we obtain (3-3).

If we define the duration D_t and D_ω of $f(t)$ and $F(\omega)$ by

$$D_t{}^2 = \frac{1}{E} \int_{-\infty}^{\infty} t^2|f(t)|^2\, dt \quad \text{and} \quad D_\omega{}^2 = \frac{1}{2\pi E} \int_{-\infty}^{\infty} \omega^2|F(\omega)|^2\, d\omega \tag{3-9}$$

respectively, then (3-2) yields

$$D_t D_\omega \geq \tfrac{1}{2} \tag{3-10}$$

Comment If D_t is defined by

$$D_t{}^2 = \frac{1}{E} \int_{-\infty}^{\infty} (t - \eta)^2|f(t)|^2\, dt = \frac{1}{E} \int_{-\infty}^{\infty} t^2|f(t + \eta)|^2\, dt$$

then (3-10) still holds because the transforms of the functions $f(t)$ and $f(t + \eta)$ have the same amplitude. If η is the "mean" of $|f(t)|^2$ [see Chap. 3, (2-18)], then D_t is its minimum, and it is more realistic to use it as a measure of the duration of $f(t)$.

Time-limited signals

Suppose now that (Fig. 3-1)

$$f(t) = 0 \quad \text{for } |t| > \frac{T}{2} \tag{3-11}$$

We maintain that†

$$TD_\omega \geq \pi \tag{3-12}$$

and that the equality holds for the signal

$$f(t) = A \cos \frac{\pi t}{T} \quad |t| < \frac{T}{2} \tag{3-13}$$

Proof We seek a function $f(t)$ which satisfies (3-11), and is such that

$$ED_\omega{}^2 = \frac{1}{2\pi} \int_{-\infty}^{\infty} \omega^2|F(\omega)|^2\, d\omega = \int_{-T/2}^{T/2} |f'(t)|^2\, dt \tag{3-14}$$

is minimum, subject to the constraint

$$E = \int_{-T/2}^{T/2} |f(t)|^2\, dt \tag{3-15}$$

† Tosio Hosono and Shuzo Ohwaku, *J. Inst. Elec. Comm. Engrs.*, Japan, August, 1965.

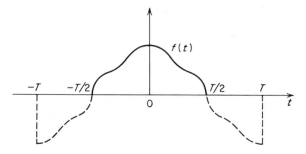

Fig. 3-1

This problem can be solved with the calculus of variations. We shall present a simpler solution based on Chap. 4, (2-10). We assume for simplicity that $f(t)$ is even. The analysis can be readily extended to arbitrary functions.

We first observe that $f(t)$ must be zero for $|t| = T/2$

$$f\left(\frac{T^-}{2}\right) = 0 \qquad f\left(-\frac{T^+}{2}\right) = 0 \tag{3-16}$$

Otherwise, $f'(t)$ would contain impulses at $|t| = T/2$, and D_ω would be infinite. We now extend $f(t)$ beyond $|t| = T/2$, as in Fig. 3-1, that is,

$$f\left(\frac{T}{2} + t\right) = -f\left(\frac{T}{2} - t\right) \qquad 0 < t < \frac{T}{2} \tag{3-17}$$

and expand it into a Fourier series in the interval $(-T, T)$. Because of (3-17), the resulting expansion will contain only odd harmonics, i.e.,

$$f(t) = \sum_{n=0}^{\infty} a_{2n+1} \cos (2n + 1)\omega_o t \qquad \omega_o = \frac{\pi}{T} \tag{3-18}$$

and will satisfy (3-16). Differentiating, we have

$$f'(t) = -\omega_o \sum_{n=0}^{\infty} a_{2n+1} \sin (2n + 1)\omega_o t \tag{3-19}$$

Our problem is thus to find the constants a_{2n+1} such that

$$ED_\omega{}^2 = \frac{\omega_o \pi}{2} \sum_{n=0}^{\infty} (2n + 1)^2 a_{2n+1}^2 \tag{3-20}$$

is minimum, subject to the constraint

$$E = \frac{T}{2} \sum_{n=0}^{\infty} a_{2n+1}^2$$

These relationships follow from (3-14), (3-15), and Chap. 4, (2-10). One can see by inspection that we must have

$$a_{2n+1} = 0 \qquad \text{for } n > 0$$

and (3-13) follows. For the optimum function $A \cos (\pi t/T)$ we readily find $D_\omega = \pi/T$; hence for any other function, D_ω cannot be less than π/T, and (3-12) results.

Reversing the roles of t and ω, we conclude from (3-12), changing T to $2\omega_c$, that if

$$F(\omega) = 0 \qquad \text{for } |\omega| > \omega_c$$

then

$$4\omega_c{}^2 \int_{-\infty}^{\infty} t^2|f(t)|^2 \, dt \geq \pi^2 \int_{-\infty}^{\infty} |f(t)|^2 \, dt \tag{3-21}$$

and that the equality holds for

$$F(\omega) = A \cos \frac{\pi \omega}{2\omega_c} \qquad |\omega| < \omega_c \tag{3-22}$$

TWO–DIMENSIONAL SIGNALS

Consider a signal $f(x,y)$ with energy

$$E = \iint_{-\infty}^{\infty} |f|^2 \, dx \, dy$$

and Fourier transforms $F(u,v)$. As an extension of the uncertainty principle, we shall show that

$$\iint_{-\infty}^{\infty} x^2|f|^2 \, dx \, dy \iint_{-\infty}^{\infty} u^2|F|^2 \, du \, dv \geq \pi^2 E^2 \tag{3-23a}$$

$$\iint_{-\infty}^{\infty} y^2|f|^2 \, dx \, dy \iint_{-\infty}^{\infty} v^2|F|^2 \, du \, dv \geq \pi^2 E^2 \tag{3-23b}$$

$$\iint_{-\infty}^{\infty} (x^2 + y^2)|f|^2 \, dx \, dy \iint_{-\infty}^{\infty} (u^2 + v^2)|F|^2 \, du \, dv \geq 4\pi^2 E^2 \tag{3-23c}$$

and that the equality holds in (3-23a), (3-23b), and (3-23c) only if

$$f(x,y) = A(y)e^{-\alpha x^2} \qquad f(x,y) = B(x)e^{-\beta y^2} \qquad f(x,y) = Ce^{-(\alpha x^2 + \beta y^2)} \tag{3-24}$$

respectively.

Proof To simplify the argument, we shall assume that $f(x,y)$ is real.   The results hold for complex signals also.   With

$$g = xf \qquad h = \frac{\partial f}{\partial x}$$
(3-25)

(1-2) yields

$$\left| \iint_{-\infty}^{\infty} xf \frac{\partial f}{\partial x} \, dx \, dy \right|^2 \leq \iint_{-\infty}^{\infty} x^2 f^2 \, dx \, dy \iint_{-\infty}^{\infty} \left(\frac{\partial f}{\partial x} \right)^2 dx \, dy$$
(3-26)

But

$$\frac{\partial f}{\partial x} \Leftrightarrow juF$$

Hence,

$$\iint_{-\infty}^{\infty} \left(\frac{\partial f}{\partial x} \right)^2 dx \, dy = \frac{1}{4\pi^2} \iint_{-\infty}^{\infty} u^2 |F|^2 \, du \, dv$$
(3-27)

Integrating by parts, we have

$$\iint_{-\infty}^{\infty} xf \frac{\partial f}{\partial x} \, dx \, dy = \frac{1}{2} \iint_{-\infty}^{\infty} x \partial_x f^2 \, dy = \left| \frac{1}{2} \int_{-\infty}^{\infty} xf^2 \, dy \right|_{x=-\infty}^{x=\infty}$$

$$- \frac{1}{2} \iint_{-\infty}^{\infty} f^2 \, dx \, dy = - \frac{E}{2}$$

The last equality follows when we assume that xf^2 is integrable [see also (3-4)].   Inserting into (3-26), we conclude, with (3-27), that

$$\frac{E^2}{4} \leq \iint_{-\infty}^{\infty} x^2 f^2 \, dx \, dy \frac{1}{4\pi^2} \iint_{-\infty}^{\infty} u^2 |F|^2 \, du \, dv$$

and (3-23a) results.   The proof of (3-23b) is identical.

To prove (3-23c), we denote by a_1 and a_2 the first and second integrals in (3-23a) and denote by b_1 and b_2 the first and second integrals in (3-23b).   Since $a_1 a_2 \geq \pi^2 E^2$, $b_1 b_2 \geq \pi^2 E^2$, we have

$$a_2 \geq \frac{\pi^2 E^2}{a_1} \qquad b_2 \geq \frac{\pi^2 E^2}{b_1}$$

But

$$(a_1 + b_1) \left(\frac{1}{a_1} + \frac{1}{b_1} \right) = 2 + \frac{a_1}{b_1} + \frac{b_1}{a_1} \geq 4$$

as it is easy to show; hence,

$$(a_1 + b_1)(a_2 + b_2) \geq (a_1 + b_1) \left(\frac{1}{a_1} + \frac{1}{b_1} \right) \pi^2 E^2 \geq 4\pi^2 E^2$$

and (3-23c) follows.

For the equality to hold in (3-23a), we must have [see (3-25) and (1-3)]

$$xf = k \frac{\partial f}{\partial x} \qquad \text{therefore} \qquad f = A(y)e^{x^2/2k}$$

and the first equation in (3-24) results, with $k = -\frac{1}{2}\alpha$. Reasoning similarly for (3-23b) and (3-23c), we can establish the other two equations in (3-24).

THE UNCERTAINTY PRINCIPLE FOR HANKEL TRANSFORMS

Consider a signal $f(r)$ with "circular energy"

$$E = 2\pi \int_0^\infty r|f(r)|^2 \, dr \qquad (3\text{-}28)$$

With $\bar{f}(w)$ the Hankel transform of $f(r)$, we shall show that

$$\int_0^\infty r^3|f(r)|^2 \, dr \int_0^\infty w^3|\bar{f}(w)|^2 \, dw \geq \frac{E^2}{4\pi^2} \qquad (3\text{-}29)$$

and that the equality holds if

$$f(r) = Ce^{-\alpha r^2} \qquad (3\text{-}30)$$

Proof It is easy to see that the energy of the two-dimensional signal $f(\sqrt{x^2 + y^2})$ equals E. Furthermore [see Chap. 5, (1-4)],

$$f(\sqrt{x^2 + y^2}) \Leftrightarrow F(u,v) = 2\pi\bar{f}(\sqrt{u^2 + v^2})$$

Inserting the above into (3-23c) and transforming the independent variables into polar coordinates, as in Chap. 5, (1-5), we conclude that

$$2\pi \int_0^\infty r^3|f(r)|^2 \, dr \, 2\pi \int_0^\infty w^3|2\pi\bar{f}(w)|^2 \, dw \geq 4\pi^2E^2$$

and (3-29) results. From the last equation in (3-24), we obtain (3-30), with $\alpha = \beta$.

4. SPECTRAL ANALYSIS; PULSE COMPRESSION; TIME SCALING

The main ideas of this section are direct consequences of known optical principles (see also Chap. 11, Sec. 2). To simplify the notations, we shall deal with low-pass complex signals. The results for real bandpass functions are self-evident corollaries (see Prob. 6-11).

In our discussion, we shall make frequent use of a filter with impulse response

$$h(t) = e^{j\alpha t^2} \qquad (4\text{-}1)$$

This function is a modulated signal with instantaneous frequency

$$\omega(t) = 2\alpha t$$

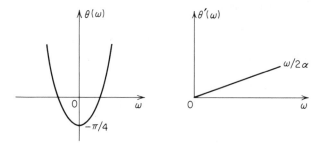

Fig. 4-1

The corresponding system function is given by [see Chap. 3, (1-31)]

$$H(\omega) = e^{j\pi/4} \sqrt{\frac{\pi}{\alpha}} \, e^{-j\omega^2/4\alpha} \tag{4-2}$$

Thus, the filter is all-pass, with quadratic phase lag (Fig. 4-1):

$$\theta(\omega) = \frac{\omega^2}{4\alpha} - \frac{\pi}{4} \tag{4-3}$$

That is, it has linear group delay

$$\theta'(\omega) = \frac{\omega}{2\alpha}$$

This filter cannot be realized exactly; however, it suffices to approximate (4-3) only in the band of the input.

The corresponding bandpass characteristics are

$$h(t) = e^{j(\alpha t^2 + \omega_o t)} \qquad H(\omega) = e^{j\pi/4} \sqrt{\frac{\pi}{\alpha}} \, e^{-j(\omega-\omega_o)^2/4\alpha} \tag{4-4}$$

REAL–TIME SPECTRAL ANALYSIS

Given a signal $f(t)$, we shall determine its Fourier transform $F(\omega)$ by means of the system shown in Fig. 4-2, which consists of the filter (4-1) and the signal generator

$$s(t) = e^{-j\alpha t^2} \tag{4-5}$$

As we see from the figure, the input to the filter is the product

$$f(t)e^{-j\alpha t^2}$$

Hence the resulting output is given by

$$g(t) = [f(t)e^{-j\alpha t^2}] * e^{j\alpha t^2} = \int_{-\infty}^{\infty} f(\tau)e^{-j\alpha\tau^2}e^{j\alpha(t-\tau)^2} \, d\tau$$

$$= e^{j\alpha t^2} \int_{-\infty}^{\infty} f(\tau)e^{-j2\alpha t\tau} \, d\tau$$

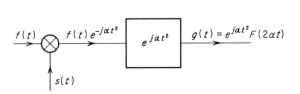

Fig. 4-2

Thus,

$$g(t) = e^{j\alpha t^2}F(2\alpha t) \tag{4-6}$$

From the above we see that the output of our system is a modulated signal whose envelope is the Fourier transform $F(2\alpha t)$ of the input $f(t)$.

If $F(\omega)$ is negligible for $|\omega| > \Omega$ and

$$\alpha \gg \Omega^2 \tag{4-7}$$

then $e^{j\alpha t^2} \simeq 1$ for $2\alpha t < \Omega$; hence,

$$g(t) \simeq F(2\alpha t) \tag{4-8}$$

Example 4-1 Suppose that

$$f(t) = \begin{cases} e^{j\omega_1 t} & |t| < T/2 \\ 0 & |t| > T/2 \end{cases} \tag{4-9}$$

In this case,

$$F(\omega) = \frac{2 \sin [(\omega - \omega_1)T/2]}{\omega - \omega_1}$$

Defining the duration Ω of $F(\omega)$ by $2\pi/T$, we conclude from (4-7) and (4-8) that if

$$\alpha T^2 \gg 1 \tag{4-10}$$

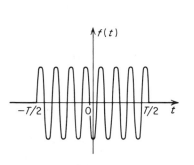

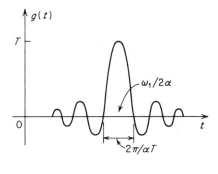

Fig. 4-3

then (Fig. 4-3)

$$g(t) \simeq \frac{2 \sin [(2\alpha t - \omega_1) T/2]}{2\alpha t - \omega_1} \qquad (4\text{-}11)$$

Thus, $g(t)$ is a pulse centered at $t = \omega_1/2\alpha$. From the position of this pulse we can, therefore, determine the frequency ω_1 of the input.

If the input contains two frequency components

$$f(t) = a_1 e^{j\omega_1 t} + a_2 e^{j\omega_2 t}$$

and the ratio a_1/a_2 is of the order of one, then the two frequencies can be resolved, provided that $\omega_1 - \omega_2 > 2\pi/T$. Hence, by increasing T we can arbitrarily increase the resolving power of the analyzer.

We note that the term $e^{j\alpha t^2}$ in (4-6) can be eliminated if two filters are used, as in Prob. 6-8. In the resulting system, (4-8) and (4-11) are exact.

PULSE COMPRESSION

The following special case of (4-11) is of particular interest [c2]. Suppose that $\omega_1 = 0$; we then have

$$g(t) \simeq \frac{\sin \alpha T t}{\alpha t} \qquad (4\text{-}12)$$

Thus if the input to the filter in (4-1) is a frequency-modulated pulse, then the output is given by (4-12), provided that (4-10) holds. Defining the duration of (4-12) by $2\pi/\alpha T$ (Fig. 4-3), we conclude that the input is "compressed" by the factor

$$\frac{\alpha T^2}{2\pi}$$

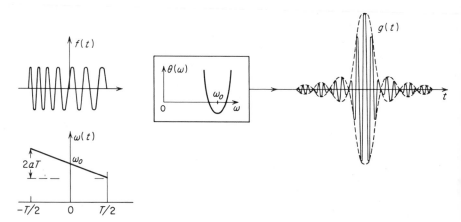

Fig. 4-4

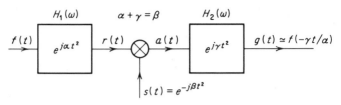

Fig. 4-5

For example, if $2\alpha T = 2\pi \times 10^8$ cycles/sec and $T = 10^{-6}$ sec, then the *compression ratio* equals 50.

We state briefly the bandpass version of the pulse-compression scheme. The input to the filter in (4-4) is the FM pulse

$$e^{-j(\alpha t^2 - \omega_o t)} p_{T/2}(t)$$

which has instantaneous frequency decreasing linearly from $\omega_o + \alpha T$ to $\omega_o - \alpha T$ (Fig. 4-4). The resulting output equals

$$g(t) = e^{j(\alpha t^2 + \omega_o t)} \frac{\sin \alpha Tt}{\alpha t}$$

and if $\alpha T^2 \gg 1$, then

$$g(t) \simeq e^{j\omega_o t} \frac{\sin \alpha Tt}{\alpha t}$$

TIME SCALING

Consider a signal $f(t)$ and a constant c. An important problem in many applications is the realization of a system whose output equals $f(ct)$. We propose to solve this problem with the system of Fig. 4-5, which consists of two all-pass filters with quadratic phase

$$h_1(t) = e^{j\alpha t^2} \qquad h_2(t) = e^{j\gamma t^2} \tag{4-13}$$

and a signal generator

$$s(t) = e^{-j\beta t^2}$$

The input to the first filter is the given signal $f(t)$. We denote by $r(t)$ its output and denote by $a(t)$ the input to the second filter. Thus

$$r(t) = f(t) * e^{j\alpha t^2} \qquad a(t) = e^{-j\beta t^2} r(t) \tag{4-14}$$

The output $g(t)$ of the second system is given by

$$g(t) = a(t) * e^{j\gamma t^2} = \{[f(t) * e^{j\alpha t^2}]e^{-j\beta t^2}\} * e^{j\gamma t^2} \tag{4-15}$$

We shall show that if the constants α, β, and γ are such that

$$\alpha + \gamma = \beta \tag{4-16}$$

(lens formula), then

$$g(t) = \frac{\pi}{\alpha} e^{j\gamma\beta t^2/\alpha f} \left(-\frac{\gamma t}{\alpha} \right) \qquad (4\text{-}17)$$

If $f(t) = 0$ for $|t| > T/2$ and

$$\left| \frac{\alpha\beta T^2}{\gamma} \right| \ll 1 \qquad (4\text{-}18)$$

then

$$e^{j\gamma\beta t^2/\alpha} \simeq 1 \qquad \text{for } \left| \frac{\gamma t}{\alpha} \right| < \frac{T}{2}$$

and (4-17) yields

$$g(t) \simeq \frac{\pi}{\alpha} f(ct) \qquad c = -\frac{\gamma}{\alpha} \qquad (4\text{-}19)$$

Proof The output $r(t)$ of the first filter is given by [see (4-14)]

$$\int_{-\infty}^{\infty} f(\tau) e^{j\alpha(t-\tau)^2} \, dt = e^{j\alpha t^2} \int_{-\infty}^{\infty} f(\tau) e^{j\alpha\tau^2} e^{-j2\alpha t\tau} \, d\tau \qquad (4\text{-}20)$$

With $F_1(\omega)$ the Fourier transform of the function

$$f_1(t) = f(t) e^{j\alpha t^2} \qquad (4\text{-}21)$$

we conclude from (4-20) that

$$r(t) = e^{j\alpha t^2} F_1(2\alpha t) \qquad (4\text{-}22)$$

Hence the input to the second filter is [see (4-16)]

$$a(t) = e^{-j\beta t^2} e^{j\alpha t^2} F_1(2\alpha t) = e^{-j\gamma t^2} F_1(2\alpha t) \qquad (4\text{-}23)$$

Finally

$$g(t) = \int_{-\infty}^{\infty} e^{-j\gamma\tau^2} F_1(2\alpha\tau) e^{j\gamma(t-\tau)^2} \, d\tau = e^{j\gamma t^2} \int_{-\infty}^{\infty} F_1(2\alpha\tau) e^{-j2\gamma t\tau} \, d\tau \quad (4\text{-}24)$$

With $2\alpha\tau = \omega$, it follows from the above and the Fourier inversion formula that

$$g(t) = \frac{\pi}{\alpha} e^{j\gamma t^2} f_1 \left(-\frac{\gamma t}{\alpha} \right) = \frac{\pi}{\alpha} e^{j\gamma t^2} e^{j\gamma^2 t^2/\alpha} f \left(-\frac{\gamma t}{\alpha} \right) \qquad (4\text{-}25)$$

and (4-17) results.

The above is of course an idealized scheme based on the assumptions that the filters are all-pass with quadratic phase for every ω and that the generator output (t) is a linear FM signal for every t. We shall now introduce deviations from these assumptions.

Pulse generator

Suppose that $s(t)$ equals zero for $|t| > a$:

$$s(t) = e^{-j\beta t^2}p_a(t) \qquad p_a(t) = \begin{cases} 1 & |t| < a \\ 0 & |t| > a \end{cases} \qquad (4\text{-}26)$$

This assumption has no effect on the first filter, and hence its output $r(t)$ is given by (4-22).   The input to the second filter is now

$$a(t) = e^{-j\gamma t^2}F_1(2\alpha t)p_a(t) \qquad (4\text{-}27)$$

Therefore, (4-24) still holds, provided that $F_1(2\alpha\tau)$ is replaced by $F_1(2\alpha\tau)p_a(\tau)$. To determine $g(t)$, it suffices therefore to replace the function $f_1(t)$ in (4-25) by the inverse Fourier transform $f_2(t)$ of the product

$$F_2(\omega) = F_1(\omega)p_a\left(\frac{\omega}{2\alpha}\right) = F_1(\omega)p_{2\alpha a}(\omega) \qquad (4\text{-}28)$$

Since

$$f_1(t) \leftrightarrow F_1(\omega) \qquad \frac{\sin 2\alpha a t}{\pi t} \leftrightarrow p_{2\alpha a}(\omega)$$

we conclude from the convolution theorem that

$$f_2(t) = f_1(t) * \frac{\sin 2\alpha a t}{\pi t} = [f(t)e^{j\alpha t^2}] * \frac{\sin 2\alpha a t}{\pi t} \qquad (4\text{-}29)$$

This expression can be simplified with the help of the following.

Lemma   If

$$y(t) = 0 \qquad \text{for } |t| > e \text{ and } \alpha e^2 \ll 1 \qquad (4\text{-}30)$$

then

$$[e^{j\alpha t^2}x(t)] * y(t) = e^{j\alpha t^2}[x(t) * y(t)] \qquad (4\text{-}31)$$

Proof   From the condition $\alpha e^2 \ll 1$ it follows that

$$e^{j\alpha(t-\tau)^2} \simeq e^{j\alpha t^2} \qquad \text{for } |\tau| < e$$

Since $y(t) = 0$ for $|t| > e$, the left side of (4-31) equals

$$\int_{-e}^{e} e^{j\alpha(t-\tau)^2}x(t-\tau)y(\tau)\, d\tau \simeq e^{j\alpha t^2}\int_{-e}^{e} x(t-\tau)y(\tau)\, d\tau$$

and (4-31) follows.

We return to (4-29).   The function $\sin 2\alpha a t/\pi t$ is negligible for $|t| > \pi/\alpha a$.   If, therefore,

$$\alpha a^2 \gg \pi^2 \qquad (4\text{-}32)$$

then [see (4-31)]

$$f_2(t) = [f(t)e^{j\alpha t^2}] * \frac{\sin 2\alpha at}{\pi t} = e^{j\alpha t^2}\left[f(t) * \frac{\sin 2\alpha at}{\pi t}\right] \qquad (4\text{-}33)$$

Thus, if the generator $s(t)$ of the time-scaling system of Fig. 4-2 is given by (4-26), then its output equals

$$g(t) = \frac{\pi}{\alpha} e^{j\gamma\beta t^2/\alpha}\varphi\left(-\frac{\gamma t}{\alpha}\right) \qquad (4\text{-}34)$$

where

$$\varphi(t) = f(t) * \frac{\sin 2\alpha at}{\pi t} \qquad (4\text{-}35)$$

Low-pass filter with quadratic phase

The all-pass requirement with quadratic phase is not realizable. If its amplitude deviates from the ideal, then it can be replaced by a filter $H_a(\omega)$ without phase distortion in cascade and with an all-pass filter with quadratic phase (Fig. 4-6).   Introducing this equivalence to the first filter of Fig. 4-2, we conclude that the preceding relationships hold, provided that the signal $f(t)$ is replaced by

$$f(t) * h_a(t)$$

where $h_a(t)$ is the impulse response of the filter $H_a(\omega)$. If $H_a(\omega)$ is an ideal low-pass filter with cutoff frequency ω_o, then $h_a(t) = \sin \omega_o t/\pi t$.

The second filter can be treated similarly. For this purpose, we replace it by the all-pass filter $H_2(\omega)$ of Fig. 4-2, which is in cascade with a filter $H_b(\omega)$ without phase distortion (Fig. 4-6). The resulting output is then given by the function $g(t)$ in (4-17), which is convolved with the impulse response $h_b(t)$ of $H_b(\omega)$.

Comment   If $c > 1$, then the output $f(ct)$ of the system of Fig. 4-2

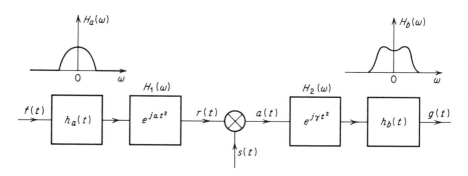

Fig. 4-6

will precede the input $f(t)$. This apparent violation of causality can be simply explained. For $c > 0$, one of the filters must have negative phase; to approximate the quadratic phase one must therefore add a linear term ωt_o to the phase $\theta(\omega)$. This term results in a t_o delay; hence, the scaling applies to the delayed signal $f(t - t_o)$.

OPTICAL ANALOGIES

The results of this section have the following optical interpretation (for details see Chap. 11, Sec. 2).

Time scaling corresponds to image formation, where t is now a space coordinate. The input $f(t)$ of Fig. 4-2 is the object, the output $g(t)$ is its image, and the generator $s(t)$ represents the lens. Assumption (4-26) means that the lens is of finite size, and condition (4-16) corresponds to the lens formula, Chap. 9, (5-16). Equation (4-17) or the equivalent

$$|g(t)| = \left| f\left(-\frac{\gamma t}{\alpha}\right) \right|$$

shows that the image is similar to the object, and the ratio α/γ equals the resulting magnification.

The optical analog of the spectrum analyzer output (4-8) is the fact that on the focal plane of a lens, the field is proportional to the Fourier transform of the incident wave.

Finally, the pulse-compression principle corresponds to the fact that a lens concentrates the incoming beam into a small region of its focal plane.

5. GENERALIZATION OF THE UNCERTAINTY PRINCIPLE

Consider a real function $f(t)$ with total energy

$$E = \int_{-\infty}^{\infty} f^2(t)\, dt \tag{5-1}$$

If we form the energy ratio

$$\alpha = \frac{1}{E} \int_{-T}^{T} f^2(t)\, dt \tag{5-2}$$

then, by selecting $f(t)$ such that $f(t) = 0$ for $|t| > T$, we can make α equal one. However, if the function $f(t)$ is band-limited, i.e.,

$$f(t) \leftrightarrow F(\omega) = 0 \qquad \text{for } |\omega| > \Omega \tag{5-3}$$

then α is strictly less than one because a band-limited function must extend to infinity (cannot be time-limited). In this section, we shall investigate the following problem. Given T and Ω, we form the class C of all functions band-limited by Ω. In this class, we seek an optimum signal $f_o(t)$ such that the corresponding energy ratio α_o is maximum; i.e., for any other $f(t)$ we have $\alpha \leq \alpha_o$.

Approximate solution for small ΩT

As we know from (1-21), for $|t| < T$, $|f(0) - f(t)|$ can be made arbitrarily small with $\Omega T \to 0$. Hence, if ΩT is small enough, then $f(t)$ is approximately a constant in the interval $(-T, T)$, and

$$\alpha = \frac{1}{E} \int_{-T}^{T} f^2(t) \, dt \simeq \frac{2f^2(0)T}{E} \tag{5-4}$$

Thus, in order to maximize α, it suffices to maximize $f(0)/\sqrt{E}$ in the class C. From the discussion of Sec. 1, it follows that this ratio is maximum for the function (1-14); hence, the optimum signal is

$$f_o(t) \simeq \sqrt{\frac{E}{\Omega \pi}} \frac{\sin \Omega t}{t} \qquad \Omega T \to 0 \tag{5-5}$$

Since $f_o(0) = \sqrt{E\Omega/\pi}$, the corresponding energy ratio is given by

$$\alpha_o \simeq \frac{2E\Omega T}{E\pi} = \frac{2}{\pi} \Omega T \qquad \Omega T \to 0 \tag{5-6}$$

Thus, if α_o is plotted as a function of ΩT, its slope at the origin equals $2/\pi$ [see also (5-10)].

Exact solution†

The optimum function $f_o(t)$ equals the eigenfunction $\varphi_o(t)$ of the integral equation [p2]

$$\int_{-T}^{T} \varphi(\tau) \frac{\sin \Omega(t - \tau)}{\pi(t - \tau)} \, d\tau = \lambda \varphi(t) \tag{5-7}$$

corresponding to the largest eigenvalue $\lambda = \lambda_o$; that is,

† D. Slepian, H. O. Pollak, and H. J. Landau, *Bell System Tech. J.*, vol. 40, January, 1961, pp. 43–84.

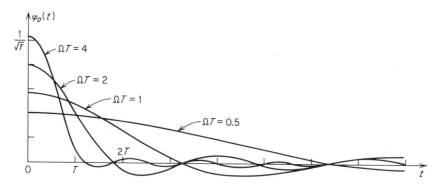

Fig. 5-1

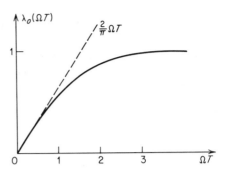

Fig. 5-2

$$f_o(t) = \varphi_c(t) \tag{5-8}$$

The maximum energy ratio α_o equals λ_o:

$$\alpha_o = \lambda_o \tag{5-9}$$

The above will follow as a special case of the corresponding two-dimensional problem (see also Prob. 6-12).

It can be easily shown by a simple scaling that the solution $\varphi_o(t)$ of (5-7) depends only on the product ΩT (see also page 216).   The signals $\varphi_o(t) = \varphi_o(t,\Omega T)$ are known in the literature as *prolate spheroidal wave functions*.

These functions are shown in Fig. 5-1 for $\Omega T = 0.5$, 1, 2, and 4. The maximum eigenvalue $\lambda_o = \lambda_o(\Omega T)$ is plotted in Fig. 5-2 as a function of ΩT.   It is of interest to observe that

$$\lambda_o(\Omega T) \simeq \frac{2}{\pi} \Omega T \qquad \text{for } \Omega T < 1 \tag{5-10}$$

and that

$$\varphi_o(t) \simeq k\, \frac{\sin \Omega t}{t} \qquad \text{for } \Omega T < 1 \tag{5-11}$$

in agreement with the approximate solution presented earlier.

Comments

1. The integral equation (5-7) can be written as a convolution

$$\varphi_T(t) * \frac{\sin \Omega t}{\pi t} = \lambda \varphi(t) \tag{5-12}$$

where $\varphi_T(t) = \varphi(t)p_T(t)$.   With $\Phi_T(\omega)$ the Fourier transform of $\varphi_T(t)$, we thus conclude from (5-12) that

$$\Phi_T(\omega)p_\Omega(\omega) = \lambda \Phi(\omega) \tag{5-13}$$

because the pulse $p_\Omega(\omega)$ is the Fourier transform of $\sin \Omega t / \pi t$. Hence, $\Phi(\omega) = 0$ for $|\omega| > \Omega$.

2. We maintain that the energy ratio of a solution $\varphi(t)$ of (5-7) equals the corresponding eigenvalue λ. Indeed, with E the energy of $\varphi(t)$, we have, from (5-13) and Parseval's formula,

$$\int_{-T}^{T} \varphi^2(t) \, dt = \int_{-\infty}^{\infty} \varphi(t)\varphi_T(t) \, dt = \frac{1}{2\pi} \int_{-\infty}^{\infty} \Phi(\omega)\Phi_T(\omega) \, d\omega$$
$$= \frac{\lambda}{2\pi} \int_{-\Omega}^{\Omega} \Phi^2(\omega) \, d\omega = \lambda E$$

3. It can be shown that (Prob. 6-13) the optimum function $\varphi_o(t)$ also satisfies the integral equation

$$\int_{-\Omega}^{\Omega} e^{j\Omega t\tau/T}\varphi(\tau) \, d\tau = \sqrt{\frac{2\pi\lambda_o T}{\Omega}} \, \varphi(t) \tag{5-14}$$

from which it follows, with $\Omega\tau/T = \omega$, that $\varphi_o(t)$ is proportional to its Fourier transform

$$\varphi_o(t) \leftrightarrow \Phi_o(\omega) = \sqrt{\frac{2\pi T}{\lambda_o \Omega}} \, \varphi_o\left(\frac{T}{\Omega} \, \omega\right) p_\Omega(\omega) \tag{5-15}$$

TWO–DIMENSIONAL SIGNALS

Consider a signal $f(x,y)$ with energy

$$E = \iint\limits_{-\infty}^{\infty} |f(x,y)|^2 \, dx \, dy \tag{5-16}$$

We assume that its spectrum is zero outside a region A of the uv plane (Fig. 5-3), i.e.,

$$f(x,y) \leftrightarrow F(u,v) = 0 \qquad (u,v) \notin A \tag{5-17}$$

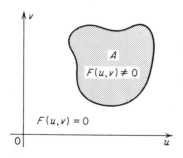
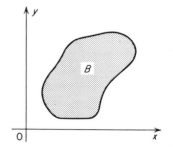

Fig. 5-3

and we form the energy ratio

$$\alpha = \frac{1}{E} \iint\limits_{B} |f(x,y)|^2 \, dx \, dy \tag{5-18}$$

where B is a region of the xy plane. With A and B specified, we seek to determine a function $f_o(x,y)$ which maximizes α.

Approximate solution for small regions

Suppose that the product of the dimensions of the regions A and B is small. Under this assumption, $f(x,y)$ is approximately constant in B [see (2-8)]; hence

$$\alpha = \frac{1}{E} \iint\limits_{B} |f(x,y)|^2 \, dx \, dy \simeq \frac{|f(0,0)|^2 B_o}{E} \tag{5-19}$$

where B_o is the area of B. It suffices, therefore, to select $f(x,y)$ so as to maximize $|f(0,0)|/\sqrt{E}$. With

$$k_A(x,y) = \frac{1}{4\pi^2} \iint\limits_{A} e^{j(ux+vy)} \, du \, dv \tag{5-20}$$

as the inverse transform of the zero-one function associated with the region A, we see from (2-7) that the optimum function is given by

$$f_o(x,y) = 2\pi \sqrt{\frac{E}{A_o}} \, k_A(x,y) \tag{5-21}$$

and it is such that $f_o(0,0) = \sqrt{EA_o}/2\pi$. Inserting into (5-19), we thus have

$$\alpha_o \simeq \frac{A_o B_o}{4\pi^2} \tag{5-22}$$

If A is a circle of radius a, then [see Chap. 3, (4-31)]

$$f_o(x,y) \simeq \sqrt{\frac{E}{\pi}} \frac{J_1(a\sqrt{x^2+y^2})}{\sqrt{x^2+y^2}} \tag{5-23}$$

Exact solution

The determination of the optimum signal is based on the following.

Lemma If the signal $f(x,y)$ is truncated outside the region B, then the signal

$$f_B(x,y) = f(x,y)p_B(x,y) \tag{5-24}$$

results where

$$p_B(x,y) = \begin{cases} 1 & (x,y) \in B \\ 0 & (x,y) \notin B \end{cases}$$

is the zero-one function associated with the region B.   Clearly, the energy of $f_B(x,y)$ equals $E\alpha$ [see (5-18)].   With $F_B(u,v)$ its Fourier transform, i.e.,

$$f_B(x,y) \Leftrightarrow F_B(u,v)$$

we maintain that the energy ratio of $F_B(u,v)$ cannot exceed the energy ratio of $f(x,y)$.   Thus,

$$\frac{1}{4\pi^2 E\alpha} \iint_A |F_B|^2 \, du \, dv \geq \alpha \tag{5-25}$$

where α is the energy ratio (5-18).

It will also follow from the proof that (5-25) is an equality only if $F_B(u,v)$ is proportional to $F(u,v)$ in the region A, that is,

$$F_B(u,v)P_A(u,v) = \lambda F(u,v) \tag{5-26}$$

where $P_A(u,v) = 1$ for $(u,v) \in A$ and zero otherwise.

Proof   Clearly,

$$E\alpha = \iint_B |f_B|^2 \, dx \, dy = \int\!\!\int_{-\infty}^{\infty} ff_B^* \, dx \, dy = \frac{1}{4\pi^2} \int\!\!\int_{-\infty}^{\infty} FF_B^* \, du \, dv$$

$$= \frac{1}{4\pi^2} \iint_A FF_B^* \, du \, dv$$

as we see from Parseval's formula and (5-17).   Applying Schwarz' inequality to the above, we have

$$(4\pi^2 E\alpha)^2 \leq \iint_A |F|^2 \, du \, dv \iint_A |F_B|^2 \, du \, dv = 4\pi^2 E \iint_A |F_B|^2 \, du \, dv$$

and (5-25) follows.   The above holds with the equality sign only if F is proportional to F_B [see (1-3)] in the region of integration, i.e., if (5-26) holds.

Theorem   The optimum function $f_o(x,y)$ equals the eigenfunction $\varphi_o(x,y)$ of the integral equation† [see (5-20)]

$$\iint_B \varphi(\xi,\eta)k_A(x - \xi, y - \eta) \, d\xi \, d\eta = \lambda \varphi(x,y) \tag{5-27}$$

corresponding to the largest eigenvalue $\lambda = \lambda_o$; that is,

$$f_o(x,y) = \varphi_o(x,y) \tag{5-28}$$

and the maximum energy ratio α_o equals λ_o:

$$\alpha_o = \lambda_o \tag{5-29}$$

† D. Slepian, *Bell System Tech. J.*, vol. 43, 1964, pp. 3009–3057; *J. Opt. Soc. Am.*, vol. 55, no. 9, 1965.

Proof   With $f_{oB}(x,y) = f_o(x,y)p_B(x,y)$ and $F_{oB}(u,v)$ the transform of f_{oB}, it follows from the lemma that

$$\frac{1}{4\pi^2 E \alpha_o} \iint\limits_A |F_{oB}|^2 \, du \, dv = \beta \geq \alpha_o \tag{5-30}$$

We now truncate F_{oB} outside the region A, forming the function

$$F_{oBA}(u,v) = F_{oB}(u,v)P_A(u,v)$$

and its inverse transform, $f_{oBA}(x,y)$.   Reversing the role of f and F in the lemma, we conclude that the energy ratio of f_{oBA} in the region B cannot be less than β.   But this ratio cannot exceed α_o because α_o is maximum; therefore, $\beta = \alpha_o$ and [see (5-26)]

$$F_{oB}(u,v)P_A(u,v) = \lambda F_o(u,v) \tag{5-31}$$

Since the inverse of P_A equals k_A [see (5-20)], (5-27) follows from the convolution theorem.   To complete the proof of the theorem, we must show that the solutions of (5-27) are band-limited in A and that their energy ratio equals λ.   Clearly (5-27) can be written in the form

$$\varphi_B(x,y) ** k_A(x,y) = \lambda \varphi(x,y) \tag{5-32}$$

where $\varphi_B(x,y) = \varphi(x,y)p_B(x,y)$.   Hence,

$$\Phi_B(u,v)P_A(u,v) = \lambda \Phi(u,v) \tag{5-33}$$

Furthermore,

$$\iint\limits_B |\varphi|^2 \, dx \, dy = \int\int\limits_{-\infty}^{\infty} \varphi \varphi_B \, dx \, dy = \frac{1}{4\pi^2} \int\int\limits_{-\infty}^{\infty} \Phi \Phi_B^* \, du \, dv$$

$$= \frac{\lambda}{4\pi^2} \iint\limits_A |\Phi|^2 = \lambda E$$

where E is the energy of φ, and this completes the proof.

Comments

1. The constant α_o depends on A and B.   From the foregoing discussion we can see that if these regions are interchanged, then α_o remains the same, i.e.,

$$\alpha_o(B,A) = \alpha_o(A,B) \tag{5-34}$$

and the corresponding optimum function (which is band-limited in the region B and maximizes the energy ratio in the region A) equals F_{oB} (elaborate).

2. The preceding lemma can be used to find a numerical solution of the integral equation (5-27).   We start with an arbitrary function [for example, the approximate solution (5-21)], truncate it as in (5-24), and form the transform F_B of f_B. If F_B is then truncated outside the region A, its inverse f_{BA} has a higher energy ratio than f. Repeating the process, we approach a solution of (5-27) (see also page 446).

Rectangular regions Suppose that the regions A and B are rectangles centered at the origin with sides $2a_1$, $2a_2$ and $2b_1$, $2b_2$, respectively. In this case, (5-27) takes the form

$$\int\int_{-b_2-b_1}^{b_2b_1} \varphi(\xi,\eta) \frac{\sin a_1(x - \xi) \sin a_2(y - \eta)}{\pi(x - \xi)\pi(y - \eta)} \, d\xi \, d\eta = \lambda\varphi(x,y) \qquad (5\text{-}35)$$

One can show that (Prob. 6-14) the eigenfunction $\varphi_o(x,y)$ of (5-35) corresponding to the maximum eigenvalue λ_o is of the form

$$\varphi_o(x,y) = \varphi_1(x)\varphi_2(y)$$

where $\varphi_1(x)$ and $\varphi_2(y)$ are solutions of

$$\int_{-b_1}^{b_1} \varphi_1(\xi) \frac{\sin a_1(x - \xi)}{\pi(x - \xi)} \, d\xi = \lambda_x\varphi_1(x)$$

$$\int_{-b_2}^{b_2} \varphi_2(\eta) \frac{\sin a_2(y - \eta)}{\pi(y - \eta)} \, d\eta = \lambda_y\varphi_2(y)$$

and $\lambda = \lambda_x\lambda_y$. Clearly, for φ_o to be optimum, φ_1 and φ_2 must be optimum. From the above it follows that the optimum solution of the one-dimensional problem satisfies (5-7), and the optimum function $f_o(x,y)$ of the two-dimensional problem is given by

$$f_o(x,y) = \varphi_o(x;a_1b_1)\varphi_o(y;a_2b_2) \qquad (5\text{-}36)$$

where $\varphi_o(x;c)$ are the prolate spheroidal wave functions.

CIRCULAR SYMMETRY AND HANKEL TRANSFORMS

Consider finally a real signal $f(r)$ with band-limited Hankel transform $\bar{f}(w)$

$$f(r) \overset{h}{\leftrightarrow} \bar{f}(w) \qquad \bar{f}(w) = 0 \qquad \text{for } w > a \qquad (5\text{-}37)$$

With

$$E = 2\pi \int_0^\infty rf^2(r) \, dr = 2\pi \int_0^a w\bar{f}^2(w) \, dw \qquad (5\text{-}38)$$

its circular energy, we form the energy ratio

$$\alpha = \frac{2\pi}{E} \int_0^b rf^2(r) \, dr \qquad (5\text{-}39)$$

where b is a given constant. Our problem is to find an optimum function $f_o(r)$ that is band-limited as in (5-37) and is such that α is maximum.

Approximate solution for small ab

If the product ab is small, then [see (2-20)]

$$\int_0^b rf^2(r)\,dr \simeq f^2(0)\int_0^b r\,dr = f^2(0)\frac{b^2}{2}$$

Hence, the optimum function must be such as to maximize $f^2(0)/E$. As we know from (2-7), this function is given by $J_1(ar)/r$ and its circular energy equals π [see Chap. 5, (1-20) and (1-13)]. For x small, $J_1(x) \simeq x/2$; hence, $f_o(0) = a/2$ and

$$f_o(r) \simeq \frac{J_1(ar)}{r} \qquad \alpha_o \simeq \frac{a^2 b^2}{8} \qquad \text{for } ab \to 0 \qquad (5\text{-}40)$$

Exact solution

The kernel $\sin \Omega(t - \tau)/\pi(t - \tau)$ of the integral equation (5-7) is the inverse Fourier transform of a truncated exponential. Since for Hankel transforms the function corresponding to $e^{j\omega\tau}$ is $J_o(\rho w)$, we might expect that the solution to our problem would satisfy a similar equation whose kernel is the inverse Hankel transform†

$$D(r,\rho) = a\frac{\rho J_1(a\rho)J_o(ar) - rJ_o(a\rho)J_1(ar)}{\rho^2 - r^2} \qquad (5\text{-}41)$$

[see Chap. 5, (1-23)] of the function $J_o(\rho w)$ truncated for $w > a$. This is indeed the case, as we shall presently show.

We maintain that $f_o(r)$ equals the eigenfunction $\psi_o(r)$ of the integral equation

$$\int_0^b \rho D(r,\rho)\psi(\rho)\,d\rho = \lambda\psi(r) \qquad (5\text{-}42)$$

corresponding to the maximum eigenvalue λ_o and that the maximum energy ratio α_o equals λ_o

$$\alpha_o = \lambda_o \qquad (5\text{-}43)$$

Proof With $f(x,y) = f(\sqrt{x^2 + y^2})$, the above is a special case of a two-dimensional problem. Forming the function

$$f_{ob}(r) = f_o(r)p_b(r)$$

and its Hankel transform $\bar{f}_{ob}(w)$, we see from (5-31) that

$$\bar{f}_{ob}(w)p_a(w) = \int_0^b \rho f_o(\rho)J_o(\rho w)p_a(w)\,d\rho = \lambda_o\bar{f}_o(w) \qquad (5\text{-}44)$$

Taking the inverse Hankel transforms of both sides, we obtain (5-42) because the inverse transform of $J_o(\rho w)p_a(w)$ equals $D(r,\rho)$.

† G. Lansraux and G. Boisin, *Can. J. Phys.*, vol. 36, p. 1696, 1958.

It is easy to show that the solutions of (5-42) have band-limited Hankel transforms and that their energy ratio equals λ (show it); therefore, (5-43) holds. This follows also from (5-29).

Comments

1. It follows by a simple scaling that if a and b are interchanged, then the new optimum function is $f_o(br/a)$ (elaborate). Except for a scaling, $f_o(r)$ and α_o depend only on the product ab.

2. We note that $f_o(r)$ is proportional to its Hankel transform properly scaled:

$$f_o(r) = \frac{a\sqrt{\alpha_o}}{b} \bar{f}_o\left(\frac{a}{b}r\right) \qquad r < b \tag{5-45}$$

Indeed, the energy of the function $f_{ob}(r) = f_o(r)p_b(r)$ and of its transform $\bar{f}_{ob}(w)$ equals $E\alpha_o$. The energy of $\bar{f}_{ob}(w)$ in the interval $(0,a)$ equals $E\alpha_o^2$ [see (5-44)], and, therefore, its energy ratio equals α_o. And since the optimum function is unique within a factor, we conclude from comment 1 that

$$\bar{f}_{ob}(w) = \frac{b}{a}\sqrt{\alpha_o}\, f_o\left(\frac{b}{a}w\right) \tag{5-46}$$

where the constant is determined by equalizing the energies on both sides. But

$$f_o\left(\frac{b}{a}r\right) \overset{h}{\leftrightarrow} \frac{a^2}{b^2}\bar{f}_o\left(\frac{a}{b}w\right)$$

Hence, $f_{ob}(r) = \dfrac{a}{b}\sqrt{\alpha_o}\,\bar{f}_o\left(\dfrac{a}{b}r\right)$, and (5-45) results.

3. The optimum function $f_o(r)$ satisfies the integral equation

$$\int_0^b \rho f_o(\rho)J_o(r\rho)\,d\rho = \frac{b}{a}\sqrt{\alpha_o}f_o\left(\frac{b}{a}r\right) \tag{5-47}$$

This follows from (5-46) by expressing $\bar{f}_{ob}(w)$ in terms of $f_o(\rho)$ and replacing w by r.

PROBLEMS

6-1. Consider a system with impulse response $h(t) = e^{-at}U(t)$ and input $f(t)$. We assume that $f(t)$ equals zero outside the interval $(0,T)$ and that its energy equals E.

    (a) Determine the form of $f(t)$ so that the output $g(t_o)$ at a given time t_o is maximum.

    (b) With $g_m(t_o)$ the resulting maximum, find t_o so that $g_m(t_o)$ is maximum.

6-2.† Show that, for any real x,

$$\left| e^{jx} - 1 - jx - \cdots - \frac{(jx)^{n-1}}{(n-1)!} \right| \le \frac{|x|^n}{n!}$$

† A. Papoulis, *IEEE Trans. Inform. Theory*, vol. IT-11, pp. 593–594, October, 1965.

6-3. (a) Given $n + 1$ functions $f(t)$, $\varphi_1(t)$, . . . , $\varphi_n(t)$, show that the constants a_1, . . . , a_n that minimize

$$e = \int_{-\infty}^{\infty} |f(t) - [a_1\varphi_1(t) + \cdots + a_n\varphi_n(t)]|^2 \, dt$$

must be such that

$$\int_{-\infty}^{\infty} \{f(t) - [a_1\varphi_1(t) + \cdots + a_n\varphi_n(t)]\} \varphi_i^*(t) \, dt = 0$$

for every $i = 1$, . . . , n, and that the minimum e is given by

$$e = \int_{-\infty}^{\infty} \{f(t) - [a_1\varphi_1(t) + \cdots + a_n\varphi_n(t)]\} f^*(t) \, dt$$

(b) With $F(\omega)$, $\Phi_1(\omega)$, . . . , $\Phi_n(\omega)$ the Fourier transforms of the above functions, show that the constants A_i that minimize

$$\int_{-\infty}^{\infty} |F(\omega) - [A_1\Phi_1(\omega) + \cdots + A_n\Phi_n(\omega)]|^2 \, d\omega$$

must be such that $A_i = a_i$.

(c) Using (a), show that the constants a_k that minimize

$$\int_{-T}^{T} \left| f(t) - \sum_{k=-n}^{n} a_k e^{jk\pi t/T} \right|^2 \, dt$$

are the coefficients of the Fourier series expansion of $f(t)$ in the interval $(-T,T)$.

6-4. The function $f(t)$ is band-limited by ω_o, and t_1, . . . , t_n are given numbers. With

$$f_n(t) = \sum_{i=1}^{n} a_i k(t - t_i) \qquad k(t) = \frac{\sin \omega_o t}{\pi t}$$

show that the constants a_i that minimize the mean-square error

$$e = \int_{-\infty}^{\infty} |f(t) - f_n(t)|^2 \, dt$$

must be such that

$$\sum_{i=1}^{n} a_i k(t_i - t_j) = f(t_j) \qquad j = 1, \ldots, n$$

and that the minimum e is given by

$$e = \int_{-\infty}^{\infty} |f(t)|^2 \, dt - \sum_{i=1}^{n} a_i f^*(t_i)$$

Hint: Use Prob. 6-3 and the fact that

$$f(t) * \frac{\sin \omega_o t}{\pi t} = f(t)$$

6-5. The energy of $f(x,y)$ equals E. With $F(u,v)$ its Fourier transform, show that

(a) If $F(u,v) = 0$ outside a square of area a^2, then

$$|f(x + \alpha, \, y + \beta) - f(x,y)| \leq \frac{a^2}{2\pi} \sqrt{2E(\alpha^2 + \beta^2)}$$

(b) If $F(u,v) = 0$ outside a circle of radius a, then

$$\left| \frac{\partial^{m+n} f(x,y)}{\partial x^m \, \partial y^n} \right| \leq \frac{\sqrt{E}}{2\pi} a^{m+n}$$

6-6. (a) Show that if $f(x,y) = 0$ for $|x| > a/2$ or $|y| > b/2$, then

$$\iint\limits_{-\infty}^{\infty} (u^2 + v^2)|F(u,v)|^2 \, du \, dv \geq \frac{\pi^4}{a^2 b^2} \iint\limits_{-\infty}^{\infty} |F(u,v)|^2 \, du \, dv$$

and equality holds only if

$$f(x,y) = \begin{cases} A \cos \dfrac{\pi x}{a} \cos \dfrac{\pi y}{b} & |x| < \dfrac{a}{2}, \ |y| < \dfrac{b}{2} \\ 0 & \text{otherwise} \end{cases}$$

(b) Show that, if $f(r) = 0$ for $r > a$, then with $\bar{f}(w)$ the Hankel transform of $f(r)$,

$$\int_0^\infty w^3 |\bar{f}(w)|^2 \, dw \geq \left(\frac{2.405}{a} \right)^4 \int_0^\infty w |\bar{f}(w)|^2 \, dw$$

and equality holds if

$$f(r) = \begin{cases} A J_o(\alpha_1 r) & r < a \\ 0 & r > a \end{cases} \qquad \alpha_1 a = 2.405$$

Hint: Show that if [see Chap. 5, (3-2)]

$$\sum_{i=1}^{\infty} b_i J_o(\alpha_i r) p_a(r) \overset{h}{\leftrightarrow} \bar{f}(w)$$

then

$$\sum_{i=1}^{\infty} b_i \alpha_i^2 J_o(\alpha_i r) p_a(r) \overset{h}{\leftrightarrow} w^2 \bar{f}(w)$$

6-7. The system of Fig. P6-7 consists of two all-pass filters with quadratic phase and a gate G opening at $t = t_1$ and closing at $t = t_2$. Show that under suitable approximations, this system is equivalent to an ideal bandpass filter with

$$H(\omega) = \begin{cases} \dfrac{\pi}{\alpha} & 2\alpha t_1 < \omega < 2\alpha t_2 \\ 0 & \text{otherwise} \end{cases}$$

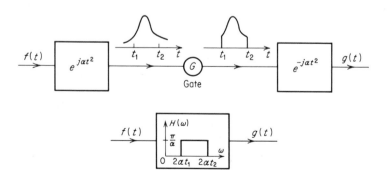

Fig. P6-7

6-8. (Exact spectrum analyzer) With $f(t) \leftrightarrow F(\omega)$, show that

$$\{[f(t) * e^{j\alpha t^2}]e^{-j\alpha t^2}\} * e^{j\alpha t^2} = \sqrt{\frac{\pi}{\alpha}}\, e^{j\pi/4} F(2\alpha t)$$

From the above it follows that the system of Fig. P6-8 yields as output the Fourier transform of the input $f(t)$.

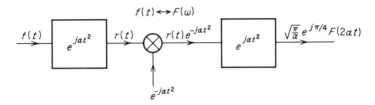

Fig. P6-8

6-9. (Pulse compression) Show that

$$e^{j(\alpha t^2 + \omega_o t)} p_{T/2}(t) \leftrightarrow e^{-j(\omega - \omega_o)^2/4\alpha} \sqrt{\frac{\pi}{2\alpha}} \left[\mathbf{F}\left(\frac{\omega - \omega_1}{2\sqrt{\alpha}}\right) + \mathbf{F}\left(\frac{\omega_2 - \omega}{2\sqrt{\alpha}}\right) \right]$$

where $\mathbf{F}(x)$ is the Fresnel integral and $\omega_1 = \omega_o - \alpha T$, $\omega_2 = \omega_o + \alpha T$. Show that if $\alpha T^2 \gg 1$, then the above Fourier transform is an ideal bandpass function (Fig. P6-9) with quadratic phase for every ω such that $|\omega - \omega_1| \gg \sqrt{\alpha}$, $|\omega - \omega_2| \gg \sqrt{\alpha}$.

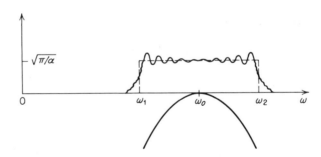

Fig. P6-9

6-10. In the time-scaling system of Fig. 4-5 the constants α, β, and γ are such that $\alpha + \gamma = \beta + \epsilon$ (defocusing). With $g(t;\epsilon)$ the resulting response, show that

$$g(t,\epsilon) = g(t,0) * e^{j\epsilon t^2}$$

6-11. (Bandpass spectrum analyzer) Show that

$$[f(t)e^{j\omega_o t}e^{-j\beta t^2}] * e^{j(\beta t^2 + \omega_1 t)} = e^{j(\beta t^2 + \omega_1 t)} F(2\beta t - \omega_o + \omega_1)$$

6-12. Given a real signal $f(t)$ that is band-limited by ω_o, we form the signal $f_T(t)$, which results from truncating $f(t)$ for $|t| > T$ (Fig. P6-12). If $f_T(t)$ is the input to an ideal low-pass filter with cutoff frequency ω_o and $g(t)$ the resulting response, show that

$$\frac{\int_{-T}^{T} f^2(t)\, dt}{\int_{-\infty}^{\infty} f^2(t)\, dt} \leq \frac{\int_{-T}^{T} g^2(t)\, dt}{\int_{-\infty}^{\infty} g^2(t)\, dt} \tag{1}$$

and that (1) holds with the equality sign only if $g(t) = \lambda f(t)$, that is, if $f(t)$ is an eigenfunction of the integral equation

$$\int_{-T}^{T} f(\tau)\, \frac{\sin \omega_o(t - \tau)}{\pi(t - \tau)}\, d\tau = \lambda f(t)$$

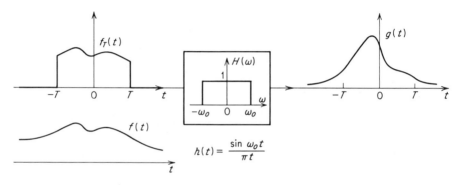

Fig. P6-12

6-13. Show that the integral equations

$$\int_{-T}^{T} \varphi(\tau)\, \frac{\sin (t - \tau)}{\pi(t - \tau)}\, d\tau = \lambda \varphi(t) \qquad \int_{-1}^{1} \psi(\tau) e^{it\tau/T}\, d\tau = \mu \psi(t)$$

have the same eigenfunctions and that their eigenvalues λ_i and μ_i are such that $\mu_i = \sqrt{2\pi\lambda_i T}$.

6-14. Show that if $\varphi_o(x,y)$ is the eigenfunction of the integral equation

$$\int_{-b_2}^{b_2} \int_{-b_1}^{b_2} \varphi(\xi,\eta) k[a_1(x - \xi)] k[a_2(y - \eta)]\, d\xi\, d\eta = \lambda \varphi(x,y) \qquad k(x) = \frac{\sin x}{\pi x}$$

which corresponds to the maximum eigenvalue λ_o, then $\varphi_o(x,y) = \varphi_1(x)\varphi_2(x)$, where $\varphi_1(x)$ and $\varphi_2(x)$ are such that

$$\int_{-b_1}^{b_1} \varphi_i(\xi) k[a_i(x - \xi)]\, d\xi = \lambda_i \varphi_i(x) \qquad i = 1,\, 2 \text{ and } \lambda_o = \lambda_1 \lambda_2$$

6-15. The input to a system $H(\omega)$ is a signal $f(t)$ such that

$$F(\omega) = 0 \qquad \text{for } |\omega| < \omega_o$$

With $g(t) = f(t) * h(t)$ the resulting output and

$$E_1 = \int_{-\infty}^{\infty} |f'(t)|^2\, dt$$

the energy of the derivative of $f(t)$, show that

$$|g(t)|^2 \leq \frac{E_1}{2\pi} \int_{|\omega| \geq \omega_o} \frac{|H(\omega)|^2}{\omega^2} d\omega \tag{1}$$

Special case† If $H(\omega) = 1$, then $g(t) = f(t)$ and (1) yields

$$|f(t)| \leq \sqrt{\frac{E_1}{\pi \omega_o}}$$

6-16. (a) Show that for any α,

$$\left| \int_a^b F(\omega) d\omega \right|^2 \leq \int_a^b (\alpha^2 + \omega^2) |F(\omega)|^2 d\omega \int_a^b \frac{d\omega}{\alpha^2 + \omega^2}$$

(b) With

$$E = \int_{-\infty}^{\infty} |f(t)|^2 dt \qquad E_1 = \int_{-\infty}^{\infty} |f'(t)|^2 dt$$

the energy of an arbitrary signal $f(t)$ and of its derivative $f'(t)$, show that for any t_o,

$$|f(t_o)| \leq \sqrt[4]{EE_1}$$

and that equality holds only if

$$f(t) = ke^{-\alpha|t-t_o|}$$

6-17.‡ (Band-limited interpolation error) Given an arbitrary signal $f(t)$ with transform $F(\omega)$, we form the function

$$s(t) = \sum_{n=-\infty}^{\infty} f(nT) \frac{\sin \omega_o(t - nT)}{\omega_o(t - nT)}$$

where T is an arbitrary constant and $\omega_o = \pi/T$. Show that

$$|f(t) - s(t)| \leq \frac{1}{\pi} \int_{|\omega| \geq \omega_o} |F(\omega)| d\omega$$

Hint: Form a suitable filter with output the "aliasing error" $f(t) - s(t)$ and show that for any ω,

$$\left| e^{j\omega t} - \sum_{n=-\infty}^{\infty} e^{jnT\omega} \frac{\sin \omega_o(t - nT)}{\omega_o(t - nT)} \right| \leq 2$$

† A. Culmone, TM-68-1, E. E. Dept., Syracuse University, Syracuse, N.Y., March, 1968.
‡ J. L. Brown, Jr., *J. of Math. Analysis and Applications,* vol. 18, April, 1967, pp. 75–84.

7

METHOD OF STATIONARY PHASE AND ASYMPTOTIC EXPANSIONS

In this chapter we investigate the asymptotic behavior of $F(\omega)$ for large ω. One of the techniques of relating this behavior to the values of $f(t)$ near the end points of its definition is the method of stationary phase. In the following we develop this method, and we extend the results to integrals of two variables. As a special case, we derive the asymptotic form of Hankel transforms.

1. THE INITIAL VALUE THEOREM

A basic problem in many applications is the determination of the behavior of the Fourier transform $F(\omega)$ or the Laplace transform

$$F_o(p) = F\left(\frac{p}{j}\right)$$

of a signal $f(t)$, for large values of ω or p. This problem is a special case of an important class of theorems on asymptotic expansions, and the purpose of this chapter is to discuss certain of these theorems that are related to Fourier transforms [d1, w2].

The most familiar form of the problem is the initial value theorem relating the derivatives of $f(t)$ at the origin to the behavior of its unilateral Laplace transform

$$F_o(p) = \int_0^\infty e^{-pt} f(t)\, dt \tag{1-1}$$

for large p. This theorem is based on the fact that the unilateral Laplace transform of a function not containing singularities at the origin tends to zero for large p:†

$$\lim F_o(p) = 0 \qquad p \to \infty \tag{1-2}$$

The proof of (1-2) follows from (1-1), but the details will be omitted.

We define the function $f'(t)$ by

$$f'(t) = \frac{df(t)}{dt} \qquad t > 0,\, f'(t) = 0,\, t \leq 0$$

This function does not contain impulses at the origin even if $f(0^+) \neq 0$, and its Laplace transform is given by

$$pF_o(p) - f(0^+)$$

From (1-2) it follows that $pF_o(p) - f(0^+)$ tends to zero for large p. Hence,

$$f(0^+) = \lim pF(p) \qquad p \to \infty$$

Repeating the foregoing argument to higher derivatives of $f(t)$, we conclude that if $f(t)$ has Laplace-transformable derivatives of order up to $n - 1$ (without singularities at the origin), then

$$F_o(p) = \frac{f(0^+)}{p} + \frac{f'(0^+)}{p^2} + \cdots + \frac{f^{(n-1)}(0^+)}{p^n} + o(p^{-n}) \tag{1-3}$$

where by

$$\varphi(x) = o(x^{-n}) \qquad x \to x_o$$

we mean that

$$\lim x^n \varphi(x) = 0 \qquad x \to x_o$$

We shall also use the notation

$$\varphi_1(x) \sim \varphi_2(x) \qquad x \to x_o$$

† In this section, the expression $p \to \infty$ will mean that p goes to infinity in a sector in the region of existence of $F_o(p)$, that is, such that

$$|\arg p| < \frac{\pi}{2} - \epsilon \tag{1-4}$$

to indicate that

$$\lim \frac{\varphi_1(x)}{\varphi_2(x)} = 1 \qquad x \to x_o$$

From (1-3) it follows that if

$$f(t) \sim kt^n \text{ for } t \to 0, \text{ then } F_o(p) \sim k \frac{n!}{p^{n+1}} \qquad \text{for } p \to \infty \qquad (1\text{-}5)$$

Thus, if the first $n - 1$ derivatives of $f(t)$ are zero at the origin, then for $p \to \infty$, $F_o(p)$ tends to zero faster than p^{-n}.

The last result can be generalized by allowing $f(t)$ to behave as t^α near the origin. For the existence of $F_o(p)$, we must, of course, have $\alpha > -1$. In this case, if

$$f(t) \sim kt^\alpha \qquad \text{for } t \to 0$$

then

$$F_o(p) \sim k \frac{\Gamma(\alpha + 1)}{p^{\alpha+1}} \qquad \text{for } p \to \infty \qquad (1\text{-}6)$$

where

$$\Gamma(\alpha + 1) = \int_0^\infty x^{-\alpha} e^{-x} \, dx$$

is the gamma function [see Chap. 3, (1-22)]. We note from the above that if $f(t)$ is not bounded, then $F_o(p)$ might tend to zero more slowly than $1/p$. For example, if

$$f(t) \sim \frac{k}{\sqrt{t}} \qquad \text{then} \qquad F_o(p) \sim k \frac{\Gamma(\frac{1}{2})}{\sqrt{p}}$$

Example 1-1

$$F_o(p) = \frac{1}{p^3 + 2p^2 + 2p + 1}$$

Since

$$\lim p^3 F_o(p) = 1 \qquad p \to \infty$$

we have

$$f(0) = f'(0) = 0 \qquad f''(0) = 1$$

Furthermore,

$$f'''(0) = \lim [p^4 F(p) - pf''(0)] = -2$$

If, in the preceding discussion, the various limits exist as p tends to infinity not only in the sector (1-4) but also along the imaginary axis, then the initial value theorem can be expressed in terms of the Fourier transform $F(\omega)$ of $f(t)$. For example, from (1-5) it follows that if $f(t) = 0$

for $t < 0$ and

$$f(t) \sim kt^n \qquad \text{for } t \to 0 \qquad \text{then} \qquad F(\omega) \sim k \frac{n!}{(j\omega)^{n+1}} \qquad \text{for } \omega \to \infty$$

$$\text{(1-7)}$$

With

$$F(\omega) = A(\omega)e^{j\varphi(\omega)}$$

the last relationship in (1-7) takes the form

$$A(\omega) \sim k \frac{n!}{\omega^{n+1}} \qquad \varphi(\omega) \sim -(n+1)\frac{\pi}{2} \qquad \text{for } \omega \to \infty \qquad \text{(1-8)}$$

We observe that $j\omega F(\omega)$ might not converge at infinity even in trivial cases. Suppose, for example, that $f(t) = U(t) - U(t-1)$. As we know,

$$F(\omega) = \frac{1 - e^{-j\omega}}{j\omega}$$

Clearly, $1 - e^{-j\omega}$ does not tend to a limit for $\omega \to \infty$, and to study the asymptotic behavior of $F(\omega)$, one needs a different version of the initial value theorem. This we plan to do in subsequent sections.

Signal-front delay Suppose that $t_o > 0$ and (Fig. 1-1)

$$f(t) = 0 \qquad \text{for } t < t_o \qquad\qquad\qquad\qquad\qquad \text{(1-9)}$$

Clearly, the signal and all its derivatives are zero at the origin, and $F_o(p)$ tends to zero faster than any power of p for $p \to \infty$. For an extension of the initial value theorem to such signals, we first determine the maximum t_o satisfying (1-9), and then relate the asymptotic behavior of $F_o(p)$ to the derivatives of $f(t)$ at $t = t_o$.

It can be seen that t_o is the least upper bound of all numbers τ such that

$$\lim e^{pt}F_o(p) = 0 \qquad p \to \infty \qquad t \leq \tau \qquad\qquad \text{(1-10)}$$

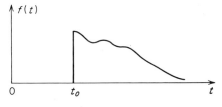 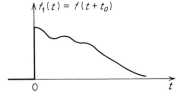

Fig. 1-1

This property of the "signal front" t_o follows from the inversion formula for Laplace transforms [p2].

With t_o determined, we form the function $f_1(t) = f(t + t_o)$, whose transform is

$$F_1(p) = e^{t_o p} F_o(p)$$

Applying the initial value theorem to the function $f_1(t)$, we obtain [see (1-3)]

$$f_1(0^+) = f(t_o^+) = \lim_{p \to \infty} p e^{t_o p} F_o(p)$$

$$f_1'(0^+) = f'(t_o^+) = \lim_{p \to \infty} [p^2 e^{t_o p} F(p) - p f(t_o^+)] \tag{1-11}$$

and similar expressions for higher derivatives.

Example 1-2

$$F_o(p) = \frac{e^{-\sqrt{p^2 + a^2}}}{p + 2}$$

It is easy to see that (1-10) is satisfied only for $\tau < 1$.   Thus

$$t_o = 1 \qquad f(t) = 0 \qquad \text{for } t < 1$$

Furthermore,

$$p - \sqrt{p^2 + a^2} = p\left[1 - \sqrt{1 + \frac{a^2}{p^2}}\right] = p\left[-\frac{a^2}{2p^2} + \cdots\right]$$

Hence [see (1-11)],

$$f(1^+) = \lim_{p \to \infty} \frac{p}{p + 2} e^{p - \sqrt{a^2 + p^2}} = 1$$

To evaluate $f'(1^+)$, we observe that

$$\frac{p^2(e^{-a^2/2p} + \cdots)}{p + 1} - p = \frac{p^2[1 - (a^2/2p + \cdots) + \cdots] - p(p + 1)}{p + 1}$$

$$\xrightarrow[p \to \infty]{} -\left(1 + \frac{a^2}{2}\right)$$

Hence,

$$f'(1^+) = -\left(1 + \frac{a^2}{2}\right)$$

Higher derivatives can be found similarly.

2. ASYMPTOTIC EXPANSION OF FOURIER TRANSFORMS

In this section, we shall study the asymptotic behavior of the Fourier integral

$$F(\omega) = \int_{-\infty}^{\infty} f(t) e^{-j\omega t}\, dt$$

for large ω.   This integral is a limiting case of

$$M(k) = \int_a^b f(t)e^{jkt}\,dt \tag{2-1}$$

In the next section we shall extend the analysis to the more general form [e1]

$$N(k) = \int_a^b f(t)e^{jk\mu(t)}\,dt \tag{2-2}$$

However, as we show in Sec. 3, one can reduce $N(k)$ to an integral of the form $M(k)$ by a change of variables.

For large k, the exponential term varies rapidly, with the result that the integrals tend to zero.   Our objective is to find out how fast they do so, and to develop an asymptotic series describing their behavior for $k \to \infty$.   As an illustration, we give below four examples:

$$I_1 = \int_a^b e^{jkt}\,dt = \frac{e^{jkb} - e^{jka}}{jk} \tag{2-3}$$

$$I_2 = \int_{-a}^a \left(1 + \cos\frac{\pi}{a}t\right)e^{jkt}\,dt = \frac{2\sin ka}{k[1 - (ak/\pi)^2]} \tag{2-4}$$

$$I_3 = \int_0^\infty t^\alpha e^{jkt}\,dt = \frac{\Gamma(\alpha+1)}{(-jk)^{\alpha+1}} = \frac{\Gamma(\alpha+1)}{k^{\alpha+1}}e^{j\pi(\alpha+1)/2} \tag{2-5}$$

$$I_4 = \int_0^\infty e^{jkt^n}\,dt = \frac{1}{n}\int_0^\infty x^{-(n-1)/n}e^{jkx}\,dx = \frac{\Gamma(1/n)}{n\sqrt[n]{-jk}} = \frac{\Gamma(1/n)}{n\sqrt[n]{k}}e^{j\pi/2n} \tag{2-6}$$

We note that the integrals I_1 and I_2 tend to zero as $1/k$ and $1/k^3$, respectively.   As we shall presently show, the reason for this difference in their asymptotic behavior is the fact that the function $f(t)$ in I_1 is different from zero at the end points of the integration interval, whereas in I_2, the function $f(t)$ and its derivative are zero for $t = \pm a$ (Fig. 2-1). In I_3, the integrand t^α tends to infinity for $t \to 0$ if $\alpha < 0$.   As a result, I_3 tends to zero more slowly than $1/k$ for $k \to \infty$.   Finally, I_4 goes to zero as $1/\sqrt[n]{k}$ because at $t = 0$ the first $n - 1$ derivatives of $\mu(t) = t^n$ are zero.

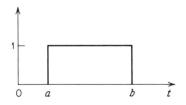
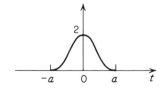

Fig. 2-1

It will be seen that the asymptotic behavior of $M(k)$ depends only on the form of $f(t)$ and its derivatives at the end points of the integration interval.   The behavior of $N(k)$ depends on the form of $f(t)$ and $\mu(t)$ at the points $t = a$ and $t = b$ and also at the points in the interior of the interval (a,b) in which $\mu(t)$ takes extreme values (stationary points).

Integration by parts

In Sec. 1, we derived the asymptotic expansion of $F_o(p)$ as follows.   We noted that $F_o \to 0$ for $p \to \infty$, and we applied this result to the transform of the derivatives of $f(t)$.   In this section, we use a related approach. We first establish the fundamental fact that $M(k) \to 0$ for $k \to \infty$ (Riemann lemma), and then we derive the subsequent terms of the expansion of $M(k)$ by repeated integration by parts.

Riemann lemma   If the function $f(t)$ is Riemann-integrable, then

$$M(k) = \int_a^b f(t)e^{jkt}\,dt \to 0 \qquad \text{for } k \to \infty \tag{2-7}$$

Proof   We shall outline a proof assuming that the interval (a,b) is finite.   From the integrability of $f(t)$ it follows that, given $\epsilon > 0$, we can find a sufficiently fine subdivision of (a,b) such that if (Fig. 2-2)

$$m_i = \min f(t) \qquad \text{for } t_i \leq t \leq t_{i+1}$$

then, for any k, the integral

$$M_n(k) = \sum_{i=0}^{n-1} \int_{t_i}^{t_{i+1}} m_i e^{jkt}\,dt$$

differs from $M(k)$ by less than ϵ.   That is,

$$|M_n(k) - M(k)| < \epsilon$$

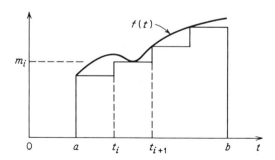

Fig. 2-2

But

$$\int_{t_i}^{t_{i+1}} m_i e^{jkt} = m_i \frac{e^{jt_{i+1}k} - e^{jt_i k}}{jk}$$

Hence

$$|M_n(k)| = \left| \sum_{i=0}^{n-1} m_i \frac{e^{jt_{i+1}k} - e^{jt_i k}}{jk} \right| \le \frac{2}{k} \sum_{i=0}^{n-1} |m_i| \xrightarrow[k \to \infty]{} 0$$

and (2-7) follows.

Comments   The above theorem also holds if the integral $M(k)$ is improper at a number of points a_i, provided that $f(t)$ is absolutely integrable in the vicinity of these points.   For the proof, one observes that the points a_i can be enclosed into subintervals such that their contribution to $M(k)$ can be made arbitrarily small.   The integral in the remaining part of the interval (a,b) is then proper, and the preceding conclusion holds.

By a limiting argument one can also prove that the lemma is true even if $a = -\infty$ or $b = \infty$.

Suppose now that the function $f(t)$ has an integrable derivative in the interval (a,b).   Integrating (2-1) by parts, we have

$$M(k) = \int_a^b f(t) \frac{de^{jkt}}{jk} = \frac{f(t)e^{jkt}}{jk}\bigg|_a^b - \frac{1}{jk}\int_a^b f'(t)e^{jkt}\, dt \qquad (2\text{-}8)$$

Applying the Riemann lemma to the last integral, we conclude that

$$\int_a^b f'(t)e^{jkt}\, dt \xrightarrow[k \to \infty]{} 0$$

Hence,

$$\frac{1}{jk} \int_a^b f'(t)e^{jkt}\, dt = o(k^{-1})$$

Therefore,

$$M(k) = \frac{f(b)e^{jkb} - f(a)e^{jka}}{jk} + o(k^{-1}) \qquad (2\text{-}9)$$

By repeated integration by parts in (2-8), we obtain the following expansion for $M(k)$.

Boundary value theorem

If the derivatives of $f(t)$ of order up to n exist and are integrable in the interval (a,b), then

$$M(k) = \sum_{m=0}^{n-1} (-1)^m \frac{f^{(m)}(b)e^{jkb} - f^{(m)}(a)e^{jka}}{(jk)^{m+1}} + o(k^{-n}) \qquad (2\text{-}10)$$

where $f^{(m)}(a)$ is the mth derivative of $f(t)$ at $t = a^+$ (from the right), and $f^{(m)}(b)$ is the corresponding derivative at $t = b^-$ (from the left).

If a function $f(t)$ is zero outside the interval (a,b), then its Fourier transform is given by

$$F(\omega) = \int_a^b f(t)e^{-j\omega t}\, dt \tag{2-11}$$

With $k = -\omega$, we thus conclude from (2-10) that if $f'(t), \ldots, f^{(n)}(t)$ are integrable in (a,b), then

$$F(\omega) = \frac{f(a)e^{-ja\omega} - f(b)e^{-jb\omega}}{j\omega} + \cdots$$
$$+ \frac{f^{(n-1)}(a)e^{-ja\omega} - f^{(n-1)}(b)e^{-jb\omega}}{(j\omega)^n} + o(\omega^{-n}) \tag{2-12}$$

If $f(t)$ is real, then, equating real and imaginary parts in (2-12), we obtain the asymptotic expansions

$$\int_a^b f(t)\cos \omega t\, dt = \frac{f(b)\sin b\omega - f(a)\sin a\omega}{\omega}$$
$$+ \frac{f'(b)\cos b\omega - f'(a)\cos a\omega}{\omega^2} - \frac{f''(b)\sin b\omega - f''(a)\sin a\omega}{\omega^3}$$
$$- \frac{f'''(b)\cos b\omega - f'''(a)\cos a\omega}{\omega^4} + \cdots \tag{2-13}$$

$$\int_a^b f(t)\sin \omega t\, dt = - \frac{f(b)\cos b\omega - f(a)\cos a\omega}{\omega}$$
$$+ \frac{f'(b)\sin b\omega - f'(a)\sin a\omega}{\omega^2} + \cdots \tag{2-14}$$

In (2-12), we can take $b = \infty$ and neglect the terms at infinity, if $f(t)$ and its pertinent derivatives tend to zero with $t \to \infty$.

If $a = 0$, $b = \infty$ and $f(t)$ and its pertinent derivatives are zero at $t = \infty$, then (2-12) yields the initial value theorem (1-4) [see also (1-7)] for the Fourier transforms of causal functions.

If $a \neq 0$, then

$$\lim_{\omega \to \infty} j\omega \int_a^\infty f(t)e^{-j\omega t}\, dt = f(a^+) \tag{2-15}$$

Comments With $F(\omega)$ as in (2-11), we see from (2-12) that if $f(t)$ and its derivatives of order up to $n - 2$ are zero at the end points of the interval (a,b), then $F(\omega)$ goes to zero as ω^{-n} for $n \to \infty$. Hence, in order to obtain a rapid attenuation of $F(\omega)$ for large ω, we should search for functions with a high order of flatness at the points $t = a$ and $t = b$. This is used in optics in the apodization problem.

If the function $f(t)$ is piecewise differentiable with discontinuous derivatives at the points $t = a_i$ in the interval (a,b), then (2-12) no longer holds. To determine the asymptotic expansion of $F(\omega)$, we write the integral in (2-11) as a sum of integrals in the intervals (a_i, a_{i+1}) and apply (2-12) to each term (see also Prob. 7-10).

Even functions If $f(-t) = f(t)$, then $f^{(m)}(-t) = (-1)^m f^{(m)}(t)$. In this case we obtain, from (2-12) with $a = -b$,

$$\frac{1}{2} \int_{-b}^{b} f(t) e^{-j\omega t} \, dt = \frac{f(b) \sin b\omega}{\omega} + \frac{f'(b) \cos b\omega}{\omega^2} - \frac{f''(b) \sin b\omega}{\omega^3}$$

$$- \frac{f'''(b) \cos b\omega}{\omega^4} + \cdots + (-1)^k \left[\frac{f^{(2k)}(b) \sin b\omega}{\omega^{2k+1}} + \frac{f^{(2k+1)}(b)}{\omega^{2k+2}} \cos b\omega \right]$$

$$+ \cdots + o(\omega^{-n}) \quad (2\text{-}16)$$

Example 2-1

$$f(t) = \begin{cases} t^n(1-t)^n & 0 < t < 1 \\ 0 & \text{otherwise} \end{cases}$$

Clearly,

$$f(0) = f'(0) = \cdots = f^{(n-1)}(0) = 0 \qquad f^{(n)}(0) = n!$$
$$f(1) = f'(1) = \cdots = f^{(n-1)}(1) = 0 \qquad {}^n(1) = n!$$

Hence [see (2-12)],

$$F(\omega) = \int_0^1 t^n(1-t)^n e^{-j\omega t} \, dt = \frac{n!(1-e^{-j\omega})}{(j\omega)^{n+1}} + o(\omega^{n+1})$$

END POINT SINGULARITIES

If $f(t) \to \infty$ for $t \to a$ or b, then the foregoing results do not hold. In the following we shall examine the behavior of $M(k)$ for this case. It will be assumed that $f(t)$ tends to infinity only for $t \to a$; to simplify the notations, we shall make $a = 0$ without loss of generality. The results can be readily extended to functions that have a singularity at the right end point $t = b$.

We shall assume that $f(t)$ tends to infinity as t^α for $t \to 0$. In other words, with

$$\varphi(t) = f(t) t^{-\alpha} \qquad f(t) = t^\alpha \varphi(t) \qquad -1 < \alpha < 0 \quad (2\text{-}17)$$

it will be assumed that $\varphi(t)$ has a continuous derivative at $t = 0$. Condition $\alpha > -1$ is necessary to insure the existence of the integral $M(k)$, which is now of the form

$$M(k) = \int_0^b f(t) e^{jkt} \, dt = \int_0^b t^\alpha \varphi(t) e^{jkt} \, dt \quad (2\text{-}18)$$

We maintain that for $k \to \infty$

$$M(k) = \varphi(0) \int_0^b t^\alpha e^{jkt} \, dt + O(k^{-1}) = \varphi(0) \frac{\Gamma(\alpha+1)}{k^{\alpha+1}} e^{j\pi(\alpha+1)/2}$$

$$+ O(k^{-1}) \quad (2\text{-}19)$$

where by

$$y(x) = O(x^{-n}) \qquad \text{for } x \to \infty$$

we mean that $x^n y(x)$ remains bounded for $x \to \infty$; that is, we can find two constants A and x_o such that

$$|y(x)| < \frac{A}{x^n} \qquad \text{for } x > x_o$$

Proof For any $\epsilon > 0$, we have

$$M(k) = \int_0^\epsilon t^\alpha \varphi(t) e^{jkt} \, dt + \int_\epsilon^b t^\alpha \varphi(t) e^{jkt} \, dt$$

The integrand of the last integral has no singularities in the integration interval (ϵ, b); hence, it goes to zero as k^{-1} for $k \to \infty$. Reasoning similarly, we have

$$\int_\epsilon^\infty t^\alpha e^{jkt} \, dt = O(k^{-1}) \qquad k \to \infty$$

Furthermore (elaborate)

$$\int_0^\epsilon t^\alpha \varphi(t) e^{jkt} \, dt = \varphi(0) \int_0^\epsilon t^\alpha e^{jkt} \, dt + O(k^{-1}) \qquad k \to \infty$$

Combining, we conclude that

$$M(k) = \varphi(0) \int_0^\infty t^\alpha e^{jkt} \, dt + O(k^{-1}) \qquad k \to \infty$$

and (2-19) follows from (2-5).

If the upper point b is singular, then with $f(t) = (b - t)^\beta \varphi(t)$ and $-1 < \beta < 0$, we obtain, as in (2-19),

$$M(k) = \int_a^b (b - t)^\beta \varphi(t) e^{jkt} \, dt = e^{jkb} \int_0^{b-a} x^\beta \varphi(x + b) e^{-jkx} \, dx$$

$$= e^{jkb} \varphi(b) \int_0^\infty x^\beta e^{-jkx} \, dx + O(k^{-1})$$

Hence, for $k \to \infty$

$$\int_a^b (b - t)^\beta \varphi(t) e^{jkt} \, dt = e^{jkb} \varphi(b) \frac{\Gamma(\beta + 1)}{k^{\beta+1}} e^{-j\pi(\beta+1)/2} + O(k^{-1}) \qquad (2\text{-}20)$$

If $f(t)$ has a singular point at $t = t_o$ and t_o is in the interior of the interval (a, b), then the asymptotic form of $M(k)$ is obtained by integrating in the (a, t_o) and (t_o, b) intervals and using (2-19) and (2-20) properly modified.

Erdélyi's theorem

The foregoing results are special cases of the following fundamental theorem.†

† A. Erdélyi, *J. Soc. Ind. Appl. Math.*, vol. 3, 1955, pp. 17–27.

Theorem   If $\varphi(t)$ is n times continuously differentiable for $a \leq t \leq b$ and

$$-1 < \lambda \leq 0 \qquad -1 < \mu \leq 0$$

then

$$\int_a^b (t - a)^\lambda (b - t)^\mu \varphi(t) e^{jkt}\, dt = B_n(k) - A_n(k) + O(k^{-n}) \qquad (2\text{-}21)$$

where

$$A_n(k) = \sum_{m=0}^{n-1} \frac{\Gamma(m + \lambda + 1) e^{j(\pi/2)(m-1+\lambda)} e^{jka}}{m! k^{m+\lambda+1}} \frac{d^m}{dt^m} \left[(b - t)^\mu \varphi(t) \right] \Big|_{t=a}$$

$$B_n(k) = \sum_{m=0}^{n-1} \frac{\Gamma(m + \mu + 1) e^{j(\pi/2)(m-1-\mu)} e^{jkb}}{m! k^{m+\mu+1}} \frac{d^m}{dt^m} \left[(t - a)^\lambda \varphi(t) \right] \Big|_{t=b}$$

In (2-21), if $\lambda = \mu = 0$, then $O(k^{-n})$ can be replaced by $o(k^{-n})$ [see also (2-10)].

With $n = 1$, we obtain

$$\int_a^b (t - a)^\lambda (b - t)^\mu \varphi(t) e^{jkt}\, dt = O(k^{-1})$$
$$+ \Gamma(\mu + 1) e^{-j(\pi/2)(\mu+1)} e^{jkb} (b - a)^\lambda \varphi(b) k^{-(\mu+1)}$$
$$+ \Gamma(\lambda + 1) e^{j(\pi/2)(\lambda+1)} e^{jka} (b - a)^\mu \varphi(a) k^{-(\lambda+1)} \qquad (2\text{-}22)$$

This follows also from (2-19) and (2-20).

We remark that the terms $A_n(k)$ and $B_n(k)$ depend on the behavior of the integrand near $t = a$ and $t = b$, respectively.   If the point $t = a$ only is singular, then the dominant term in the expansion of $M(k)$ goes to zero as $k^{-(\lambda+1)}$.   The next term is obtained from the upper limit $t = b$, and it goes to zero as k^{-1} [see also (2-9)].

Example 2-2   Suppose that

$$M(k) = \int_0^b t^{-\frac{1}{2}} e^{jkt}\, dt$$

With $\varphi(t) = 1$, $\alpha = -\frac{1}{2}$, the first term of the expansion of $M(k)$ equals [see (2-19)]

$$\frac{\Gamma(\frac{1}{2})}{k^{\frac{1}{2}}} e^{j\pi/4}$$

The next term results from the integration near the upper limit.   Its value is

$$\frac{b^{-\frac{1}{2}} e^{jkb}}{jk}$$

as we see from (2-9) with $f(b) = b^{-\frac{1}{2}}$.   Hence

$$M(k) = \sqrt{\frac{\pi}{k}} e^{j\pi/4} + \frac{e^{jkb}}{jk \sqrt{b}} + \cdots$$

Example 2-3   We shall determine the asymptotic behavior of the Bessel function

$$J_o(x) = \frac{1}{\pi} \int_{-1}^1 \frac{e^{jxt}}{\sqrt{1 - t^2}}\, dt$$

The above integral is of the form (2-21), with

$$\lambda = \mu = -\tfrac{1}{2} \qquad b = -a = 1 \qquad \varphi(t) = 1$$

Since $\Gamma(\tfrac{1}{2}) = \sqrt{\pi}$, we conclude from (2-22) that

$$J_o(x) = \sqrt{\frac{2}{\pi x}} \cos\left(x - \frac{\pi}{4}\right) + O(x^{-1})$$

The complete expansion of $J_o(x)$ is given by (Poisson)

$$J_o(x) = \sqrt{\frac{2}{\pi x}} \cos\left(x - \frac{\pi}{4}\right) \left[1 - \frac{1^2 \cdot 3^2}{2!(2x)^2} + \frac{1^2 \cdot 3^2 \cdot 5^2 \cdot 7^2}{4!(8x)^4} - \cdots\right]$$
$$+ \sqrt{\frac{2}{\pi x}} \sin\left(x - \frac{\pi}{4}\right) \left[\frac{1^2}{1!8x} - \frac{1^2 \cdot 3^2 \cdot 5^2}{3!(8x)^3} + \cdots\right]$$

as one can show with some effort from (2-21) and the fact that $\Gamma(\alpha + 1) = \alpha\Gamma(\alpha)$. The expansion of $J_n(x)$ is discussed in Prob. 7-2.

3. METHOD OF STATIONARY PHASE

Consider the integral

$$N(k) = \int_a^b f(t)e^{jk\mu(t)} \, dt \tag{3-1}$$

We maintain that if $\mu(t)$ is twice-differentiable and has no maximum or minimum (stationary point) in the interval (a,b), that is, if

$$\mu'(t) \neq 0 \qquad \text{for } a \leq t \leq b \tag{3-2}$$

then for $k \to \infty$

$$N(k) \sim \frac{1}{jk} \left[\frac{f(b)e^{jk\mu(b)}}{\mu'(b)} - \frac{f(a)e^{jk\mu(a)}}{\mu'(a)}\right] \tag{3-3}$$

Proof   We integrate (3-1) by parts:

$$M(k) = \int_a^b f(t) \frac{de^{jk\mu(t)}}{jk\mu'(t)} = \frac{f(t)e^{jk\mu(t)}}{jk\mu'(t)} \Big|_a^b - \frac{1}{jk} \int_a^b e^{jk\mu(t)} \frac{d}{dt}\left[\frac{f(t)}{\mu'(t)}\right] dt$$

But the last integral tends to zero as we can see by introducing the transformation $\mu(t) = x$ and using (3-7); hence, the last term is of the order of $o(k^{-1})$ for $k \to \infty$, and (3-3) follows.

STATIONARY POINTS

If the derivative of $\mu(t)$ is zero at a point t_o in the interval (a,b), then $N(k)$ goes to zero more slowly than $1/k$ for $k \to \infty$, and (3-3) no longer holds. By writing $N(k)$ as sum of two integrals in the intervals (a,t_o) and (t_o,b), respectively, we can assume that the stationary points of $\mu(t)$ are at the end points of the interval of integration. We shall carry out the analysis, assuming first that only the left end point a is stationary.

The discussion will be limited to the determination of the principal term in the expansion of $N(k)$; other terms can be found as outlined in Sec. 2.

Suppose then that $t_o = a$ and

$$\mu'(t_o) = \cdots = \mu^{(n-1)}(t_o) = 0 \qquad \mu^{(n)}(t_o) \neq 0 \qquad \mu'(t) \neq 0 \qquad a < t \leq b \quad (3\text{-}4)$$

We shall show that for $k \to \infty$

$$N(k) \sim f(a)e^{jk\mu(a)} \frac{\Gamma(1/n)}{n \sqrt[n]{k\mu^{(n)}(a)/n!}} e^{j\pi/2n} \quad (3\text{-}5)$$

Proof Without loss of generality, we can assume that $a = 0$ and that $\mu(a) = 0$. This can be done with a shift of the origin and the introduction of the factor $e^{jk\mu(a)}$ in (3-1). With this assumption, the integration interval becomes $(0,b)$, and $\mu(t)$ varies monotonically from 0 to $\mu(b)$ (Fig. 3-1). We can therefore introduce the change of variable

$$\mu(t) = x \qquad \mu(0) = 0 \quad (3\text{-}6)$$

in (3-1). Thus $N(k)$ takes the form

$$N(k) = \int_0^b f(t)e^{jk\mu(t)} \, dt = \int_0^{\mu(b)} \frac{f(t)}{\mu'(t)} e^{jkx} \, dx \quad (3\text{-}7)$$

where, in the last integral, t is a function of x specified by (3-6). This is an integral of the form (2-18), and in order to determine its asymptotic behavior, it suffices to find α and $\varphi(0)$. Since for $t \to 0$

$$\mu(t) \sim \mu^{(n)}(0) \frac{t^n}{n!}$$

we have

$$\mu'(t) \sim \frac{\mu^{(n)}(0)}{(n-1)!} t^{n-1} \sim \frac{\mu^{(n)}(0)}{(n-1)!} \left[\frac{\mu(t)n!}{\mu^{(n)}(0)} \right]^{(n-1)/n} = n \sqrt[n]{\frac{\mu^n(0)}{n!}} x^{(n-1)/n}$$

and

$$\frac{f(t)}{\mu'(t)} \sim x^{(1-n)/n} \frac{f(t)}{n \sqrt[n]{\mu^{(n)}(0)/n!}} = x^{(1-n)/n} \varphi(x)$$

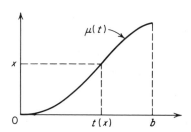

Fig. 3-1

where $\varphi(x)$ is the last fraction. Hence, with

$$\alpha = \frac{1-n}{n} \qquad \varphi(0) = \frac{f(0)}{n \sqrt[n]{\mu^{(n)}(0)/n!}}$$

(3-5) follows from (2-19).

Example 3-1   From (3-5) we obtain, with $f(t) = 1$ and $\mu(t) = t^3$,

$$\int_0^1 e^{ikt^3}\, dt \sim \frac{\Gamma(\frac{1}{3})}{3 \sqrt[3]{k}}\, e^{i\pi/6} \qquad k \to \infty$$

Indeed, $t = 0$ is the stationary point of $\mu(t)$ and

$$\mu(0) = \mu'(0) = \mu''(0) = 0 \qquad \mu'''(0) = 6$$

Comment   By the transformation (3-6), the integral $N(k)$ is reduced to the integral $M(k)$ [see (3-7)], and Erdélyi's theorem can be used to derive higher terms of its expansion.   The next term will, of course, be contributed by the integration near $t = b$ and will be given by (3-3), as we show in the next example.

Example 3-2

$$N(k) = \int_0^b e^{ikt^2}\, dt \qquad \mu(t) = t^2 \qquad n = 2$$

The dominant term is obtained from (3-5):

$$\frac{\Gamma(\frac{1}{2})}{2 \sqrt{k}}\, e^{i\pi/4}$$

The next term is obtained from (3-3) with $f(b) = 1$, $\mu'(b) = 2b$:

$$\frac{e^{ikb^2}}{jk2b}$$

Hence,

$$\int_0^b e^{ikt^2}\, dt = \frac{1}{2} \sqrt{\frac{\pi}{k}}\, e^{i\pi/4} + \frac{e^{ikb^2}}{2jbk} + \cdots$$

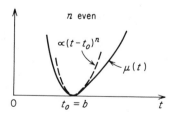

Fig. 3-2

From (3-5) we see that the value of $N(k)$ for large k depends on $f(a)$ and the behavior of $\mu(t)$ near the stationary point $t_o = a$.

Suppose now that t_o coincides with the upper end point b. If n is even, then (Fig. 3-2) $\mu(t)$ is even about t_o [see (3-4)]; hence, $N(k)$ is given again by (3-5) with a replaced by b. If n is odd, then $\mu(t)$ is odd about t_o; hence, $N(k)$ is given by the right side of (3-5) multiplied by $e^{-j\pi/n}$ (elaborate).

Interior stationary points

Suppose finally that t_o is an interior point, that is,

$$a < t_o < b$$

and that $\mu(t)$ has no other extrema in the interval (a,b). Since

$$N(k) = \int_a^{t_o} f(t)e^{jk\mu(t)}\, dt + \int_{t_o}^b f(t)e^{jk\mu(t)}\, dt$$

we conclude from the preceding discussion that if n is even, then the last two integrals are equal. Hence [see (3-5)]

$$N(k) \sim 2f(t_o)e^{jk\mu(t_o)} \frac{\Gamma(1/n)e^{j\pi/2n}}{n\sqrt[n]{k\mu^{(n)}(t_o)/n!}} \qquad n \text{ even} \tag{3-8}$$

If n is odd, then the second integral equals $e^{-j\pi/n}$ times the first integral. Therefore,

$$N(k) \sim 2f(t_o)e^{jk\mu(t_o)} \frac{\Gamma(1/n)\cos(\pi/2n)}{n\sqrt[n]{k\mu^{(n)}(t_o)/n!}} \qquad n \text{ odd} \tag{3-9}$$

because $\cos(\pi/2n) = \operatorname{Re} e^{j\pi/2n}$. The number n is defined in (3-4).

Thus, the dominant term is of the order of $1/\sqrt[n]{k}$. The next term is found from the integration near the end points a and b, and it is given by (3-3).

For $n = 2$, we have

$$N(k) \sim f(t_o)e^{jk\mu(t_o)} \sqrt{\frac{2\pi}{k\mu''(t_o)}}\, e^{j\pi/4} \tag{3-10}$$

and for $n = 3$, we have

$$N(k) \sim f(t_o)e^{jk\mu(t_o)} \frac{\Gamma(\frac{1}{3})}{\sqrt{3}} \left[\frac{6}{k\mu'''(t_o)}\right]^{\frac{1}{3}} \tag{3-11}$$

because $\cos(\pi/6) = \sqrt{3}/2$.

Example 3-3

$$N(k) = \int_a^b e^{jk(\alpha t^2 - \beta t)}\, dt \qquad a < \frac{\beta}{2\alpha} < b$$

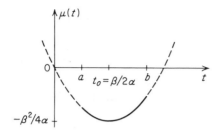

Fig. 3-3

With $\mu(t) = \alpha t^2 - \beta t$ (Fig. 3-3) we have

$$\mu'(t) = 2\alpha t - \beta \qquad t_o = \frac{\beta}{2\alpha} \qquad \mu(t_o) = \frac{-\beta^2}{4\alpha} \qquad \mu''(t_o) = 2\alpha$$

From (3-10) and (3-3) we obtain

$$\int_a^b e^{ik(\alpha t^2 - \beta t)} \, dt = \sqrt{\frac{\pi}{\alpha k}} \, e^{i\pi/4} e^{-jk\beta^2/4\alpha} + \frac{1}{jk} \left[\frac{e^{jk(\alpha b^2 - \beta b)}}{2\alpha b - \beta} - \frac{e^{jk(\alpha a^2 - \beta a)}}{2\alpha a - \beta} \right] + \cdots$$

If $\beta/2\alpha$ is outside the interval (a,b), then there are no stationary points, and the expansion of $N(k)$ starts with the k^{-1} term.

Example 3-4 (Fermat's principle and Snell's law)   Consider the expression

$$N(k) = \sqrt{k} \int_a^b e^{ikr(x)} \, dx$$

where $r(x) = r_1(x) + r_2(x) = \sqrt{d^2 + x^2} + \sqrt{e^2 + (c - x)^2}$ (Fig. 3-4). This expression gives the reflected field at P due to a line source S in front of a mirror on the seg-

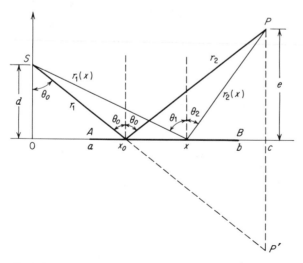

Fig. 3-4

ment (a,b) of the x axis.   The integration results from Kirchhoff's formula.   To find the asymptotic form of $N(k)$, we must determine the point x_o that minimizes $r(x)$:

$$\frac{dr(x)}{dx} = \frac{x}{r_1} - \frac{c - x}{r_2}$$

Hence, x_o is such that

$$\frac{x_o}{r_1} = \frac{c - x_o}{r_2}$$

That is,

$$\sin \theta_1 = \sin \theta_2$$

Case I   If $a < x_o < b$, then the integral goes to zero as $1/\sqrt{k}$ and [see (3-10)]

$$N(k) \sim e^{ikr(x_o)} \sqrt{\frac{2\pi}{r''(x_o)}}\, e^{i\pi/4}$$

where

$$r''(x_o) = \cos^2 \theta_o \left(\frac{1}{r_1} + \frac{1}{r_2} \right)$$

Thus if the point P is in the visible region of geometric optics, then the value of $N(k)$ is determined by integrating near the point x_o.   At this point, the optical path $r(x)$ is minimum (Fermat's principle), and the angle of incidence θ_1 equals the angle of reflection θ_2 (Snell's law).

Case II   If x_o is outside the interval (a,b), then $N(k)$ goes to zero as $1/\sqrt{k}$ and [see (3-3)]

$$N(k) \sim \frac{1}{j\sqrt{k}} \left[\frac{e^{ikr(b)}}{r'(b)} - \frac{e^{ikr(a)}}{r'(a)} \right]$$

Comments   If there are several stationary points t_i in the interval (a,b), then, by expressing $N(k)$ as a sum of integrals in intervals with only one stationary point, one can proceed as above.

The foregoing analysis can be applied to other integrals involving a large parameter if with a suitable change of variable they can be reduced to the form (3-1).   This is illustrated in the following examples.

Example 3-5   (Fresnel integral)   We shall determine the asymptotic form of the integral

$$\mathbf{F}(x) = \sqrt{\frac{2}{\pi}} \int_0^x e^{iy^2}\, dy$$

for large x.   With b a fixed constant and

$$x = \sqrt{k}\, b \qquad y = \sqrt{k}\, t$$

we have

$$\mathbf{F}(x) = \sqrt{\frac{2k}{\pi}} \int_0^b e^{ikt^2}\, dt$$

Clearly, $k \to \infty$ with $x \to \infty$; hence (see Example 3-2),

$$\mathbf{F}(x) = \frac{e^{j\pi/4}}{\sqrt{2}} + \frac{e^{jx^2}}{jx\sqrt{2\pi}} + o(x^{-1})$$

Example 3-6

$$F(\omega) = \int_0^T e^{j(\alpha t^3 + \beta t)} e^{-j\omega t}\, dt$$

With k and x defined by

$$\alpha t^3 = \frac{kx^3}{3} \qquad (\omega - \beta)t = kx \qquad k = \sqrt{\frac{(\omega - \beta)^3}{3\alpha}}$$

we have, assuming that $\omega > \beta$,

$$F(\omega) = \sqrt[3]{\frac{k}{3\alpha}} \int_0^b e^{jk(x^3/3 - x)}\, dx \qquad b = T \sqrt[3]{\frac{3\alpha}{k}} = T\sqrt{\frac{3\alpha}{\omega - \beta}}$$

The above integral is of the form (3-1), with

$$\mu(x) = \frac{x^3}{3} - x \qquad \mu'(x) = x^2 - 1$$

Clearly,

$$\mu'(x) = 0 \qquad \text{for } x = x_o = 1$$

Case I   If $b > 1$, that is, if

$$\beta < \omega < 3\alpha T^2 + \beta$$

then the stationary point $x_o = 1$ is in the interval $(0,b)$. With

$$\mu(1) = -\tfrac{2}{3} \qquad \mu''(1) = 2$$

we obtain from (3-10)

$$\int_0^b e^{jk(x^3/3 - x)}\, dx \sim e^{-j2k/3} \sqrt{\frac{\pi}{k}} e^{j\pi/4}$$

Hence, for $k \to \infty$

$$F(\omega) \sim \frac{\sqrt{\pi}}{\sqrt[4]{3\alpha(\omega - \beta)}} e^{-j2\sqrt{(\omega-\beta)^3/27\alpha}} e^{j\pi/4} \qquad (3\text{-}12)$$

Case II   If $0 < b < 1$, that is, if

$$\omega > 3\alpha T^2 + \beta$$

then there are no stationary points in the interval of integration. Since $\mu'(x) = x^2 - 1$, we have, from (3-3),

$$\int_0^b e^{jk(x^3/3 - x)}\, dx \sim \frac{1}{jk} \left[\frac{e^{jk(b^3/3 - b)}}{b^2 - 1} + 1 \right]$$

Hence

$$F(\omega) \sim \frac{1}{j(\omega - \beta)} \left[1 + \frac{(\omega - \beta)e^{j(\alpha T^3 + \beta T - \omega T)}}{3\alpha T^2 + \beta - \omega} \right] \qquad (3\text{-}13)$$

Case III If $\omega < \beta$ then with $(\beta - \omega)t = kx$, $\mu(x) = x^3/3 + x$, we see that $\mu(x)$ has no stationary points, and $F(\omega)$ is again given by (3-13).

4. STATIONARY PHASE FOR TWO–DIMENSIONAL INTEGRALS

The preceding results will now be extended to two-dimensional signals.† As we show in this section, this can be done by viewing a double integral as a repeated integral.   For brevity, we shall examine only the most common cases and shall develop only the dominant term of their asymptotic expansions.

Consider the integral

$$N(k) = \iint\limits_{R} f(x,y)e^{jk\mu(x,y)} \, dx \, dy \tag{4-1}$$

where R is a region in the xy plane, as in Fig. 4-1.   We assume that $\mu(x,y)$ is twice-continuously differentiable in R, and we shall determine the asymptotic behavior of $N(k)$ for $k \to \infty$.

Interior stationary point

Suppose that $\mu(x,y)$ takes an extreme value at a single point (x_o,y_o) in R:

$$\frac{\partial \mu}{\partial x} = \mu_x(x_o,y_o) = 0 \qquad \frac{\partial \mu}{\partial y} = \mu_y(x_o,y_o) = 0 \qquad (x_o,y_o) \in R \tag{4-2}$$

We assume that $f(x,y)$ is continuous at x_o, y_o and that

$$\mu_{xx}\mu_{yy} - \mu_{xy}{}^2 \neq 0 \qquad \mu_{yy} \neq 0 \tag{4-3}$$

where μ_{xx}, μ_{yy}, μ_{xy} are partial derivatives evaluated at (x_o,y_o).   We shall show that for $k \to \infty$

$$\iint\limits_{R} f(x,y)e^{jk\mu(x,y)} \, dx \, dy \sim \frac{2\pi j f(x_o,y_o)}{k \sqrt{\mu_{xx}\mu_{yy} - \mu_{xy}{}^2}} \, e^{jk\mu(x_o,y_o)} \tag{4-4}$$

Proof   The intersection of the surface $\mu(x,y)$ by a plane perpendicular to the x axis is a curve $\mu(x,y)$ (x constant).   This curve has a maximum at a point x, $\bar{y}(x)$, where $\bar{y}(x)$ is the solution of the equation

$$\frac{\partial \mu}{\partial y} = \mu_y = 0 \qquad \text{that is} \qquad \mu_y[x,\bar{y}(x)] = 0 \tag{4-5}$$

Varying x, we thus obtain a curve $\bar{y}(x)$ in the xy plane, which is specified by (4-5).   Since $\mu(x,y)$ has an extremum at (x_o,y_o), such a curve exists, and it passes through (x_o,y_o).   Clearly, the function $\bar{y}(x)$ is given implicitly by (4-5) and it is such that $\bar{y}(x_o) = y_o$.   We shall assume that it is single-valued; i.e., for one x there is at most one $\bar{y}(x)$.   We shall further assume that any line parallel to the x axis intersects the boundary of

† J. S. Jones and M. Kline, *J. Math. Phys.*, vol. 37, no. 1, 1958, pp. 1–28.

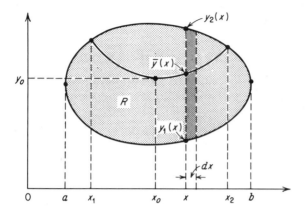

Fig. 4-1

the region R at no more than two points.   These assumptions are made for brevity of notation, and they can be easily relaxed.

The integral $N(k)$ can thus be written in the form

$$N(k) = \int_a^b \int_{y_1(x)}^{y_2(x)} f(x,y)e^{jk\mu(x,y)} \, dy \, dx \tag{4-6}$$

where $y_1(x)$, $y_2(x)$, a, and b are as in Fig. 4-1.   The inner integral

$$N_1(k,x) = \int_{y_1(x)}^{y_2(x)} f(x,y)e^{jk\mu(x,y)} \, dy \tag{4-7}$$

is of the form (3-1).   With x_1 and x_2 the x coordinates of the end points of the curve $\bar{y}(x)$, if

$$x_1 < x < x_2$$

then $N_1(k,x)$ has an interior stationary point for $y = \bar{y}(x)$ [see (4-5)]. As we shall presently see, the asymptotic form of $N(k)$ depends on the behavior of $N_1(k,x)$ near x_o.   At least in this vicinity, $\mu_{yy} \neq 0$ [see (4-3)]; hence, with $n = 2$, we have, from (3-10),

$$N_1(k,x) \sim f[x,\bar{y}(x)]e^{jk\mu[x,\bar{y}(x)]} \sqrt{\frac{2\pi}{k\mu_{yy}[x,\bar{y}(x)]}} \, e^{j\pi/4} \tag{4-8}$$

For x not in the interval (x_1,x_2), $N_1(k,x)$ has no stationary points; hence, it goes to zero as k^{-1} for $k \to \infty$.   For large k we can therefore neglect in (4-6) the integration outside the interval (x_1,x_2) in the determination of the dominant part of $N(k)$.   Thus

$$N(k) \sim \int_{x_1}^{x_2} N_1(k,x) \, dx \sim \sqrt{\frac{2\pi}{k}} \, e^{j\pi/4} \int_{x_1}^{x_2} \frac{f[x,\bar{y}(x)]}{\sqrt{\mu_{yy}[x,\bar{y}(x)]}} \, e^{jk\mu[x,\bar{y}(x)]} \, dx \tag{4-9}$$

This is an integral of the form (3-1), and to determine its asymptotic behavior, we need its stationary points, i.e., the roots of

$$\frac{d\mu[x,\bar{y}(x)]}{dx} = \mu_x + \mu_y \frac{d\bar{y}(x)}{dx} = 0$$

Since $\mu_y[x,\bar{y}(x)] \equiv 0$, we see that at a stationary point, we must have

$$\mu_x[x,\bar{y}(x)] = 0 \qquad \mu_y[x,\bar{y}(x)] = 0$$

This is satisfied only for $x = x_o$ [see (4-2)] and at that point, $\bar{y}(x_o) = y_o$. To complete the evaluation of $N(k)$, we need the second derivative of $\mu[x,\bar{y}(x)]$. Differentiating the identity $\mu_y[x,\bar{y}(x)] \equiv 0$ with respect to x, we find

$$\mu_{yx} + \mu_{yy}\bar{y}'(x) = 0$$

Hence

$$\bar{y}'(x) = -\frac{\mu_{yx}}{\mu_{yy}}$$

Thus,

$$\frac{d^2\mu[x,\bar{y}(x)]}{dx^2} = \mu_{xx} + \mu_{xy}\bar{y}' + (\mu_{yx} + \mu_{yy}\bar{y}')\bar{y}' + \mu_y\bar{y}'' = \mu_{xx} - \frac{\mu_{xy}^2}{\mu_{yy}}$$

and with $\bar{y}(x_o) = y_o$, we have, applying (3-10) to (4-9),

$$N(k) \sim \sqrt{\frac{2\pi}{k}} \, e^{j\pi/4} \frac{f}{\sqrt{\mu_{yy}}} \, e^{jk\mu} \sqrt{\frac{2\pi}{k(\mu_{xx} - \mu_{xy}^2/\mu_{yy})}} \, e^{j\pi/4}$$

where all functions are evaluated at (x_o,y_o), and (4-4) follows.

Comments If $\mu(x,y)$ has several distinct stationary points in R, then the dominant term in the expansion of $N(k)$ is determined by summing (4-4) over all these points.

If the stationary points of $\mu(x,y)$ form a curve (horizontal ridge) such that

$$\mu[x,\bar{y}(x)] = \mu = \text{const} \qquad \text{for } x \text{ in the interval } (x_3,x_4)$$

then (4-9) yields

$$N(k) \sim \sqrt{\frac{2\pi}{k}} \, e^{j\pi/4} e^{jk\mu} \int_{x_3}^{x_4} \frac{f[x,\bar{y}]}{\sqrt{\mu_{yy}[x,\bar{y}]}} \, dx \tag{4-10}$$

The last integral is independent of k, and $N(k)$ goes to zero as $1/\sqrt{k}$ for $k \to \infty$.

If $\mu(x,y)$ has no stationary points but (4-5) has a solution $\bar{y}(x)$ (ridge without peak in R), then $N_1(k,x)$ is again given by (4-8). However, the last integral in (4-9) has no stationary points because the equation

$\mu_x + \mu_y \bar{y}'(x) = 0$ has no solution for $x_1 < x < x_2$. Its value depends on the integration near the end points x_1, x_2, and it can be determined from (3-3). Inserting (3-3) into (4-9), we conclude that the dominant term of $N(k)$ depends on the value of f and μ_{yy} at the points $[x_1, \bar{y}(x_1)]$ and $[x_2, \bar{y}(x_2)]$, and it goes to zero as $k^{-3/2}$.

Suppose finally that $\mu(x,y)$ is monotone increasing or decreasing with increasing x or y (no peaks or ridges). In this case, the asymptotic form of $N_1(k,x)$ will depend on the integration near the boundary points $y_1(x)$ and $y_2(x)$, and it will be given by (3-3), with dominant term proportional to k^{-1}. As a result, $N(k)$ will depend on the behavior of f and μ near the boundary of R, and it will go to zero faster than $1/k$. Since the analysis is essentially the same for an arbitrary μ as for a μ depending linearly on x and y, we shall carry out the details for $\mu(x,y) = ax + by$, which is essentially the exponent in a two-dimensional Fourier transform.

ASYMPTOTIC FORM OF THE TWO–DIMENSIONAL FOURIER TRANSFORMS

Consider a region R with a smooth boundary C (twice-differentiable). If the function $f(x,y)$ equals zero outside the region R, then its Fourier transform is given by

$$F(u,v) = \iint_R f(x,y)e^{-j(ux+vy)} \, dx \, dy \tag{4-11}$$

We shall study the behavior of $F(u,v)$ for u and v tending to infinity along the line

$$\frac{v}{u} = \gamma \tag{4-12}$$

With $v = \gamma u$, the integral $F(u,v)$ takes the form

$$F(u,\gamma u) = \iint_R f(x,y)e^{-ju(x+\gamma y)} \, dx \, dy \tag{4-13}$$

which is similar to (4-1), with $u = -k$ and $\mu(x,y) = x + \gamma y$. Since $\mu_x = 1$, $\mu_y = \gamma$, this integral has no stationary points.

We denote by $P_i(\alpha_i, \beta_i)$ the points of the boundary curve C such that the tangent to C is perpendicular to the line $y = \gamma x$ and denote by ρ_i the radius of curvature of the curve C at these points (Fig. 4-2). We shall show that the dominant term of the asymptotic expansion of $F(u,v)$ depends on $f(\alpha_i, \beta_i)$ and ρ_i. Specifically,

$$F(u,v) \sim \sum_i \frac{f(\alpha_i,\beta_i) \sqrt{2\pi\rho_i}}{\sqrt[4]{(u^2 + v^2)^3}} e^{j(u\alpha_i + v\beta_i \mp 3\pi/4)} \tag{4-14}$$

where the sign of $3\pi/4$ is negative if $u\alpha_i + v\beta_i > 0$; otherwise it is positive.

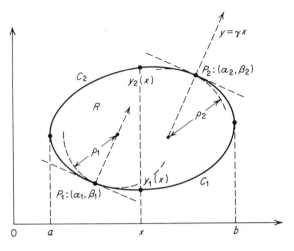

Fig. 4-2

Proof With $y_1(x)$ and $y_2(x)$ the upper and lower parts of the curve C and

$$F_1(x,v) = \int_{y_1(x)}^{y_2(x)} f(x,y)e^{-jvy} \, dy \tag{4-15}$$

we have from (2-9), with $k = -v$,

$$F_1(x,v) \sim (jv)^{-1}\{f[x,y_1(x)]e^{-jvy_1(x)} - f[x,y_2(x)]e^{-jvy_2(x)}\} \tag{4-16}$$

Clearly,

$$F(u,v) = \int_a^b F_1(x,v)e^{-jux} \, dx \tag{4-17}$$

To evaluate the asymptotic form of $F(u,v)$, we insert (4-16) in the above integral and use the method of stationary phase for one variable. Consider the term

$$I = \int_a^b f[x,y_1(x)]e^{-ju[x+\gamma y_1(x)]} \, dx$$

It is of the form of (3-1), with $\mu(x) = x + \gamma y_1(x)$ and $k = -u$. Its stationary points x_i are the roots of

$$\mu'(x) = 1 + \gamma y_1'(x) = 0 \qquad y_1'(x_i) = -\frac{1}{\gamma} = -\frac{u}{v}$$

From the above, we see that the tangent to the boundary curve C at the points $[x_i,y_1(x_i)]$ is perpendicular to the line $y = \gamma x$; hence, these points are the points P_i of the lower branch C_1 of C and $y_1(\alpha_i) = \beta_i$. From

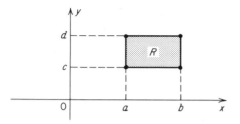

Fig. 4-3

(3-10) we have

$$I \sim \sum_i f(\alpha_i,\beta_i) e^{-ju(\alpha_i+\gamma\beta_i)} \sqrt{\frac{2\pi}{-u\mu''(\alpha_i)}} \; e^{j\pi/4}$$

where $\mu''(\alpha_i) = \gamma y_1''(\alpha_i)$, and the summation extends over all i in C_1. At P_i the radius of curvature ρ_i of C is given by

$$\rho_i = \frac{[1 + (y_1')^2]^{3/2}}{\pm y_1''} = \frac{\sqrt{(1 + u^2/v^2)^3}}{\pm y_1''}$$

Hence

$$\mu''(\alpha_i) = \gamma y_1''(\alpha_i) = \mp \frac{\sqrt{(u^2 + v^2)^3}}{\rho_i u v^2}$$

Inserting into the asymptotic form of I, we obtain, with (4-16) and (4-17), the terms of (4-14) which result from the points P_i in C_1. The second term in (4-16) is handled similarly.

Comments   For the validity of (4-14) and its extensions, the function $f(x,y)$ must satisfy various differentiability conditions. These conditions follow from the corresponding requirements of the one-dimensional cases on which the proof of (4-14) was based.

The dominant term of $F(u,v)$ is not always given by (4-14). Suppose, for example, that $f(x,y) = 0$ everywhere on the curve C. In this case, the dominant term of $F_1(x,v)$ is [see (2-10)]

$$F_1(x,v) \sim (jv)^{-2}\{f_1'[x,y_1(x)]e^{-jvy_1(x)} - f_2'[x,y_2(x)]e^{-jvy_2(x)}\}$$

where

$$f_i'[x,y_i(x)] = \frac{df[x,y_i(x)]}{dx} = f_x[x,y_i(x)] + f_y[x,y_i(x)]\frac{dy_i(x)}{dx} \qquad i = 1, 2$$

Inserting into (4-17), we can proceed as before.

As a last application, we shall assume that the boundary C of the region R is a polygon. In this case, the dominant term of $F(u,v)$ depends on the values of $f(x,y)$ at the corners of the polygon. We shall carry out the details for a region bounded by a rectangle (Fig. 4-3).   The integral $F(u,v)$ takes the form

$$F(u,v) = \int_c^d \int_a^b f(x,y)e^{-j(ux+vy)} \, dx \, dy$$

We shall assume that both u and v tend to infinity, i.e., that γ is different from 0 or ∞.   By repeated application of (2-9), we obtain

$$\int_a^b f(x,y)e^{-jux} \, dx \sim \frac{f(b,y)e^{-jub} - f(a,y)e^{-jua}}{-jv}$$

$$\int_c^d \int_a^b f(x,y)e^{-j(ux+vy)} \, dx \, dy \sim \frac{1}{uv} \left[f(b,d)e^{-j(ub+vd)} - f(b,c)e^{-j(ub+vc)} \right.$$
$$\left. - f(a,d)e^{-j(ua+vd)} + f(a,c)e^{-j(ua+vc)} \right]$$

ASYMPTOTIC EXPANSION OF HANKEL TRANSFORMS

We shall finally show that the asymptotic form of the Hankel transform

$$\tilde{f}(w) = \int_0^a rf(r)J_o(wr) \, dr \tag{4-18}$$

is

$$\tilde{f}(w) \sim \sqrt{\frac{2a}{\pi w^3}} \, f(a) \sin\left(wa - \frac{\pi}{4}\right) \qquad \text{for } w \to \infty \tag{4-19}$$

Proof   Since $2\pi \tilde{f}(\sqrt{u^2 + v^2})$ is the Fourier transform of $f(\sqrt{x^2 + y^2})$, we have

$$\tilde{f}(\sqrt{u^2 + v^2}) = \frac{1}{2\pi} \iint_R f(\sqrt{x^2 + y^2})e^{-j(ux+vy)} \, dx \, dy \tag{4-20}$$

where R is a circle of radius a.   We can therefore use (4-14).   For any u/v, there are two stationary boundary points P_1 and P_2 (Fig. 4-4), where

$$\alpha_1 = -\alpha_2 = \frac{ua}{w} \qquad \beta_1 = -\beta_2 = \frac{va}{w}$$

$$\alpha_1 u + \beta_1 v = -(\alpha_2 u + \beta_2 v) = \frac{(u^2 + v^2)a}{w} = aw$$

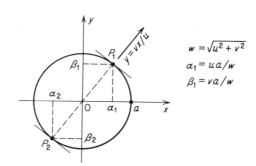

Fig. 4-4

But $f(\sqrt{\alpha_i{}^2 + \beta_i{}^2}) = f(a)$, $\rho_i = a$; hence (4-14) yields

$$\bar{f}(w) \sim \frac{1}{2\pi} \frac{f(a)\sqrt{2\pi a}}{\sqrt[4]{w^6}} [e^{j(aw-3\pi/4)} + e^{-j(aw-3\pi/4)}]$$

and (4-19) follows.

Comments   The above result can also be obtained from the asymptotic form of $J_o(x)$ (see Example 2-3).

$$J_o(x) \sim \sqrt{\frac{2}{\pi x}} \cos\left(x - \frac{\pi}{4}\right)$$

Inserting into (4-18), we have

$$\bar{f}(w) \sim \sqrt{\frac{2}{\pi w}} \int_0^a \sqrt{r}\, f(r) \cos\left(wr - \frac{\pi}{4}\right) dr$$

$$= \sqrt{\frac{2}{\pi w}} \operatorname{Re} \int_0^a \sqrt{r}\, f(r) e^{j(wr-\pi/4)}\, dr$$

The last integral is of the form of (2-1).   Applying (2-9), we obtain

$$\bar{f}(w) \sim \sqrt{\frac{2}{\pi w}} \operatorname{Re} \frac{1}{jw} \sqrt{a}\, f(a) e^{j(wa-\pi/4)}$$

and (4-19) results.

In (4-19) the number $f(a)$ is, of course, $f(a^-)$.

If $f(a) = 0$, then, as we shall presently show, $\bar{f}(w)$ goes to zero faster than $w^{-3/2}$.

Example 4-1   From the pair of Hankel transforms

$$\left.\begin{array}{ll} 1 & 0 \le r \le a \\ 0 & r > a \end{array}\right\} \overset{h}{\leftrightarrow} \frac{a J_1(aw)}{w}$$

and (4-19) we have

$$\frac{a J_1(aw)}{w} \sim \sqrt{\frac{2a}{\pi w^3}} \sin\left(aw - \frac{\pi}{4}\right) \qquad w \to \infty$$

from which the asymptotic form of the Bessel function $J_1(x)$ results.

$$J_1(x) \sim \sqrt{\frac{2}{\pi x}} \cos\left(x - \frac{3\pi}{4}\right)$$

Higher-order terms

We shall use the differentiation theorem [see Chap. 5, (1-10)]

$$f''(r) + \frac{1}{r} f'(r) \overset{h}{\leftrightarrow} -w^2 \bar{f}(w) \tag{4-21}$$

to obtain higher-order terms in the asymptotic expansion of $\bar{f}(w)$.   We shall assume that $f(r)$ is twice-differentiable in the interval $0 < r < a$.

Suppose first that

$$f(a) = 0 \qquad f'(a) = 0$$

We then have, from (4-18) and (4-21),

$$\bar{f}(w) \sim -\sqrt{\frac{2a}{\pi w^7}}\, f''(a) \sin\left(aw - \frac{\pi}{4}\right) \qquad w \to \infty \qquad (4\text{-}22)$$

Similarly, if

$$f^{(k)}(a) = 0 \qquad k = 0, 1, \ldots, 2n - 1$$

then, reasoning similarly, we have

$$\bar{f}(w) \sim (-1)^n \sqrt{\frac{2a}{\pi w^{4n+3}}}\, f^{(2n)}(a) \sin\left(aw - \frac{\pi}{4}\right) \qquad w \to \infty \qquad (4\text{-}23)$$

Suppose next that $f(a) \neq 0$, $f'(a) = 0$.   The function

$$\varphi(r) = f(r) - f(a)p_a(r)$$

is zero for $r > a$, and its Hankel transform equals

$$\bar{\varphi}(w) = \bar{f}(w) - f(a)\frac{aJ_1(aw)}{w} \qquad (4\text{-}24)$$

Clearly, $\varphi(a) = 0$, $\varphi'(a) = 0$.   Hence we can use (4-22) for $\bar{\varphi}(w)$.   Since $\varphi''(a) = f''(a)$, we conclude from (4-24) that

$$\bar{f}(w) \sim \frac{af(a)J_1(aw)}{w} - \sqrt{\frac{2a}{\pi w^7}}\, f''(a) \sin\left(aw - \frac{\pi}{4}\right) \qquad (4\text{-}25)$$

Retaining the first term in the asymptotic expansion of $J_1(aw)$ (Prob. 7-2), we thus obtain the first two terms in the expansion of $\bar{f}(w)$.   The dominant term agrees, of course, with (4-19) (see Example 4-1).

Suppose finally that $f(a) = 0$, $f'(a) \neq 0$.   The second derivative of $f(r)$ contains an impulse $f'(a)\delta(r - a)$.   With $f''(r)$ as the derivative in the interval $0 < r < a$, (4-21) reads

$$f''(r) + \frac{1}{r}f'(r) - f'(a)\delta(r - a) \overset{h}{\leftrightarrow} -w^2\bar{f}(w)$$

Hence

$$f''(r) + \frac{1}{r}f'(r) \overset{h}{\leftrightarrow} -w^2\bar{f}(w) + af'(a)J_o(aw)$$

Since there are no singularities in the left side, we can apply (4-19).

The result is

$$\tilde{f}(w) \sim af'(a)\frac{J_o(aw)}{w^2} - \sqrt{\frac{2a}{\pi w^7}}\left[f''(a) + \frac{1}{a}f'(a)\right]\sin\left(aw - \frac{\pi}{4}\right)$$

(4-26)

The dominant term is (see Example 2-3)

$$\tilde{f}(w) \sim f'(a)\sqrt{\frac{2a}{\pi w^5}}\cos\left(aw - \frac{\pi}{4}\right)$$

(4-27)

Repeating the foregoing arguments, we can determine any number of terms in the expansion of $\tilde{f}(w)$.

5. THE MEANING OF AN ASYMPTOTIC EXPANSION

By

$$f(x) \sim \varphi(x) \qquad x \to x_o$$

one means that

$$\lim \frac{f(x)}{\varphi(x)} = 1 \qquad x \to x_o$$

We write

$$f(x) = o[\varphi(x)] \qquad x \to x_o$$

to indicate that

$$\lim \frac{f(x)}{\varphi(x)} = 0 \qquad x \to x_o$$

Finally,

$$f(x) = O[\varphi(x)] \qquad x \to x_o$$

means that the ratio $f(x)/\varphi(x)$ is bounded in some neighborhood of x_o; that is, there exist two constants $A > 0$ and $\epsilon > 0$ such that

$$|f(x)| < A|\varphi(x)| \qquad \text{for } |x - x_o| \le \epsilon$$

If $x_o = \infty$, then $|x - x_o| \le \epsilon$ should be replaced by $x > \epsilon$.
It follows from the above that for any a

$$O[a\varphi(x)] = O[\varphi(x)] \qquad o[a\varphi(x)] = o[\varphi(x)]$$

We also note that

$$f(x) \sim \varphi(x) \qquad \text{iff} \qquad f(x) - \varphi(x) = o[\varphi(x)]$$

(5-1)

Indeed

$$\lim \frac{f(x) - \varphi(x)}{\varphi(x)} = \lim \frac{f(x)}{\varphi(x)} - 1 = 0 \qquad x \to x_o$$

Similarly, if $f(x) \sim \varphi(x)$, then

$$f(x) = O[\varphi(x)] \qquad x \to x_o$$

However, the converse is not true.

Asymptotic sequences and series

We say that the functions $\varphi_o(x)$, $\varphi_1(x)$, . . . form an asymptotic sequence for $x \to x_o$ if [e1]

$$\varphi_{n+1}(x) = o[\varphi_n(x)] \qquad x \to x_o \tag{5-2}$$

For example, x^n is an asymptotic sequence for $x \to 0$, and x^{-n} is such a sequence for $x \to \infty$.

Suppose that $\varphi_n(x)$ is an asymptotic sequence, and

$$f(x) \sim \sum_{n=0}^{N} a_n \varphi_n(x) \qquad x \to x_o \tag{5-3}$$

It then follows from (5-1) that

$$f(x) - \sum_{n=0}^{N} a_n \varphi_n(x) = o[\varphi_N(x)] \qquad x \to x_o \tag{5-4}$$

With $\varphi_n(x)$ as above, we say that $f(x)$ is given by an asymptotic series expansion

$$f(x) \sim \sum_{n=0}^{\infty} a_n \varphi_n(x) \qquad x \to x_o \tag{5-5}$$

if we can find a sequence of numbers a_1, a_2, . . . such that (5-3) is true for any N. We elaborate on the meaning of the series (5-5). Given an integer N and a number δ, we can find a number $\epsilon > 0$ such that

$$\left| f(x) - \sum_{n=0}^{N} a_n \varphi_n(x) \right| < \delta \varphi_N(x) \qquad \text{for } |x - x_o| < \epsilon \tag{5-6}$$

If $x_o = \infty$, then $|x - x_o| < \epsilon$ is replaced by $x > \epsilon$.

An important special case of (5-5) is the asymptotic power series

$$f(x) \sim a_0 + \frac{a_1}{x} + \frac{a_2}{x^2} + \cdots + \frac{a_n}{x^n} + \cdots \qquad x \to \infty \tag{5-7}$$

In this case

$$f(x) - \left(a_0 + \frac{a_1}{x} + \cdots + \frac{a_n}{x^n} \right) = o(x^{-n}) \qquad x \to \infty$$

or, equivalently,

$$\lim x^n \left[f(x) - \left(a_0 + \cdots + \frac{a_n}{x^n} \right) \right] = 0 \qquad x \to \infty$$

Comments Suppose that for any n

$$\varphi_n(x) \to 0 \qquad x \to x_o$$

In this case, we have [see (5-4)]

$$r_N(x) = f(x) - \sum_{n=0}^{N} a_n \varphi_n(x) \to 0 \qquad x \to x_o \tag{5-8}$$

From this, *it does not follow* that

$$f(x) = \sum_{n=0}^{\infty} a_n \varphi_n(x) \tag{5-9}$$

In fact, for any $x \neq x_o$, the above sum might be infinite; i.e., it might represent a divergent series. This does not, of course, contradict (5-8). In order for the series (5-9) to converge for a *specific* x, the rest term $r_N(x)$ should be small for *any* N sufficiently large. For (5-8) to be true, $r_N(x)$ should be small for a specific N and for x in a small neighborhood (depending on N) of x_o.

If the series in (5-5) is divergent, then we can construct a convergent series that is asymptotically equal to $f(x)$. For this purpose, we form the functions

$$\psi_n(x) = \begin{cases} \varphi_n(x) & |x - x_o| < 2^{-n} \\ 0 & |x - x_o| > 2^{-n} \end{cases}$$

These functions form an asymptotic sequence as in (5-2), and they are such that

$$f(x) \sim \sum_{n=0}^{\infty} a_n \psi_n(x) \qquad x \to x_o$$

because, for a given N, $\psi_n(x) = \varphi_n(x)$ if x is sufficiently close to x_o and $n \leq N$. Furthermore, if $x \neq x_o$, then the series converges because $\psi_n(x) = 0$ for n sufficiently large.

PROBLEMS

7-1.† The Laplace transform of the step response $f(t)$ of a transmission line without leakage is given by

$$F(p) = \frac{e^{-b\sqrt{p(p+a)}}}{p}$$

Find the front t_o of $f(t)$. Show that

$$f(t_o) = e^{-ab/2} \qquad f'(t_o) = \frac{a^2 b}{8} e^{-ab/2} \qquad f''(t_o) = -\frac{a^3 b}{32} e^{-ab/2}\left(1 - \frac{ab}{4}\right)$$

† G. F. Ross, *IEEE, PGCT*, vol. GT-13, p. 220, June, 1966.

7-2. Show that the asymptotic expansion of $J_n(x)$ is given by

$$J_n(x) \sim \sqrt{\frac{2}{\pi x}} \cos\left(x - \frac{n\pi}{2} - \frac{\pi}{4}\right)\left[1 - \frac{(4n^2 - 1^2)(4n^2 - 3^2)}{2!(8x)^2}\right.$$
$$\left. + \frac{(4n^2 - 1^2)(4n^2 - 3^2)(4n^2 - 5^2)(4n^2 - 7^2)}{4!(8x)^4} - \cdots\right] - \sqrt{\frac{2}{\pi x}} \sin\left(x - \frac{n\pi}{2} - \frac{\pi}{4}\right)$$
$$\left[\frac{4n^2 - 1^2}{1!8x} - \frac{(4n^2 - 1^2)(4n^2 - 3^2)(4n^2 - 5^2)}{3!(8x)^3} + \cdots\right]$$

7-3. Show that

$$\int_{-a}^{a} \sqrt{a^2 - t^2}\, e^{-j\omega t}\, dt \sim \sqrt{\frac{8a\pi}{\omega^3}} \cos\left(a\omega - \frac{3\pi}{4}\right) \qquad \text{for } \omega \to \infty$$

7-4. With

$$\mu(x,y) = r = \sqrt{(x - x_o)^2 + (y - y_o)^2 + z_o^2}$$

show that if the point (x_o, y_o) is in S, then

$$g(x_o, y_o, z_o) = \frac{-jk}{4\pi} \iint_S \frac{1}{r}\left(1 - \frac{\partial r}{\partial z}\right) f(x,y) e^{jkr}\, dx\, dy \xrightarrow[k \to \infty]{} f(x_o, y_o) e^{jkz_o}$$

7-5. With $\bar{f}(w)$ the Hankel transform of $J_o(br)p_a(r)$, show that for $w \to \infty$

$$\bar{f}(w) \sim J_o(ab) \sqrt{\frac{2a}{\pi w^3}} \sin\left(aw - \frac{\pi}{4}\right) \qquad \text{if} \qquad J_o(ab) \neq 0$$

$$\bar{f}(w) \sim bJ_1(ab) \sqrt{\frac{2a}{\pi w^5}} \cos\left(aw + \frac{3\pi}{4}\right) \qquad \text{if} \qquad J_o(ab) = 0$$

7-6. If $f(r) = 0$ for $r > a$, then its profile $\varphi(x)$ is given by

$$\varphi(x) = 2 \int_0^{\sqrt{a^2 - x^2}} f(r)\, dy \qquad \text{for } |x| < a$$

Derive the asymptotic expansion (4-19) for $\bar{f}(w)$, using the result of Prob. 7-5 and the fact that if

$$f(r) \overset{h}{\leftrightarrow} \bar{f}(w)$$

then

$$\varphi(u) \leftrightarrow 2\pi\bar{f}(u)$$

Hint: For x near a, $\varphi(x) \simeq 2f(a)\sqrt{a^2 - x^2}$.

7-7. Show that for $x \to x_o$

(a) $O[\varphi_1(x)]O[\varphi_2(x)] = O[\varphi_1(x)\varphi_2(x)]$

(b) $O[\varphi_1(x)]o[\varphi_2(x)] = o[\varphi_1(x)]o[\varphi_2(x)] = o[\varphi_1(x)\varphi_2(x)]$

7-8. Show that if for $x \to x_o$

$$f_i(x) = O[\varphi_i(x)] \qquad i = 1, 2, \ldots, n$$

then

$$a_1 f_1(x) + \cdots + a_n f_n(x) = O[|a_1|\varphi_1(x) + \cdots + |a_n|\varphi_n(x)]$$

7-9. Show that if

$$f(x) \sim \sum_{n=0}^{N} a_n \varphi_n(x) \qquad x \to x_o$$

then

$$a_n = \lim_{x \to x_o} \frac{f(x) - \sum_{i=0}^{n-1} a_i \varphi_i(x)}{\varphi_n(x)} \qquad n = 0, \ldots, N$$

7-10. In this problem, it is shown that the points of discontinuity of the first n derivatives of a signal $f(t)$ can be determined if the asymptotic expansion of order $n + 1$ of its Fourier transform $F(\omega)$ is known. Show that if

$$F(\omega) = \frac{c_o}{j\omega} e^{-ja_o\omega} + \cdots + \frac{c_n}{(j\omega)^{n+1}} + o\left(\frac{1}{\omega^{n+1}}\right) \qquad \omega \to \infty$$

then the ith derivative $f^{(i)}(t)$ of $f(t)$ is discontinuous at $t = a_i$ with discontinuity

$$f^{(i)}(a_i{}^+) - f^{(i)}(a_i{}^-) = c_i \qquad i = 0, \ldots, n$$

Hint. Express $F(\omega)$ as a sum of integrals in the intervals (a_i, a_{i+1}); use (2-12).
Illustration If $F(\omega) = 1/(\omega^4 + 1) = 1/\omega^4 - 1/\omega^8 + \cdots$, then $f(t)$ and all its derivatives are continuous for $t \neq 0$. Furthermore,

$$f^{(i)}(0^+) - f^{(i)}(0^-) = \begin{cases} 1 & i = 4n + 3 \\ 0 & i \neq 4n + 3 \end{cases} \qquad n = 0, 1, \ldots$$

Special case If $\lim [j\omega e^{ja\omega}F(\omega)] = c$ for $\omega \to \infty$, then $f(a^+) - f(a^-) = c$.

8
RANDOM SIGNALS

We now turn our investigation to stochastic processes, i.e., to signals $f(t)$ that are specified not by their point properties, but by their averages. Stochastic processes and averages (E) can be given two different interpretations. In the first interpretation, $f(t)$ means a family of stationary random functions, and E denotes expected value. In the second interpretation, $f(t)$ is a single time function, and E is a time average. Both interpretations lead to identical results formally.

Our analysis is limited to the investigation of correlation functions (second-order moments) and power spectra. These quantities give only a partial description of the average properties of $f(t)$; however, they suffice in a large number of applications.

In Sec. 2, we deal with signals defined in a general space, and we derive the correlation of the output of linear operators (systems). The one-dimensional case is treated with some elaboration in Secs. 3 and 4. For emphasis, we reestablish the main results in Sec. 5 in the form of time averages. We conclude with a brief discussion of two-dimensional signals.

1. INTRODUCTION

In the preceding chapters we dealt with "deterministic" functions that can usually be described by a small number of analytic pieces. We now turn our attention to "random" signals that are specified by "irregular" curves, as in Fig. 1-1. We should point out that the two cases are treated differently not because deterministic signals are "known" and random signals are "unknown." The essential reason is that in a deterministic analysis we are dealing with point properties of various functions, whereas in the theory of random signals we study averages.

The *time average* $\langle x(t) \rangle$ of a signal $x(t)$ is defined by the limit

$$\langle x(t) \rangle = \lim \frac{1}{2T} \int_{-T}^{T} x(t)\, dt \qquad T \to \infty \tag{1-1}$$

This limit is a number (functional) associated with $x(t)$ such that (see Prob. 8-1)

$$\langle ax(t + b) \rangle = a\langle x(t) \rangle \tag{1-2}$$

$$\langle a_1 x_1(t) + \cdots + a_n x_n(t) \rangle = a_1\langle x_1(t) \rangle + \cdots + a_n\langle x_n(t) \rangle \tag{1-3}$$

The average of a random signal can be given a different interpretation. One assumes that $\mathbf{x}(t)$ is a member of a stochastic process,[†] i.e., of a family of functions defined on a probability space. For a given t, $\mathbf{x}(t)$ is then a random variable with an expected value

$$\eta(t) = E\{\mathbf{x}(t)\}$$

which defines the *ensemble average* of the random signal $\mathbf{x}(t)$.

The quantities $\langle x(t) \rangle$ and $\eta(t)$ are, in general, unrelated. In fact, $\langle x(t) \rangle$ is a constant, whereas $\eta(t)$ depends on t. However, if the process $\mathbf{x}(t)$ is stationary and it satisfies certain conditions (ergodicity, page 278), then the time-average $\langle \mathbf{x}(t) \rangle$ performed on each member of the family is "almost certainly" a constant equal to the ensemble average $E\{\mathbf{x}(t)\}$.

The question is then which of these two approaches should one adopt in the study of averages. It would seem that if one deals with a single function, time averaging should be used, since it is related directly to the observable signal; this, however, is not the case. A physical signal is available only over a finite interval of time; the limit in (1-1) is, therefore, not a physical quantity but a theoretical concept. It is no more an abstraction to assume that $\mathbf{x}(t)$ is a "typical" member of a family of functions and to define its average properties as expected values. This approach also permits the investigation of averages for nonstationary signals (Fig. 1-2), whereas this is not possible in terms of time averages.

[†] Boldface letters will be used to denote stochastic processes.

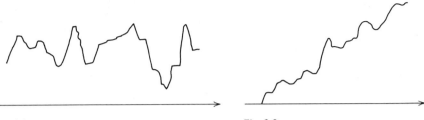

Fig. 1-1   **Fig. 1-2**

Finally, even if one is interested only in a single signal, its properties might be related to the known properties of an ensemble.

The following analysis will be phrased primarily in terms of stochastic processes and ensemble averages [p1, p3]. From the theory of probability we shall use only the fact that

$$E\{|\mathbf{x}(t)|^2\} \geq 0 \tag{1-4}$$

and the linearity of expected values: With $\mathbf{x}_1$, $\mathbf{x}_2$, . . . a sequence of random variables, and a_1, a_2, . . . a sequence of numbers,

$$E\{a_1\mathbf{x}_1 + \cdots + a_n\mathbf{x}_n\} = a_1E\{\mathbf{x}_1\} + \cdots + a_nE\{\mathbf{x}_n\} \tag{1-5}$$

We note that all our results concerning stationary stochastic processes hold also for time averages of a single signal. This follows from the equivalence of (1-5) and (1-3). In Sec. 5 we discuss briefly the time-average form of various theorems.

In this investigation, we shall study the second-order moments of the input $\mathbf{x}(t)$ and the output $\mathbf{y}(t)$ of a linear system. The quantities of primary interest are the average amplitudes $E\{\mathbf{x}(t)\}$, $E\{\mathbf{y}(t)\}$ and the intensities $E\{|\mathbf{x}(t)|^2\}$, $E\{|\mathbf{y}(t)|^2\}$. It will be seen that, whereas $E\{\mathbf{y}(t)\}$ can be expressed in terms of $E\{\mathbf{x}(t)\}$ only, $E\{|\mathbf{y}(t)|^2\}$ cannot be determined from a mere knowledge of $E\{|\mathbf{x}(t)|^2\}$. The *autocorrelation*

$$R(t_1,t_2) = E\{\mathbf{x}(t_1)\mathbf{x}^*(t_2)\} \tag{1-6}$$

of the input $\mathbf{x}(t)$ must be known for every t_1, t_2.

The preceding notions were formulated in terms of time functions; however, they also hold if the independent variable is a vector in an arbitrary space. In the next section we develop our main results in terms of signals defined on a general space and of linear operators. In subsequent sections we consider the special features of one- and two-dimensional signals.

2. LINEAR SYSTEMS AND SECOND-ORDER MOMENTS

We are given a stochastic process $\mathbf{x}(P)$, where P is a point in a general space (space-time). The *expected value* or *mean* $\eta_x(P)$, defined by

$$\eta_x(P) = E\{\mathbf{x}(P)\} \tag{2-1}$$

is a deterministic function of P.

Suppose that the process $\mathbf{x}(P)$ is the input to a system L. The resulting output

$$\mathbf{y}(Q) = L[\mathbf{x}(P)] \tag{2-2}$$

is also a stochastic process, and Q is either a point of the input space or of another space. We shall determine its mean

$$\eta_y(Q) = E\{\mathbf{y}(Q)\} \tag{2-3}$$

In general, this function cannot be expressed in terms of $\eta_x(P)$ only. For its determination, other statistical properties of the input must be known. However, as we shall presently show, if the system is linear, then $\eta_y(Q)$ can be found from a mere knowledge of $\eta_x(P)$.

Fundamental theorem   If the system L is linear, then

$$\eta_y(Q) = L[\eta_x(P)] \tag{2-4}$$

Thus the expected value of the output is the response of the system to the deterministic input $\eta_x(P)$.

Proof   The proof of the above is an immediate consequence of the linearity of expected values [see (1-5)]:

$$E\{\mathbf{y}(Q)\} = E\{L[\mathbf{x}(P)]\} = L[E\{\mathbf{x}(P)\}]$$

It can be derived more concretely by expressing the system as a convolution

$$\mathbf{y}(Q) = \int_V \mathbf{x}(P)h(P;Q)\,dP \tag{2-5}$$

where $h(P;Q)$ is its impulse response [see Chap. 2, (3-9) and (3-32)], and the integration extends over the space V of the input. Taking expected values of both sides of (2-5) and using (1-5) (extended to infinite sums and integrals), we conclude that

$$E\{\mathbf{y}(Q)\} = \int_V E\{\mathbf{x}(P)\}h(P;Q)\,dP \tag{2-6}$$

and (2-4) follows.

Comments

1. For the validity of the above theorem, linearity suffices. It is not necessary to assume that the system is shift-invariant.

2. The theorem is true only if the system is deterministic, i.e., if its impulse response $h(P;Q)$ is not random. Only then does the relationship

$$E\{\mathbf{x}(P)h(P;Q)\,dP\} = E\{\mathbf{x}(P)\}h(P;Q)\,dP$$

on which (2-6) is based, hold. A system specified internally, either by its elements (lumped parameters or propagation media) or by a differential equation, is deterministic if the elements or the coefficients of the defining equation are deterministic.

CORRELATION

In the study of random signals, an observable quantity is the average *intensity* (or *power*) $E\{|\mathbf{x}(P)|^2\}$. Unlike the case of the mean, the average intensity $E\{|\mathbf{y}(Q)|^2\}$ of the output $\mathbf{y}(Q)$ of a linear system cannot be determined in terms of the average intensity $E\{|\mathbf{x}(P)|^2\}$ of the input. What is needed is the mean of the product $\mathbf{x}(P_1)\mathbf{x}^*(P_2)$ for *every* P_1 and P_2.

Definitions   The *autocorrelation*

$$R(P_1,P_2) \qquad \text{or} \qquad R_{xx}(P_1,P_2)$$

of a process $\mathbf{x}(P)$ is defined by

$$R_{xx}(P_1,P_2) = E\{\mathbf{x}(P_1)\mathbf{x}^*(P_2)\} \tag{2-7}$$

Given two processes $\mathbf{x}(P)$ and $\mathbf{y}(Q)$, we define their *cross correlation* $R_{xy}(P,Q)$ by

$$R_{xy}(P,Q) = E\{\mathbf{x}(P)\mathbf{y}^*(Q)\} \tag{2-8}$$

If the above definitions are applied to the processes

$$\mathbf{x}(P) - E\{\mathbf{x}(P)\} \qquad \text{and} \qquad \mathbf{y}(Q) - E\{\mathbf{y}(Q)\}$$

the resulting quantities are known as the autocovariance and the cross-covariance functions $C_{xx}(P_1,P_2)$ and $C_{xy}(P,Q)$. Thus the cross covariance of the processes $\mathbf{x}(P)$ and $\mathbf{y}(Q)$ is given by

$$C_{xy}(P,Q) = R_{xy}(P,Q) - E\{\mathbf{x}(P)\}E\{\mathbf{y}^*(Q)\} \tag{2-9}$$

This is the covariance of the random variables $\mathbf{x}(P)$ and $\mathbf{y}(Q)$. In optics, C_{xx} and C_{xy} are known as self- and mutual-*coherence functions*, respectively. The ratio

$$r_{xy}(P,Q) = \frac{C_{xy}(P,Q)}{\sqrt{C_{xx}(P,P)C_{yy}(Q,Q)}} \tag{2-10}$$

is known as the *complex degree of coherence*. It is the correlation coefficient of the random variables $\mathbf{x}(P)$ and $\mathbf{y}(Q)$, and it satisfies

$$|r_{xy}(P,Q)| \leq 1 \tag{2-11}$$

which results readily from (1-4) (see Prob. 8-3).

Comment We shall now show that the cross correlation $R_{xy}(P,Q)$ can be expressed as the average intensity of a linear combination of $\mathbf{x}(P)$ and $\mathbf{y}(Q)$. For this purpose, we form the function

$$
\begin{aligned}
I(a,b) &= E\{|a\mathbf{x}(P) + b\mathbf{y}(Q)|^2\} \\
&= E\{[a\mathbf{x}(P) + b\mathbf{y}(Q)][a^*\mathbf{x}^*(P) + b^*\mathbf{y}^*(Q)]\} \\
&= |a|^2 R_{xx}(P,P) + ab^* R_{xy}(P,Q) + a^*b R_{xy}^*(P,Q) + |b|^2 R_{yy}(Q,Q)
\end{aligned}
$$

From the above it follows that

$$I(1,0) = R_{xx}(P,P) \qquad I(0,1) = R_{yy}(Q,Q)$$

$$I(1,1) = R_{xx}(P,P) + 2 \operatorname{Re} R_{xy}(P,Q) + R_{yy}(Q,Q)$$

$$I(1,j) = R_{xx}(P,P) + 2 \operatorname{Im} R_{xy}(P,Q) + R_{yy}(Q,Q)$$

Thus, by measuring $I(1,0)$, $I(0,1)$, $I(1,1)$ and $I(1,j)$, we can determine the real numbers $R_{xx}(P,P)$, $R_{yy}(Q,Q)$ and the real and imaginary parts of $R_{xy}(P,Q)$. The autocorrelation $R_{xx}(P_1,P_2)$ can be found similarly.

OUTPUT CORRELATION

Our objective is to determine the autocorrelation of the output of a linear system L. This will permit us to find not only $E\{|\mathbf{y}(Q)|^2\}$ but also the average intensity of any other process linearly dependent on $\mathbf{y}(Q)$. As a preparation, we shall first evaluate the cross correlation between input and output.

Conjugate system In this analysis, it will be desirable to define the conjugate L^* of the system L. This system is such that

$$\text{If} \qquad \mathbf{y}(Q) = L[\mathbf{x}(P)] \qquad \text{then} \qquad \mathbf{y}^*(Q) = L^*[\mathbf{x}^*(P)] \tag{2-12}$$

It is easy to see that L^* is linear. If L is specified by its impulse response $h(P,Q)$, then the impulse response of L^* is $h^*(P,Q)$. We shall say that the system L is real if $L = L^*$. In this case, $h(P,Q)$ is a real function.

From the linearity of L^* it follows that with P_1 a fixed point,

$$L^*[\mathbf{x}(P_1)\mathbf{x}^*(P)] = \mathbf{x}(P_1)L^*[\mathbf{x}^*(P)] = \mathbf{x}(P_1)\mathbf{y}^*(Q)$$

In this expression, L^* operates on the function $\mathbf{x}^*(P)$, with $\mathbf{x}(P_1)$ treated as a constant. To emphasize this fact, we write the above in the form

$$\mathbf{x}(P_1)\mathbf{y}^*(Q_2) = L_2^*[\mathbf{x}(P_1)\mathbf{x}^*(P_2)]$$

Taking expected values of both sides, we obtain, as in (2-4),

$$E\{\mathbf{x}(P_1)\mathbf{y}^*(Q_2)\} = L_2^*[E\{\mathbf{x}(P_1)\mathbf{x}^*(P_2)\}]$$

Hence,

$$R_{xy}(P_1,Q_2) = L_2^*[R_{xx}(P_1,P_2)] \tag{2-13}$$

Thus, $R_{xy}(P_1,Q_2)$ is the output of the linear operator L^* with input $R_{xx}(P_1,P_2)$. The subscript 2 in L_2^* indicates that the system operates on $R_{xx}(P_1,P_2)$, which is considered as a function of P_2, with P_1 a parameter.

Multiplying both sides of (2-2) by $\mathbf{y}^*(Q_2)$, we have

$$\mathbf{y}(Q_1)\mathbf{y}^*(Q_2) = L_1[\mathbf{x}(P_1)\mathbf{y}^*(Q_2)]$$

Taking expected values, we finally conclude that

$$R_{yy}(Q_1,Q_2) = L_1[R_{xy}(P_1,Q_2)] \tag{2-14}$$

Combining (2-13) with (2-14), we can thus express the autocorrelation of the output $\mathbf{y}(Q)$ in terms of the autocorrelation of the input $\mathbf{x}(P)$ by

$$R_{yy}(Q_1,Q_2) = L_1[L_2^*[R_{xx}(P_1,P_2)]] \tag{2-15}$$

Example 2-1 In a propagation problem, the field $y(Q)$ at a point Q in space (Fig. 2-1) due to a certain source distribution $x(P)$ is determined by solving a suitable wave equation. If the medium is linear, then this process defines a linear operator L with input $x(P)$ and output $y(Q)$. The conjugate operator L^* results when the wave equation is replaced by its conjugate (conjugate coefficients).

Suppose now that the source $\mathbf{x}(P)$ is random with autocorrelation $R_{xx}(P_1,P_2)$. This function is assumed known for every P_1 and P_2 in the space of the source. We want to determine the average power $E\{|\mathbf{y}(Q)|^2\}$ or, more generally, the autocorrelation $R_{yy}(Q_1,Q_2)$ of the resulting random field $\mathbf{y}(Q)$. From (2-13) we see that the cross correlation $R_{xy}(P_1,Q_2)$ between the source $\mathbf{x}(P_1)$ and the field $\mathbf{y}(Q_2)$ is found by solving the conjugate wave equation whose source is the autocorrelation $R_{xx}(P_1,P_2)$, which is considered as a function of P_2. To determine $R_{yy}(Q_1,Q_2)$, we then apply (2-14). This means that we solve the wave equation whose source is the cross correlation $R_{xy}(P_1,Q_2)$, which is considered as a function of P_1.

Consider, finally, two linear systems L^1 and L^2 (Fig. 2-2) with inputs

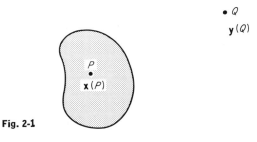

Fig. 2-1

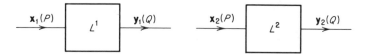

Fig. 2-2

$\mathbf{x}_1(P)$, $\mathbf{x}_2(P)$ and outputs $\mathbf{y}_1(Q)$, $\mathbf{y}_2(Q)$

$$\mathbf{y}_1(Q) = L^1[\mathbf{x}_1(P)] \qquad \mathbf{y}_2(Q) = L^2[\mathbf{x}_2(P)] \tag{2-16}$$

Reasoning as in (2-13) and (2-14), we find (elaborate)

$$E\{\mathbf{x}_1(P_1)\mathbf{y}_2^*(Q_2)\} = R_{x_1 y_2}(P_1, Q_2) = L_2^{2*}[R_{x_1 x_2}(P_1, P_2)] \tag{2-17}$$

$$E\{\mathbf{y}_1(Q_1)\mathbf{y}_2^*(Q_2)\} = R_{y_1 y_2}(Q_1, Q_2) = L_1^1[R_{x_1 y_2}(P_1, Q_2)] \tag{2-18}$$

In (2-17), L_2^{2*} is the conjugate of the system L^2 and it operates on the variable P_2.

3. ONE–DIMENSIONAL PROCESSES

We are given a stochastic process $\mathbf{x}(t)$ with mean

$$\eta_x(t) = E\{\mathbf{x}(t)\}$$

and autocorrelation

$$R_{xx}(t_1, t_2) = E\{\mathbf{x}(t_1)\mathbf{x}^*(t_2)\}$$

where

$$E\{|\mathbf{x}(t)|^2\} = R_{xx}(t, t) \geq 0 \tag{3-1}$$

If $\varphi(t)$ is a deterministic signal and

$$\mathbf{w}(t) = \varphi(t)\mathbf{x}(t)$$

then, since

$$E\{\varphi(t_1)\mathbf{x}(t_1)\varphi^*(t_2)\mathbf{x}^*(t_2)\} = \varphi(t_1)\varphi^*(t_2)E\{\mathbf{x}(t_1)\mathbf{x}^*(t_2)\}$$

we have

$$R_{ww}(t_1, t_2) = \varphi(t_1)\varphi^*(t_2)R_{xx}(t_1, t_2) \tag{3-2}$$

The cross correlation of two processes $\mathbf{x}(t)$ and $\mathbf{y}(t)$ is defined by

$$R_{xy}(t_1, t_2) = E\{\mathbf{x}(t_1)\mathbf{y}^*(t_2)\}$$

We say that these processes are orthogonal (uncorrelated if their mean is zero) if $R_{xy}(t_1, t_2) = 0$ for every t_1, t_2.

SYSTEMS

Suppose that $\mathbf{x}(t)$ is the input to a linear time-invariant system L with impulse response $h(t)$. The resulting output

$$\mathbf{y}(t) = \int_{-\infty}^{\infty} \mathbf{x}(t - \alpha)h(\alpha)\, d\alpha = \mathbf{x}(t) * h(t) \tag{3-3}$$

is also a stochastic process. A specific function of $\mathbf{y}(t)$ (associated with an experimental outcome) is determined by convolving the corresponding member of $\mathbf{x}(t)$ with the impulse response of the system. We shall determine the mean and autocorrelation of $\mathbf{y}(t)$.

Taking expected values of both sides of (3-3), we conclude [as in (2-6)] that

$$\eta_y(t) = \int_{-\infty}^{\infty} \eta_x(t - \alpha)h(\alpha)\, d\alpha = \eta_x(t) * h(t) \tag{3-4}$$

Multiplying the conjugate of (3-3) by $\mathbf{x}(t_1)$ and taking expected values, we have [p1]

$$E\{\mathbf{x}(t_1)\mathbf{y}^*(t)\} = \int_{-\infty}^{\infty} E\{\mathbf{x}(t_1)\mathbf{x}^*(t - \alpha)\}h^*(\alpha)\, d\alpha$$

With $t = t_2$, we thus obtain

$$R_{xy}(t_1,t_2) = \int_{-\infty}^{\infty} R_{xx}(t_1; t_2 - \alpha)h^*(\alpha)\, d\alpha = R_{xx}(t_1,t_2) * h^*(t_2) \tag{3-5}$$

The last expression means that we convolve $R_{xx}(t_1,t_2)$, which is considered as a function of t_2, with the impulse response $h^*(t_2)$ (the variable t_1 is treated as a parameter).

Multiplying (3-3) by $\mathbf{y}^*(t_2)$ and taking expected values, we find, similarly,

$$R_{yy}(t_1,t_2) = \int_{-\infty}^{\infty} R_{xy}(t_1 - \alpha, t_2)h(\alpha)\, d\alpha = R_{xy}(t_1,t_2) * h(t_1) \tag{3-6}$$

These results are special cases of (2-13) and (2-14). They also hold if the correlations are replaced by the corresponding covariance functions.

White noise   We shall say that the process $\mathbf{x}(t)$ is white noise if

$$R_{xx}(t_1,t_2) = 0 \qquad \text{for } t_1 \neq t_2 \tag{3-7}$$

or, equivalently, if its complex degree of coherence equals zero for $t_1 \neq t_2$; that is, if

$$r_{xx}(t_1,t_2) = 0 \qquad t_1 \neq t_2 \tag{3-7a}$$

(We assumed zero mean.)   The term incoherence is also used in place of white noise; however, we shall reserve it for space-dependent processes.

If the process $\mathbf{x}(t)$ is white noise and its autocorrelation does not contain impulses, then its effects, i.e., moments of the output of a system with input $\mathbf{x}(t)$, are identically zero [see (3-5) and (3-6)]. Hence, the autocorrelation of a nontrivial white noise must be of the form

$$R_{xx}(t_1,t_2) = q(t_1)\delta(t_2 - t_1) \tag{3-8}$$

If $\mathbf{x}(t)$ is the input to a linear system and $\mathbf{y}(t)$ is the resulting output, then (3-5) and (3-6) yield

$$R_{xy}(t_1,t_2) = [q(t_1)\delta(t_2 - t_1)] * h^*(t_2) = q(t_1)h^*(t_2 - t_1)$$
$$R_{yy}(t_1,t_2) = [q(t_1)h^*(t_2 - t_1)] * h(t_1)$$
$$= \int_{-\infty}^{\infty} q(t_1 - \alpha)h^*(t_2 - t_1 - \alpha)h(\alpha)\,d\alpha \tag{3-9}$$

With $t_1 = t_2 = t$, we obtain the important relationship

$$E\{|\mathbf{y}(t)|^2\} = R_{yy}(t,t) = \int_{-\infty}^{\infty} q(t - \alpha)|h(\alpha)|^2\,d\alpha = q(t) * |h(t)|^2 \tag{3-10}$$

Thus the average intensity of the output is obtained by convolving $q(t)$ with $|h(t)|^2$.

If

$$h(t) = 0 \qquad \text{for } |t| < a$$

and a is sufficiently small so that $q(t)$ can be approximated by a constant in any interval of length $2a$, then

$$E\{|\mathbf{y}(t)|^2\} \simeq q(t) \int_{-a}^{a} |h(t)|^2\,dt \tag{3-11}$$

In other words, the average intensity of the output of a system with "short" impulse response is proportional to $q(t)$. For this reason, $q(t)$ is often called the "average intensity" of $\mathbf{x}(t)$ although

$$E\{|\mathbf{x}(t)|^2\} = \infty$$

We shall retain this practice.

From (3-11) we also conclude that

$$q(t) \geq 0 \tag{3-12}$$

Comment White noise is an extreme case of a process with $\mathbf{x}(t_1)$ and $\mathbf{x}(t_2)$ uncorrelated. At the other extreme (complete coherence) the absolute value of the coherence ratio equals one:

$$|r_{xx}(t_1,t_2)| = 1 \qquad \text{all } t_1,\, t_2 \tag{3-13}$$

This is the case if

$$R_{xx}(t_1,t_2) = p(t_1)p^*(t_2) \tag{3-14}$$

Fig. 3-1

A process $\mathbf{x}(t)$ that satisfies (3-14) must be such that

$$E\left\{\left|\mathbf{x}(t_1) - \frac{p(t_1)}{p(t_2)}\mathbf{x}(t_2)\right|^2\right\} = 0 \qquad \text{all } t_1, t_2 \tag{3-15}$$

as it is easy to see.

We return to systems. Suppose that $\mathbf{x}_1(t)$, $\mathbf{x}_2(t)$ are the inputs to the two systems of Fig. 3-1 and

$$\mathbf{y}_1(t) = \mathbf{x}_1(t) * h_1(t) \qquad \mathbf{y}_2(t) = \mathbf{x}_2(t) * h_2(t) \tag{3-16}$$

are the resulting outputs. Reasoning as in (3-5), we conclude that [see also (2-17) and (2-18)]

$$R_{x_1 y_2}(t_1,t_2) = R_{x_1 x_2}(t_1,t_2) * h_2^*(t_2)$$
$$R_{y_1 y_2}(t_1,t_2) = R_{x_1 y_2}(t_1,t_2) * h_1(t_1) \tag{3-17}$$

Example 3-1

a. We shall determine the mean and autocorrelation of the derivative $\mathbf{x}'(t)$ of a process $\mathbf{x}(t)$. Clearly, $\mathbf{x}'$ can be considered as the output of a linear system L (differentiator) with input $\mathbf{x}(t)$. Hence [see (2-4)],

$$E\{\mathbf{x}'(t)\} = \frac{dE\{\mathbf{x}(t)\}}{dt} \tag{3-18}$$

With

$$R_{xx'}(t_1,t_2) = E\{\mathbf{x}(t_1)\mathbf{x}'^*(t_2)\}$$

we conclude from (2-13) and the fact that L is a real system that

$$R_{xx'}(t_1,t_2) = L_2[R_{xx}(t_1,t_2)] = \frac{\partial R_{xx}(t_1,t_2)}{\partial t_2} \tag{3-19}$$

because L_2 signifies differentiation with respect to the variable t_2. Similarly [see (2-14)],

$$R_{x'x'}(t_1,t_2) = L_1\left[\frac{\partial R_{xx}(t_1,t_2)}{\partial t_2}\right] = \frac{\partial^2 R_{xx}(t_1,t_2)}{\partial t_1\,\partial t_2} \tag{3-20}$$

b. With L^1, L^2 two systems such that

$$L^1[x(t)] = \frac{d^n x(t)}{dt^n} = x^{(n)}(t) \qquad L^2[x(t)] = x^{(r)}(t)$$

we obtain from (2-17) and (2-18), setting $\mathbf{x}_1(t) = \mathbf{x}_2(t) = \mathbf{x}(t)$,

$$R_{x^{(n)}x^{(r)}}(t_1,t_2) = \frac{\partial^{n+r}R_{xx}(t_1,t_2)}{\partial t_1^n\,\partial t_2^r} \tag{3-21}$$

DIFFERENTIAL EQUATIONS

Suppose that the process $\mathbf{y}(t)$ is the solution of an nth-order differential equation

$$a_n\mathbf{y}^{(n)}(t) + \cdots + a_1\mathbf{y}'(t) + a_0\mathbf{y}(t) = \mathbf{x}(t) \qquad t \geq 0 \tag{3-22}$$

with initial conditions

$$\mathbf{y}(0) = \mathbf{y}'(0) = \cdots = \mathbf{y}^{(n-1)}(0) = 0 \tag{3-23}$$

It is well known that if we assume $\mathbf{y}(t) = 0$ for $t < 0$, then $\mathbf{y}(t)$ can be considered as the output of a linear system L with input $\mathbf{x}(t)U(t)$. The system is specified by (3-22) and (3-23), and its impulse response $h(t)$ can be found by solving the equation

$$a_nh^{(n)}(t) + \cdots + a_0h(t) = \delta(t) \qquad h(0^-) = \cdots = h^{(n-1)}(0^-) = 0$$

or, equivalently, the equation

$$a_nh^{(n)}(t) + \cdots + a_0h(t) = 0 \qquad h(0) = \cdots = h^{(n-2)}(0) = 0$$

$$h^{(n-1)}(0) = \frac{1}{a_n}$$

The conjugate L^* of L is specified by the differential equation (3-22), whose coefficients are the conjugates a_k^* of a_k, and which has initial conditions (3-23).

We shall determine the mean $\eta_y(t)$ and the autocorrelation $R_{yy}(t_1,t_2)$ of the solution $\mathbf{y}(t)$ in terms of the mean $\eta_x(t)$ and of the autocorrelation $R_{xx}(t_1,t_2)$ of the input $\mathbf{x}(t)$. All time instances will be assumed positive.

From (2-4) it follows that $\eta_y(t)$ is the solution of the equation

$$a_n\eta_y^{(n)}(t) + \cdots + a_0\eta_y(t) = \eta_x(t)$$
$$\eta_y(0) = \cdots = \eta_y^{(n-1)}(0) = 0 \tag{3-24}$$

From (2-13) we conclude that the cross correlation $R_{xy}(t_1,t_2)$ satisfies the equation

$$a_n^* \frac{\partial^n R_{xy}(t_1,t_2)}{\partial t_2{}^n} + \cdots + a_0^* R_{xy}(t_1,t_2) = R_{xx}(t_1,t_2) \tag{3-25}$$

with initial conditions

$$R_{xy}(t_1,0) = \frac{\partial R_{xy}(t_1,0)}{\partial t_2} = \cdots = \frac{\partial^{n-1} R_{xy}(t_1,0)}{\partial t_2{}^{n-1}} = 0 \tag{3-26}$$

Finally, $R_{yy}(t_1,t_2)$ is found by solving [see (2-14)]

$$a_n \frac{\partial^n R_{yy}(t_1,t_2)}{\partial t_1{}^n} + \cdots + a_0 R_{yy}(t_1,t_2) = R_{xy}(t_1,t_2) \tag{3-27}$$

with initial conditions

$$R_{yy}(0,t_2) = \frac{\partial R_{yy}(0,t_2)}{\partial t_1} = \cdots = \frac{\partial^{n-1}R_{yy}(0,t_2)}{\partial t_1^{n-1}} = 0 \qquad (3\text{-}28)$$

Thus, solving (3-25) (an ordinary differential equation in t_2 with t_1 a parameter), we obtain $R_{xy}(t_1,t_2)$; inserting the solution in (3-27) and solving, we obtain $R_{yy}(t_1,t_2)$.

Example 3-2   Consider the equation

$$\frac{d\mathbf{y}(t)}{dt} + \alpha\mathbf{y}(t) = \mathbf{x}(t) \qquad y(0) = 0 \qquad \alpha > 0$$

where $\mathbf{x}(t)$ is a stochastic process with

$$\eta_x(t) = 0 \qquad R_{xx}(t_1,t_2) = k\delta(t_1 - t_2)$$

If follows readily from (3-24) that $\eta_y(t) = 0$.   From (3-25) we see that

$$\frac{\partial R_{xy}(t_1,t_2)}{\partial t_2} + \alpha R_{xy}(t_1,t_2) = k\delta(t_1 - t_2) \qquad R_{xy}(t_1,0) = 0$$

Solving, we find

$$R_{xy}(t_1,t_2) = ke^{-\alpha(t_2-t_1)}U(t_2 - t_1)$$

The above is shown in Fig. 3-2a as a function of t_2 (t_1 fixed) and in Fig. 3-2b as a function of t_1 (t_2 fixed).   Finally, (3-27) yields

$$\frac{\partial R_{yy}(t_1,t_2)}{\partial t_1} + \alpha R_{yy}(t_1,t_2) = ke^{\alpha(t_1-t_2)}U(t_2 - t_1) \qquad R_{yy}(0,t_2) = 0$$

For $t_1 < t_2$, the solution of this equation is

$$R_{yy}(t_1,t_2) = \frac{k}{2\alpha} e^{\alpha(t_1-t_2)}(1 - e^{-2\alpha t_1}) \qquad (3\text{-}29)$$

For $t_1 > t_2$ we reverse, in the above, the roles of t_1 and t_2 because $R_{yy}(t_1,t_2) = R_{yy}(t_2,t_1)$. We note that

$$E\{\mathbf{y}^2(t)\} = R_{yy}(t,t) = \frac{k}{2\alpha}(1 - e^{-2\alpha t}) \qquad (3\text{-}30)$$

Special case   If $\alpha = 0$, then

$$\frac{d\mathbf{y}(t)}{dt} = \mathbf{x}(t) \qquad y(t) = \int_0^t \mathbf{x}(\tau)\,d\tau$$

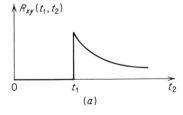

(a)

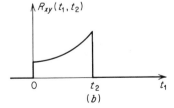

(b)

Fig. 3-2

and (3-29) [or, directly, (3-6)] yields

$$R_{yy}(t_1,t_2) = \begin{cases} kt_1 & 0 < t_1 < t_2 \\ kt_2 & 0 < t_2 < t_1 \end{cases}$$

Transforms of correlations

Transforms are used mainly in the study of stationary processes (power spectra). We introduce them here briefly for general processes.

Given two processes $\mathbf{x}(t)$ and $\mathbf{y}(t)$, we form the double Fourier transform

$$S_{xy}(u,v) = \iint\limits_{-\infty}^{\infty} R_{xy}(t_1,t_2)e^{-j(ut_1+vt_2)} \, dt_1 \, dt_2 \tag{3-31}$$

and the corresponding quantities $S_{xx}(u,v)$, $S_{yy}(u,v)$. Suppose that $\mathbf{y}(t)$ is the output of a system with input $\mathbf{x}(t)$ and system function $H(\omega)$. Since

$$h^*(t) \leftrightarrow H^*(-\omega) \tag{3-32}$$

we conclude, taking transforms of both sides of (3-5) and using the convolution theorem, that

$$S_{xy}(u,v) = S_{xx}(u,v)H^*(-v) \tag{3-33}$$

By using similar reasoning, we note that (3-6) yields

$$S_{yy}(u,v) = S_{xy}(u,v)H(u) = S_{xx}(u,v)H(u)H^*(-v) \tag{3-34}$$

4. STATIONARY PROCESSES

We say that a stochastic process $\mathbf{x}(t)$ is stationary (in the wide sense) if its mean is constant and its autocorrelation depends on $t_1 - t_2$ only:

$$E\{\mathbf{x}(t)\} = \eta = \text{const} \qquad R(t_1,t_2) = R(t_1 - t_2) \tag{4-1}$$

With $t_1 - t_2 = \tau$, $t_2 = t$, we thus have

$$E\{\mathbf{x}(t + \tau)\mathbf{x}^*(t)\} = R(\tau) \tag{4-2}$$

We note that

$$R(-\tau) = R^*(\tau) \tag{4-3}$$

and if $\mathbf{x}(t)$ is real, then $R(\tau)$ is real and even.

The autocorrelation $R(\tau)$ can be expressed as average intensity. Indeed,

$$R(0) = E\{|\mathbf{x}(t)|^2\} \geq 0 \tag{4-4}$$

Furthermore,

$$E\{|\mathbf{x}(t+\tau) - \mathbf{x}(t)|^2\} = 2[R(0) - \text{Re } R(\tau)]$$
$$E\{|\mathbf{x}(t+\tau) - j\mathbf{x}(t)|^2\} = 2[R(0) - \text{Im } R(\tau)]$$

(4-5)

Hence, $R(\tau)$ can be found from $R(0)$ and from the average intensity of $\mathbf{x}(t+\tau) - a\mathbf{x}(t)$ evaluated for $a = 1$ and $a = j$.

Two processes $\mathbf{x}(t)$ and $\mathbf{y}(t)$ are called jointly stationary if each is stationary and their correlation depends on $t_1 - t_2$ only:

$$E\{\mathbf{x}(t+\tau)\mathbf{y}^*(t)\} = R_{xy}(\tau)$$

(4-6)

SYSTEMS

We shall now show that if the input $\mathbf{x}(t)$ to a linear system is stationary, then it is jointly stationary with the output $\mathbf{y}(t)$. With $\eta_x(t) = \eta_x$, we conclude from (3-4) that

$$\eta_y(t) = \eta_x \int_{-\infty}^{\infty} h(t) \, dt = \text{const}$$

(4-7)

From the stationarity of $\mathbf{x}(t)$ it follows that

$$R_{xx}(t_1, t_2 - \alpha) = R_{xx}(\tau + \alpha) \qquad t_1 - t_2 = \tau$$

and (3-5) yields

$$R_{xy}(t_1, t_2) = \int_{-\infty}^{\infty} R_{xx}(\tau + \alpha)h^*(\alpha) \, d\alpha$$

(4-8)

Thus, $R_{xy}(t_1, t_2)$ depends on $t_1 - t_2 = \tau$ only, and it is given by

$$R_{xy}(\tau) = R_{xx}(\tau) * h^*(-\tau)$$

(4-9)

This follows from (4-8), with $\alpha = -\beta$. By a similar argument we deduce from (3-6) that

$$R_{yy}(\tau) = \int_{-\infty}^{\infty} R_{xy}(\tau - \alpha)h(\alpha) \, d\alpha = R_{xy}(\tau) * h(\tau)$$

(4-10)

Thus, $\mathbf{y}(t)$ is stationary with autocorrelation

$$R_{yy}(\tau) = R_{xx}(\tau) * h^*(-\tau) * h(\tau)$$

(4-11)

White noise The autocorrelation of a stationary white noise is an impulse [see (3-8)]

$$R_{xx}(\tau) = q\delta(\tau)$$

(4-12)

From (4-11) it follows that the autocorrelation of the corresponding output $\mathbf{y}(t)$ is given by

$$R_{yy}(\tau) = qh^*(-\tau) * h(\tau) = q \int_{-\infty}^{\infty} h(\tau + \alpha)h^*(\alpha) \, d\alpha$$

(4-13)

In particular,

$$E\{|\mathbf{y}(t)|^2\} = R_{yy}(0) = q \int_{-\infty}^{\infty} |h(t)|^2 \, dt \tag{4-14}$$

Comment With $\mathbf{x}(t)$ as in (4-12) and with $\varphi(t)$ as a deterministic signal, the process

$$\mathbf{w}(t) = \varphi(t)\mathbf{x}(t)$$

is nonstationary white noise with autocorrelation [see (3-2)]

$$R_{ww}(t_1,t_2) = q\varphi(t_1)\varphi^*(t_2)\delta(t_2 - t_1) = q|\varphi(t_1)|^2\delta(t_2 - t_1) \tag{4-15}$$

Conversely, if $\mathbf{w}(t)$ is such that

$$R_{ww}(t_1,t_2) = q(t_1)\delta(t_2 - t_1)$$

then the process

$$\mathbf{x}(t) = \frac{\mathbf{w}(t)}{\sqrt{q(t)}}$$

is stationary white noise with $R_{xx}(\tau) = \delta(\tau)$.

POWER SPECTRA

We define the power spectrum $S(\omega)$ of a stationary process $\mathbf{x}(t)$ as the Fourier transform of its autocorrelation

$$R(\tau) \leftrightarrow S(\omega) = \int_{-\infty}^{\infty} R(\tau)e^{-j\omega\tau} \, d\tau \tag{4-16}$$

Since $R(-\tau) = R^*(\tau)$, we conclude that $S(\omega)$ is real.

If $\mathbf{x}(t)$ is real, then $R(\tau)$ is also real and

$$R(-\tau) = R(\tau) \qquad S(-\omega) = S(\omega)$$

The cross-power spectrum $S_{xy}(\omega)$ of two jointly stationary processes $\mathbf{x}(t)$ and $\mathbf{y}(t)$ is the Fourier transform of their cross correlation

$$R_{xy}(\tau) \leftrightarrow S_{xy}(\omega)$$

With $\mathbf{x}(t)$ the input to a system specified by (3-3), we conclude, taking transforms of both sides of (4-9) and (4-10), that [see (3-32)]

$$S_{xy}(\omega) = S_{xx}(\omega)H^*(\omega) \qquad S_{yy}(\omega) = S_{xy}(\omega)H(\omega) \tag{4-17}$$

Hence,

$$S_{yy}(\omega) = S_{xx}(\omega)|H(\omega)|^2 \tag{4-18}$$

Using the above basic relationship, we shall show that the power spectrum $S(\omega)$ of an arbitrary process $\mathbf{x}(t)$ is nonnegative; that is,

$$S(\omega) \geq 0 \tag{4-19}$$

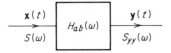

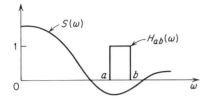 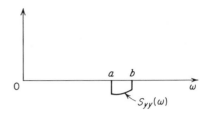

Fig. 4-1

We first observe that [see (4-16)]

$$E\{|\mathbf{x}(t)|^2\} = R(0) = \frac{1}{2\pi} \int_{-\infty}^{\infty} S(\omega)\, d\omega \geq 0 \qquad (4\text{-}20)$$

Suppose that $S(\omega)$ is negative in an interval (a,b) (Fig. 4-1). Using $\mathbf{x}(t)$ as the input to the bandpass system

$$H_{ab}(\omega) = \begin{cases} 1 & a < \omega < b \\ 0 & \text{otherwise} \end{cases} \qquad (4\text{-}21)$$

we obtain as output a process $\mathbf{y}(t)$ with power spectrum

$$S_{yy}(\omega) = \begin{cases} S(\omega) & a < \omega < b \\ 0 & \text{otherwise} \end{cases}$$

This follows from (4-18). Thus,

$$E\{|\mathbf{y}(t)|^2\} = R_{yy}(0) = \frac{1}{2\pi} \int_{-\infty}^{\infty} S_{yy}(\omega)\, d\omega = \frac{1}{2\pi} \int_{a}^{b} S(\omega)\, d\omega < 0$$

But this is impossible, and hence $S(\omega)$ cannot be negative in any interval, and (4-19) follows.

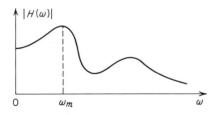 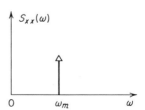

Fig. 4-2

Output bounds Suppose that the input to a system is a process $\mathbf{x}(t)$ with average power $R_{xx}(0)$. We shall establish bounds on the average power $R_{yy}(0)$ of the resulting output $\mathbf{y}(t)$.

With ω_m the value of ω such that $|H(\omega)|$ is maximum (Fig. 4-2)

$$|H(\omega)| \leq |H(\omega_m)|$$

it follows from (4-19) that

$$\int_{-\infty}^{\infty} |H(\omega)|^2 S_{xx}(\omega) \, d\omega \leq |H(\omega_m)|^2 \int_{-\infty}^{\infty} S_{xx}(\omega) \, d\omega$$

Hence [see (4-18)],

$$R_{yy}(0) = \frac{1}{2\pi} \int_{-\infty}^{\infty} S_{yy}(\omega) \, d\omega \leq |H(\omega_m)|^2 R_{xx}(0) \tag{4-22}$$

The above holds with the equality sign only if

$$S_{xx}(\omega) = k\delta(\omega - \omega_m)$$

that is, if

$$R_{xx}(\tau) = k_1 e^{j\omega_m \tau}$$

From (4-22) it follows that

$$E\{|\mathbf{y}(t)|^2\} \leq |H(\omega_m)|^2 E\{|\mathbf{x}(t)|^2\}$$

Example 4-1 Suppose that $\mathbf{y}(t)$ satisfies the differential equation

$$a_n \mathbf{y}^{(n)}(t) + \cdots + a_0 \mathbf{y}(t) = \mathbf{x}(t) \qquad \text{all } t$$

where $\mathbf{x}(t)$ is a stationary process with power spectrum $S_{xx}(\omega)$. As it is known, $\mathbf{y}(t)$ can be considered as the output of a linear system with input $\mathbf{x}(t)$ and system function

$$H(\omega) = \frac{1}{a_n(j\omega)^n + \cdots + a_0}$$

Hence, $\mathbf{y}(t)$ is stationary, and its power spectrum is given by [see (4-18)]

$$S_{yy}(\omega) = \frac{S_{xx}(\omega)}{|a_n(j\omega)^n + \cdots + a_0|^2}$$

Example 4-2 Given a stationary process $\mathbf{x}(t)$ with power spectrum $S(\omega)$, we form the "sampled mean"

$$\mathbf{y}(t) = \frac{1}{2n+1} [\mathbf{x}(t - nT) + \cdots + \mathbf{x}(t) + \cdots + \mathbf{x}(t + nT)]$$

Clearly, $\mathbf{y}(t)$ can be considered as the output of a linear system with input $\mathbf{x}(t)$ and system function

$$H(\omega) = \frac{1}{2n+1} (e^{-jnT\omega} + \cdots + 1 + \cdots + e^{jnT\omega})$$

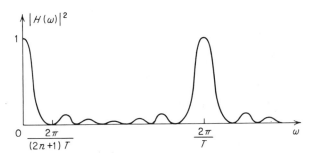

Fig. 4-3

Since (Fig. 4-3)

$$|H(\omega)|^2 = \frac{\sin^2 (n + \tfrac{1}{2})T\omega}{(2n + 1)^2 \sin^2 (T\omega/2)} \tag{4-23}$$

it follows from (4-18) that the power spectrum of $y(t)$ is given by

$$S_{yy}(\omega) = \frac{S(\omega) \sin^2 (n + \tfrac{1}{2})T\omega}{(2n + 1)^2 \sin^2 (T\omega/2)} \tag{4-24}$$

Hence,

$$E\{|y(t)|^2\} = \frac{1}{2\pi} \int_{-\infty}^{\infty} \frac{S(\omega) \sin^2 (n + \tfrac{1}{2})T\omega}{(2n + 1)^2 \sin^2 (T\omega/2)}\, d\omega \tag{4-25}$$

We note that

$$E\{y(t)\} = E\{x(t)\} = \eta \tag{4-26}$$

Furthermore [see (4-23)],

$$H(0) = 1 \quad \text{and} \quad H(\omega) \xrightarrow[n \to \infty]{} 0 \quad \omega \neq \frac{2\pi r}{T}$$

If, therefore,

$$S(\omega) = S_1(\omega) + 2\pi|\eta|^2\delta(\omega) \tag{4-27}$$

and $S_1(\omega)$ is integrable without singularities, then

$$E\{|y(t)|^2\} \xrightarrow[n \to \infty]{} |\eta|^2 \tag{4-28}$$

This follows from (4-25). We thus conclude, with (4-26) and (4-28), that (elaborate)

$$E\{|y(t) - \eta|^2\} \to 0 \qquad n \to \infty$$

In other words, the variance of the random variable $y(t)$ tends to zero; i.e., if (4-27) holds, then the "sample mean" $y(t)$ tends to η in the mean-square sense with $n \to \infty$ (ergodicity).

Consider, finally, the two systems of Fig. 3-1 specified by

$$y_1(t) = x_1(t) * h_1(t) \qquad y_2(t) = x_2(t) * h_2(t) \tag{4-29}$$

Assuming that the inputs $x_1(t)$ and $x_2(t)$ are jointly stationary, we conclude, reasoning as in (4-9) and (4-10), that

$$R_{x_1y_2}(\tau) = R_{x_1x_2}(\tau) * h_2^*(-\tau) \qquad R_{y_1y_2}(\tau) = R_{x_1y_2}(\tau) * h_1(\tau) \qquad (4\text{-}30)$$

Hence,

$$S_{x_1y_2}(\omega) = S_{x_1x_2}(\omega)H_2^*(\omega) \qquad S_{y_1y_2}(\omega) = S_{x_1y_2}(\omega)H_1(\omega) \qquad (4\text{-}31)$$

HILBERT TRANSFORMS

Given a real stationary process $\mathbf{x}(t)$ with autocorrelation $R_{xx}(\tau)$ and power spectrum $S_{xx}(\omega)$, we form its Hilbert transform [see Chap. 3, (3-16)]:

$$\hat{\mathbf{x}}(t) = \frac{1}{\pi}\int_{-\infty}^{\infty}\frac{\mathbf{x}(\tau)}{t-\tau}\,d\tau = \mathbf{x}(t) * \frac{1}{\pi t} \qquad (4\text{-}32)$$

As we know, $\hat{\mathbf{x}}(t)$ is the output of the quadrature filter

$$h(t) = \frac{1}{\pi t} \leftrightarrow -j\,\text{sgn}\,\omega = H(\omega)$$

with input $\mathbf{x}(t)$. From the above and (4-18) it follows that

$$S_{\hat{x}\hat{x}}(\omega) = S_{xx}(\omega) \qquad \text{hence} \qquad R_{\hat{x}\hat{x}}(\tau) = R_{xx}(\tau) \qquad (4\text{-}33)$$

Similarly, (4-17) yields

$$S_{x\hat{x}}(\omega) = jS_{xx}(\omega)\,\text{sgn}\,\omega \qquad (4\text{-}34)$$

Hence,

$$R_{x\hat{x}}(\tau) = -R_{xx}(\tau) * \frac{1}{\pi\tau} = -\hat{R}_{xx}(\tau) \qquad (4\text{-}35)$$

where $\hat{R}_{xx}(\tau)$ is the Hilbert transform of $R_{xx}(\tau)$.

Since $\mathbf{x}(t)$ is real, $R_{xx}(\tau)$ is even; hence, $\hat{R}_{xx}(\tau)$ is odd. Therefore,

$$E\{\mathbf{x}(t)\hat{\mathbf{x}}(t)\} = R_{x\hat{x}}(0) = 0 \qquad (4\text{-}36)$$

With

$$\mathbf{z}(t) = \mathbf{x}(t) + j\hat{\mathbf{x}}(t) \qquad (4\text{-}37)$$

as the analytic signal associated with $\mathbf{x}(t)$, we have

$$\begin{aligned}
R_{zz}(\tau) &= E\{[\mathbf{x}(t+\tau) + j\hat{\mathbf{x}}(t+\tau)][\mathbf{x}(t) - j\hat{\mathbf{x}}(t)]\} \\
&= R_{xx}(\tau) + R_{\hat{x}\hat{x}}(\tau) - jR_{x\hat{x}}(\tau) + jR_{x\hat{x}}(-\tau)
\end{aligned}$$

But $R_{x\hat{x}}(\tau)$ is odd. Hence [see (4-35)],

$$R_{zz}(\tau) = 2[R_{xx}(\tau) + j\hat{R}_{xx}(\tau)] \qquad (4\text{-}38)$$

Thus, $R_{zz}(\tau)$ equals twice the analytic signal associated with $R_{xx}(\tau)$. Taking transforms of both sides of (4-38), we conclude, with (4-34), that

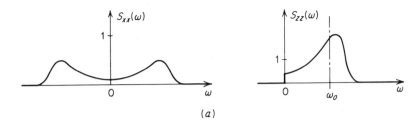

(a)

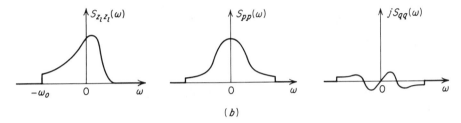

(b)

Fig. 4-4

the power spectrum of $z(t)$ is given by

$$S_{zz}(\omega) = 2[S_{xx}(\omega) - jS_{x\hat{x}}(\omega)] = 4S_{xx}(\omega)U(\omega) \qquad (4\text{-}39)$$

as in Fig. 4-4.

Modulation

Given an arbitrary constant ω_o, we form the process

$$z_i(t) = z(t)e^{-j\omega_o t} = p(t) + jq(t) \qquad (4\text{-}40)$$

Since

$$E\{z(t + \tau)e^{-j\omega_o(t+\tau)}z^*(t)e^{j\omega_o t}\} = E\{z(t + \tau)z^*(t)\}e^{-j\omega_o\tau}$$

we have

$$R_{z_i z_i}(\tau) = R_{zz}(\tau)e^{-j\omega_o\tau} \qquad \text{and hence} \qquad S_{z_i z_i}(\omega) = S_{zz}(\omega + \omega_o) \tag{4-41}$$

From [see (4-37) and (4-40)]

$$x(t) + j\hat{x}(t) = [p(t) + jq(t)]e^{j\omega_o t}$$

it follows that

$$\begin{aligned} x(t) &= p(t)\cos\omega_o t - q(t)\sin\omega_o t \\ \hat{x}(t) &= p(t)\sin\omega_o t + q(t)\cos\omega_o t \end{aligned} \qquad (4\text{-}42)$$

It can be shown that [p1] the processes $\mathbf{p}(t)$ and $\mathbf{q}(t)$ are jointly stationary with

$$R_{pp}(\tau) = R_{qq}(\tau) \qquad R_{pq}(\tau) = -R_{qp}(\tau)$$

and

$$R_{pp}(\tau) + jR_{qp}(\tau) = \tfrac{1}{2}R_{zz}(\tau)e^{-j\omega_o\tau} \tag{4-43}$$

Therefore,

$$S_{pp}(\omega) + jS_{qp}(\omega) = \tfrac{1}{2}S_{z_1z_1}(\omega) \tag{4-44}$$

Equating real and imaginary parts, we finally conclude that

$$2S_{pp}(\omega) = S_{z_1z_1}(\omega) + S_{z_1z_1}(-\omega) \qquad 2jS_{qp}(\omega) = S_{z_1z_1}(\omega) - S_{z_1z_1}(-\omega)$$

(show it) as in Fig. 4-4b.

INEQUALITIES

Given two jointly stationary real or complex processes $\mathbf{x}(t)$ and $\mathbf{y}(t)$, we shall show that

$$|R_{xy}(\tau)|^2 \leq R_{xx}(0)R_{yy}(0) \tag{4-45}$$

Proof With a a real constant, we have

$$E\{|\mathbf{x}(t+\tau) + aR_{xy}(\tau)\mathbf{y}(t)|^2\}$$
$$= R_{xx}(0) + 2a|R_{xy}(\tau)|^2 + a^2|R_{xy}(\tau)|^2 R_{yy}(0) \geq 0$$

as it is easy to show. The above quadratic is nonnegative for every a; hence its discriminant is nonpositive, and (4-45) follows. Clearly, (4-45) is also true for $\mathbf{x}(t) = \mathbf{y}(t)$.

Using (4-45), we shall prove that for any a and b

$$\left| \int_a^b S_{xy}(\omega)e^{j\omega\tau}\,d\omega \right|^2 \leq \int_a^b S_{xx}(\omega)\,d\omega \int_a^b S_{yy}(\omega)\,d\omega \tag{4-46}$$

Proof We form two identical bandpass systems $H_{ab}(\omega)$, as in Fig.

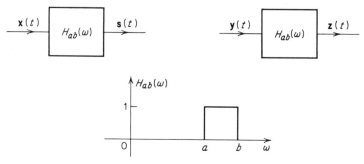

Fig. 4-5

4-5 [see (4-21)]. With $\mathbf{x}(t)$ and $\mathbf{y}(t)$ as respective inputs, the resulting outputs $\mathbf{s}(t)$ and $\mathbf{z}(t)$ are such that

$$S_{ss}(\omega) = S_{xx}(\omega)H_{ab}^2(\omega) \qquad S_{zz}(\omega) = S_{yy}(\omega)H_{ab}^2(\omega)$$
$$S_{sz}(\omega) = S_{xy}(\omega)H_{ab}^2(\omega)$$

This follows from (4-18) and (4-31). Hence,

$$R_{ss}(0) = \frac{1}{2\pi} \int_a^b S_{xx}(\omega) \, d\omega \qquad R_{zz}(0) = \frac{1}{2\pi} \int_a^b S_{yy}(\omega) \, d\omega$$

$$R_{sz}(\tau) = \frac{1}{2\pi} \int_a^b S_{xy}(\omega)e^{j\omega\tau} \, d\omega$$

Applying (4-45) to the processes $\mathbf{s}(t)$ and $\mathbf{z}(t)$, we obtain (4-46).

As a consequence, we note that if $S_{xx}(\omega)$ or $S_{yy}(\omega)$ is zero in an interval (a,b), then $S_{xy}(\omega)$ must also be zero in this interval (elaborate). The following special case is of particular interest:

Suppose that

$$R_{xx}(\tau) = Ae^{j\omega_o\tau} \qquad S_{xx}(\omega) = 2\pi A\delta(\omega - \omega_o)$$

In this case, if $S_{yy}(\omega)$ does not contain an impulse at ω_o, then $R_{xy}(\tau) \equiv 0$. If $S_{yy}(\omega)$ contains the impulse $2\pi B\delta(\omega - \omega_o)$, then

$$R_{xy}(\tau) = Ce^{j\omega_o\tau} \qquad \text{with } |C|^2 \leq AB \qquad (4\text{-}47)$$

This follows from (4-46).

MONOCHROMATIC PROCESSES

A complex process $\mathbf{x}(t)$ is called monochromatic if its power spectrum is an impulse

$$R(\tau) = Ae^{j\omega_o\tau} \qquad S(\omega) = 2\pi A\delta(\omega - \omega_o) \qquad (4\text{-}48)$$

It is easy to show that if the above is true, then

$$E\{|\mathbf{x}(t + \tau) - \mathbf{x}(t)e^{j\omega_o\tau}|^2\} = 0 \qquad (4\text{-}49)$$

for any τ. The process

$$\mathbf{x}(t) = \mathbf{a}e^{j\omega_o t}$$

is obviously monochromatic; however, the converse is true only if the equality is interpreted in the mean-square sense (Prob. 8-6).

If $S(\omega)$ is not an ideal impulse, but occupies a "narrow" band, as in Fig. 4-6 with $\omega_c \ll \omega_o$, then the process $\mathbf{x}(t)$ is called *quasi-monochromatic*.

We shall say that a real process $\mathbf{x}(t)$ is monochromatic if its autocorrelation is given by

$$R(\tau) = A \cos \omega_o\tau \qquad (4\text{-}50)$$

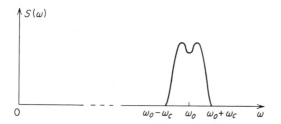

Fig. 4-6

With $\mathbf{z}(t) = \mathbf{x}(t) + j\hat{\mathbf{x}}(t)$ as the analytic signal associated with $\mathbf{x}(t)$, we have [see (4-38)]

$$R_{zz}(\tau) = 2Ae^{j\omega_o\tau} \tag{4-51}$$

Forming the processes

$$\mathbf{p}(t) + j\mathbf{q}(t) = [\mathbf{x}(t) + j\hat{\mathbf{x}}(t)]e^{-j\omega_o t}$$

we have

$$\mathbf{x}(t) = \mathbf{p}(t)\cos \omega_o t - \mathbf{q}(t)\sin \omega_o t \tag{4-52}$$

as in (4-42). From (4-51) and (4-43) it follows that

$$R_{pp}(\tau) = R_{qq}(\tau) = A \qquad R_{qp}(\tau) = 0$$

Thus a real monochromatic process $\mathbf{x}(t)$ is of the form (4-52), where the process $\mathbf{p}(t)$ and $\mathbf{q}(t)$ are such that

$$E\{|\mathbf{p}(t+\tau) - \mathbf{p}(t)|^2\}$$
$$= E\{|\mathbf{q}(t+\tau) - \mathbf{q}(t)|^2\} = E\{\mathbf{p}(t+\tau)\mathbf{q}(t)\} = 0 \tag{4-53}$$

for any τ. This is the case if

$$\mathbf{x}(t) = \mathbf{a}\cos \omega_o t + \mathbf{b}\sin \omega_o t \qquad E\{\mathbf{ab}\} = 0 \qquad E\{\mathbf{a}^2\} = E\{\mathbf{b}^2\}$$

However, a monochromatic process is not necessarily of the above form.

We finally remark that if $\mathbf{x}(t)$ is monochromatic, as in (4-48), and $\mathbf{y}(t)$ is an arbitrary process, then [see (4-47)]

$$R_{xy}(\tau) = Ce^{j\omega_o\tau}$$

If $S_{yy}(\omega)$ does not contain an impulse at ω_o, then $R_{xy}(\tau) \equiv 0$.

ERGODICITY

Given a stationary stochastic process $\mathbf{x}(t)$, we form its time average

$$\langle \mathbf{x}(t) \rangle = \lim_{T \to \infty} \frac{1}{2T} \int_{-T}^{T} \mathbf{x}(t)\, dt \tag{4-54}$$

We shall examine, briefly, the conditions that $\mathbf{x}(t)$ must satisfy so that its time average $\langle \mathbf{x}(t) \rangle$ will equal the ensemble average $E\{\mathbf{x}(t)\}$. That is,

$$\langle \mathbf{x}(t) \rangle = E\{\mathbf{x}(t)\} = \eta \tag{4-55}$$

We are faced here with two questions: (1) Does the time average (4-54) exist as a limit for every curve of the process $\mathbf{x}(t)$? (2) If it exists, it defines, in general, a random variable $\langle \mathbf{x}(t) \rangle$. Under what conditions is this random variable equal to the constant $E\{\mathbf{x}(t)\}$?

It can be shown that† (ergodicity theorem) the first question has an affirmative answer: the limit (4-54) exists for (almost) all curves of $\mathbf{x}(t)$. It remains to investigate the second question. The random variable $\langle \mathbf{x}(t) \rangle$ will equal the constant $E\{\mathbf{x}(t)\}$ (almost certainly) only if its variance is zero. To determine this variance, we form the finite average [p1]

$$\mathbf{n}_T = \frac{1}{2T} \int_{-T}^{T} \mathbf{x}(t) \, dt \tag{4-56}$$

This average is a random variable with mean

$$E\{\mathbf{n}_T\} = \frac{1}{2T} \int_{-T}^{T} E\{\mathbf{x}(t)\} \, dt = \eta \tag{4-57}$$

We shall find its second moment $E\{|\mathbf{n}_T|^2\}$. For this purpose, we form the process

$$\mathbf{y}(t) = \frac{1}{2T} \int_{t-T}^{t+T} \mathbf{x}(\tau) \, d\tau \tag{4-58}$$

It is easy to see that $\mathbf{y}(t)$ is the output of a linear system with input $\mathbf{x}(t)$ and impulse response (Fig. 4-7)

$$h(t) = \begin{cases} \dfrac{1}{2T} & |t| < T \\ 0 & |t| > T \end{cases}$$

Since the corresponding system function is given by

$$H(\omega) = \frac{\sin T\omega}{T\omega}$$

† G. D. Birkoff, Proof of the Ergodic Theorem, *Proc. Natl. Acad. Sci. U.S.A.*, vol. 17, 1931, pp. 656–660.

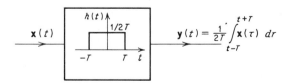

Fig. 4-7

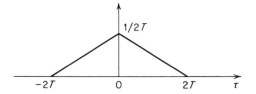

Fig. 4-8

it follows from (4-18) that

$$S_{yy}(\omega) = S_{xx}(\omega) \frac{\sin^2 T\omega}{T^2\omega^2} \tag{4-59}$$

The inverse Fourier transform of $\sin^2 T\omega/T^2\omega^2$ is the triangle [see Chap. 3, (2-5)]

$$\frac{1}{2T}\left(1 - \frac{|\tau|}{2T}\right) p_{2T}(\tau)$$

shown in Fig. 4-8. Therefore,

$$R_{yy}(\tau) = \frac{1}{2T}\int_{-2T}^{2T}\left(1 - \frac{|\alpha|}{2T}\right) R_{xx}(\tau - \alpha)\, d\alpha \tag{4-60}$$

as we see from (4-59) and the convolution theorem.

Clearly, $\mathbf{n}_T = \mathbf{y}(0)$; therefore (4-60) yields, with $\tau = 0$,

$$E\{|\mathbf{n}_T|^2\} = R_{yy}(0) = \frac{1}{2T}\int_{-2T}^{2T}\left(1 - \frac{|\alpha|}{2T}\right) R_{xx}(\alpha)\, d\alpha \tag{4-61}$$

From the above and (4-57) it follows that the variance of the random variable $\mathbf{n}_T$ is given by

$$\sigma_{\eta_T}^2 = E\{|\mathbf{n}_T|^2\} - |\eta|^2 = \frac{1}{2T}\int_{-2T}^{2T}\left(1 - \frac{|\alpha|}{2T}\right) R_{xx}(\alpha)\, d\alpha - |\eta|^2 \tag{4-62}$$

If this quantity tends to zero with $T \to \infty$, then $\mathbf{n}_T$ tends to the constant η. Thus, the process $\mathbf{x}(t)$ is ergodic with respect to its mean if

$$\lim_{T\to\infty} \frac{1}{2T}\int_{-2T}^{2T}\left(1 - \frac{|\alpha|}{2T}\right) R_{xx}(\alpha)\, d\alpha = |\eta|^2 \tag{4-63}$$

The above can be expressed in terms of the autocovariance $C_{xx}(\tau)$ of $\mathbf{x}(t)$. It is easy to see that (4-63) is equivalent to

$$\sigma_{\eta_T}^2 = \frac{1}{2T}\int_{-2T}^{2T}\left(1 - \frac{|\alpha|}{2T}\right) C_{xx}(\alpha)\, d\alpha \xrightarrow[T\to\infty]{} 0 \tag{4-64}$$

This follows from (4-62) and the fact that $C_{xx}(\tau) = R_{xx}(\tau) - |\eta|^2$.

5. TIME AVERAGES AND SAMPLING EXPANSION

Consider a deterministic signal $x(t)$ with finite average power

$$0 < \lim_{T \to \infty} \frac{1}{2T} \int_{-T}^{T} |x(t)|^2 \, dt < \infty \tag{5-1}$$

We define its mean

$$\bar{\eta}_x = \langle x(t) \rangle = \lim_{T \to \infty} \frac{1}{2T} \int_{-T}^{T} x(t) \, dt = \lim_{T \to \infty} \frac{1}{2T} \int_{-T}^{T} x(t + \tau) \, dt \tag{5-2}$$

and autocorrelation

$$\bar{R}_{xx}(\tau) = \lim_{T \to \infty} \frac{1}{2T} \int_{-T}^{T} x(t + \tau)x^*(t) \, dt = \langle x(t + \tau)x^*(t) \rangle \tag{5-3}$$

In the last expression, τ is treated as a parameter, and the averaging is with respect to t.

If $y(t)$ is a second signal with finite power, the cross correlation $\bar{R}_{xy}(\tau)$ is defined by

$$\bar{R}_{xy}(\tau) = \lim_{T \to \infty} \frac{1}{2T} \int_{-T}^{T} x(t + \tau)y^*(t) \, dt = \langle x(t + \tau)y^*(t) \rangle \tag{5-4}$$

Example 5-1

a. If

$$x(t) = ae^{j\omega_1 t} \qquad y(t) = be^{j\omega_2 t}$$

then $\bar{\eta}_x = \bar{\eta}_y = 0$, and

$$\bar{R}_{xx}(\tau) = |a|^2 e^{j\omega_1 \tau}$$
$$\bar{R}_{yy}(\tau) = |b|^2 e^{j\omega_2 \tau} \qquad \bar{R}_{xy}(\tau) = \begin{cases} ab^* e^{j\omega_1 \tau} & \omega_1 = \omega_2 \\ 0 & \omega_1 \neq \omega_2 \end{cases}$$

as it is easy to show.
b. If the constants a and b are real and

$$x(t) = a \cos (\omega_1 t + \varphi_1) \qquad y(t) = b \cos (\omega_2 t + \varphi_2)$$

then $\bar{\eta}_x = \bar{\eta}_y = 0$, and

$$\bar{R}_{xx}(\tau) = \frac{a^2}{2} \cos \omega_1 \tau$$
$$\bar{R}_{yy}(\tau) = \frac{b^2}{2} \cos \omega_2 \tau \qquad \bar{R}_{xy}(\tau) = \begin{cases} \dfrac{ab}{2} \cos (\omega_1 \tau + \varphi_1 - \varphi_2) & \omega_1 = \omega_2 \\ 0 & \omega_1 \neq \omega_2 \end{cases}$$

As we noted, time averaging is a linear operation. Thus

$$\langle a_1 x_1(t) + \cdots + a_n x_n(t) \rangle = a_1 \langle x_1(t) \rangle + \cdots + a_n \langle x_n(t) \rangle \tag{5-5}$$

And since the analysis of the preceding section was based on the linearity of expected values, we conclude that all results concerning stationary stochastic processes hold also for time averages with the proper identification of the various parameters. We shall discuss briefly some of the conclusions related to linear systems [12, p2].

Consider a linear system with input $x(t)$ and output

$$y(t) = \int_{-\infty}^{\infty} x(t - \alpha)h(\alpha)\, d\alpha \tag{5-6}$$

(For the following it is essential to use the above form of the convolution integral.) Integrating both sides and changing the order of integration, we have

$$\frac{1}{2T} \int_{-T}^{T} y(t)\, dt = \int_{-\infty}^{\infty} \left[\frac{1}{2T} \int_{-T}^{T} x(t - \alpha)\, dt \right] h(\alpha)\, d\alpha$$

If we take the limit under the integral sign, we conclude (with $T \to \infty$) that [see (5-2)]

$$\bar{\eta}_y = \langle y(t) \rangle = \int_{-\infty}^{\infty} \langle x(t - \alpha) \rangle h(\alpha)\, d\alpha = \bar{\eta}_x \int_{-\infty}^{\infty} h(\alpha)\, d\alpha$$

as in (4-7). Formally, this means that we can take the time average under the integral sign, remembering to average with respect to t. This is a consequence of (5-5), and will be used repeatedly.

Multiplying the conjugate of (5-6) by $x(t + \tau)$, we have

$$x(t + \tau)y^*(t) = \int_{-\infty}^{\infty} x(t + \tau)x^*(t - \alpha)h^*(\alpha)\, d\alpha \tag{5-7}$$

But [see (1-2)]

$$\langle x(t + \tau)x^*(t - \alpha) \rangle = \langle x(t + \tau + \alpha)x^*(t) \rangle = \bar{R}_{xx}(\tau + \alpha) \tag{5-8}$$

Taking the time averages of both sides of (5-7), we thus obtain

$$\bar{R}_{xy}(\tau) = \int_{-\infty}^{\infty} \bar{R}_{xx}(\tau + \alpha)h^*(\alpha)\, d\alpha = \bar{R}_{xx}(\tau) * h^*(-\tau) \tag{5-9}$$

A similar argument yields

$$\bar{R}_{yy}(\tau) = \bar{R}_{xy}(\tau) * h(\tau) \tag{5-10}$$

as in (4-9) and (4-10).

The power spectrum $\bar{S}(\omega)$ of $x(t)$ is defined as the Fourier transform of $\bar{R}(\tau)$, and it has the same properties as the power spectrum $S(\omega)$ of a stochastic process. For example, from (5-9) and (5-10) it follows that [see (4-18)]

$$\bar{S}_{yy}(\omega) = \bar{S}_{xx}(\omega)|H(\omega)|^2$$

We note that $\bar{S}(\omega)$ can be expressed directly in terms of $x(t)$ by the limit (see Prob. 8-4)

$$\bar{S}(\omega) = \lim_{T \to \infty} \frac{1}{2T} \left| \int_{-T}^{T} x(t) e^{-j\omega t} \, dt \right|^2 \tag{5-11}$$

The cross-power spectrum $\bar{S}_{xy}(\omega)$ of two signals $x(t)$ and $y(t)$ of finite power is the Fourier transform of their cross correlation $\bar{R}_{xy}(\tau)$, and it is given by (Prob. 8-4)

$$\bar{S}_{xy}(\omega) = \lim_{T \to \infty} \frac{1}{2T} \left[\int_{-T}^{T} x(t) e^{-j\omega t} \, dt \int_{-T}^{T} y^*(t) e^{j\omega t} \, dt \right] \tag{5-12}$$

Equations (5-11) and (5-12) are not always true for stochastic processes.

We further note that if a signal $x(t)$ satisfies (5-1), then, in general, its Fourier transform does not exist. From (5-11) it follows that

$$\lim_{T \to \infty} \int_{-T}^{T} x(t) e^{-j\omega t} \, dt = \infty \qquad \lim_{T \to \infty} \frac{1}{2T} \int_{-T}^{T} x(t) e^{-j\omega t} \, dt = 0$$

We conclude with an observation on the meaning of the term "monochromatic signal" as applied to deterministic functions. A complex signal $x(t)$ of finite power is called monochromatic if its autocorrelation is an exponential

$$\bar{R}(\tau) = A e^{j\omega_0 \tau} \tag{5-13}$$

The above obviously holds if (see Example 5-1)

$$x(t) = \sqrt{A} \, e^{j\omega_0 t}$$

However, this is not necessary. If $\bar{R}(\tau)$ is given by (5-13), then the signal $x(t)$ must be such that for any τ

$$\lim_{T \to \infty} \frac{1}{2T} \int_{-T}^{T} |x(t + \tau) - x(t) e^{j\omega_0 \tau}|^2 \, dt = 0 \tag{5-14}$$

as in (4-49) (show it). Thus, with

$$x(t) = a(t) e^{j\omega_0 t}$$

the envelope $a(t)$ must satisfy

$$\langle |a(t + \tau) - a(t)|^2 \rangle = 0$$

For real monochromatic processes, conditions similar to (4-53) hold.

SAMPLING THEOREM

In Chap. 4 we developed the sampling theorem for signals with finite energy. Signals with finite power, or stationary stochastic processes, have, in general, no Fourier transforms†; therefore, the theorem is not directly applicable to them. The purpose of the following is to show that if the power spectrum $S(\omega)$ or $\bar{S}(\omega)$ is band-limited, then the sampling expansion holds in the mean-square sense.

Stationary processes Consider a stationary stochastic process $\mathbf{x}(t)$ with power spectrum $S(\omega)$. It can be shown that if

$$S(\omega) = 0 \qquad \text{for } |\omega| \geq \omega_c$$

then

$$E\left\{\left|\mathbf{x}(t) - \sum_{n=-\infty}^{\infty} \mathbf{x}(nT)\frac{\sin \omega_c(t - nT)}{\omega_c(t - nT)}\right|^2\right\} = 0 \qquad (5\text{-}15)$$

provided that $T \leq \pi/\omega_c$. The proof of the above is identical to the following proof of the corresponding result for time averages.

Finite power signals

We are given a deterministic signal $x(t)$, as in (5-1), with autocorrelation $\bar{R}(\tau)$ and power spectrum $\bar{S}(\omega)$. We assume that

$$\bar{S}(\omega) = 0 \qquad \text{for } |\omega| \geq \omega_c \qquad (5\text{-}16)$$

In general it is not true that $x(t)$ equals its sampling expansion

$$x(t + \tau) \neq \sum_{n=-\infty}^{\infty} x(t + nT)\frac{\sin \omega_c(\tau - nT)}{\omega_c(\tau - nT)} \qquad T = \frac{\pi}{\omega_c}$$

We shall show, however, that

$$\lim_{T \to \infty} \frac{1}{2T}\int_{-T}^{T}\left|x(t + \tau) - \sum_{n=-\infty}^{\infty} x(t + nT)\frac{\sin \omega_c(\tau - nT)}{\omega_c(\tau - nT)}\right|^2 dt = 0$$

$$(5\text{-}17)$$

or, equivalently, that

$$\left\langle\left|x(t + \tau) - \sum_{n=-\infty}^{\infty} x(t + nT)\frac{\sin \omega_c(\tau - nT)}{\omega_c(\tau - nT)}\right|^2\right\rangle = 0 \qquad (5\text{-}18)$$

for any τ. In the above and in all following equations, the symbol $\langle\ \rangle$ means averaging with respect to the variable t.

Proof To prove (5-18), we form the truncation error

$$e_N(t + \tau) = x(t + \tau) - \sum_{n=-N}^{N} x(t + nT)\frac{\sin \omega_c(\tau - nT)}{\omega_c(\tau - nT)} \qquad (5\text{-}19)$$

---

† A function $f(t)$ with finite power can be written as a Stieltjes integral in terms of its "generalized Fourier" transform. We have decided, however, not to use this concept and to describe the spectral properties of $f(t)$ in terms of the ordinary Fourier transform $S(\omega)$ of its autocorrelation $R(\tau)$.

We shall evaluate the mean square $\langle|e_N(t + \tau)|^2\rangle$ of this error, and will show that it tends to zero with $N \to \infty$. Clearly, $e_N(t + \tau)$ can be considered as the output of a linear system with input $x(t)$ and system function

$$H(\omega) = e^{j\tau\omega} - \sum_{n=-N}^{N} e^{jnT\omega} \frac{\sin \omega_c(\tau - nT)}{\omega_c(\tau - nT)} \tag{5-20}$$

Hence [see (4-18)],

$$\langle|e_N(t + \tau)|^2\rangle = \frac{1}{2\pi} \int_{-\omega_c}^{\omega_c} \bar{S}(\omega)|H(\omega)|^2 \, d\omega \leq \bar{R}(0)|H(\omega_m)|^2 \tag{5-21}$$

where $|H(\omega_m)|$ is the maximum of $|H(\omega)|$ in the interval $(-\omega_c, \omega_c)$ [see also (4-22)]. The function $H(\omega)$ has the following interpretation. The coefficients of the Fourier series expansion of $e^{j\tau\omega}$ in the interval $(-\omega_c, \omega_c)$ are given by

$$\frac{1}{2\omega_c} \int_{-\omega_c}^{\omega_c} e^{j\tau\omega} e^{-jnT\omega} \, d\omega = \frac{\sin \omega_c(\tau - nT)}{\omega_c(\tau - nT)}$$

Hence, $H(\omega)$ equals the error in the approximation of the function $e^{j\tau\omega}$ by a truncated Fourier series. Thus, $\langle|e_N(t + \tau)|^2\rangle$ is bounded by the maximum value $|H(\omega_m)|$ of this error. Since $e^{j\tau\omega}$ is continuous, it follows from the theory of Fourier series that $H(\omega_m)$ tends to zero with $N \to \infty$. Hence,

$$\langle|e_N(t + \tau)|^2\rangle \xrightarrow[N \to \infty]{} 0$$

and (5-18) follows.

We note that for a specified $\bar{R}(0)$ the mean-square value of the truncation error is maximum if

$$\bar{R}(\tau) = k e^{j\omega_m\tau}$$

that is, if $x(t)$ is monochromatic with frequency ω_m.

6. TWO-DIMENSIONAL PROCESSES

We shall now extend, briefly, the preceding results to two-dimensional processes. The autocorrelation of a process $\mathbf{f}(x,y)$ is given by

$$R_{ff}(x_1,y_1;x_2,y_2) = E\{\mathbf{f}(x_1,y_1)\mathbf{f}^*(x_2,y_2)\} \tag{6-1}$$

and its average intensity by

$$R_{ff}(x,y;x,y) = E\{|\mathbf{f}(x,y)|^2\} \geq 0 \tag{6-2}$$

We say that this process is *incoherent* if

$$R_{ff}(x_1,y_1;x_2,y_2 = q(x_1,y_1)\delta(x_2 - x_1)\delta(y_2 - y_1) \tag{6-3}$$

A process is called stationary if its autocorrelation depends on $x_1 - x_2$ and $y_1 - y_2$ only:

$$R_{ff}(x_1,y_1;x_2,y_2) = R_{ff}(x_1 - x_2, y_1 - y_2) \tag{6-4}$$

Thus,

$$R_{ff}(\xi,\eta) = E\{\mathbf{f}(x + \xi, y + \eta)\mathbf{f}^*(x,y)\} \tag{6-5}$$

If (6-4) holds only for $(x,y) \in A$, then we say that $\mathbf{f}(x,y)$ is stationary in the region A.

Suppose that a process $\mathbf{f}(x,y)$ is incoherent, as in (6-3), and that $q(x,y) > 0$ for every (x,y). It is then easy to show that the process

$$\mathbf{w}(x,y) = \frac{\mathbf{f}(x,y)}{\sqrt{q(x,y)}} \tag{6-6}$$

is incoherent and stationary, with autocorrelation

$$R_{ww}(\xi,\eta) = \delta(\xi)\delta(\eta) \tag{6-7}$$

SYSTEMS

We now assume that $\mathbf{f}(x,y)$ is the input to a linear shift-invariant system with point spread $h(x,y)$. The resulting output $\mathbf{g}(x,y)$ is a stochastic process specified by

$$\mathbf{g}(x,y) = \int\limits_{-\infty}^{\infty}\!\!\int \mathbf{f}(\alpha,\beta)h(x - \alpha, y - \beta)\, d\alpha\, d\beta = \mathbf{f}(x,y) ** h(x,y) \tag{6-8}$$

The cross correlation

$$R_{fg}(x_1,y_1;x_2,y_2) = E\{\mathbf{f}(x_1,y_1)\mathbf{g}^*(x_2,y_2)\}$$

between the input and the output is given by

$$R_{fg}(x_1,y_1;x_2,y_2) = R_{ff}(x_1,y_1;x_2,y_2) ** h^*(x_2,y_2) \tag{6-9}$$

This follows from (2-13) or by a direct reasoning, as in (3-5). The above is a double convolution of $h^*(x_2,y_2)$, with R_{ff} considered as a function of x_2, y_2 (x_1, y_1 are treated as parameters). Similarly,

$$R_{gg}(x_1,y_1;x_2,y_2) = R_{fg}(x_1,y_1;h_2,y_2) ** h(x_1,y_1) \tag{6-10}$$

as in (3-6).

If $\mathbf{f}(x,y)$ is incoherent [see (6-3)], then (6-9) yields

$$R_{fg}(x_1,y_1;x_2,y_2) = q(x_1,y_1)h^*(x_2 - x_1, y_2 - y_1) \tag{6-11}$$

Inserting into (6-10), we obtain

$$R_{gg}(x_1,y_1;x_2,y_2) = [q(x_1,y_1)h^*(x_2 - x_1, y_2 - y_1)] ** h(x_1,y_1) \tag{6-12}$$

In particular,

$$E\{|\mathbf{g}(x,y)|^2\} = q(x,y) ** |h(x,y)|^2 \tag{6-13}$$

We observe again that if $h(x,y)$ takes significant values only in a "small" region A near the origin, then (6-13) takes the form

$$E\{|\mathbf{g}(x,y)|^2\} \simeq q(x,y) \iint\limits_A |h(x,y)|^2 \, dx \, dy \tag{6-14}$$

If the process $\mathbf{f}(x,y)$ is stationary with autocorrelation as in (6-4), then it is jointly stationary with $\mathbf{g}(x,y)$, and

$$R_{fg}(\xi,\eta) = E\{\mathbf{f}(x+\xi, y+\eta)\mathbf{g}^*(x,y)\} = R_{ff}(\xi,\eta) ** h^*(-\xi,-\eta) \tag{6-15}$$

This follows from (6-9) after some thought. Similarly, (6-10) yields

$$R_{gg}(\xi,\eta) = R_{fg}(\xi,\eta) ** h(\xi,\eta) \tag{6-16}$$

With S_{ff}, S_{fg}, S_{gg} the double Fourier transforms of R_{ff}, R_{fg}, R_{gg} and with $H(u,v)$ the system function, the above yields

$$\begin{aligned} S_{fg}(u,v) &= S_{ff}(u,v)H^*(u,v) \\ S_{gg}(u,v) &= S_{fg}(u,v)H(u,v) = S_{gg}(u,v)|H(u,v)|^2 \end{aligned} \tag{6-17}$$

as in (4-18).

If R_{ff} and h have circular symmetry, that is, if

$$R_{ff}(\xi,\eta) = R_{ff}(\rho) \qquad h(\xi,\eta) = h(\rho) \qquad \rho = \sqrt{\xi^2 + \eta^2}$$

then R_{fg} and R_{gg} also have circular symmetry, and

$$\begin{aligned} \bar{R}_{fg}(w) &= 2\pi\bar{R}_{ff}(w)\bar{h}^*(w) \\ \bar{R}_{gg}(w) &= 2\pi\bar{R}_{fg}(w)\bar{h}(w) = 4\pi^2\bar{R}_{ff}(w)|\bar{h}(w)|^2 \end{aligned} \tag{6-18}$$

where overbars indicate Hankel transforms. The above follows from (6-17) and Chap. 5, (1-4).

FOURIER TRANSFORMS OF STOCHASTIC PROCESSES

Consider a one-dimensional stochastic process $\mathbf{f}(t)$. If each member of this process has a Fourier transform, then the resulting family of functions

$$\mathbf{F}(\omega) = \int_{-\infty}^{\infty} \mathbf{f}(t)e^{-j\omega t} \, dt \tag{6-19}$$

is a stochastic process in ω. We shall determine its mean and autocorrelation. These functions can be obtained from (6-19). However, by viewing (6-19) as an operator

$$\mathbf{F}(\omega) = L[\mathbf{f}(t)] \tag{6-20}$$

we can apply the results of Sec. 2. This operator is obviously linear, but it is not time-invariant. Its impulse response is given by

$$L[\delta(t - \tau)] = e^{-j\omega\tau} \tag{6-21}$$

Hence, the conjugate operator L^* is such that [see (2-12)]

$$L^*[f(t)] = \int_{-\infty}^{\infty} f(t)e^{j\omega t}\, dt = F(-\omega) \tag{6-22}$$

that is, it assigns to $f(t)$ its transform with a reversal in the sign of ω.

From (2-4) [or directly from (6-19)], it follows that

$$E\{\mathbf{F}(\omega)\} = L[E\{\mathbf{f}(t)\}] = \int_{-\infty}^{\infty} E\{\mathbf{f}(t)\}e^{-j\omega t}\, dt \tag{6-23}$$

Thus the Fourier transform of the expected value of $\mathbf{f}(t)$ equals the expected value of $\mathbf{F}(\omega)$.

Correlation

With $R_{ff}(t_1,t_2)$ as the autocorrelation of $\mathbf{f}(t)$, we introduce the transforms [see Chap. 3, (4-4)]

$$R_{ff}(t_1,t_2) \overset{t_2}{\leftrightarrow} s_{ff}(t_1,v) \overset{t_1}{\leftrightarrow} S_{ff}(u,v) \tag{6-24}$$

Clearly, $S_{ff}(u,v)$ is the two-dimensional transform of $R_{ff}(t_1,t_2)$:

$$S_{ff}(u,v) = \iint_{-\infty}^{\infty} R_{ff}(t_1,t_2)e^{-j(ut_1+vt_2)}\, dt_1\, dt_2 \tag{6-25}$$

From (2-13) it follows that

$$E\{\mathbf{f}(t_1)\mathbf{F}^*(\omega_2)\} = R_{fF}(t_1,\omega_2) = L_2^*[R_{ff}(t_1,t_2)]$$

The last expression is the Fourier transform of $R_{ff}(t_1,t_2)$ in the variable t_2, with reversal of sign in v [see (6-22)], hence,

$$R_{fF}(t_1,\omega_2) = s_{ff}(t_1, -\omega_2) \tag{6-26}$$

From the above and (2-14) we conclude that

$$R_{FF}(\omega_1,\omega_2) = L_1[R_{fF}(t_1,\omega_2)] = L_1[s_{ff}(t_1, -\omega_2)]$$

This is the transform of $s_{ff}(t_1, -\omega_2)$ with respect to t_1; hence,

$$R_{FF}(\omega_1,\omega_2) = S_{ff}(\omega_1, -\omega_2) \tag{6-27}$$

as we see from (6-24).

Thus the autocorrelation of the Fourier transform of a process $\mathbf{f}(t)$ equals the two-dimensional Fourier transform of $R_{ff}(t_1,t_2)$, with reversal in the sign of the second variable.

We note that

$$E\{|\mathbf{F}(\omega)|^2\} = S_{ff}(\omega,-\omega) = \iint\limits_{-\infty}^{\infty} R_{ff}(t_1,t_2)e^{-j\omega(t_1-t_2)}\, dt_1\, dt_2 \qquad (6\text{-}28)$$

Special cases

1. Suppose that $\mathbf{f}(t)$ is white noise, as in (3-8):

$$R_{ff}(t_1,t_2) = q(t_1)\delta(t_2 - t_1)$$

With $Q(\omega)$ the Fourier transform of $q(t)$, that is,

$$q(t) \leftrightarrow Q(\omega) \qquad (6\text{-}29)$$

we have

$$q(t_1)\delta(t_2 - t_1) \overset{t_2}{\leftrightarrow} q(t_1)e^{-jvt_1} \leftrightarrow Q(u + v) \qquad (6\text{-}30)$$

Thus, $S_{ff}(u,v) = Q(u + v)$, and (6-27) yields

$$R_{FF}(\omega_1,\omega_2) = Q(\omega_1 - \omega_2) \qquad (6\text{-}31)$$

From the above we see that if $\mathbf{f}(t)$ is white noise, then its Fourier transform $\mathbf{F}(\omega)$ is a stationary process. The average intensity of $\mathbf{F}(\omega)$ is, therefore, constant:

$$E\{|\mathbf{F}(\omega)|^2\} = Q(0) = \int_{-\infty}^{\infty} q(t)\, dt \qquad (6\text{-}32)$$

2. We now assume that the process $\mathbf{f}(t)$ is stationary; thus

$$R_{ff}(t_1,t_2) = R(t_1 - t_2)$$

With

$$R(\tau) \leftrightarrow S(\omega)$$

we have

$$R(t_1 - t_2) \overset{t_2}{\leftrightarrow} S(-v)e^{-jvt_1} \overset{t_1}{\leftrightarrow} 2\pi S(-v)\delta(u + v)$$

Thus, $S_{ff}(u,v) = 2\pi S(-v)\delta(u + v)$, and

$$R_{FF}(\omega_1,\omega_2) = 2\pi S(\omega_2)\delta(\omega_1 - \omega_2) \qquad (6\text{-}33)$$

In other words, the Fourier transform of a stationary process is white noise whose "average intensity" (in the sense of page 264) equals 2π times the power spectrum of the process.

3. Suppose finally that [see also Chap. 10, (1-33)]

$$R(t_1,t_2) = p(t_1)p^*(t_2)$$

With $P(\omega)$ the Fourier transform of $p(t)$, we have

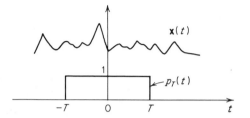 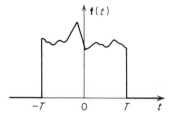

Fig. 6-1

$$p(t_1)p^*(t_2) \Leftrightarrow P(u)P^*(-v)$$

Hence

$$R_{FF}(\omega_1,\omega_2) = P(\omega_1)P^*(\omega_2) \tag{6-34}$$

and

$$E\{|\mathbf{F}(\omega)|^2\} = |P(\omega)|^2 \tag{6-35}$$

Example 6-1   Given a stationary process $\mathbf{x}(t)$ with autocorrelation $k\delta(\tau)$, we form the process

$$\mathbf{f}(t) = a\mathbf{x}(t)p_T(t)$$

where $p_T(t)$ is a pulse (Fig. 6-1).   Clearly, $\mathbf{f}(t)$ is nonstationary white noise with autocorrelation [see (3-2)]

$$R_{ff}(t_1,t_2) = a^2 p_T(t_1)\delta(t_2 - t_1)$$

because $p_T{}^2(t) = p_T(t)$.   Since

$$q(t) \equiv a^2 p_T(t) \leftrightarrow \frac{2a^2 \sin \omega T}{\omega}$$

we conclude from (6-31) that the autocorrelation of the Fourier transform $\mathbf{F}(\omega)$ is given by

$$R_{FF}(\omega_1,\omega_2) = \frac{2a^2 \sin (\omega_1 - \omega_2)T}{\omega_1 - \omega_2}$$

Example 6-2

a. Consider a stationary process $\mathbf{x}(t)$ with autocorrelation $R(\tau)$.   We form the process

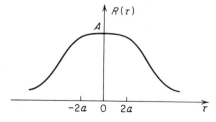

Fig. 6-2

(Fig. 6-2)

$$\mathbf{f}(t) = p_a(t)\mathbf{x}(t)$$

where a is small enough so that

$$R(\tau) \simeq R(0) = A \qquad \text{for } |\tau| < 2a$$

It is easy to see that

$$R_{ff}(t_1,t_2) = A p_a(t_1)p_a(t_2)$$

Hence

$$S_{ff}(u,v) = 4A \frac{\sin au}{u} \frac{\sin av}{v}$$

Inserting into (6-35), we obtain the average intensity

$$E\{|\mathbf{F}(\omega)|^2\} = 4A \frac{\sin^2 a\omega}{\omega^2}$$

b. With $\mathbf{x}(t)$ as in (a), we form the process

$$\mathbf{f}(t) = p_a(t - b)\mathbf{x}(t) + p_a(t + b)\mathbf{x}(t)$$

(Fig. 6-3a), and we assume that

$$R(\tau) \simeq R(2b) = B \qquad \text{for } |\tau - 2b| < 2a$$

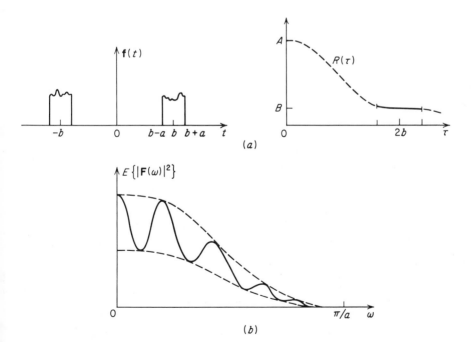

(a)

(b)

Fig. 6-3

It then follows that (elaborate)

$$R_{ff}(t_1,t_2) = Ap_a(t_1 - b)p_a(t_2 - b) + Ap_a(t_1 + b)p_a(t_2 + b)$$
$$+ Bp_a(t_1 - b)p_a(t_2 + b) + B^*p_a(t_1 + b)p_a(t_2 - b)$$

Hence (Fig. 6-3b),

$$E\{|\mathbf{F}(\omega)|^2\} = 8\frac{\sin^2 a\omega}{\omega^2}(A + \mathrm{Re}\, B\cos 2b\omega)$$

Two dimensions

The preceding results can be readily extended to a two-dimensional signal $\mathbf{f}(x,y)$ with transform

$$\mathbf{F}(u,v) = \int\limits_{-\infty}^{\infty}\!\!\int \mathbf{f}(x,y)e^{-j(ux+vy)}\,dx\,dy \tag{6-36}$$

With $R_{ff}(x_1,y_1;x_2,y_2)$ as the autocorrelation of $\mathbf{f}(u,v)$, we form the transforms

$$R_{ff}(x_1,y_1;x_2,y_2) \overset{x_2,y_2}{\Leftrightarrow} s_{ff}(x_1,y_1;u_2,v_2) \overset{x_1,y_1}{\Leftrightarrow} S(u_1,v_1;u_2,v_2) \tag{6-37}$$

We shall determine the correlations

$$R_{fF}(x_1,y_1;u_2,v_2) = E\{\mathbf{f}(x_1,y_1)\mathbf{F}^*(u_2,v_2)\}$$
$$R_{FF}(u_1,v_1;u_2,v_2) = E\{\mathbf{F}(u_1,v_1)\mathbf{F}^*(u_2,v_2)\}$$

Reasoning as in (6-26) and (6-27), we find

$$R_{fF}(x_1,y_1;u_2,v_2) = s_{ff}(x_1,y_1;-u_2,-v_2)$$
$$R_{FF}(u_1,v_1;u_2,v_2) = S_{ff}(u_1,v_1;-u_2,-v_2) \tag{6-38}$$

If $\mathbf{f}(x,y)$ is incoherent, with

$$R_{ff}(x_1,y_1;x_2,y_2) = q(x_1,y_1)\delta(x_2 - x_1)\delta(y_2 - y_1)$$

then $\mathbf{F}(u,v)$ is stationary, with

$$R_{FF}(u_1,v_1;u_2,v_2) = Q(u_1 - u_2, v_1 - v_2) \qquad \text{where } q(x,y) \Leftrightarrow Q(u,v) \tag{6-39}$$

If $\mathbf{f}(x,y)$ is stationary, then $\mathbf{F}(u,v)$ is incoherent.

Finally, if the coherence ratio of $\mathbf{f}(x,y)$ equals one, and

$$E\{|\mathbf{f}(x,y)|^2\} = |p(x,y)|^2$$

then

$$E\{|\mathbf{F}(\omega)|^2\} = |P(u,v)|^2 \qquad \text{where } p(x,y) \Leftrightarrow P(u,v)$$

Example 6-3 The process $\mathbf{w}(x,y)$ is incoherent and its autocorrelation equals

$$k\delta(x_1 - x_2)\delta(y_1 - y_2)$$

With $p_a(r)$ a circular disk of radius a, we form the process

$$\mathbf{f}(x,y) = p_a(r)\mathbf{w}(x,y) \qquad r = \sqrt{x^2 + y^2}$$

It is easy to show, as in (3-2), that

$$R_{ff}(x_1,y_1;x_2,y_2) = kp_a(r_1)\delta(x_2 - x_1)\delta(y_2 - y_1)$$

Since [see Chap. 3, (4-31)]

$$p_a(r) \Leftrightarrow 2\pi a \frac{J_1(aw)}{w} \qquad w = \sqrt{u^2 + v^2}$$

we conclude from (6-39) that

$$R_{FF}(u_1,v_1;u_2,v_2) = 2\pi a \frac{J_1(a\sqrt{(u_1 - u_2)^2 + (v_1 - v_2)^2})}{\sqrt{(u_1 - u_2)^2 + (v_1 - v_2)^2}}$$

PROBLEMS

8-1. Show that

$$\lim_{T\to\infty} \frac{1}{2T} \int_{-T}^{T} x(t + b)\, dt = \lim_{T\to\infty} \frac{1}{2T} \int_{-T}^{T} x(t)\, dt$$

8-2. (a) Using (4-19), show that $|R(\tau)| \leq R(0)$.

(b) Show that if $R(\tau_1) = R(0)$ and $\tau_1 \neq 0$, then $R(\tau)$ is periodic.

8-3. (a) Show that if $E\{\mathbf{xy}^*\} = |E\{\mathbf{xy}^*\}|e^{j\varphi}$, then [see also Chap. 6, (1-1)]

$$E\{|\mathbf{x} - ze^{j\varphi}\mathbf{y}|^2\} = E\{|\mathbf{x}|^2\} - 2z|E\{\mathbf{xy}^*\}| + z^2 E\{|\mathbf{y}|^2\}$$

(b) Using the above, show that $|r_{xy}(P,Q)| \leq 1$ [see (2-10)].

8-4. With

$$\bar{R}_{xy}(\tau) = \lim_{T\to\infty} \frac{1}{2T} \int_{-T}^{T} x(t + \tau)y^*(t)\, dt \qquad \text{and} \qquad \bar{S}_{xy}(\omega) = \int_{-\infty}^{\infty} R_{xy}(\tau)e^{-j\omega\tau}\, d\tau$$

show that

$$\bar{S}_{xy}(\omega) = \lim_{T\to\infty} \frac{1}{2T} \left[\int_{-T}^{T} x(t)e^{-j\omega t}\, dt \int_{-T}^{T} y^*(t)e^{j\omega t}\, dt \right]$$

8-5. The process $\mathbf{x}(t)$ is stationary with autocorrelation $R(\tau)$ and power spectrum $S(\omega)$.

(a) Show that the autocorrelation of its nth derivative $\mathbf{x}^{(n)}(t)$ equals

$$(-1)^n R^{(2n)}(\tau)$$

(b) If $S(\omega) = 0$ for $|\omega| > \omega_o$, then the average power of $\mathbf{x}^{(n)}(t)$ cannot exceed $\omega_o^{2n}R(0)$.

8-6. Given a monochromatic process $\mathbf{x}(t)$ with autocorrelation $R(\tau) = ke^{j\omega_o\tau}$, show that a random variable $\mathbf{a}$ can be found such that $\mathbf{x}(t)$ equals $\mathbf{a}e^{j\omega_o t}$ in the mean-square sense, that is,

$$E\{|\mathbf{x}(t) - \mathbf{a}e^{j\omega_o t}|^2\} = 0$$

8-7. The input to a system is a real process $\mathbf{x}(t)$. With $h(t) = e^{-\alpha t}U(t)$ its impulse response and $\mathbf{y}(t)$ the resulting output, show that

(a) If $R_{xx}(\tau) = k\delta(\tau)$, then $R_{yy}(\tau) = k\rho(\tau)$ where

$$\rho(\tau) = h(\tau) * h(-\tau) = \frac{1}{2\alpha} e^{-\alpha|\tau|}$$

(b) If $R_{xx}(\tau)$ is of short duration with area m_o and second moment m_2 [see Chap. 3, (2-17)], then

$$R_{yy}(\tau) \simeq m_o\rho(\tau) + \frac{m_2}{2} \rho''(\tau)$$

8-8. Given a stationary process $x(t)$ with autocorrelation $R(\tau)$ and power spectrum $S(\omega)$, we form the process $f(t) = p(t)x(t)$.

(a) Show that $R_{ff}(t_1,t_2) = p(t_1)p^*(t_2)R(t_1 - t_2)$.

(b) With $P(\omega)$ and $F(\omega)$, the Fourier transforms of $p(t)$ and $f(t)$, respectively, show that

$$R_{FF}(\omega_1,\omega_2) = \frac{1}{2\pi} \int_{-\infty}^{\infty} P(\omega_1 - \alpha)S(\alpha)P^*(\omega_2 - \alpha) \, d\alpha$$

$$E\{|F(\omega)|^2\} = |P(\omega)|^2 * S(\omega)$$

8-9. Given a stationary process $x(t)$ with autocorrelation $R(\tau)$ and power spectrum $S(\omega)$, show that

$$R(t_1 - t_2) \Leftrightarrow 2\pi S(-v)\delta(u + v) = 2\pi S(u)\delta(u + v)$$

part two

APPLICATIONS IN OPTICS

9
DIFFRACTION

In the following chapters, we apply the concepts of systems and transforms to optics. The analysis is limited to the scalar theory of light. This simplifying assumption is restrictive, but is adequate for many applications. The results are also valid for any field satisfying the wave equation. However, the various approximations are acceptable only if the wavelength is small in some sense. The required preparation for a vector theory is beyond our objectives.

In this chapter, we deal mainly with monochromatic signals. *The entire analysis is based on Kirchhoff's formula.* This important formula is proved in the first section. The proof starts from first principles (the scalar wave equation), and it is given for signals with arbitrary time dependence.

In Sec. 2 we introduce Kirchhoff's approximation, and we show that, with its help, the determination of the diffraction field can be reduced to the evaluation of an integral. In Secs. 3 and 4 we discuss in some detail the field in the Fresnel and Fraunhofer region of a diffracting aperture. Finally, in the last section we consider the effect of thin lenses. We show that for narrow angles such lenses are equivalent to transparencies with quadratically varying phase.

1. KIRCHHOFF'S FORMULA

Consider a scalar quantity $v(x,y,z,t)$, which satisfies the wave equation

$$\nabla^2 v - \frac{1}{c^2} \frac{\partial^2 v}{\partial t^2} = -s \tag{1-1}$$

where c is a constant (velocity of propagation) and $s(x,y,z,t)$ a given function (source density). At the end of this section, we shall show that if V_o is a region of space containing the point (x_o, y_o, z_o) and is bounded by the closed surface S_o, then $v(x_o, y_o, z_o, t)$ is given by [b5, s5]:

$$v(x_o, y_o, z_o, t) = \frac{1}{4\pi} \iiint_{V_o} \frac{1}{r} [s] \, dV$$

$$+ \frac{1}{4\pi} \iint_{S_o} \left\{ \frac{\partial(1/r)}{\partial n} [v] - \frac{1}{cr} \frac{\partial r}{\partial n} \left[\frac{\partial v}{\partial t} \right] - \frac{1}{r} \left[\frac{\partial v}{\partial n} \right] \right\} dS \tag{1-2}$$

where r is the distance from the fixed point (x_o, y_o, z_o) to the point of integration, and $\partial/\partial n$ denotes differentiation along a line normal to the surface S_o toward its interior (Fig. 1-1). The expression $[\varphi]$ means "retardation" in the following sense:

$$[\varphi] = \varphi \left(x, y, z, t - \frac{r}{c} \right) \qquad r = \sqrt{(x - x_o)^2 + (y - y_o)^2 + (z - z_o)^2}$$

If $s = 0$ everywhere in V_o, then (1-2) yields

$$v(x_o, y_o, z_o, t) = \frac{1}{4\pi} \iint_{S_o} \left\{ \frac{\partial(1/r)}{\partial n} [v] - \frac{1}{cr} \frac{\partial r}{\partial n} \left[\frac{\partial v}{\partial t} \right] - \frac{1}{r} \left[\frac{\partial v}{\partial n} \right] \right\} dS \tag{1-3}$$

This fundamental relationship, known as Kirchhoff's formula, will form the basis of our analysis. We note that it expresses $v(x_o, y_o, z_o, t)$ in terms of the values of v, $\partial v/\partial n$, $\partial v/\partial t$ on the surface S_o at the retarded times $t - r/c$.

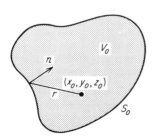

Fig. 1-1

If the source density s occupies a bounded region V in space, and it is zero prior to some time t_o, then

$$v(x_o,y_o,z_o,t) = \frac{1}{4\pi} \iiint_V \frac{1}{r} [s] \, dV \tag{1-4}$$

Indeed, from (1-2) it follows that $v = 0$ for $t < t_o$. If, therefore, V_o is a sphere of radius R enclosing V and the point (x_o,y_o,z_o), and R is large enough so that the minimum distance from S_o to (x_o,y_o,z_o) exceeds $c(t - t_o)$, then the surface integral in (1-2) vanishes, and (1-4) follows. By a limiting argument we can extend the validity of (1-4) to unbounded regions.

As a special case, suppose that s is a point source at the origin

$$s = 4\pi w(t)\delta(x)\delta(y)\delta(z)$$

where $w(t)$ is an arbitrary function. It then follows from (1-4) that the resulting field is

$$v(x_o,y_o,z_o,t) = \frac{w(t - r/c)}{r} \qquad r = \sqrt{x_o{}^2 + y_o{}^2 + z_o{}^2} \tag{1-5}$$

If s is a line source with line density $4\pi w(t)$ along the y axis,

$$s = 4\pi w(t)\delta(x)\delta(z)$$

then $v(x_o,y_o,z_o,t)$ is given by

$$v(x_o,y_o,z_o,t) = \int_{-\infty}^{\infty} \frac{w(t - r/c)}{r} \, dy$$

With

$$\rho = \sqrt{x_o{}^2 + z_o{}^2} \qquad y - y_o = \rho \sinh \eta$$

$$r = \sqrt{\rho^2 + (y - y_o)^2} = \rho \cosh \eta \tag{1-6}$$

the above yields

$$v(x_o,y_o,z_o,t) = \int_{-\infty}^{\infty} w\left(t - \frac{\rho}{c} \cosh \eta\right) d\eta \tag{1-7}$$

Harmonic signals

We now assume that v varies harmonically with time:

$$v(x,y,z,t) = g(x,y,z)e^{-j\omega t} \qquad \frac{\omega}{c} = \frac{2\pi}{\lambda} = k \tag{1-8}$$

We then have, for every point in a source-free region V_o,

$$g(x_o,y_o,z_o) = \frac{1}{4\pi} \iint_{S_o} \left[g \frac{\partial}{\partial n}\left(\frac{e^{jkr}}{r}\right) - \frac{e^{jkr}}{r} \frac{\partial g}{\partial n} \right] dS \tag{1-9}$$

This follows from (1-3) because

$$[v] = ge^{j(kr-\omega t)} \qquad \left[\frac{\partial v}{\partial t}\right] = -j\omega g e^{j(kr-\omega t)} \qquad \left[\frac{\partial v}{\partial n}\right] = \frac{\partial g}{\partial n} e^{j(kr-\omega t)}$$

For harmonic signals, the wave equation reduces to

$$\nabla^2 v + k^2 v = -s \tag{1-10}$$

Using this formula, one can establish (1-9) directly. By representing an arbitrary signal as a linear combination of exponentials, one can then deduce the general form (1-3) of Kirchhoff's formula. However, such an approach is not suitable for our analysis because optical signals have no ordinary Fourier transforms (see Chap. 10). To insure the generality of the formula, we shall give a direct proof of (1-3).

TWO-DIMENSIONAL SIGNALS

Suppose that $v(x,z,t)$ is independent of y and it satisfies the two-dimensional wave equation

$$\frac{\partial^2 v}{\partial x^2} + \frac{\partial^2 v}{\partial z^2} - \frac{1}{\mathbf{c}^2}\frac{\partial^2 v}{\partial t^2} = -s \tag{1-11}$$

We shall first express v in terms of the source function $s(x,z,t)$ by a formula similar to (1-4). If v is viewed as a three-dimensional signal independent of y, then (1-11) is a special case of (1-1); hence, (1-4) holds [b1]. Performing the integration with respect to y first, we obtain, with the transformation (1-6),

$$v(x_o,z_o,t) = \frac{1}{4\pi} \iint_S \int_{-\infty}^{\infty} s\left(x, z, t - \frac{\rho}{\mathbf{c}}\cosh\eta\right) d\eta\, dx\, dz \tag{1-12}$$

where ρ is the distance from the point (x_o,z_o) to the point (x,z) in the region S of the sources. Clearly, (1-7) is a special case of the above.

Comment If a function v satisfies the homogeneous wave equation $(s = 0)$ everywhere except at the origin, and it depends only on r, then it is given by

$$\frac{w(t \pm r/\mathbf{c})}{r}$$

where $w(t)$ is an arbitrary twice-differentiable function [see (1-5)]. The general solution of the corresponding two-dimensional problem is the more complicated expression [see (1-7)]

$$\int_{-\infty}^{\infty} w\left(t \pm \frac{\rho}{\mathbf{c}}\cosh\eta\right) d\eta$$

Kirchhoff's formula   Suppose now that Γ_o is a closed curve on the xz plane, and (x_o,z_o) is a point in its interior.   Using for S_o the surface of a cylinder of length $2Y$ whose axis is parallel to the y axis and whose cross section is the curve Γ_o (Fig. 1-2), we can find $v(x_o,z_o,t)$ from its values on Γ_o by integrating over S_o [as in (1-3)] and evaluating the limit of the integral for $Y \rightarrow \infty$.   We shall carry out the details for the harmonic case

$$v(x,z,t) = g(x,z)e^{-j\omega t}$$

The surface S_o consists of the cylindrical part S_1 and the planes $y = \pm Y$, forming the surfaces S_2 and S_3.   For every point of S_2 and S_3, we have

$$\frac{\partial g}{\partial n} = \pm \frac{\partial g}{\partial y} = 0 \qquad \frac{1}{r}\frac{\partial r}{\partial n} \xrightarrow[Y \rightarrow \infty]{} 0$$

Furthermore, the area of these surfaces is finite and independent of Y. It suffices, therefore, to limit the integration in (1-9) to the surface S_1. With

$$dS = dl\, dy$$

and $Y \rightarrow \infty$, we thus have

$$\iint_{S_o} \left[g\frac{\partial}{\partial n}\left(\frac{e^{jkr}}{r}\right) - \frac{e^{jkr}}{r}\frac{\partial g}{\partial n} \right] dS = \int_{\Gamma_o} dl \int_{-\infty}^{\infty} [\quad] dy$$

Since the functions g and $\partial g/\partial n$ are independent of y, we can take them outside the second integral, and (1-9) yields

$$g(x_o,z_o) = \frac{1}{4\pi}\int_{\Gamma_o}\left[g\frac{\partial}{\partial n}\int_{-\infty}^{\infty}\frac{e^{jkr}}{r}\,dy - \frac{\partial g}{\partial n}\int_{-\infty}^{\infty}\frac{e^{jkr}}{r}\,dy \right] dl \qquad (1\text{-}13)$$

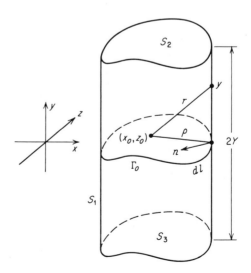

Fig. 1-2

With

$$H_o(x) = \frac{1}{\pi} \int_{-\infty}^{\infty} e^{jx \cosh \eta} \, d\eta \tag{1-14}$$

the Hankel function of order zero (first kind) and

$$r = \sqrt{\rho^2 + y^2} = \rho \cosh \eta \qquad \rho = \sqrt{(x - x_o)^2 + (z - z_o)^2}$$

we conclude, as in (1-7), that

$$\int_{-\infty}^{\infty} \frac{e^{jkr}}{r} \, d\eta = \int_{-\infty}^{\infty} e^{jk\rho \cosh \eta} \, d\eta = \pi H_o(k\rho)$$

Inserting into (1-13), we thus obtain the line integral

$$g(x_o, z_o) = \frac{1}{4} \int_{\Gamma_o} \left[g \frac{\partial H_o(k\rho)}{\partial n} - H_o(k\rho) \frac{\partial g}{\partial n} \right] dl \tag{1-15}$$

where, as in (1-9), $\partial/\partial n$ denotes differentiation along a line normal to the curve Γ_o, toward its interior. This is the two-dimensional form of Kirchhoff's formula for harmonic signals.

If $k\rho \gg 1$, that is, if the minimum distance from the point of observation (x_o, z_o) to the boundary Γ_o is large compared with the wavelength λ, then (1-15) can be simplified with the method of *stationary phase*. Clearly, (1-14) is an integral of the form of Eq. (3-1), Chap. 7, where

$$\mu(\eta) = \cosh \eta$$

Since $\mu'(\eta) = 0$ for $\eta = 0$ only, (1-14) has one interior stationary point $\eta_o = 0$, with

$$\mu(\eta_o) = 1 \qquad \mu''(\eta_o) = 1$$

Applying Eq. (3-10), Chap. 7, we thus have

$$H_o(x) = \frac{1}{\pi} \int_{-\infty}^{\infty} e^{jx \cosh \eta} \, d\eta \xrightarrow[x \to \infty]{} \sqrt{\frac{2}{\pi x}} \, e^{j(x + \pi/4)} \tag{1-16}$$

and (1-15) yields

$$g(x_o, z_o) = \frac{e^{j\pi/4}}{\sqrt{8\pi k}} \int_{\Gamma_o} \left[g \frac{\partial}{\partial n} \left(\frac{e^{jk\rho}}{\sqrt{\rho}} \right) - \frac{e^{jk\rho}}{\sqrt{\rho}} \frac{\partial g}{\partial n} \right] dl \tag{1-17}$$

for $k\rho \gg 1$, that is, for $\rho \gg \lambda$.

Sources Suppose, finally, that the source density s in (1-12) varies harmonically with time, i.e., that

$$s(x, z, t) = p(x, z)e^{-j\omega t}$$

Since [see (1-14)]

$$\int_{-\infty}^{\infty} e^{-j\omega(t-\rho\cosh\eta/c)} \, d\eta = \pi e^{-j\omega t} H_o(k\rho)$$

we conclude from (1-12) and (1-16) that

$$g(x_o,z_o) = \frac{1}{4} \iint_S p(x,z) H_o(k\rho) \, dx \, dz \xrightarrow[\lambda\to0]{} \frac{\sqrt{\lambda}}{4\pi} e^{j\pi/4} \iint_S \frac{p(x,z)}{\sqrt{\rho}} e^{jk\rho} \, dx \, dz$$

For a line source along the y axis with density

$$s(x,z,t) = 4\pi e^{-j\omega t} \, \delta(x) \, \delta(z) \tag{1-18}$$

the above yields

$$g(x_o,z_o) = \pi H_o(k\rho) \to \sqrt{\frac{\lambda}{\rho}} e^{j(k\rho+\pi/4)} \qquad \text{for } \rho \gg \lambda \tag{1-19}$$

PROOF OF KIRCHHOFF'S FORMULA

The proof of (1-2) will be based on the fact that if a function $h(t)$ is continuous and

$$\int_a^b w(t) h(t) \, dt = 0 \tag{1-20}$$

for any $w(t)$, then $h(t)$ is identically zero in the interval (a,b).

It is well known that if the functions ψ and φ have continuous first and second derivatives everywhere in the closed region V and its boundary surface S, then (Green's theorem)

$$\iiint_V (\psi\nabla^2\varphi - \varphi\nabla^2\psi) \, dV = \iint_S \left(-\psi\frac{\partial\varphi}{\partial n} + \varphi\frac{\partial\psi}{\partial n} \right) dS \tag{1-21}$$

where $\partial/\partial n$ is taken toward the interior [s5] of S. The region V can be simply connected (Fig. 1-3) or multiply connected (Fig. 1-4). In the latter case, S consists of two pieces $S = S_o + S_1$.

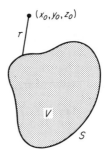

Fig. 1-3

With $w(t)$ an arbitrary twice-differentiable function and (x_o,y_o,z_o) a fixed point outside the region V, we form the function

$$\psi(x,y,z,t) = \frac{w(t + r/\mathbf{c})}{r} \qquad r = \sqrt{(x - x_o)^2 + (y - y_o)^2 + (z - z_o)^2}$$

$$(1\text{-}22)$$

It is easy to see that ψ satisfies the wave equation

$$\nabla^2\psi = \frac{1}{\mathbf{c}^2}\frac{\partial^2\psi}{\partial t^2}$$

for every $r \neq 0$ [see also (1-5)]. With $\varphi = v$, as in (1-1), we thus have

$$\psi\nabla^2v - v\nabla^2\psi = \psi\left(\frac{1}{\mathbf{c}^2}\frac{\partial^2v}{\partial t^2} - s\right) - v\frac{1}{\mathbf{c}^2}\frac{\partial^2\psi}{\partial t^2}$$

Inserting into (1-21), we obtain

$$\frac{1}{\mathbf{c}^2}\iiint_V\left(\frac{w}{r}\frac{\partial^2v}{\partial t^2} - \frac{v}{r}w''\right)dV = \iint_S\left(-\frac{w}{r}\frac{\partial v}{\partial n} + v\frac{\partial(w/r)}{\partial n}\right)dS$$

$$+ \iiint_V\frac{ws}{r}dV \quad (1\text{-}23)$$

where w and its second derivative w'' are evaluated at $t + r/\mathbf{c}$.

We now denote by r_m the maximum distance from the fixed point (x_o,y_o,z_o) to the points of the region V, and we choose $w(t)$ such that

$$w(t) \equiv 0 \qquad \text{for } |t| \geq \frac{2r_m}{\mathbf{c}} \tag{1-24}$$

With $T = 3r_m/\mathbf{c}$, we have for every (x,y,z) in V

$$-\int_{-T}^{T}\left(w\frac{\partial^2v}{\partial t^2} - vw''\right)dt = \left[w\left(t + \frac{r}{\mathbf{c}}\right)\frac{\partial v}{\partial t} - vw'\left(t + \frac{r}{\mathbf{c}}\right)\right]\Big|_{-T}^{T} = 0$$

$$(1\text{-}25)$$

(integration by parts) because

$$|\pm T + r/\mathbf{c}| > 2r_m/\mathbf{c}$$

Since (1-25) is true for every point in V, it follows that if the left side of (1-23) is integrated with respect to t in the interval $(-T,T)$, the result is zero; hence, the integral of the right side must also be zero. Changing the order of integration, we thus have

$$\iint_S\int_{-T}^{T}\left(-\frac{w}{r}\frac{\partial v}{\partial n} + v\frac{\partial(w/r)}{\partial n}\right)dt\,dS + \iiint_V\int_{-T}^{T}\frac{ws}{r}dt\,dV = 0$$

$$(1\text{-}26)$$

But

$$\frac{\partial}{\partial n} \frac{w(t + r/\mathbf{c})}{r} = \frac{\partial(1/r)}{\partial n} w + \frac{1}{r\mathbf{c}} \frac{\partial r}{\partial n} w'$$

and [see (1-24)]

$$\int_{-T}^{T} vw' \, dt = w\left(t + \frac{r}{\mathbf{c}}\right) v \Big|_{-T}^{T} - \int_{-T}^{T} w \frac{\partial v}{\partial t} \, dt = -\int_{-T}^{T} w \frac{\partial v}{\partial t} \, dt$$

$$(1\text{-}27)$$

We insert the above into (1-26) and introduce the transformation

$$t' = t + r/\mathbf{c}$$

The new limits of integration $-T + r/\mathbf{c}$ and $T + r/\mathbf{c}$ are now functions of (x,y,z); however, since $w(t)$ is zero for $|t| > 2r_m/\mathbf{c}$, they can be replaced by the constant limits $-T$ and T. Hence the order of space and time integration can again be changed. We also note that $w(t')$ is independent of space coordinates and that, therefore, it can be taken outside the space integration. With these changes, (1-26) yields [see (1-27)]

$$\int_{-T}^{T} w(t') \left\{ \iint_S \left(-\frac{1}{r}\left[\frac{\partial v}{\partial n}\right] + [v]\frac{\partial(1/r)}{\partial n} - \frac{1}{r\mathbf{c}}\frac{\partial r}{\partial n}\left[\frac{\partial v}{\partial t}\right] \right) dS \right.$$

$$\left. + \iiint_V \frac{[s]}{r} \, dV \right\} dt' = 0 \quad (1\text{-}28)$$

The retarded times are as shown because $\partial v/\partial t$ was evaluated before the transformation $t = t' - r/\mathbf{c}$ was introduced. The above is true for every $|t'| < 2r_m/\mathbf{c}$, that is, for every $|t| < r_m/\mathbf{c}$. And since $w(t)$ and the time origin are arbitrary, it follows that the quantity in braces in (1-28) must equal zero for every t and for every (x_0,y_0,z_0) outside the region V.

To complete the proof of (1-2), we choose $S = S_o + S_1$, as in Fig. 1-4. Assuming that S_1 is a spherical surface of radius a centered at the

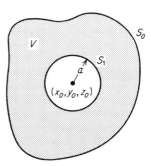

Fig. 1-4

point of observation (x_o, y_o, z_o), we have

$$\frac{\partial r}{\partial n} = 1 \qquad \frac{\partial (1/r)}{\partial n} = -\frac{1}{a^2} \qquad r = a$$

for every point on S_1. Since the function v and its derivatives are continuous, we conclude, with $(\cdot \cdot \cdot)$ the parentheses in (1-28), that

$$\iint\limits_{S_1} (\cdot \cdot \cdot) \, dS = \iint\limits_{S_1} \left(-\frac{1}{a}\left[\frac{\partial v}{\partial n}\right] - \frac{[v]}{a^2} - \frac{1}{a\mathbf{c}}\left[\frac{\partial v}{\partial t}\right] \right) dS \xrightarrow[a \to 0]{} -4\pi v$$

because

$$[v] = v\left(x, \, y, \, z, \, t - \frac{a}{\mathbf{c}}\right) \to v(x_o, y_o, z_o, t)$$

with $a \to 0$. Hence, the quantity in braces in (1-28), integrated over the surface S_o, equals $4\pi v$. The proof of (1-2) is thus complete.

2. KIRCHHOFF'S APPROXIMATION

Consider an optical field v^i due to light sources in the half-space $z < 0$. If an opaque screen $\bar{S}$ bounded by a curve Γ is placed in the region $z \geq 0$ (Fig. 2-1), a new field v results, and the object of diffraction theory is to determine the perturbed field v. If the sources are specified, then the incident field v^i can be evaluated from (1-4); in any case, it will be con-

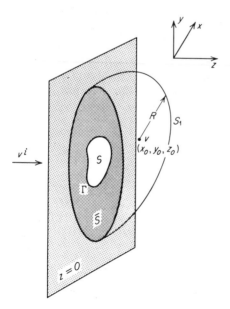

Fig. 2-1

sidered known. We shall assume that the boundary Γ is a plane curve on the plane $z = 0$.

Since there are no sources for $z \geq 0$, v satisfies the homogeneous wave equation in this region; therefore, it is given by (1-3) for every point (x_o,y_o,z_o) inside a closed surface S_o in the right half-space. By the aperture S of the screen $\tilde{S}$ we shall mean the interior of the curve Γ on the plane $z = 0$. With S_1 the surface of a sphere of radius $R > z_o$ centered at (x_o,y_o,z_o), S_o will consist of the aperture S, the spherical surface S_1, and the portion of the screen $\tilde{S}$ between S and S_1.

Suppose that the incident field v^i is established at some time t_o:

$$v^i(x,y,z,t') = 0 \qquad \text{for } t' < t_o$$

With t the time of observation, if R is so large that

$$t - \frac{R}{\mathbf{c}} < t_o$$

then v vanishes on the surface S_1 at the retarded times $t - R/\mathbf{c}$. With $R \to \infty$, we thus conclude that the integration can be limited to the plane $z = 0$ consisting of the aperture S and the screen $\tilde{S}$.

Comment The contribution of the spherical surface S_1 to the integration is zero because we assumed that v^i vanishes prior to t_o. Clearly, if v^i is a harmonic function of time, then this assumption is not true; hence, the integration over S_1 does not necessarily tend to zero with $R \to \infty$, and the open-surface formula [Chap. 1, (1-19)] is not always correct. For its validity, the field g must satisfy certain general radiation conditions. However, for our objectives, this restriction can be ignored.

Kirchhoff's formula (1-3) expresses the perturbed field v in terms of its boundary values, i.e., in terms of unknown quantities. It cannot, therefore, be used in the above form, and for the exact determination of v one must seek other methods. However, for optical waves, it seems reasonable to assume that *the disturbed field equals zero everywhere on the dark side of the screen, and at its aperture it equals the incident wave v^i* [b5]. Thus

$$v, \frac{\partial v}{\partial n}, \frac{\partial v}{\partial t} = \begin{cases} v^i, \dfrac{\partial v^i}{\partial n}, \dfrac{\partial v^i}{\partial t} & \text{for } (x,y,z) \in S \\ 0 & \text{for } (x,y,z) \in \tilde{S} \end{cases} \tag{2-1}$$

Inserting the above into (1-3), we can determine $v(x_o,y_o,z_o,t)$ in terms of the unperturbed field v^i and of its derivatives on the aperture surface S at the retarded times $t - r/\mathbf{c}$. Assumption (2-1), known as Kirchhoff's approximation, thus permits us to reduce the theory of diffraction to the evaluation of an integral. One can show that if the largest wave-

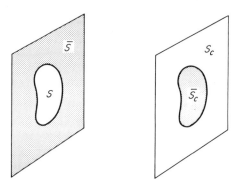

Fig. 2-2

length λ_m of the spectrum of v^i is small compared with z_o and with the dimensions of S, then the approximation error is negligible; however, its estimate is not simple.

Transparent aperture   Suppose now that the aperture is not air but a thin film.   We shall assume again that (2-1) still holds, provided that $v^i(x,y,z,t)$ is replaced by

$$v^i[x, y, z, t - \tau(x,y)]a(x,y) \tag{2-2}$$

where the "delay" $\tau(x,y)$ and the "attenuation" $a(x,y)$ are characteristic of the film.

Babinet's principle   If the aperture S is the entire $z = 0$ plane (no screen), then the diffracted field equals the incident field.   Hence,

$$\frac{1}{4\pi} \iint\limits_{-\infty}^{\infty} \{\quad\} \, dx \, dy = v^i(x_o,y_o,z_o,t)$$

where the quantity in the braces is as in (1-2).   This permits us to express the diffraction field v_c of a complementary screen in terms of the diffraction field v of the original screen.   Defining the complementary screen as the screen whose aperture S_c is the opaque part $\bar{S}$ of a given screen (Fig. 2-2), we conclude that

$$4\pi v_c = \iint\limits_{\bar{S}} \{\quad\} \, dx \, dy = \iint\limits_{-\infty}^{\infty} \{\quad\} \, dx \, dy - \iint\limits_{S} \{\quad\} \, dx \, dy$$

$$= 4\pi(v^i - v)$$

where the quantity in the braces is as in (1-2).   Thus

$$v_c = v^i - v \tag{2-3}$$

everywhere in the region $z > 0$.

PLANE-WAVE INCIDENCE

We next assume that the unperturbed field v^i is a plane wave propagating in the z direction:

$$v^i = v^i\left(x, y, t - \frac{z}{c}\right)$$

Since the surface S is part of the z plane, we have

$$\frac{\partial v^i}{\partial n} = \frac{\partial v^i}{\partial z} = -\frac{1}{c}\frac{\partial v^i}{\partial t}$$

for every point on S, and with $dS = dx\,dy$, (1-3) yields

$$v(x_0,y_0,z_0,t) = \frac{1}{4\pi}\iint_S \left\{\frac{1}{r^2}\frac{\partial r}{\partial z}[v^i] + \frac{1}{cr}\left(1 - \frac{\partial r}{\partial z}\right)\left[\frac{\partial v^i}{\partial t}\right]\right\}\,dx\,dy \qquad (2\text{-}4)$$

Suppose now that the point of observation (x_0,y_0,z_0) is sufficiently far from the screen so that

$$\frac{|v^i|}{z_0} \ll \frac{1}{c}\left|\frac{\partial v^i}{\partial t}\right| \qquad (2\text{-}5)$$

From

$$r = \sqrt{(x - x_0)^2 + (y - y_0)^2 + z_0^2} \geq z_0 \qquad \left|\frac{\partial r}{\partial z}\right| \leq 1$$

and (2-5) it follows that the first term in the integral (2-4) can be neglected as compared with the others, and the approximation

$$v(x_0,y_0,z_0,t) = \frac{1}{4\pi c}\iint_S \frac{1}{r}\left(1 - \frac{\partial r}{\partial z}\right)\left[\frac{\partial v^i}{\partial t}\right]\,dx\,dy \qquad (2\text{-}6)$$

results.

Assumption (2-5) states that with $t_o = z_0/c$ as the propagation time of the incident wave from the screen $z = 0$ to the point of observation (x_0,y_0,z_0), the slope v^i/t_o (Fig. 2-3) is small compared with the slope $\partial v^i/\partial t$. Since in optics we are interested only in time averages over several oscil-

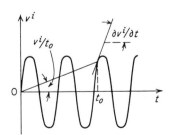

Fig. 2-3

lations, this condition need be true only in some mean sense, and this is the case if

$$z_0 \gg \lambda_m$$

where λ_m is the largest wavelength in the spectrum of v^i.

Self-luminous objects   At a distance r that is large compared with the dimensions of S, (2-6) reduces to

$$v(x_0,y_0,z_0,t) = \frac{1 + \gamma_o}{4\pi c r_o} \iint_S \left[\frac{\partial v^i}{\partial t} \right] dx\, dy \qquad (2\text{-}6a)$$

because

$$\frac{\partial r}{\partial z} \simeq \frac{\partial r}{\partial z_0} = -\frac{z_0}{r_o} = -\gamma_o \qquad r_o = \sqrt{x_o{}^2 + y_o{}^2 + z_o{}^2}$$

Suppose now that the aperture is replaced by surface sources (self-luminous objects)

$$s(x,y,z,t) = \varphi(x,y,t)\,\delta(z)$$

on the $z = 0$ plane.   The resulting far field is then given by [see (1-4)]

$$v_s(x_0,y_0,z_0,t) = \frac{1}{4\pi} \iint_S \frac{1}{r} [\varphi]\, dx\, dy \simeq \frac{1}{4\pi r_o} \iint_S [\varphi]\, dx\, dy \qquad (2\text{-}6b)$$

Hence, if

$$\varphi(x,y,t) = \frac{2}{c} \frac{\partial}{\partial t}\, v^i(x,y,0,t)$$

then $v_s = v$ in the small-angle region $\gamma_o \simeq 1$.   Thus, the diffracted field is the same as the field due to a self-luminous object of suitable density. This equivalence is valid in a small-angle region along the z axis; however, as we shall soon see, this is often the region where v takes significant values.

Point source   The incident field v^i due to a point source $4\pi w(t)$ placed at the point (x_s,y_s,z_s) is given by [see (1-5)]

$$v^i(x,y,z,t) = \frac{w(t - r_s/c)}{r_s} \qquad r_s = \sqrt{(x_s - x)^2 + (y_s - y)^2 + z_s{}^2}$$
$$(2\text{-}7)$$

With $w'(t)$ the derivative of $w(t)$, we have

$$\frac{\partial v^i}{\partial t} = \frac{w'}{r_s} \qquad \frac{\partial v^i}{\partial n} = -\left(\frac{w'}{r_s c} + \frac{w}{r_s{}^2} \right) \frac{\partial r_s}{\partial n} \qquad (2\text{-}8)$$

Inserting into (1-2), and assuming that $w(t)$ varies sufficiently rapidly so that

$$\frac{w(t)}{r} \ll \frac{w'(t)}{c} \qquad \frac{w(t)}{r_s} \ll \frac{w'(t)}{c} \tag{2-9}$$

we obtain as in (2-6)

$$v(x_0,y_0,z_0,t) = \frac{1}{4\pi c} \iint\limits_{S} \frac{1}{rr_s} w'\left(t - \frac{r + r_s}{c}\right)\left(\frac{\partial r_s}{\partial z} - \frac{\partial r}{\partial z}\right) dx \, dy \tag{2-10}$$

This result can be used to derive the diffraction field due to a uniform plane wave

$$v^i = w_o[t - (\alpha_s x + \beta_s y + \gamma_s z)] \tag{2-11}$$

which propagates in an arbitrary direction with directional cosines α_s, β_s, γ_s. Indeed, with

$$\frac{w(t)}{r_s} \to w_o(t) \qquad \frac{\partial r_s}{\partial z} \to \gamma_s \qquad \text{for } r_s \to \infty$$

we conclude from (2-10), omitting a constant delay, that

$$v(x_0,y_0,z_0,t) = \frac{1}{4\pi c} \iint\limits_{S} \frac{1}{r}\left(\gamma_s - \frac{\partial r}{\partial z}\right) w_o'\left(t - \frac{\alpha_s x + \beta_s \gamma + \gamma_s z + r}{c}\right) dx \, dy$$
$$\tag{2-12}$$

Harmonic signals

Suppose now that the incident field is harmonic in time:

$$v^i = f(x,y)e^{-j\omega(t-z/c)} \tag{2-13}$$

The diffracted field is then of the form (1-8)

$$v = g(x,y,z)e^{-j\omega t}$$

On the $z = 0$ plane, we have

$$\left[\frac{\partial v^i}{\partial t}\right] = -j\omega f(x,y)e^{-j\omega(t-r/c)}$$

Inserting into (2-6), we obtain

$$g(x_0,y_0,z_0) = \frac{-j}{2\lambda} \iint\limits_{S} \frac{1}{r}\left(1 - \frac{\partial r}{\partial z}\right) f(x,y)e^{jkr} dx \, dy \tag{2-14}$$

which is subject to condition (2-5). For harmonic signals this condition reduces to

$$z_0 \gg \lambda$$

If the aperture contains a transparency with attenuation $a(x,y)$ and delay $\tau(x,y)$ [see (2-2)], then (2-14) still holds, provided that $f(x,y)$ is multiplied by the *transmission function*

$$T(x,y) = a(x,y)e^{j\omega\tau(x,y)} \tag{2-15}$$

If v^i is due to a point source, as in (2-7), then with

$$w(t) = e^{-j\omega t}$$

(2-10) yields

$$g(x_o,y_o,z_o) = \frac{-j}{2\lambda} \iint_S \frac{1}{rr_s} \left(\frac{\partial r_s}{\partial z} - \frac{\partial r}{\partial z} \right) e^{jk(r+r_s)} \, dx \, dy \tag{2-16}$$

provided that $r, r_s \gg \lambda$.

For a plane wave as in (2-11), we conclude with $w_o(t) = e^{-j\omega t}$ that [see (2-12)]

$$g(x_o,y_o,z_o) = \frac{-j}{2\lambda} \iint_S \frac{1}{r} \left(\gamma_s - \frac{\partial r}{\partial z} \right) e^{jk(\alpha_s x + \beta_s y + \gamma_s z)} e^{jkr} \, dx \, dy \tag{2-17}$$

The preceding relationships were obtained as special cases of the approximate formula (2-6), which is valid for arbitrary signals and is based on condition (2-5). They can also be derived by introducing the condition $z_o \gg \lambda$ directly in the harmonic form (1-9) of Kirchhoff's formula. This approach will be used in the two-dimensional case.

TWO-DIMENSIONAL SIGNALS

Consider a harmonic plane wave, uniform in y, propagating in the z direction:

$$v^i = f(x)e^{-j\omega(t-z/c)} \tag{2-18}$$

We place an opaque screen on the plane $z = 0$ with a strip aperture of width $2a$ in the y direction (Fig. 2-4). The disturbed field v is independent of y, that is,

$$v(x,y,z,t) = g(x,z)e^{-j\omega t}$$

and $g(x_o,z_o)$ is given by the two-dimensional form (1-15) of Kirchhoff's formula or the approximate form (1-17) for $z_o \gg \lambda$.

Choosing for Γ_o the closed curve of Fig. 2-4, which consists of the straight-line segment $(-a,a)$ on the aperture, two line segments on the screen along the x axis, and a semicircle of radius R, we conclude, as we did on page 307—assuming that g and $\partial g/\partial n$ are zero on the dark side of the screen (Kirchhoff's approximation)—that the integration can be limited to the $(-a,a)$ segment of the x axis.

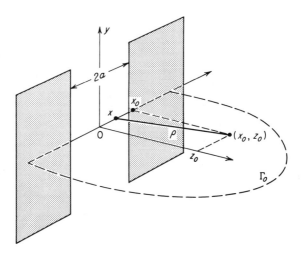

Fig. 2-4

For $z = 0$ we have [see (2-18)]

$$g = f(x) \qquad \frac{\partial g}{\partial n} = \frac{\partial g}{\partial z} = jkf(x)$$

and (1-17) yields

$$g(x_o,z_o) = \frac{e^{j\pi/4}}{\sqrt{8k\pi}} \int_{-a}^{a} f(x) \left(\frac{\partial}{\partial z} \frac{e^{jk\rho}}{\sqrt{\rho}} - \frac{jk}{\sqrt{\rho}} e^{jk\rho} \right) dx \qquad (2\text{-}19)$$

where

$$\rho = \sqrt{(x - x_o)^2 + z_o^2} \qquad \frac{\partial \rho}{\partial z} = \frac{-z_o}{\rho}$$

Clearly,

$$\frac{\partial}{\partial z} \left(\frac{e^{jk\rho}}{\sqrt{\rho}} \right) = \frac{jk}{\sqrt{\rho}} e^{jk\rho} \frac{\partial \rho}{\partial z} - \frac{1}{2\rho \sqrt{\rho}} e^{jk\rho} \qquad (2\text{-}20)$$

If $z_o \gg \lambda$ [an assumption implicit in (1-17)], then the second term on the right side of the above equation can be omitted, and (2-19) yields

$$g(x_o,z_o) = \frac{e^{-j\pi/4}}{2\sqrt{\lambda}} \int_{-a}^{a} \frac{1}{\sqrt{\rho}} \left(1 - \frac{\partial \rho}{\partial z} \right) f(x) e^{jk\rho} \, dx \qquad (2\text{-}21)$$

Comment   If $\rho \gg a$, then (2-21) yields

$$g(x_o,y_o) = \frac{e^{-j\pi/4}}{2\sqrt{\lambda\rho_o}} (1 + \gamma_o) \int_{-a}^{a} f(x) e^{jk\rho} \, dx \qquad (2\text{-}21a)$$

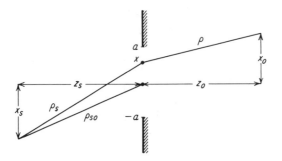

Fig. 2-5

as in (2-6a).   If the aperture is self-luminous with surface sources

$$s = \varphi(x)\delta(z)e^{-j\omega t}$$

then the resulting field at a distance $\rho \gg a$ is given by

$$g_s(x_o, z_o) = \frac{1}{4\pi} \sqrt{\frac{\lambda}{\rho_o}} \, e^{j\pi/4} \int_{-a}^{a} \varphi(x) e^{jk\rho} \, dx \tag{2-21b}$$

as we see from (1-19).   Hence, if

$$\varphi(x) = -2jkf(x)$$

then $g_s = g$ in the small-angle region $\gamma_o \simeq 1$.

Line sources   We now assume that the incident wave is due to a line
source (Fig. 2-5)

$$s = 4\pi e^{-j\omega t}\delta(x - x_s)\delta(z - z_s) \qquad z_s < 0$$

at the point (x_s, z_s).   In this case [see (1-19)]

$$g^i(x, z) = \sqrt{\frac{\lambda}{\rho_s}} \, e^{j(k\rho_s + \pi/4)} \qquad \rho_s = \sqrt{(x - x_s)^2 + z_s^2} \tag{2-22}$$

If we insert the above into (1-17) and use (2-20), we find that the disturbed field g is given by

$$g(x_o, z_o) = \frac{1}{2} \int_{-a}^{a} \frac{1}{\sqrt{\rho\rho_s}} \left(\frac{\partial\rho_s}{\partial z} - \frac{\partial\rho}{\partial z} \right) e^{jk(\rho + \rho_s)} \, dx \tag{2-23}$$

provided that $\rho, \rho_s \gg \lambda$.

The above can be used to determine the diffraction field due to a
plane wave

$$g^i(x, z) = e^{jk(\alpha_s x + \gamma_s z)} \tag{2-24}$$

as the far field of the line source

$$4\pi \sqrt{\frac{\rho_s}{\lambda}} e^{-j(\omega t + \pi/4)} \delta(x - x_s)\delta(z - z_s)$$

Indeed, if ρ_s is large, then (see Fig. 2-5)

$$\rho_s \simeq \rho_{so} + \alpha_s x \qquad \alpha_s = \frac{x_s}{\rho_{so}} \tag{2-25}$$

Multiplying (2-23) by $e^{-j\pi/4} \sqrt{\rho_s/\lambda}$ and making $\rho_s \to \infty$ along the line with directional cosines α_s, γ_s, we obtain

$$g(x_o, z_o) = \frac{e^{-j\pi/4}}{2\sqrt{\lambda}} \int_{-a}^{a} \frac{1}{\sqrt{\rho}} \left(\gamma_s - \frac{\partial\rho}{\partial z}\right) e^{jk\alpha_s x} e^{jk\rho} \, dx \tag{2-26}$$

Details of the approximation (2-25) are given in Sec. 4.

3. FRESNEL DIFFRACTION

In this section we shall study the diffraction patterns of various apertures illuminated by harmonic sources. The following approximation will be often used.

Fresnel approximation

If (Fig. 3-1)

$$r = \sqrt{d^2 + z^2} \qquad \text{and} \qquad d \ll r$$

then

$$r - z = \frac{d^2}{r + z} \simeq \frac{d^2}{2r} \simeq \frac{d^2}{2z} \tag{3-1}$$

The error of the first approximation is

$$\frac{d^2}{r + z} - \frac{d^2}{2r} = \frac{d^2(r - z)}{2r(r + z)} \simeq \frac{d^4}{(2r)^3} \simeq \frac{d^4}{(2z)^3} \tag{3-2}$$

The error is essentially the same for the second approximation.

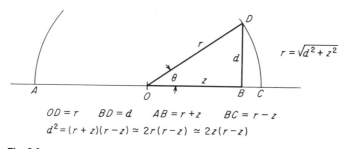

$$OD = r \qquad BD = d \qquad AB = r + z \qquad BC = r - z$$
$$d^2 = (r + z)(r - z) \simeq 2r(r - z) \simeq 2z(r - z)$$

Fig. 3-1

The above will be used in exponentials of the form e^{jkr}. Assuming that an angle error equal to, say, $\pi/100$, is tolerated, we can use the approximation

$$r \simeq z + \frac{d^2}{2z}$$

provided that [see (3-2)]

$$k \frac{d^4}{(2z)^3} < \frac{\pi}{100} \qquad \text{that is} \qquad \frac{25d}{\lambda} < \left(\frac{z}{d}\right)^3 \tag{3-3}$$

This conservative condition can be expressed in terms of the angle θ of Fig. 3-1:

$$\frac{d}{z} = \tan \theta \simeq \theta < \sqrt[4]{\frac{\lambda}{25z}} \tag{3-3a}$$

TWO–DIMENSIONAL SIGNALS

We have seen that the diffraction field of an infinite strip illuminated by a plane wave propagating in the z direction is given by [see (2-20)]

$$g(x_o,z_o) = \frac{e^{-j\pi/4}}{2\sqrt{\lambda}} \int_{-a}^{a} \frac{1+\gamma}{\sqrt{\rho}} f(x) e^{jk\rho}\, dx \tag{3-4}$$

where $f(x)$ is the amplitude of the incident wave and

$$\rho = \sqrt{(x-x_o)^2 + z_o{}^2} \qquad \gamma = -\frac{\partial \rho}{\partial z} = \frac{z_o}{\rho} \tag{3-5}$$

If the aperture contains a transparency with attenuation $a(x)$ and delay $\tau(x)$, then (3-4) still holds, provided that $f(x)$ is multiplied by the transmission function [see (2-15)]

$$T(x) = a(x) e^{j\omega\tau(x)}$$

Remembering that a small change in ρ is negligible in $\sqrt{\rho}$ but not in the exponent $k\rho$ of (3-4), we conclude from (3-1) that if $|x - x_o| \ll z_o$ [see also (3-9)], then

$$\rho \simeq z_o + \frac{(x-x_o)^2}{2z_o} \qquad \frac{1+\gamma}{\sqrt{\rho}} \simeq \frac{2}{\sqrt{z_o}} \tag{3-6}$$

With these approximations, (3-4) yields the fundamental formula

$$g(x_o,z_o) = \frac{1}{\sqrt{\lambda z_o}} e^{j(kz_o - \pi/4)} \int_{-a}^{a} f(x) e^{jk\frac{(x-x_o)^2}{2z_o}}\, dx \tag{3-7}$$

Denoting by ρ_o the distance from the origin to the point of observation

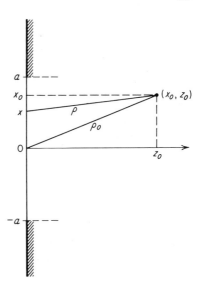

Fig. 3-2

(x_o,z_o) (Fig. 3-2), we have, as in (3-1),

$$\rho_o = \sqrt{x_o{}^2 + z_o{}^2} \simeq z_o + \frac{x_o{}^2}{2z_o}$$

Hence,

$$z_o + \frac{(x - x_o)^2}{2z_o} \simeq \rho_o + \frac{x^2}{2z_o} - \frac{xx_o}{z_o}$$

and (3-7) can thus be written in the form

$$g(x_o,z_o) = \frac{1}{\sqrt{\lambda z_o}}\, e^{j(k\rho_o - \pi/4)} \int_{-a}^{a} f(x) e^{jk(x^2/2z_o)} e^{-jk(xx_o/z_o)}\, dx \tag{3-7a}$$

In (3-4), the integration is limited to the interval $(-a,a)$; hence $|x - x_o|$ is at most $a + |x_o|$. If, therefore [see (3-3)]

$$\frac{25(a + |x_o|)}{\lambda} < \left(\frac{z_o}{a + |x_o|}\right)^3 \tag{3-8}$$

then the diffracted field is given by (3-7). The locus of points (x_o,z_o) satisfying (3-8) defines the so-called Fresnel region.

Fundamental observation As we shall presently show, the Fresnel approximation can be used not only in the region specified by (3-8), but also for points nearer the aperture such that

$$z_o > 400\lambda \qquad |x_o| < a \tag{3-8a}$$

provided $f(x)$ does not vary too rapidly. This is certainly the case if $f(x) = 1$, that is, if the aperture contains no transparency and it is illuminated by a uniform plane wave.

Near zone and stationary phase

We shall now determine the asymptotic behavior of (3-4) for $k \to \infty$. This integral is of the form of Eq. (3-1), Chap. 7, with

$$\mu(x) = \rho(x) = \sqrt{(x - x_o)^2 + z_o{}^2} \qquad \mu'(x) = 0 \qquad \text{for } x = x_o$$

If $|x_o| > a$, then there is no interior stationary point. In this case [see Chap. 7, (3-3)]

$$\int_a^b \varphi(t)e^{jk\mu(t)} \, dt \sim \frac{1}{jk} \left[\frac{\varphi(b)}{\mu'(b)} e^{jk\mu(b)} - \frac{\varphi(a)}{\mu'(a)} e^{jk\mu(a)} \right] \tag{3-9}$$

With

$$\rho(a) = \rho_1 \qquad \rho(-a) = \rho_2 \qquad \rho'(x) = \frac{x - x_o}{\rho} \qquad \gamma(x) = \frac{z_o}{\rho}$$

we obtain, from (3-4) and (3-9),

$$g(x_o, z_o) = \frac{\sqrt{\lambda}}{4\pi} e^{-j3\pi/4} \left[\frac{(\rho_1 + z_o)f(a)}{(a - x_o) \sqrt{\rho_1}} e^{jk\rho_1} + \frac{(\rho_2 + z_o)f(-a)}{(a + x_o) \sqrt{\rho_2}} e^{jk\rho_2} \right] \tag{3-10}$$

This is the dominant term in the asymptotic expansion of the diffraction field in the dark region $|x_o| > a$ of geometric optics, and it goes to zero as $\sqrt{\lambda}$.

If $|x_o| < a$, then x_o is an interior stationary point. From Chap. 7, (3-10), we have

$$\int_a^b \varphi(t)e^{jk\mu(t)} \, dt \sim \varphi(t_o) \sqrt{\frac{2\pi}{k\mu''(t_o)}} \, e^{j[k\mu(t_o) + \pi/4]} \tag{3-11}$$

Applying the above to (3-4) and noting that

$$\rho(x_o) = z_o \qquad \gamma(x_o) = 1 \qquad \rho''(x_o) = \frac{1}{z_o}$$

we obtain

$$g(x_o, z_o) = \frac{e^{-j\pi/4}}{2 \sqrt{\lambda}} \frac{2}{\sqrt{z_o}} f(x_o) \sqrt{\frac{2\pi z_o}{k}} \, e^{j(kz_o + \pi/4)} = f(x_o)e^{jkz_o} \tag{3-12}$$

Thus, in the illuminated region $|x_o| < a$, the diffracted field tends to the incident field for $\lambda \to 0$. The next term in the asymptotic expansion of $g(x_o, z_o)$ is the right side of (3-10).

From the above, we see that the diffracted field is the sum of the incident field (3-12)—limited to the illuminated region of space—and the field (3-10), which can be considered as a wave emanating from the edges $x = \pm a$ of the aperture.   In the dark region $|x_o| > a$, only the edges of the aperture are visible.   If $f(a) = f(-a) = 0$ (this can be achieved with suitable transparencies), then the right side of (3-11) is zero.   In this case, $g(x_o,z_o)$ is given by the next term of its expansion, and it goes to zero as $\lambda^{3/2}$ [see Chap. 7, (2-21)].   The region is then "darker."

We shall now investigate the validity of the approximation (3-7). For this purpose, we show in Fig. 3-3 the quantities

$$\cos k\rho(x) \qquad \text{and} \qquad \sin k\rho(x)$$

as functions of x for $z_o \gg \lambda$.   Because of the rapid variation of these quantities away from the stationary point x_o, if $f(x)$ is sufficiently smooth, then only the integration in a small region near x_o contributes significantly to the integral in (3-4).   Defining somewhat arbitrarily this region by the condition

$$k[\rho(x) - \rho(x_o)] \leq 4\pi$$

we see that only the strip

$$|x - x_o| \leq 2 \sqrt{\lambda z_o} \tag{3-13}$$

of the aperture contributes significantly to the illumination of the point (x_o,z_o).   If x satisfies (3-13) and $z_o > 400\lambda$, then

$$\frac{25|x - x_o|}{\lambda} < \frac{z_o{}^3}{|x - x_o|^3}$$

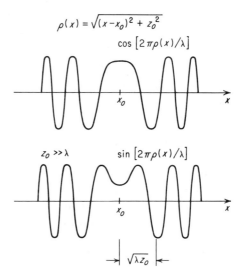

$$\rho(x) = \sqrt{(x-x_0)^2 + z_0{}^2}$$

$$\cos\left[2\pi\rho(x)/\lambda\right]$$

$$z_0 \gg \lambda \qquad \sin\left[2\pi\rho(x)/\lambda\right]$$

$$\sqrt{\lambda z_0}$$

Fig. 3-3

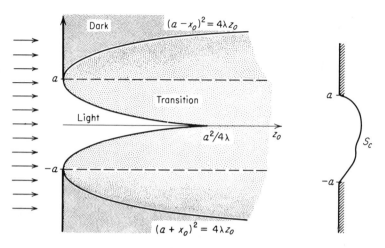

Fig. 3-4   **Fig. 3-5**

Hence [see (3-3)] the approximation (3-6) and its consequence (3-7) can be used not only in the region (3-8) but also for

$$z_o > 400\lambda \qquad |x_o| < a$$

If x_o is near $\pm a$ in the sense that

$$a - |x_o| < 2 \sqrt{\lambda z_o}$$

then only part of the region (3-13) is in the interval of integration $(-a,a)$. If $|x_o| - a > 2 \sqrt{\lambda z_o}$, this region is outside the interval $(-a,a)$, and $g(x_o,z_o)$ tends to zero as $\sqrt{\lambda}$ [see (3-10)].

The space can thus be divided into a light region, where the diffracted field is comparable to the incident field, a transition region, and a dark region. These regions are bounded by the parabolas (Fig. 3-4)

$$(a - x_o)^2 = 4\lambda z_o \qquad (a + x_o)^2 = 4\lambda z_o \tag{3-14}$$

For

$$z_o > a^2/4\lambda$$

there is no light region.

We finally remark that the region near the aperture, in which the diffracted field equals the incident field, as in (3-12), depends on the frequency content of $f(x)$. If $f(x)$ is expanded into a Fourier series in the interval $(-a,a)$, and its components higher than n are negligible, then the "near zone" approximation (3-12) holds for

$$z_o \leq \frac{a^2}{4n^2\lambda} \qquad -a + 2 \sqrt{\lambda z_o} < x_o < a - 2 \sqrt{\lambda z_o} \tag{3-15}$$

From the above we see that if in Kirchhoff's formula (2-4) the integration extends over a nonplane surface S_c, as in Fig. 3-5, Kirchhoff's approximation (2-1) can still be used, provided that S_c is in the region (3-15).

Example 3-1 If the incident field is a uniform plane wave, then

$$f(x) = 1$$

With

$$\mathbf{F}(x) = \sqrt{\frac{2}{\pi}} \int_0^x e^{iv^2}\, dy \tag{3-16}$$

the Fresnel integral [see Chap. 3, (1-35)] (3-7) yields

$$g(x_o, z_o) = e^{i(kz_o - \pi/4)} \frac{1}{\sqrt{2}} \left\{ \mathbf{F}\left[(a - x_o)\sqrt{\frac{\pi}{\lambda z_o}} \right] + \mathbf{F}\left[(a + x_o)\sqrt{\frac{\pi}{\lambda z_o}} \right] \right\} \tag{3-17}$$

In Fig. 3-6 we show $|g(x_o, z_o)|$ as a function of x_o for various values of z_o.

Along the z axis (Fig. 3-7)

$$g(0, z_o) = \sqrt{2}\, e^{i(kz_o - \pi/4)} \mathbf{F}\left(a\sqrt{\frac{\pi}{\lambda z_o}} \right) \tag{3-18}$$

Since [see Chap. 3, (1-38) and (1-41)]

$$\mathbf{F}(x) \sim \sqrt{\frac{2}{\pi}}\, x \qquad \text{for } x \to 0$$

$$\mathbf{F}(x) \sim \frac{1}{\sqrt{2}}\, e^{i\pi/4} + \frac{1}{jx}\frac{1}{\sqrt{2\pi}}\, e^{ix^2} \qquad \text{for } x \to \infty$$

we conclude that for large z_o,

$$g(0, z_o) \sim \frac{2a}{\sqrt{\lambda z_o}}\, e^{i(kz_o - \pi/4)}$$

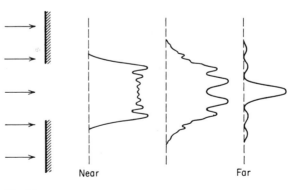

Near   Far

Fig. 3-6

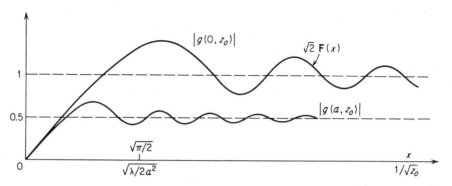

Fig. 3-7

and for small z_o,

$$g(0,z_o) = e^{ikz_o} \left[1 + e^{-j3\pi/4} \frac{\sqrt{\lambda z_o}}{a\pi} e^{j\pi a^2/\lambda z_o} \right]$$

Along the boundary $x_o = a$ of the geometric shadow

$$g(a,z_o) = \frac{1}{\sqrt{2}} e^{i(kz_o - \pi/4)} \mathbf{F}\left(2a \sqrt{\frac{\pi}{\lambda z_o}} \right)$$

Thus,

$$|g(0,z_o)| = 2|g(a,4z_o)|$$

FRESNEL TRANSFORMS

In the study of the Fresnel diffraction, one can use either (3-7) or (3-7a). The first equation is more suitable for the near zone. The second leads more naturally to the Fraunhofer region. In this study we find it convenient to introduce the following concept.

Definition   Given a function $f(x)$, we define its Fresnel transform $F_\sigma(\omega)$ by the integral

$$F_\sigma(\omega) = \frac{1}{\sigma\sqrt{2\pi}} \int_{-\infty}^{\infty} f(x) e^{jx^2/2\sigma^2} e^{-jx\omega} \, dx \qquad (3\text{-}19)$$

Denoting as usual by

$$f(x) \leftrightarrow F(\omega)$$

a Fourier transform pair, we see from the definition that

$$\frac{e^{jx^2/2\sigma^2}}{\sigma\sqrt{2\pi}} f(x) \leftrightarrow F_\sigma(\omega) \qquad (3\text{-}20)$$

Hence (Fourier inversion formula)

$$f(x) = \frac{\sigma e^{-jx^2/2\sigma^2}}{\sqrt{2\pi}} \int_{-\infty}^{\infty} F_\sigma(\omega) e^{jx\omega} \, d\omega \tag{3-21}$$

The function $F_\sigma(\omega)$ can be expressed in terms of the Fourier transform $F(\omega)$ of $f(x)$. Indeed, from

$$\frac{1}{\sigma\sqrt{2\pi}} e^{jx^2/2\sigma^2} \leftrightarrow e^{j\pi/4}e^{-j\sigma^2\omega^2/2} \tag{3-22}$$

[see Chap. 3, (1-31)] and the frequency convolution theorem [Chap. 3, (2-4)], it follows that

$$F_\sigma(\omega) = e^{j\pi/4}F(\omega) * e^{-j\sigma^2\omega^2/2} \tag{3-23}$$

As we see from (3-19), if $f(x) = 0$ for $|x| > a$ and $\sigma \gg a$, then $F_\sigma(\omega)$ is proportional to $F(\omega)$ (Fraunhofer approximation):

$$F_\sigma(\omega) \simeq \frac{F(\omega)}{\sigma\sqrt{2\pi}} \qquad \sigma \to \infty \tag{3-24}$$

We also note that the right side of (3-22) tends to the constant $e^{j\pi/4}$ for $\sigma \to 0$. Therefore, the left side (interpreted as a distribution operating on functions of bounded variation) tends to an impulse

$$\frac{1}{\sigma\sqrt{2\pi}} e^{-j\pi/4}e^{jx^2/2\sigma^2} \xrightarrow[\sigma\to 0]{} \delta(x) \tag{3-25}$$

Writing (3-19) in the form

$$e^{j\sigma^2\omega^2/2}F_\sigma(\omega) = \frac{1}{\sigma\sqrt{2\pi}} \int_{-\infty}^{\infty} f(x) e^{j(x-\sigma^2\omega)^2/2\sigma^2} \, dx \tag{3-26}$$

(elaborate), we conclude, with (3-25), that

$$e^{j(\sigma^2\omega^2/2-\pi/4)} F_\sigma(\omega) \simeq f(\sigma^2\omega) \qquad \sigma \to 0 \tag{3-27}$$

Example 3-2 If

$$f(x) = \begin{cases} 1 & |x| < a \\ 0 & |x| > a \end{cases}$$

then

$$\sqrt{2}\, e^{j\omega^2\sigma^2/2}F_\sigma(\omega) = \mathbf{F}\left(\frac{a}{\sigma\sqrt{2}} - \frac{\sigma\omega}{\sqrt{2}}\right) + \mathbf{F}\left(\frac{a}{\sigma\sqrt{2}} + \frac{\sigma\omega}{\sqrt{2}}\right) \tag{3-28}$$

as we see from (3-26) and (3-16).

The diffraction field $g(x_o, z_o)$ can be expressed in terms of the Fresnel transform $F_\sigma(\omega)$ of $f(x)$. With $\sigma = \sqrt{z_o/k}$, we conclude from (3-7a) and

(3-19) that

$$g(x_o, z_o) = e^{j(k\rho_o - \pi/4)} F_{\sqrt{z_o/k}}\left(k\frac{x_o}{z_o}\right) \tag{3-29}$$

This holds, of course, if we assume that

$$f(x) = 0 \qquad \text{for } |x| > a \tag{3-30}$$

Thus, the diffraction field on the surface of a cylinder centered at the origin is proportional to the Fresnel transform of the aperture. On the plane $z_o = $ constant:

$$|g(x_o, z_o)| = \left| F_{\sqrt{z_o/k}}\left(k\frac{x_o}{z_o}\right) \right| \tag{3-31}$$

For small z_o, (3-29) reduces to the near zone approximation [see (3-27) and (3-6)]

$$g(x_o, z_o) = e^{jkz_o} f(x_o)$$

For large z_o, (3-29) yields [see (3-24)]

$$g(x_o, z_o) = \frac{1}{\sqrt{\lambda z_o}} e^{j(k\rho_o - \pi/4)} F\left(k\frac{x_o}{z_o}\right) \tag{3-32}$$

This is the Fraunhofer approximation to be discussed in the next section.

Scaling From the Fourier scaling theorem

$$f(\alpha x) \leftrightarrow \frac{1}{|\alpha|} F\left(\frac{\omega}{\alpha}\right)$$

or directly from (3-19) it follows that

$$\frac{e^{jx^2/2\sigma^2}}{\sigma\sqrt{2\pi}} f(\alpha x) \leftrightarrow F_{|\alpha|\sigma}\left(\frac{\omega}{\alpha}\right) \tag{3-33}$$

Thus if the Fresnel transform of $f(x)$ equals $F_\sigma(\omega)$, then the Fresnel transform of $f(\alpha x)$ equals $F_{|\alpha|\sigma}(\omega/\alpha)$. This result will be used often. We give below two simple applications.

If the wavelength of the incident wave is changed from λ to λ_1, a new diffraction field $g_1(x_o, z_o)$ results. From (3-31) it follows that

$$|g(x_o, z_o)| = \left| g_1\left(x_o, \frac{\lambda z_o}{\lambda_1}\right) \right| \tag{3-34}$$

Thus, the intensity of the new field on the plane $z = \lambda z_o/\lambda_1$ equals the intensity of the original field on the plane $z = z_o$ (Fig. 3-8).

We shall now express the diffraction field $g_\alpha(x_o, z_o)$, due to the aperture function $f(\alpha x)$, in terms of the field $g(x_o, z_o)$ due to $f(x)$. With $F_\sigma(\omega)$

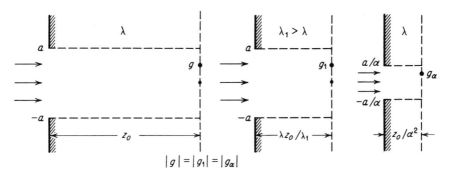

Fig. 3-8

the Fresnel transform of $f(x)$, we see from (3-33) and (3-29) that

$$g_\alpha(x_o,z_o) = e^{j(k\rho_o-\pi/4)}F_{\alpha\sqrt{z_o/k}}\left(\frac{kx_o}{\alpha z_o}\right) \tag{3-35}$$

Hence,

$$\left| g_\alpha\left(\frac{x_o}{\alpha}, \frac{z_o}{\alpha^2}\right) \right| = |g(x_o,z_o)| \tag{3-36}$$

as in Fig. 3-8.

Line sources

If the aperture is illuminated by the line source

$$s = 4\pi e^{-j\omega t}\delta(x)\delta(z + z_s) \qquad z_s > 0$$

at the point $(0,-z_s)$, then the resulting diffraction field $g_s(x_o,z_o)$ is given by (2-23). If

$$\frac{25a}{\lambda} < \left(\frac{z_s}{a}\right)^3$$

then [see (3-3)] we can use the approximations

$$\rho_s = \sqrt{x^2 + z_s^2} \simeq z_s + \frac{x^2}{2z_s} \qquad \frac{1}{\sqrt{\rho_s}}\frac{\partial\rho_s}{\partial z} \simeq \frac{1}{\sqrt{z_s}}$$

and (2-23) yields

$$g_s(x_o,z_o) = \frac{e^{jk(\rho_o+z_s)}}{\sqrt{z_s z_o}} \int_{-a}^{a} f(x)e^{j(k/2)x^2[(1/z_s)+(1/z_o)]}e^{-jkxx_o/z_o}\,dx \tag{3-37}$$

where

$$f(x) = 1 \qquad \text{or} \qquad a(x)e^{j\omega\tau(x)}$$

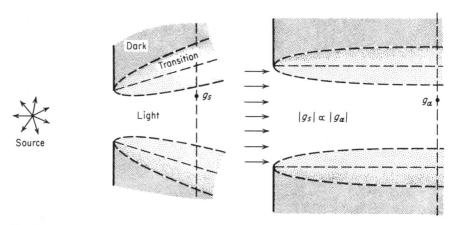

Fig. 3-9

With c defined by

$$\frac{1}{z_s} + \frac{1}{z_o} = \frac{1}{c} \tag{3-38}$$

we conclude from (3-37) and (3-19) that

$$g_s(x_o, z_o) = \sqrt{\frac{c\lambda}{z_s z_o}}\, e^{jk(\rho_o + z_s)} F_{\sqrt{c/k}}\left(k\frac{x_o}{z_o}\right) \tag{3-39}$$

If $f(x) = 1$, then the above Fresnel transform is given by (3-28).

It is of interest to observe that the diffraction pattern (3-39) is the same as the pattern of the aperture function $f(\alpha x)$ illuminated by a plane wave. Indeed, with

$$\alpha = \frac{c}{z_o} = \frac{z_s}{z_s + z_o} \tag{3-40}$$

and $g_\alpha(x_o, z_o)$ as in (3-35), we see that

$$\left| g_\alpha\left(x_o, \frac{z_o}{\alpha}\right) \right| = \sqrt{\frac{\lambda}{z_s + z_o}}\, |g_s(x_o, z_o)| \tag{3-41}$$

Thus if an aperture of width $2a$ is illuminated by a line source, then the intensity of the field on the plane $z = z_o$ is proportional to the intensity of the field of an aperture of width $2a/\alpha$ on the plane $z = z_o/\alpha$, illuminated by a plane wave (Fig. 3-9). In this scaling the boundary of the geometric shadow is preserved, and the curves separating the light, transition, and dark regions are given by

$$\left[a\left(1 + \frac{z_0}{z_s}\right) \pm x_0\right]^2 = 4\lambda z_0\left(1 + \frac{z_0}{z_s}\right)$$

as we see from (3-40) and (3-14).

Wide-angle diffraction and oblique incidence

The Fresnel approximation was based on the assumption that the directional cosine $\gamma_0 = z_0/\rho_0$ was small in the sense of (3-8). If this is not the case, then (3-6), on which (3-7) was based, no longer holds. We shall now assume that the point of observation (x_0, z_0) is sufficiently far so that

$$a\gamma_0 < \sqrt[4]{\frac{\lambda\rho_0^3}{25}} \tag{3-42}$$

In this case, the distance ρ from $(x, 0)$ to the point (x_0, z_0) can be approximated by [see (3-3a) and (3-1)]

$$\rho \simeq \rho_0 - \alpha_0 x + \frac{d^2}{2\rho_0} \qquad d^2 = x^2 - (\alpha_0 x)^2 = \gamma_0^2 x^2 \tag{3-43}$$

where $\alpha_0 = x_0/\rho_0$, as in Fig. 3-10. With

$$\frac{1 + \gamma}{\sqrt{\rho}} \simeq \frac{1 + \gamma_0}{\sqrt{\rho_0}}$$

(3-4) yields the wide-angle Fresnel approximation

$$g_0(\alpha_0, \rho_0) = \frac{1 + \gamma_0}{2\sqrt{\lambda\rho_0}} e^{j(k\rho_0 - \pi/4)} \int_{-a}^{a} f(x) e^{jk\gamma_0^2 x^2/2\rho_0} e^{-jk\alpha_0 x} \, dx \tag{3-44}$$

This result is of interest if the aperture is illuminated by a plane wave in an oblique incidence or by a line source off the z axis. In the first case (Fig. 3-11a), $f(x)$ is replaced by

$$f(x)e^{jk\alpha_s x}$$

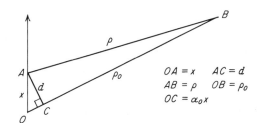

$$OA = x \qquad AC = d$$
$$AB = \rho \qquad OB = \rho_0$$
$$OC = \alpha_0 x$$

Fig. 3-10

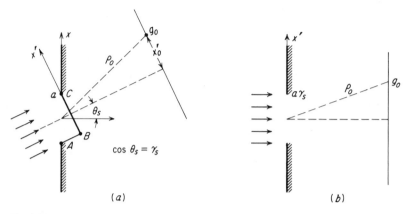

Fig. 3-11

and the term $1 + \gamma_o$ by the term $\gamma_s + \gamma_o$ [see (2-26)]. With $F_\sigma(\omega)$ as in (3-19) and $\sigma^2 = \rho_o/k\gamma_o^2$, (3-44) yields

$$g_o(\alpha_o,\rho_o) = \frac{\gamma_s + \gamma_o}{2\gamma_o} \, e^{j(k\rho_o - \pi/4)} F_\sigma[k(\alpha_o - \alpha_s)] \tag{3-45}$$

The above takes significant values in the region $\gamma_o - \gamma_s \ll 1$ near the direction of propagation γ_s of the incident wave. In this region,

$$\frac{\gamma_s + \gamma_o}{2\gamma_o} \simeq 1 \qquad \alpha_o - \alpha_s \simeq \frac{x_o'\gamma_s}{\rho_o} \tag{3-46}$$

Equivalence with normal incidence From (3-35) and (3-45) it follows that the field $g_o(\alpha_o,\rho_o)$ equals the field due to an aperture with aperture function $f(x'/\gamma_s)$ illuminated by a normally incident plane wave (Fig. 3-11b). This conclusion can also be reached by a proper modification of the region of integration. Indeed, in Kirchhoff's formula, the surface of integration is arbitrary. We can choose, therefore, as the interior of the aperture a surface whose cross section is the line ABC of Fig. 3-11a. If the angle of incidence is not close to 90°, then this line is in the near zone where the diffracted field equals the incident field (see also Fig. 3-5). Therefore, we can apply Kirchhoff's approximation to the integration along ABC. It can be seen from (1-17) that the integration along AB is negligible because, for points in the region of interest, $\gamma_o \simeq \gamma_s$; hence, $\partial\rho/\partial n \simeq 0$. And since along the line BC the field equals $f(x) = f(x'/\gamma_s)$, the equivalence between normal and oblique incidence follows.

THREE-DIMENSIONAL SIGNALS

We shall extend briefly the preceding results to the three-dimensional signals. With the approximations

$$r = \sqrt{(x - x_o)^2 + (y - y_o)^2 + z_o^2} = z_o$$

$$+ \frac{1}{2z_o}[(x - x_o)^2 + (y - y_o)^2]$$

$$r_o = \sqrt{x_o^2 + y_o^2 + z_o^2} \simeq z_o + \frac{1}{2z_o}(x_o^2 + y_o^2), \qquad (3\text{-}47)$$

$$\frac{1}{r}\left(1 - \frac{\partial r}{\partial z}\right) \simeq \frac{2}{z_o}$$

the diffraction integral [see (2-14)]

$$g(x_o, y_o, z_o) = \frac{-j}{2\lambda} \iint_S \frac{1}{r}\left(1 - \frac{\partial r}{\partial z}\right) f(x,y) e^{jkr}\, dx\, dy \qquad (3\text{-}48)$$

takes the form

$$g(x_o, y_o, z_o) = \frac{-j}{\lambda z_o} e^{jkz_o} \iint_S f(x,y) e^{j\frac{k}{2z_o}[(x-x_o)^2 + (y-y_o)^2]}\, dx\, dy \qquad (3\text{-}49)$$

or the equivalent form

$$g(x_o, y_o, z_o) = \frac{-j}{\lambda z_o} e^{jkr_o} \iint_S f(x,y) e^{j\frac{k}{2z_o}(x^2+y^2)} e^{-j\frac{k}{z_o}(xx_o+yy_o)}\, dx\, dy \qquad (3\text{-}49a)$$

The last integral is the two-dimensional Fourier transform of the function [see Chap. 3, (4-1)]

$$f(x,y) e^{jk(x^2+y^2)/2z_o}$$

evaluated at

$$u = \frac{kx_o}{z_o} \qquad v = \frac{ky_o}{z_o}$$

If the aperture S is a slit of length $2a$ on the x axis, then with

$$f(x,y) = f(x)\delta(y)$$

(3-49) yields

$$g(x_o, y_o, z_o) = \frac{-j}{\lambda z_o} e^{jkz_o} \int_{-a}^{a} f(x) e^{jk(x-x_o)^2/2z_o}\, dx$$

Thus, g is independent of y_o, and it equals the corresponding two-dimensional field (3-7) multiplied by $(1 - j)/\sqrt{2\lambda z_o}$.

If S is a circle of radius b, and $f(x,y)$ has circular symmetry, that is,

$$f(x,y) = f(\rho) \qquad \rho = \sqrt{x^2 + y^2}$$

then $g(x_o,y_o,z_o)$ also has circular symmetry:

$$g(x_o,y_o,z_o) = g(\rho_o,z_o) \qquad \rho_o = \sqrt{x_o^2 + y_o^2}$$

And thus it is given by

$$g(\rho_o,z_o) = \frac{-2\pi j}{\lambda z_o} e^{jkr_o} \int_0^b \rho f(\rho) e^{jk\rho^2/2z_o} J_o\left(k\,\frac{\rho\rho_o}{z_o}\right) d\rho \tag{3-50}$$

This follows from (3-49a), as in Chap. 5, (1-4). The above integral is the Hankel transform of the function

$$f(\rho)e^{jk\rho^2/2z_o}$$

evaluated at $w = k\rho_o/z_o$.

The approximations (3-47) hold in the region

$$25(b + \rho_o)^4 < \gamma z_o^3 \tag{3-51}$$

where b is the radius of the smallest circle enclosing S [see (3-8)]. However, (3-50) also holds for points closer to the aperture, provided that $f(\rho)$ is sufficiently smooth *and* $\rho_o \neq 0$.

Comment   If the opaque part $\bar{S}$ occupies a finite region of the plane, then the aperture S extends to infinity; hence, the above approximations cannot be used. However, with g_c the diffraction field of the complementary screen and g^i the incident field, we know from Babinet's principle (2-3) that

$$g = g^i - g_c$$

The Fresnel form of g is then determined by expressing g_c by the integral (3-49), where the integration extends over the bounded region $\bar{S}$.

Example 3-3   A circular aperture of radius b is illuminated by a uniform plane wave

$$v^i = e^{-j\omega(t-z/c)}$$

The resulting diffraction field $g(\rho_o,z_o)$ is given by

$$g(\rho_o,z_o) = \frac{-2\pi j}{\lambda z_o} e^{jkr_o} \int_0^b \rho e^{jk\rho_2/2z_o} J_o\left(k\,\frac{\rho\rho_o}{z_o}\right) d\rho \tag{3-52}$$

This is valid—subject to (3-51)—whereas for $\rho_o \neq 0$, (3-52) also holds for points near the aperture.

Along the z axis we have $\rho_o = 0$, $r_o = z_o$, and (3-52) yields

$$g(0,z_o) = e^{jkz_o}(1 - e^{jkb^2/2z_o}) \tag{3-53}$$

as we see, with $\rho^2 = x$ and $J_o(0) = 1$. We note that

$$|g(0,z_o)|^2 = 4\sin^2\frac{kb^2}{4z_o} \tag{3-54}$$

The integral in (3-52) can be expressed in terms of Lommel's functions $U_1(a,w)$ and $U_2(a,w)$, which are defined in Chap. 5, (5-30). With a simple scaling, (3-52) yields [see Chap. 5, (5-35)]

$$g(\rho_o,z_o) = e^{jk(r_o+b^2/2z_o)}\left[U_2\left(\frac{kb^2}{z_o},\frac{kb\rho_o}{z_o}\right) - jU_1\left(\frac{kb^2}{z_o},\frac{kb\rho_o}{z_o}\right)\right] \tag{3-55}$$

Since [see Chap. 5, (5-36)]

$$U_1(a,a) = \frac{\sin a}{2} \qquad U_2(a,a) = \tfrac{1}{2}[J_o(a) - \cos a]$$

we conclude from (3-55) that, along the boundary $\rho_o = b$ of the geometric shadow [b5],

$$|g(b,z_o)|^2 = \frac{1}{4}\left[1 - 2J_o\left(\frac{kb^2}{z_o}\right)\cos\frac{kb^2}{z_o} + J_o^2\left(\frac{kb^2}{z_o}\right)\right] \tag{3-56}$$

As we show in Sec. 5, these results give, with scaling modifications, the field off the focal plane of a lens.

In three dimensions, the wide-angle Fresnel approximation (3-43) takes the following form (Fig. 4-1):

$$r = \sqrt{[r_o - (\alpha_o x + \beta_o y)]^2 + d^2} \simeq r_o - (\alpha_o x + \beta_o y) + \frac{d^2}{2r_o}$$

$$d^2 = (x^2 + y^2) - (\alpha_o x + \beta_o y)^2$$

We finally remark that if the point (x_o,y_o,z_o) is in the visible part of the space, then the field g in (3-48) tends to the incident field for $k \to \infty$ (Prob. 7-4). In the dark region, g tends to zero as $\sqrt{\lambda}$. In this region, the main contribution to the diffracted field results from the points P_i of the boundary Γ of S (Fig. 3-12). At these points, the tangent to Γ is perpendicular to the line from the origin to the projection (x_o,y_o) of the point of observation [see Chap. 7, (4-14)].

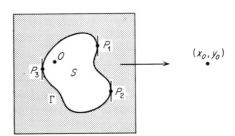

Fig. 3-12

4. FRAUNHOFER DIFFRACTION

The Fraunhofer diffraction is the limiting form of Fresnel diffraction for large z_o. We shall, however, develop it directly, using the following approximation:

$$\text{If} \quad r = \sqrt{d^2 + z^2} \quad \text{and} \quad d <<< r \quad \text{then} \quad r \simeq z$$
(4-1)

The approximation error is

$$r - z = \frac{d^2}{r + z} \simeq \frac{d^2}{2r}$$

and it can be neglected in e^{jkr} if [see (3-3)]

$$k\frac{d^2}{2r} < \frac{\pi}{100} \quad \text{that is, if} \quad r > \frac{100d^2}{\lambda}$$
(4-2)

Applying the above to the quantities in Fig. 4-1, we conclude that

$$r = \sqrt{[r_o - (\alpha_o x + \beta_o y)]^2 + d^2} \simeq r_o - (\alpha_o x + \beta_o y)$$
(4-3)

where

$$\alpha_o = \frac{x_o}{r_o} \qquad \beta_o = \frac{y_o}{r_o}$$

If a is the maximum distance of the points of the region S from the origin, then for (x,y) in S, $d \leq a$. Hence, (4-3) holds for

$$r_o > \frac{100a^2}{\lambda}$$
(4-4)

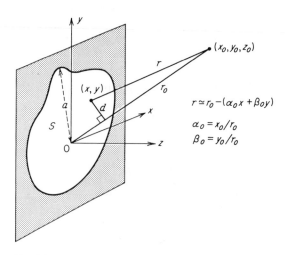

$$r \simeq r_0 - (\alpha_0 x + \beta_0 y)$$
$$\alpha_0 = x_0/r_0$$
$$\beta_0 = y_0/r_0$$

Fig. 4-1

Since $r_o \gg a$, we also have

$$\frac{1}{r}\left(1 - \frac{\partial r}{\partial z}\right) \simeq \frac{1 + \gamma_o}{r_o} \qquad \gamma_o = \frac{z_o}{r_o} \tag{4-5}$$

Inserting into (2-14), we thus obtain the field

$$g(x_o,y_o,z_o) = \frac{-j(1 + \gamma_o)}{2\lambda r_o} e^{jkr_o} \iint\limits_{S} f(x,y)e^{-jk(\alpha_o x + \beta_o y)} \, dx \, dy \tag{4-6}$$

in the Fraunhofer region (4-4). This rather loosely defined region is located at distances that are large for most optical applications. However, as we show in the next section, if a lens is placed in front of the aperture S, then (4-6) holds for points close to S.

With $F(u,v)$ the Fourier transform of $f(x,y)$, (4-6) yields

$$g(x_o,y_o,z_o) = \frac{-j(1 + \gamma_o)}{2\lambda r_o} e^{jkr_o} F(k\alpha_o,k\beta_o) \tag{4-6a}$$

As we know from Sec. 3, Chap. 6, if $f(x,y)$ does not vary rapidly, then the circle in the uv plane, in which $F(u,v)$ takes significant values, is of the order of $2\pi/a$. Hence, $g(x_o,y_o,z_o)$ is concentrated in the cone

$$k\sqrt{\alpha_o^2 + \beta_o^2} \leq \frac{2\pi}{a} \qquad \text{that is} \qquad \sqrt{x_o^2 + y_o^2} \leq \frac{z_o\lambda}{a} \tag{4-7}$$

Thus, if the dimensions of the aperture are large compared with λ, then, in the region of interest, $\gamma_o \simeq 1$, $r_o \simeq z_o$.

We see from (4-6) that on the surface of a sphere centered at the origin, the *amplitude* g of the diffraction field is proportional to $F(k\alpha_o,k\beta_o)$ because the critical term e^{jkr_o} is constant. However, *this is not the case* on the plane $z = z_o$ no matter how large z_o is. With $\alpha_o \simeq x_o/z_o$, $\beta_o \simeq y_o/z_o$ and [see (3-47)],

$$r_o = z_o + \frac{x_o^2 + y_o^2}{2z_o}$$

(4-7) takes the form (Fraunhofer-Fresnel)

$$g(x_o,y_o,z_o) = \frac{-j}{\lambda r_o} e^{jkz_o} e^{jk(x_o^2 + y_o^2)/2z_o} F\left(k\frac{x_o}{z_o}, \, k\frac{y_o}{z_o}\right) \tag{4-8}$$

On the plane $z = z_o$, the term e^{jkz_o} is constant. The second exponential in (4-8) is small near the z axis, but it cannot be neglected in the region of interest (4-7). Indeed, on the boundary of that region

$$k\frac{x_o^2 + y_o^2}{2z_o} = \frac{k\lambda^2 z_o}{2a^2}$$

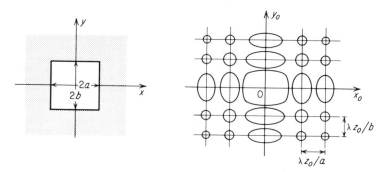

Fig. 4-2

If z_o is large enough to satisfy the Fraunhofer condition (4-4), then the above quantity equals 100π.

However, on the plane $z = z_o$, the *intensity* of the diffraction field is proportional to the energy spectrum of $f(x,y)$:

$$|g(x_o,y_o,z_o)|^2 = \frac{1}{\lambda^2 r_o^2} \left| F\left(k\,\frac{x_o}{r_o},\, k\,\frac{y_o}{r_o}\right) \right|^2 \tag{4-9}$$

Example 4-1 The intensity of the diffraction pattern of a rectangular aperture with dimensions $2a$ and $2b$, illuminated by a uniform plane wave, is given by

$$|g(x_o,y_o,z_o)|^2 = \frac{16}{\lambda^2 z_o^2} \frac{\sin^2{(akx_o/z_o)}}{(kx_o/z_o)^2} \frac{\sin^2{(bky_o/z_o)}}{(ky_o/z_o)^2} \tag{4-10}$$

This follows from (4-9) and Chap. 3, (4-30), with $r_o \simeq z_o$. The above function is maximum along the z axis, i.e.,

$$|g(0,0,z_o)|^2 = \left(\frac{4ab}{\lambda z_o}\right)^2$$

And at the points

$$x_o = \left(m + \frac{1}{2}\right)\frac{\lambda z_o}{a} \qquad y_o = \left(n + \frac{1}{2}\right)\frac{\lambda z_o}{b}$$

of the $z = z_o$ plane it has secondary maxima with decreasing intensity as m and n increase (Fig. 4-2).

Example 4-2

a. An opaque screen contains a rectangular $(2M + 1)$ by $(2N + 1)$ array of apertures which is generated by shifting $f_o(x,y)$ as in Fig. 4-3. With $F_o(u,v)$ the Fourier

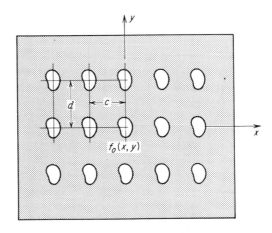

Fig. 4-3

transform of $f_o(x,y)$, the transform of the entire aperture is given by

$$F(u,v) = F_o(u,v) \frac{\sin (M + \frac{1}{2})cu}{\sin (cu/2)} \sin \frac{(N + \frac{1}{2}) dv}{\sin (dv/2)} \qquad (4\text{-}11)$$

as on page 106. Inserting into (4-6a), we obtain the resulting Fraunhofer field.

If each aperture is a circle of radius a, then [see Chap. 5, (1-20)]

$$F_o(u,v) = \frac{aJ_1(a \sqrt{u^2 + v^2})}{\sqrt{u^2 + v^2}}$$

b. If $N = 0$ and $f_o(x,y)$ is a rectangle, as in Example 4-1, then the grid of Fig. 4-4 results, and (4-11) yields

$$F(u,v) = \frac{4 \sin au}{u} \frac{\sin bv}{v} \frac{\sin (M + \frac{1}{2})cu}{\sin (cu/2)}$$

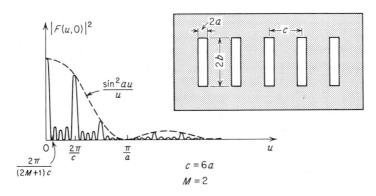

Fig. 4-4

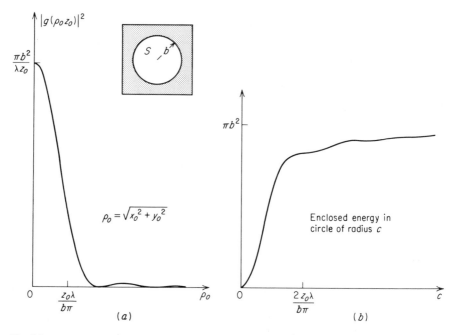

Fig. 4-5

If $f(x,y) = f(\rho)$ has circular symmetry, then with $\tilde{f}(w)$ as its Hankel transform, i.e.,

$$f(\rho) \overset{h}{\leftrightarrow} \tilde{f}(w)$$

(4-6) yields [see Chap. 5, (1-4)]

$$g(\rho_o, z_o) = \frac{-jk(1 + \gamma_o)}{2r_o} e^{jkr_o} \tilde{f}\left(\frac{k\rho_o}{r_o}\right) \qquad \rho_o = \sqrt{x_o{}^2 + y_o{}^2} \qquad (4\text{-}12)$$

Example 4-3

a. The diffraction pattern of a disc of radius b,

$$f(\rho) = p_b(\rho)$$

is given by [see Chap. 5, (1-20), and Fig. 4-5a]

$$|g(\rho_o, z_o)| = \frac{b}{\rho_o}\left|J_1\left(\frac{kb\rho_o}{z_o}\right)\right| \qquad (4\text{-}13)$$

for points in the cone (4-7). Since [see Chap. 5, (5-15)]

$$\frac{d}{dx}\left[\frac{J_1(x)}{x}\right] = -\frac{J_2(x)}{x} \qquad (4\text{-}14)$$

g is maximum at the rings of radius ρ_i where

$$\rho_i = \frac{x_i z_o}{kb} \qquad J_2(x_i) = 0$$

The energy of the diffraction pattern included in a circle of radius c in the $z = z_o$ plane equals [b5]

$$2\pi \int_0^c \rho_o |g|^2 \, d\rho_o = \pi b^2 \left[1 - J_o{}^2\left(\frac{kbc}{z_o}\right) - J_1{}^2\left(\frac{kbc}{z_o}\right) \right] \tag{4-15}$$

[see Chap. 5, (5-21)]. This quantity is shown in Fig. 4-5b.

We remark that the disk can be considered as a point only in the small-angle cone $kb\rho_o/z_o \ll 1$. In this region (4-13) yields $|g| = kb^2/2z_o$.

b. If the aperture is annular with outer radius b and inner radius ϵb, i.e., if

$$f(\rho) = p_b(\rho) - p_{\epsilon b}(\rho)$$

then

$$|g(\rho_o, z_o)|^2 = \frac{b^2}{\rho_o{}^2} \left[J_1\left(\frac{kb\rho_o}{z_o}\right) - \epsilon J_1\left(\frac{k\epsilon b\rho_o}{z_o}\right) \right]^2 \tag{4-16}$$

This function is shown in Fig. 4-6 for $\epsilon = \frac{1}{2}$.

c. If $b_2 - b_1 \ll b_2$ (ring aperture), then the limiting form of (4-16) is best determined by assuming that $f(\rho)$ is an impulse

$$f(\rho) = \delta(\rho - b)$$

In this case [see Chap. 5, (1-21)]

$$|g(\rho_o, z_o)|^2 = \left[\frac{kb}{z_o} J_o\left(\frac{kb\rho_o}{z_o}\right) \right]^2 \tag{4-17}$$

as in Fig. 4-6.

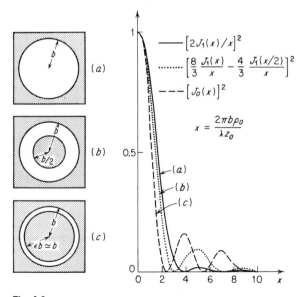

Fig. 4-6

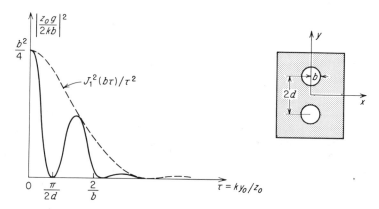

Fig. 4-7

Using the scaling theorem [Chap. 3, (4-11)], we can find from the above the diffraction patterns of elliptical discs and rings.

d. We shall finally determine the pattern of the two discs

$$f(x,y) = p_b[\sqrt{x^2 + (y-d)^2}] + p_b[\sqrt{x^2 + (y+d)^2}]$$

as shown in Fig. 4-7. From the shifting theorem [Chap. 5, (4-9)] it follows that

$$f(x,y) \Leftrightarrow \frac{2\pi b J_1(b\sqrt{u^2 + v^2})}{\sqrt{u^2 + v^2}}(e^{jdv} + e^{-jdv})$$

Inserting into (4-6), we find g. Along the line $x_o = 0$ of the $z = z_o$ plane, the above yields

$$|g(0,y_o,z_o)| = 2b\left|\frac{J_1(kby_o/z_o)}{y_o}\cos\frac{kdy_o}{z_o}\right| \tag{4-18}$$

as in Fig. 4-7.

Change of reference sphere

We shall now determine the diffraction field on the surface of a sphere of radius r_1, centered at the point $z = -d$ (Fig. 4-8). With

$$r_o \simeq z_o + \frac{\rho_o^2}{2r_o} \qquad r_1 \simeq z_o + d + \frac{\rho_o^2}{2r_1}$$

and

$$\frac{1}{r_o} - \frac{1}{r_1} = \frac{1}{a}$$

we have

$$r_o \simeq r_1 - d + \frac{\rho_o^2}{2a}$$

Inserting into (4-6), we conclude that in the small-angle region (4-7) of the new sphere, g is proportional to

$$e^{jk\rho_o{}^2/2a}F(k\alpha_o,k\beta_o) \tag{4-19}$$

If $d \ll r_o$, then $a \simeq r_o{}^2/d$. If $r_1 \to \infty$, then $a \to r_o \simeq z_o$, and the above tends to (4-8).

Point source and oblique incidence

Suppose that the aperture is illuminated by a source at the point $z = -z_s$ of the z axis. The resulting field is given by (2-16), and if $z_s > 100b^2/\lambda$, then [see (4-1)] $r_s \simeq z_s$. Hence, the source can be replaced by a plane wave. If z_s satisfies the Fresnel condition $z_s{}^3 > 25a^4/\lambda$, then on the $z = 0$ plane

$$r_s \simeq z_s + \frac{x^2 + y^2}{2z_s}$$

Inserting into (2-16), we conclude that the resulting far field is given by

$$g(x_o,y_o,z_o) = \frac{-j(1 + \gamma_o)}{2\lambda z_s r_o} e^{jk(r_o+z_s)}F_1(k\alpha_o,k\beta_o) \tag{4-20}$$

where $F_1(u,v)$ is the Fourier transform of

$$f(x,y)e^{jk(x^2+y^2)/2z_s}, \tag{4-21}$$

(Fresnel-Fraunhofer approximation). Thus, $g(x_o,y_o,z_o)$ equals the Fraunhofer field of the aperture function (4-21) illuminated by a plane wave. The above conclusion can also be deduced from (3-39), with $z_o \gg z_s \simeq c$.

If the incident field is a plane wave propagating in the $(\alpha_s,\beta_s,\gamma_s)$ direction, or if the source is off the z axis in the same direction, then

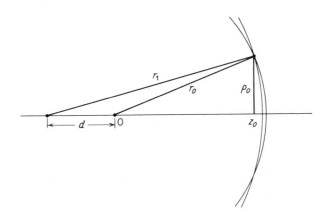

Fig. 4-8

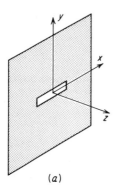

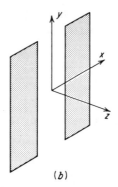

Fig. 4-9

(4-6) and (4-20) still hold, provided that the variables α_o, β_o, $1 + \gamma_o$ are replaced by $\alpha_o - \alpha_s$, $\beta_o - \beta_s$, $\gamma_s + \gamma_o$.

ONE–DIMENSIONAL TRANSFORMS

The Fraunhofer region of the diffraction pattern reduces to a one-dimensional Fourier transform if the aperture is a narrow slit (Fig. 4-9a) and the incident wave is arbitrary, or if the aperture is an infinite strip (Fig. 4-9b) and the incident wave is two-dimensional.

Slit apertures

Suppose that the aperture is a slit on the x axis. If it is sufficiently narrow, then its aperture function can be represented by a line mass [see (4-24)]

$$f(x,y) = f(x)\delta(y) \tag{4-22}$$

With $F(u)$ the Fourier transform of $f(x)$, we have [see Chap. 4, (1-16)]

$$f(x)\delta(y) \Leftrightarrow F(u)$$

Inserting into (4-6) and omitting the proportionality factor, we conclude that

$$g(x_o,y_o,z_o) \propto F(k\alpha_o) \qquad \alpha_o = \frac{x_o}{r_o} \simeq \frac{x_o}{z_o} \tag{4-23}$$

Thus, the diffraction pattern is independent of β_o.

In a real case, the slit has a finite width $2c$. With $p_c(y)$ a pulse and

$$f(x,y) = f(x)\frac{p_c(y)}{2c} \Leftrightarrow F(u)\frac{\sin cv}{cv} \tag{4-24}$$

we have

$$g \propto F(k\alpha_o) \frac{\sin kc\beta_o}{kc\beta_o}$$

Hence (4-22) is a satisfactory approximation in the cylinder

$$\beta_o < \frac{\lambda}{8c} \tag{4-25}$$

Example 4-4 Suppose that the aperture is a grid, as in Fig. 4-10. In this case, the line density $f(x)$ in (4-22) is given by

$$f(x) = \sum_{n=-N}^{N} p_a(x - nb)$$

Hence [see Chap. 4, (1-10)]

$$F(u) = \frac{2 \sin au}{u} \frac{\sin (N + \frac{1}{2})bu}{\sin (bu/2)} \tag{4-26}$$

The intensity $|g|^2$ of the resulting field is shown in Fig. 4-10 for $N = 2$ and $a = b/6$, $a \ll b$.

Two-dimensional signals

In the two-dimensional case, the Fraunhofer approximation (4-3) yields

$$\rho = \rho_o - \alpha_o x$$

Inserting into (2-21a), we conclude, as in (4-6), that

$$g(x_o, z_o) = \frac{1 + \gamma_o}{2\sqrt{\lambda\rho_o}} e^{j(k\rho_o - \pi/4)} \int_{-a}^{a} f(x) e^{-jk\alpha_o x} \, dx \tag{4-27}$$

With $F(u)$ the Fourier transform of $f(x)$, the above yields

$$g(x_o, z_o) = \frac{1 + \gamma_o}{2\sqrt{\lambda\rho_o}} e^{j(k\rho_o - \pi/4)} F(k\alpha_o) \tag{4-28}$$

Thus, on the surface of a cylinder, the diffraction field is proportional to the Fourier transform of the aperture function. On the plane $z = z_o$ in the narrow-edge region $x_o \leq z_o\lambda/b \ll 1$, we have, as in (4-8),

$$g(x_o, z_o) \propto e^{jkx_o^2/2z_o} F\left(\frac{kx_o}{z_o}\right) \qquad |g| \propto |F| \tag{4-29}$$

Example 4-5 Suppose that a dielectric with cross section

$$z = \varphi(x)$$

is placed at the opening of an aperture of length $2a$, which is illuminated by a uniform plane wave propagating in the z direction. With n the refractive index of the material,

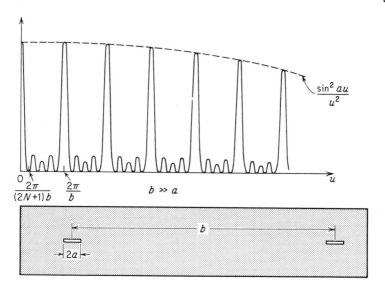

$$\frac{\sin^2 au}{u^2}$$

$$\frac{0}{(2N+1)b} \quad \frac{2\pi}{b}$$

$b \gg a$

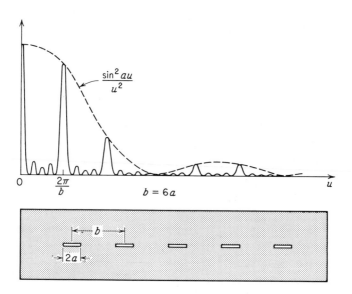

$$\frac{\sin^2 au}{u^2}$$

$$\frac{2\pi}{b}$$

$b = 6a$

Fig. 4-10

it is easy to see that the resulting delay is

$$\tau(x) = \frac{n-1}{c} \varphi(x) \tag{4-30}$$

Hence, the transmission function of the aperture is given by [see (2-15)]

$$T(x) = e^{ik(n-1)\varphi(x)} \tag{4-31}$$

We shall assume that $\varphi(x)$ is a periodic repetition of the function $\varphi_o(x)$ as in Fig. 4-11. With

$$T_o(x) = \begin{cases} T(x) & |x| \le \dfrac{b}{2} \\ 0 & \text{otherwise} \end{cases}$$

the truncated transmission function and $\Gamma(u)$ its Fourier transform, we have

$$T(x) = \sum_{m=-N}^{N} T_o(x - mb) \qquad (2N+1)b = 2a$$

The transform of $T(x)$ is given by [see Chap. 4, (1-10)]

$$\Gamma(u) \frac{\sin\,[(N+\frac{1}{2})bu]}{\sin\,(bu/2)}$$

Hence [see (4-28)]

$$|g(x_o,z_o)|^2 \propto |\Gamma(k\alpha_o)|^2 \frac{\sin^2\,[(N+\frac{1}{2})kb\alpha_o]}{\sin^2\,(kb\alpha_o/2)} \tag{4-32}$$

a. Suppose first that $\varphi(x)$ is a saw tooth (Fig. 4-11*a*):

$$\varphi_o(x) = p + qx \qquad |x| \le \frac{b}{2}$$

In this case,

$$\Gamma(u) = e^{ik(n-1)p} \frac{2\sin\,[(u - k\delta)b/2]}{u - k\delta} \qquad \delta = (n-1)q$$

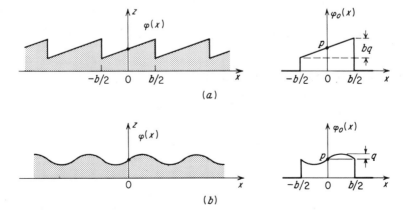

Fig. 4-11

(See also Example 1-2, Chap. 3.)   The resulting pattern (4-32) is similar to the pattern of Example 4-4, with the maximum of the envelope shifted in the direction $\alpha_o = \delta$.

b. If $\varphi(x)$ is a square wave

$$\varphi_o(x) = \begin{cases} p + q & 0 < x \leq \dfrac{b}{2} \\ p - q & \dfrac{-b}{2} < x \leq 0 \end{cases}$$

then

$$\Gamma(u) = 2e^{jk(n-1)p} \frac{\sin k\delta + \sin (bu/2 - k\delta)}{u}$$

c. Suppose finally that (Fig. 4-11*b*)

$$\varphi_o(x) = p + q \sin \frac{2\pi x}{b} \qquad |x| \leq \frac{b}{2}$$

If N is sufficiently large, then (4-32) takes significant values only near the points

$$\alpha_o = \frac{2\pi n}{kb}$$

Hence, it suffices to determine $\Gamma(2\pi n/b)$.   As we see from Chap. 5, (5-3),

$$\Gamma\left(\frac{2\pi n}{b}\right) = e^{jk(n-1)p} \int_{-b/2}^{b/2} e^{jk\delta \cos (2\pi x/b)} e^{-j(2\pi n x/b)} \, dx = b e^{jk(n-1)p} J_n(k\delta)$$

where $\delta = (n - 1)q$.

NONHARMONIC SIGNALS

We shall now determine the Fraunhofer diffraction of an aperture S illuminated by a plane wave of the form

$$v^i(x,y,z,t) = f(x,y)\varphi\left(t - \frac{z}{c}\right) \tag{4-33}$$

This is a special case of (2-3).   Hence [see (2-6*a*)],

$$v(x_o,y_o,z_o,t) = \frac{1 + \gamma_o}{4\pi c r_o} \iint_S f(x,y)\varphi'\left(t - \frac{r}{c}\right) dx \, dy \tag{4-34}$$

With $\Phi(\omega)$ the Fourier transform of $\varphi(t)$, we have

$$\varphi'(t) = \frac{1}{2\pi} \int_{-\infty}^{\infty} (-j\omega)\Phi(-\omega)e^{-j\omega t} \, d\omega$$

Inserting into (4-34) and changing the order of integration, we obtain [see (4-3)]

$$v(x_o,y_o,z_o,t)$$
$$= \frac{-j(1 + \gamma_o)}{8\pi^2 c r_o} \int_{-\infty}^{\infty} \omega\Phi(-\omega)e^{-j\omega(t - r_o/c)} \iint_S f(x,y)e^{-jk(\alpha_o x + \beta_o y)} \, dx \, dy \, d\omega$$

This holds for $r_o > 100b^2/\lambda_m$, where λ_m is the wavelength of the maximum-frequency component in $\varphi(t)$. Hence,

$$v\left(x_o,\ y_o,\ z_o,\ t + \frac{r_o}{c}\right) = \frac{-j(1 + \gamma_o)}{8\pi^2 c r_o} \int_{-\infty}^{\infty} \omega\Phi(-\omega)F(k\alpha_o,k\beta_o)e^{-j\omega t}\ d\omega$$

$$(4\text{-}35)$$

where, as always, $k = \omega/c$.

Suppose that $\varphi(t)$ is a modulated signal

$$\varphi(t) = w(t)e^{-j\omega_o t} \tag{4-36}$$

with narrow-band envelope

$$w(t) \leftrightarrow W(\omega) \qquad W(\omega) = 0 \qquad \text{for } |\omega| \geq \omega_c \tag{4-37}$$

Inserting into (4-35) and replacing $\omega_o - \omega$ by ω, we find

$$v = \frac{-j(1 + \gamma_o)}{4\pi c r_o}\ e^{-j\omega_o t}$$
$$\int_{-\omega_c}^{\omega_c} (\omega_o - \omega)W(\omega)F[(k_o - k)\alpha_o,(k_o - k)\beta_o] \frac{e^{j\omega t}}{2\pi}\ d\omega \quad (4\text{-}38)$$

If $F(u,v)$ is sufficiently smooth in the rectangle

$$(k_o - k_c)\alpha_o \leq u \leq (k_o + k_c)\alpha_o \qquad (k_o - k_c)\beta_o \leq v \leq (k_o + k_c)\beta_o$$

then

$$F[(k_o - k)\alpha_o,(k_o - k)\beta_o] \simeq F - \alpha_o k \frac{\partial F}{\partial u} - \beta_o k \frac{\partial F}{\partial v}$$

where all functions on the right side are evaluated at $u = k_o\alpha_o$, $v = k_o\beta_o$. With this approximation, the integral in (4-38) equals

$$[\omega_o w(t) + jw'(t)]F + \frac{\alpha_o}{c}\ [j\omega_o w'(t) - w''(t)] \frac{\partial F}{\partial u}$$
$$+ \frac{\beta_o}{c}\ [j\omega_o w'(t) - w''(t)] \frac{\partial F}{\partial v}$$

If $w(t) = 1$, then the above yields (4-6a).

5. THIN LENSES

In this section, we shall study the diffraction pattern of apertures containing thin lenses. We start with the two-dimensional case, assuming that the lens consists of two cylindrical surfaces with circular cross sections, as in Fig. 5-1. Such a lens will be treated as a transparency, which introduces no attenuation but merely a delay [see (2-2)] of the form

$$\tau(x) = \tau_o - \frac{x^2}{2fc} \qquad \tau_o = \frac{a^2}{2fc} \tag{5-1}$$

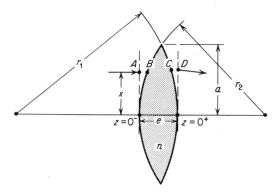

Fig. 5-1

where c is the velocity of light in air, and f is a constant characteristic of the lens (focal length). If $f > 0$, then the lens is convex (positive); if $f < 0$, the lens is concave (negative). As we shall explain, the above is an approximation giving a satisfactory characterization of the lens for small angles of incidence and for a small compared with the radii r_1 and r_2. If the incident field at the left side $z = 0^-$ of the lens is $v^i(x, 0^-, t)$, then the field at $z = 0^+$ equals

$$v^i\left(x,\ 0^+,\ t - \tau_o + \frac{x^2}{2fc}\right) \tag{5-2}$$

Since the time origin is arbitrary, the constant τ_o can be omitted.

As we see from (5-2) and (2-15), for harmonic signals the lens can be represented by the transmission function

$$T(x) = e^{-jkx^2/2f} \tag{5-3}$$

In the three-dimensional case, the surfaces of the lens are spherical, yielding the delay

$$\tau(x,y) = \tau_o - \frac{\rho^2}{2cf} \qquad \rho = \sqrt{x^2 + y^2} \tag{5-4}$$

and the corresponding transmission for harmonic signals is

$$T(x,y) = e^{-jk\rho^2/2f} \tag{5-5}$$

Plausible justification of lens characterization

A wave, incident upon a cylindrical lens of refractive index n, is refracted twice. If $a \ll r_1$, r_2, then its path from $z = -e$ to $z = 0$ is approximately rectilinear. The velocity of propagation in the lens is given by

$$\bar{c} = \frac{c}{n}$$

At the center $x = 0$, the path through the lens equals e (Fig. 5-1), which causes a delay

$$\tau_o = \frac{e}{\bar{c}} - \frac{e}{c} = \frac{e(n-1)}{c} \tag{5-6}$$

At a distance x from the center, the lens path is reduced by $AB + CD$. Applying the Fresnel approximation (3-1), we have

$$AB \simeq \frac{x^2}{2r_2} \qquad CD \simeq \frac{x^2}{2r_1} \qquad e \simeq \frac{a^2}{2r_1} + \frac{a^2}{2r_2}$$

(this is exact for parabolic lenses); with **f** defined by

$$\frac{1}{\mathbf{f}} = (n-1)\left(\frac{1}{r_1} + \frac{1}{r_2}\right) \tag{5-7}$$

(5-1) follows readily. If one or both surfaces are concave (Fig. 5-2), then (5-7) still holds, provided that r_1 or r_2 or both are negative. Formula (5-4) for spherical lenses can be similarly justified.

TWO–DIMENSIONAL SIGNALS

A cylindrical lens located on the $z = 0$ plane is illuminated by a harmonic plane wave

$$v^i = f(x)e^{-j\omega(t-z/c)}$$

Using Kirchhoff's formula, we shall determine the resulting diffraction field

$$g(x,z)e^{-j\omega t}$$

in the region $z > 0$.

We assume first that an opaque screen is placed on the portion $|x| > a$ of the $z = 0$ plane, containing the lens at its opening. From (5-3) it follows that

$$g(x,0^+) = f(x)e^{-jkx^2/2\mathbf{f}} \tag{5-8}$$

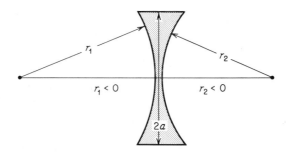

Fig. 5-2

Hence, all the results of the last two sections hold, provided that the function $f(x)$ in (3-4) is multiplied by $e^{-jkx^2/2f}$. Thus, the Fresnel formula (3-7a) yields

$$g(x_o,z_o) = \frac{1}{\sqrt{\lambda z_o}} e^{j(k\rho_o - \pi/4)} \int_{-a}^{a} f(x) e^{j\frac{kx^2}{2}\left(\frac{1}{z_o}-\frac{1}{f}\right)} e^{-jk\frac{xx_o}{z_o}} dx \qquad (5-9)$$

For $z_o = f$ (focal plane), the above reduces to

$$g(x_o,f) = \frac{1}{\sqrt{\lambda f}} e^{j(k\rho_o-\pi/4)} F\left(k\frac{x_o}{f}\right) \qquad \rho_o = \sqrt{x_o^2 + f^2} \qquad (5-10)$$

where $F(\omega)$ is the Fourier transform of $f(x)$. Thus on the focal plane $z_o = f$, the intensity $|g|^2$ of the diffraction pattern is proportional to the energy spectrum $|F|^2$ of the aperture function $f(x)$, as in the Fraunhofer region [see (4-29)].

If the incident wave is uniform, then $f(x) = 1$ for $|x| < a$, and (5-10) yields

$$|g(x_o,f)| = \frac{2}{\sqrt{\lambda f}} \left| \frac{\sin (akx_o/f)}{kx_o/f} \right|$$

This function tends to an impulse of area $2\pi/\sqrt{\lambda f}$ with $a \to \infty$.

We shall now determine $g(x_o,z_o)$ for $z_o \neq f$ (off the focal plane). With $F_\sigma(\omega)$ the Fresnel transform of $f(x)$ [see (3-19)] and

$$\frac{1}{z_o} - \frac{1}{f} = \frac{1}{\epsilon} \qquad (5-11)$$

(5-9) yields

$$g(x_o,z_o) = \sqrt{\frac{\epsilon}{z_o}} e^{j(k\rho_o-\pi/4)} F_{\sqrt{\epsilon/k}}\left(k\frac{x_o}{z_o}\right) \qquad (5-12)$$

It is of interest to observe that this function is proportional to the diffraction pattern g_α of a *lensless* aperture with aperture function $f(\alpha x)$ (Fig. 5-3). Indeed, with

$$\alpha = \frac{\epsilon}{z_o} = \frac{f}{f - z_o}$$

we conclude from (5-12) and (3-35) that [see also (3-41)]

$$\left| g_\alpha\left(x_o, \frac{z_o}{\alpha}\right) \right| = \sqrt{\frac{\epsilon}{z_o}} |g(x_o,z_o)| \qquad (5-13)$$

We note that in this equivalence, the boundaries

$$x_o = \pm a\left(1 - \frac{z_o}{f}\right) = \pm\frac{a}{\alpha}$$

of the geometric shadow are preserved.

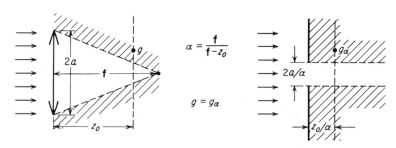

Fig. 5-3

If $\mathbf{f} - z_o = d \ll z_o$ (region near the focal plane), then

$$\epsilon \simeq \mathbf{f}^2/d \qquad \alpha \simeq \mathbf{f}/d$$

For $z_o \to \mathbf{f}$, $\alpha \to \infty$, and the equivalent lensless aperture tends to a slit.

If the incident wave is uniform, then the diffraction field near the focal plane is given by

$$|g(x_o,z_o)| = \sqrt{\frac{\mathbf{f}}{2d}} \left| \mathbf{F}\left(\frac{a}{\mathbf{f}}\sqrt{\frac{dk}{2}} - x_o\sqrt{\frac{k}{2d}}\right) + \mathbf{F}\left(\frac{a}{\mathbf{f}}\sqrt{\frac{dk}{2}} + x_o\sqrt{\frac{k}{2d}}\right)\right| \quad (5\text{-}14)$$

where $\mathbf{F}(x)$ is the Fresnel integral (3-16). This follows from (3-28) and (5-12), with $\epsilon \simeq \mathbf{f}^2/d$, $z_o \simeq \mathbf{f}$.

Image formation and lens formulas

Consider an object

$$-jkf(x)\delta(z + z_s)e^{-j\omega t} \qquad (5\text{-}15)$$

in the strip $|x| \le a_s$ of the object plane $z = -z_s$ (Fig. 5-4). We place a

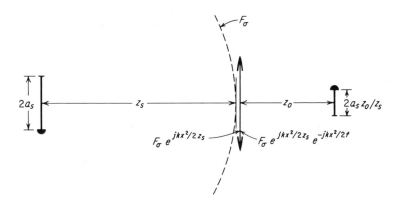

Fig. 5-4

cylindrical lens on the $z = 0$ plane, and we shall determine the "image" of $f(x)$ on the image plane $z = z_o$, where z_o is such that

$$\frac{1}{z_s} + \frac{1}{z_o} = \frac{1}{f} \tag{5-16}$$

This image will be viewed as the diffraction pattern of a lens that is illuminated by the field due to the object. As we see from (2-21b), this field is given by (3-7), with appropriate changes in the various constants. With $F_\sigma(\omega)$ the Fourier transform of

$$\frac{1}{\sqrt{\lambda z_s}} f(x) e^{jkx^2/2z_s} \tag{5-17}$$

it follows from the discussion of Sec. 3 that at $z = 0^-$, the incident field is

$$A e^{jkx^2/2z_s} F_\sigma\left(\frac{kx}{z_s}\right) \qquad \text{where} \qquad A = e^{j(kz_s - \pi/4)} \tag{5-18}$$

Introducing the transmission function (5-3) of the lens, we thus conclude that at $z = 0^+$, the field is

$$A e^{j\frac{kx^2}{2}\left(\frac{1}{z_s} - \frac{1}{f}\right)} F_\sigma(kx/z_s) \tag{5-19}$$

Hence, on the image plane $z = z_o$

$$g(x_o, z_o) = B \int_{-a}^{a} F_\sigma(kx/z_s) e^{-jkxx_o/z_o} \, dx \tag{5-20}$$

where

$$B = \frac{A}{\sqrt{\lambda z_o}} e^{j(k\rho_o - \pi/4)}$$

This follows from (3-7a) and (5-16).

If the lens is sufficiently large to assume that

$$F_\sigma\left(\frac{kx}{z_s}\right) \simeq 0 \qquad \text{for } |x| > a \tag{5-21}$$

then with $kx/z_s = \omega$, (5-20) yields

$$g(x_o, z_o) = B \sqrt{\lambda z_s} \, f\left(-\frac{z_s}{z_o} x_o\right) e^{jkz_s x_o^2/2z_o^2} \tag{5-22}$$

because the inverse Fourier transform of $F_\sigma(\omega)$ is the function in (5-17). Hence,

$$|g(x_o, z_o)| = \sqrt{\frac{z_s}{z_o}} \left| f\left(-\frac{z_s}{z_o} x_o\right) \right| \tag{5-23}$$

Thus, on the image plane $z = z_o$, the image $|g(x_o,z_o)|$ is similar to the object $|f(x)|$, provided that (5-23) holds. As we see from (5-23), the size of the image equals $2a_s z_o/z_s$; that is, the object is imaged with a magnification

$$m = \frac{z_o}{z_s} \tag{5-24}$$

Formulas (5-16) and (5-24) agree with the equations of geometric optics.

We note that the amplitudes of the object and its image are not similar. Because of the term

$$e^{jkp_o}e^{jkz_s x_o^2/2z_o^2} = e^{jkz_o}e^{jkz_s x_o^2/2fz_o}$$

a phase distortion results.

We now abandon assumption (5-21), and with

$$f_1(x) = [f(x)e^{jkx^2/2z_s}] * \frac{\sin (akx/z_s)}{\pi x} \tag{5-25}$$

we conclude from (5-20) that

$$g(x_o,z_o) = \frac{2\pi B z_s}{k} f_1\left(-\frac{z_s}{z_o}x_o\right) \tag{5-26}$$

(elaborate). One can show that [see Chap. 11, (2-29)] if $f(x)$ is sufficiently smooth, then

$$|f_1(x)| \propto \left| f(x) * \frac{\sin (akx/z_s)}{\pi x} \right| \tag{5-27}$$

Example 5-1 Suppose that the object is a line source

$$f(x) = \delta(x)$$

In this case,

$$F_\sigma(\omega) = \frac{1}{\sqrt{\lambda z_s}}$$

and (5-20) yields

$$g(x_o,z_o) = \frac{B}{\sqrt{\lambda z_s}} \frac{2 \sin (akx_o/z_o)}{(kx_o/z_o)} \tag{5-28}$$

THREE-DIMENSIONAL SIGNALS

The preceding results can be readily extended to spherical lenses and three-dimensional signals. Thus, if the incident field is a plane wave

$$f(x,y)e^{-j\omega(t-z/c)}$$

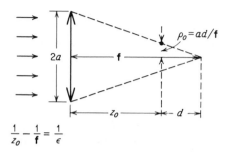

$$\frac{1}{z_o} - \frac{1}{f} = \frac{1}{\epsilon}$$

Fig. 5-5

then the resulting field is given by (3-49a), where, in the first exponential under the integral, z_o is replaced by the constant ϵ, which is introduced in (5-11). If the incident wave is uniform, then (3-49a) yields

$$g(\rho_o, z_o) = \frac{-2\pi j}{\lambda z_o} e^{jkr_o} \int_0^a \rho e^{jk\rho^2/2\epsilon} J_o\left(k\frac{\rho\rho_o}{z_o}\right) d\rho \qquad (5\text{-}29)$$

as in (3-50).

On the focal $z_o = \mathbf{f}$ (Fig. 5-5)

$$g(\rho_o, \mathbf{f}) = -je^{jkr_o} a \frac{J_1(ak\rho_o/\mathbf{f})}{\rho_o} \qquad (5\text{-}30)$$

as we see from (5-29) and Chap. 5, (1-20), with $1/\epsilon = 0$. Thus, the intensity of the diffraction field is given by the *Airy* formula

$$|g(\rho_o, \mathbf{f})|^2 = a^2 \frac{J_1^2(ak\rho_o/\mathbf{f})}{\rho_o^2} \qquad (5\text{-}31)$$

as in (4-13).

Along the z axis we have $\rho_o = 0$, and (5-29) yields [see also (3-53)]

$$g(0, z_o) = \frac{\epsilon}{z_o} e^{jkz_o}(1 - e^{jka^2/2\epsilon}) \qquad (5\text{-}32)$$

Finally, off the focal plane

$$g(\rho_o, z_o) = \frac{\epsilon}{z_o} e^{jk(r_o + a^2/2)} \left[U_2\left(\frac{ka^2}{\epsilon}, \frac{ka\rho_o}{z_o}\right) - jU_1\left(\frac{ka^2}{\epsilon}, \frac{ka\rho_o}{z_o}\right) \right] \qquad (5\text{-}33)$$

as in (3-55). With the approximation $\epsilon \simeq \mathbf{f}^2/d$, the intensity of the field along the boundary

$$\rho_o = \frac{ad}{\mathbf{f}} \qquad d = \mathbf{f} - z_o$$

of the geometric shadow is given by [see (3-56)]

$$|g(\rho_o, z_o)|^2 = \left(\frac{f}{2d}\right)^2 [1 - 2J_o(w)\cos w + J_o^2(w)] \qquad (5\text{-}34)$$

where

$$w = \frac{ka^2d}{f^2}$$

The above function is shown in Fig. 5-6.

Example 5-2   We shall determine the image $g(\rho_o, z_o)$ of a point source

$$4\pi\,\delta(x)\,\delta(y)\,\delta(z + z_s)$$

The incident field at $z = 0^-$ equals

$$A_1 e^{-jk\rho^2/2z_s} \qquad \text{where} \qquad A_1 = \frac{1}{z_s}\, e^{jkz_s}$$

Hence, $g(\rho_o, z_o)$ is the diffraction pattern of the aperture function [see (5-5)]

$$f(\rho) = A_1 e^{jk\rho^2/2z_s} e^{-jk\rho^2/2f}$$

Inserting into (3-50), we conclude that on the image plane $z = z_o$ [see (5-16)]

$$g(\rho_o, z_o) = A_2 \int_0^a \rho J_o\left(\frac{k\rho\rho_o}{z_o}\right) d\rho = aA_2\,\frac{J_1(ak\rho_o/z_o)}{k\rho_o/z_o} \qquad (5\text{-}35)$$

Off the focal plane, g is given by Lommel's functions, as in (5-33), but properly modified.

Stationary optical paths

We shall conclude with the following property of thin lenses.   In the arrangement of Fig. 5-7, $P_o{:}(x_o, y_o, z_o)$ is the image of a point source

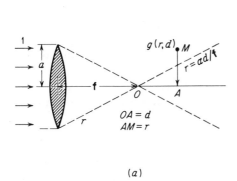

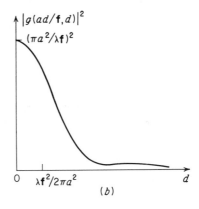

(a)

(b)

Fig. 5-6

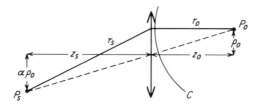

Fig. 5-7

$P_s:(-\alpha x_o, -\alpha y_o, -\alpha z_o)$, where

$$\alpha = \frac{z_s}{z_o} \qquad \frac{1}{z_s} + \frac{1}{z_o} = \frac{1}{f} \tag{5-36}$$

With r_o and r_s the distances from P_o and P_s to the point (x,y) on the plane of the lens, we maintain that

$$r_o + r_s - \frac{x^2 + y^2}{2f} = \overline{P_o P_s} = \text{const} \tag{5-37}$$

(independent of x and y), within the Fresnel approximation error. Indeed, since

$$r_o = \sqrt{z_o^2 + (x_o - x)^2 + (y_o - y)^2} \simeq z_o$$
$$+ \frac{1}{2z_o}[(x_o - x)^2 + (y_o - y)^2]$$
$$r_s = \sqrt{z_s^2 + (\alpha x_o + x)^2 + (\alpha y_o + y)^2} \simeq z_s$$
$$+ \frac{1}{2z_s}[(\alpha x_o + x)^2 + (\alpha y_o + y)]^2$$

(5-37) follows from (5-36).

As an application, we form the diffracted field

$$g(P) = A \iint_S e^{jk(r_o+r_s)} e^{-j(x^2+y^2)/2f} \, dx \, dy$$

If $P = P_o$, then the integrand is constant; hence, $|g(P_o)|$ is maximum, and it equals $|A|$ times the area of the lens.

We finally note, reasoning as in (4-19), that on the surface C of a sphere centered at P_o the amplitude of the diffracted field is constant (elaborate).

PROBLEMS

9-1. The diffraction field $g(P)$ due to a point source M (Fig. P9-1) is given by (2-16). Using the method of stationary phase [see Chap. 7, (4-4)] show that in the "visible" region of M, $g(P)$ tends to the incoming wave

$$g(P) = \frac{-j}{2\lambda} \iint_S \frac{\cos \theta_s + \cos \theta}{r r_s} e^{jk(r_s+r)} \, dx \, dy \xrightarrow[k \to \infty]{} \frac{1}{r_1} e^{jkr_1}$$

and in the "dark" region it tends to zero.

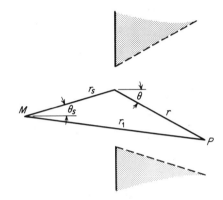

Fig. P9-1

9-2. We denote by $g(\rho)$ the Fraunhofer field of an aperture of outer radius b and inner radius ϵb illuminated by a uniform plane wave of intensity C (Fig. P9-2).

(a) Show that the intensity $|g(0)|^2$ at the center of the pattern equals

$$C \left[\frac{\pi b^2 (1 - \epsilon^2)}{\lambda z_0} \right]^2$$

(b) Show that the maxima and minima (zeros) of $|g(\rho)|^2$ are at $\rho = \alpha_i z_0 \lambda / 2 \pi b$ and $\rho = \beta_i z_0 \lambda / 2 \pi b$, where α_i and β_i are the roots of

$$J_1(\alpha_i) - \epsilon J_1(\epsilon \alpha_i) = 0 \qquad J_2(\beta_i) - \epsilon J_2(\epsilon \beta_i) = 0$$

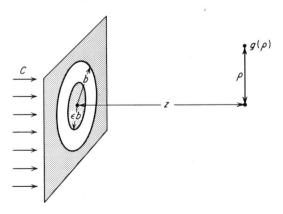

Fig. P9-2

9-3. (Doppler shift) A particle of mass $m = w(t)$ is moving with constant velocity u producing a field $f(t)$ at a distant point P in the direction of motion (Fig. P9-3). With $W(\omega)$ and $F(\omega)$ the transforms of $w(t)$ and $f(t)$, respectively, show that $F(\omega) = A W(\omega/\alpha)$, where $\alpha = 1 + u/c$.

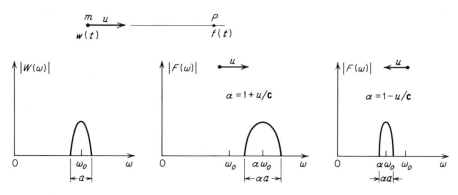

Fig. P9-3

9-4. An aperture S is illuminated by a distant monochromatic point source M (Fig. P9-4), and the resulting Fraunhofer pattern on a plane P equals $I(r)$. Show that if the source moves normally to P with velocity u, then the new pattern equals $I(\alpha r)$, where $\alpha = 1 + u/c$.

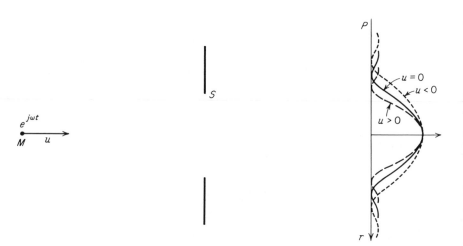

Fig. P9-4

9-5. The image of a point source $me^{j\omega t}$ at the center of the plane P (Fig. P9-5) is $g(0)$. Show that if the radius of the lens is a, then

$$|g(0)| = \frac{\pi a^2 m}{2\lambda z_0 z_s}$$

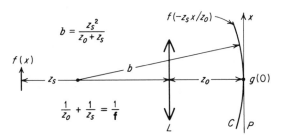

Fig. P9-5

9-6. The lens L of Fig. P9-5 is perfect.   Show that the image of an object $f(x,y)$ on a sphere C of radius $b = z_s^2/(z_o + z_s)$ equals $f(-z_s x/z_o, -z_s y/z_o)$ (no phase distortion).

9-7.† An aperture S of area A is illuminated by a uniform plane wave of amplitude B. With $g(P)$ the resulting far field on the plane $z = z_o$, show that

$$(a) \qquad |g(P)| \leq AB/\lambda z_o$$

and

$$(b) \qquad |g(P_1) - g(P_2)| \leq \frac{2\pi l a A B}{\lambda^2 z_o^2} \qquad a = \overline{P_1 P_2}$$

where l is the maximum projection of the points of S in a direction L that is parallel to the line $P_1 P_2$ (Fig. P9-7).

  Hint: $|1 - \cos x| \leq x^2/2$.

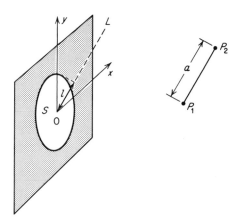

Fig. P9-7

9-8. A circular aperture is illuminated by a plane wave of amplitude $\varphi(t)f(\rho)$.   With

$$s(x) = \int f(\rho)\, dy \qquad \rho = \sqrt{x^2 + y^2}$$

the x profile of $f(\rho)$, show that the resulting far field is given by [use (4-35) and Chap.

† A. Papoulis, *J. Opt. Soc. Am.*, vol. 57, no. 3, March, 1967, pp. 362–366.

5, (2-4)]

$$g\left(\rho_o,\, z_o,\, t + \frac{r_o}{c}\right) = \frac{1 + \gamma_o}{4\pi\rho_o}\, \varphi'(t) * s\left(\frac{cr_o}{\rho_o}t\right) = \frac{(1 + \gamma_o)cr_o}{4\pi\rho_o{}^2}\, \varphi(t) * s'\left(\frac{cr_o}{\rho_o}t\right)$$

Show that if $\varphi(t) = e^{-j\omega t}$, then the above yields (4-12).

From the above it follows that g, considered as a time signal, is the output of a system with input $\varphi(t)$ and system function

$$\frac{j\omega(1 + \gamma_o)}{2cr_o}\, \bar{f}\left(\frac{\rho_o}{cr_o}\,\omega\right)$$

where $\bar{f}(w)$ is the Hankel transform of $f(\rho)$.

9-9. (a) Show that if

$$w(x,y,z) = \frac{1}{z}\, e^{jk[(x-\xi)^2+(y-\eta)^2]/2z}$$

then

$$\frac{\partial^2 w}{\partial x^2} + \frac{\partial^2 w}{\partial y^2} + 2jk\,\frac{\partial w}{\partial z} = 0 \qquad\qquad (1)$$

(b) With $g(x,y,z)$ the Fresnel diffraction field (3-49a), show that the function

$$w(x,y,z) = g(x,y,z)e^{-jkz} = \frac{-j}{\lambda z}\iint f(\xi,\eta)e^{jk[(x-\xi)^2+(y-\eta)^2]/2z}\,d\xi\,d\eta$$

satisfies the diffusion equation (1). Thus, the approximate (Fresnel) solution of the wave equation $\nabla^2 g + k^2 g = 0$ multiplied by e^{-jkz} satisfies exactly the approximate equation (1).

10
COHERENCE

Optical waves cannot be characterized by harmonic signals. Even if they are monochromatic, their phase is a complicated function that is not specified by its point properties, but by various averages. In this chapter, we develop the theory of such averages, but limit the discussion to second-order moments (coherence). The results follow directly from applying the theory of Chap. 8 to optical fields. It is true, of course, that coherent monochromatic signals can be treated as harmonic waves; however, even in this very special case, the random interpretation is preferable.

In the first section, we introduce the coherence function and the corresponding spectrum of arbitrary random scalar fields. In the next section, we discuss the various interferometers as instruments measuring the average intensity of two or more additive random signals. In Sec. 3, we derive the wave equation for the coherence function, and we show that it can be found by solving two equivalent deterministic problems. In the last section, we apply the results to the Fraunhofer diffraction.

1. OPTICAL SIGNALS, CORRELATION, COHERENCE

An optical field is a function of the space coordinates and of the time. At a fixed point in space, this field is a time signal $f(t)$, and the purpose of this section is to study its spectral properties. If the energy of $f(t)$ is finite, then

$$f(t) = \frac{1}{2\pi} \int_{-\infty}^{\infty} F(\omega)e^{j\omega t}\,d\omega$$

This relationship reduces the investigation of the propagation of $f(t)$ through linear media to the study of harmonic functions.

The above representation is not suitable for optical signals. It is more appropriate to consider them as random functions (with finite average power) and to describe their spectral properties (color) in terms of the power spectrum

$$S(\omega) = \lim_{T \to \infty} \frac{1}{2T} \left| \int_{-T}^{T} \mathbf{f}(t)e^{-j\omega t}\,dt \right|^2 \tag{1-1}$$

In a physical problem the quantities $|F(\omega)|^2$ and $S(\omega)$ are approximated by the finite integrals

$$|F_T(\omega)|^2 = \left| \int_{-T}^{T} f(t)e^{-j\omega t}\,dt \right|^2$$

$$\mathbf{S}_T(\omega) = \frac{1}{2T} \left| \int_{-T}^{T} \mathbf{f}(t)e^{-j\omega t}\,dt \right|^2$$

One might, therefore, argue that except for the scale factor $\frac{1}{2}T$, these quantities are the same. The fact is that if T is sufficiently large, then $\mathbf{S}_T(\omega)$ is invariant to an arbitrary shift of the interval of integration, and this is certainly not the case for the transform $F_T(\omega)$ of signals with finite energy.

The inverse Fourier transform of $S(\omega)$ is the autocorrelation of $\mathbf{f}(t)$. Following the general convention in optics, we shall denote this function by $\Gamma(\tau)$ and will call it the *coherence function* of $\mathbf{f}(t)$. As we know (Prob. 8-4), $\Gamma(\tau)$ can be expressed directly in terms of $\mathbf{f}(t)$:

$$\Gamma(\tau) = \lim_{T \to \infty} \frac{1}{2T} \int_{-T}^{T} \mathbf{f}(t + \tau)\mathbf{f}^*(t)\,dt$$

This average will be written in the form

$$\Gamma(\tau) = E\{\mathbf{f}(t + \tau)\mathbf{f}^*(t)\}$$

The following analysis is also valid if $\mathbf{f}(t)$ is interpreted as a stationary stochastic process and E as an expected value (ensemble average). The power spectrum $S(\omega)$ is then defined as the Fourier transform of $\Gamma(\tau)$. We note that for stochastic processes, the time average $\mathbf{S}_T(\omega)$ is a random quantity; it tends to the deterministic function $S(\omega)$ only if $\mathbf{f}(t)$ satisfies certain conditions (ergodicity) [p2].

If we use the expression E as a time average applied to a stochastic process $\mathbf{f}(t)$, we shall assume that the process is ergodic.

The signal $\mathbf{f}(t)$ is *monochromatic* if

$$\Gamma(\tau) = |a|^2 e^{j\omega_o \tau} \qquad S(\omega) = 2\pi |a|^2 \delta(\omega - \omega_o)$$

If $\mathbf{f}(t)$ is harmonic, i.e., if

$$\mathbf{f}(t) = ae^{j\omega_o t}$$

then it is monochromatic (Example 5-1, Chap. 8).   However, as we point out in Sec. 4, Chap. 8, a monochromatic signal is not necessarily harmonic.

We shall say that $\mathbf{f}(t)$ is *quasi-monochromatic* (or *narrow-band*) if its power spectrum is negligible outside the interval $(\omega_o - \omega_c, \omega_o + \omega_c)$ and (Fig. 1-1)

$$\omega_c \ll \omega_o$$

The corresponding coherence function $\Gamma(\tau)$ is then a modulated signal

$$\Gamma(\tau) = a(\tau)e^{j\omega_o t}$$

with slowly varying envelope $a(\tau)$ [see Chap. 6, (1-21)].

Properties of $\Gamma(\tau)$

The following properties of $\Gamma(\tau)$ are based on the fact that $S(\omega) \geq 0$ [see Chap. 8, (4-19)].

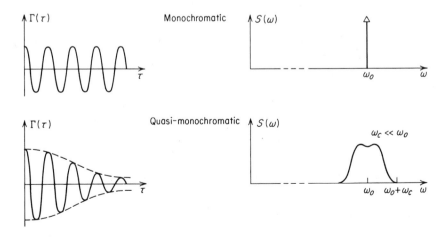

Fig. 1-1

We shall first show that

$$|\Gamma(\tau)| \leq \Gamma(0) \tag{1-2}$$

Indeed,

$$|\Gamma(\tau)| = \left| \frac{1}{2\pi} \int_{-\infty}^{\infty} S(\omega) e^{j\omega\tau} \, d\omega \right| \leq \frac{1}{2\pi} \int_{-\infty}^{\infty} S(\omega) \, d\omega = \Gamma(0)$$

Suppose now that (1-2) is satisfied with the equality sign for some $\tau = \tau_1$:

$$|\Gamma(\tau_1)| = \Gamma(0) \qquad \tau_1 \neq 0 \tag{1-3}$$

We maintain that, in this case, $\Gamma(\tau)$ is of the form

$$\Gamma(\tau) = e^{j\alpha\tau} w(\tau) \tag{1-4}$$

where $w(\tau)$ is a periodic function with period τ_1

$$w(\tau + \tau_1) = w(\tau)$$

Proof Denoting by φ the phase angle of $\Gamma(\tau_1)$, we conclude from (1-3) that

$$\Gamma(\tau_1) = \Gamma(0) e^{j\varphi}$$

Hence (inversion formula),

$$\Gamma(0) - e^{-j\varphi}\Gamma(\tau_1) = \frac{1}{2\pi} \int_{-\infty}^{\infty} S(\omega)(1 - e^{-j\varphi}e^{j\omega\tau_1}) \, d\omega = 0$$

The real part of the above integrand, given by

$$S(\omega)[1 - \cos(\omega\tau_1 - \varphi)]$$

is obviously nonnegative. Therefore, the integral is zero only if $S(\omega) = 0$ everywhere except at the zeros of

$$1 - \cos(\omega\tau_1 - \varphi) = 0$$

that is, at the points [see also Chap. 4, (2-6)]

$$\omega = \frac{2\pi n}{\tau_1} + \frac{\varphi}{\tau_1}$$

Hence, unless $\Gamma(\tau) \equiv 0$, $S(\omega)$ must consist of impulses at the above points. Thus

$$S(\omega) = \sum_{n=-\infty}^{\infty} A_n \delta(\omega - n\omega_1 - \alpha) \qquad \omega_1 = \frac{2\pi}{\tau_1} \qquad \alpha = \frac{\varphi}{\tau_1}$$

and with

$$w(t) = \frac{1}{2\pi} \sum_{n=-\infty}^{\infty} A_n e^{jn\omega_1}$$

(1-4) follows.

Corollary Suppose that

$$|\Gamma(\tau_1)| = |\Gamma(\tau_2)| = \Gamma(0) \tag{1-5}$$

where τ_1 and τ_2 are two noncommensurate numbers. We shall show that in this case, the process $\mathbf{f}(t)$ is monochromatic, i.e.,

$$\Gamma(\tau) = A e^{j\alpha\tau} \tag{1-6}$$

To prove (1-6), we note from (1-5) and (1-4) that

$$\Gamma(\tau) = e^{j\alpha_1\tau} w_1(\tau) = e^{j\alpha_2\tau} w_2(\tau)$$

Clearly, the functions $w_1(\tau)$ and $w_2(\tau)$ are periodic, with respective periods τ_1 and τ_2. Since the ratio τ_1/τ_2 is an irrational number by assumption, the above is possible only if

$$\alpha_1 = \alpha_2 \qquad w_1(\tau) = w_2(\tau) = \text{const}$$

(elaborate), and (1-6) results.

From the above it follows that if $|\Gamma(\tau)|$ is constant for every τ in an interval containing the origin, then the process $\mathbf{f}(t)$ is monochromatic.

Evaluation of the power spectrum

We shall discuss two methods for evaluating the power spectrum $S(\omega)$. In the first method, the coherence function $\Gamma(\tau)$ is determined experimentally, and $S(\omega)$ is found by computing the integral

$$S(\omega) = \int_{-\infty}^{\infty} \Gamma(\tau) e^{-j\omega\tau}\, d\tau$$

for various values of ω. In the second method, $S(\omega)$ is evaluated directly by passing $\mathbf{f}(t)$ through a suitable filter.

Correlometer In Fig. 1-2a we show an experimental arrangement for measuring the coherence function of a *real* process $\mathbf{f}(t)$. It consists of a delay line with an adjustable delay τ, a multiplier, and an integrator. The output of the integrator yields

$$\frac{1}{2T} \int_{-T}^{T} \mathbf{f}(t)\mathbf{f}(t-\tau)\, dt$$

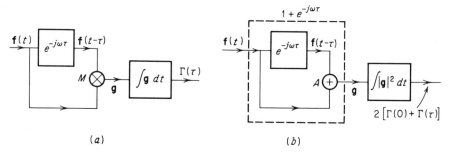

Fig. 1-2

This quantity is close to $\Gamma(\tau)$, provided that T is sufficiently large. A precise statement about the required value of T involves higher-order moments. However, the following example gives an idea of the necessary order of magnitude. If (Example 5-1, Chap. 8)

$$\mathbf{f}(t) = a \cos \omega_o t \qquad \text{then} \qquad \Gamma(\tau) = \frac{a^2}{2} \cos \omega_o \tau$$

and

$$\frac{1}{2T} \int_{-T}^{T} \mathbf{f}(t)\mathbf{f}(t - \tau) \, dt = \frac{a^2}{2} \cos \omega_o \tau \left(1 + \frac{\sin 2\omega_o T}{2\omega_o T}\right)$$

If $\omega_o T \gg 1$, then the error is small.

An alternate approach, more suitable for optical applications, is based on the relationship

$$E\{[\mathbf{f}(t) + \mathbf{f}(t - \tau)]^2\} = 2[\Gamma(0) + \Gamma(\tau)] \tag{1-7}$$

We now need a delay line, an adder, and a square-law detector (Fig. 1-2b). The output of the detector equals

$$\frac{1}{2T} \int_{-T}^{T} [\mathbf{f}(t) + \mathbf{f}(t - \tau)]^2 \, dt$$

If $\mathbf{f}(t) = a \cos \omega_o t$, then the above average yields

$$a^2(1 + \cos \omega_o \tau) \left(1 + \frac{\sin 2\omega_o T}{2\omega_o T} \cos \omega_o \tau\right)$$

and it approaches $2[\Gamma(0) + \Gamma(\tau)]$ if the interval of observation $2T$ is large compared with $1/\omega_o$.

The method can also be used to evaluate the mutual coherence function (cross correlation) $\Gamma_{12}(\tau)$ of two signals $\mathbf{f}_1(t)$ and $\mathbf{f}_2(t)$:

$$E\{[\mathbf{f}_1(t) + a\mathbf{f}_2(t - \tau)]^2\} = \Gamma_{11}(0) + 2a\Gamma_{12}(\tau) + a^2\Gamma_{12}(0) \tag{1-8}$$

as on page 260.

Spectrum analyzer   Using the relationship

$$S_g(\omega) = S(\omega)|H(\omega)|^2 \tag{1-9}$$

between the spectrum $S_g(\omega)$ of the output $\mathbf{g}(t)$ of a linear system and the spectrum $S(\omega)$ of the input $\mathbf{f}(t)$ [see Chap. 8, (4-18)], we can determine $S(\omega)$ directly. This is done by selecting a suitable system function $H(\omega)$ and measuring the average intensity (power) of the output. Indeed, suppose that the system is an ideal bandpass filter, as in Fig. 1-3. We then have, from (1-9),

$$S_g(\omega) = \begin{cases} S(\omega) & \text{for } \omega_o - \epsilon < \omega < \omega_o + \epsilon \\ 0 & \text{otherwise} \end{cases}$$

Hence,

$$E\{|\mathbf{g}(t)|^2\} = \Gamma_g(0) = \frac{1}{2\pi}\int_{-\infty}^{\infty} S_g(\omega)\, d\omega = \frac{1}{2\pi}\int_{\omega_o-\epsilon}^{\omega_o+\epsilon} S(\omega)\, d\omega \tag{1-10}$$

If ϵ is sufficiently small, then

$$E\{|\mathbf{g}(t)|^2\} \simeq \frac{\epsilon}{\pi} S(\omega_o) \tag{1-11}$$

that is, the average intensity of the output of the filter is proportional to the power spectrum $S(\omega_o)$. By varying ω_o, we can thus determine $S(\omega)$.

Comment   The underlying principles in the preceding two methods are essentially the same: the measured quantity is the average intensity of the output of a linear system with input $\mathbf{f}(t)$. In the spectrum analyzer, the system function $H(\omega)$ is a narrow-band filter. In the cor-

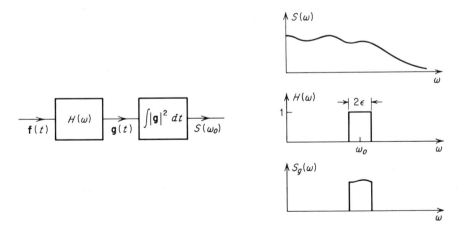

Fig. 1-3

relometer (Fig. 1-2b),

$$H(\omega) = 1 + e^{-j\omega\tau_o}$$

which yields, as output, the signal

$$\mathbf{g}(t) = \mathbf{f}(t) + \mathbf{f}(t - \tau_o)$$

with power spectrum

$$S_\varrho(\omega) = 4S(\omega) \cos^2 \frac{\omega\tau_o}{2}$$

In Sec. 2, we discuss physical arrangements for implementing these two methods.

SPACE DEPENDENCE

If the point of observation P is variable, then the optical field is a function $\mathbf{f}(P,t)$ of P and t. The cross correlation of the time functions $\mathbf{f}(P_1,t)$ and $\mathbf{f}(P_2,t)$ we shall call the (mutual) *coherence function* of the given field:

$$\Gamma(P_1,P_2;t_1,t_2) = E\{\mathbf{f}(P_1,t_1)\mathbf{f}^*(P_2,t_2)\} \tag{1-12}$$

In most cases of interest, the process $\mathbf{f}(P,t)$ is stationary in time. Hence, Γ depends only on $t_1 - t_2 = \tau$. If E is interpreted as a time average, then

$$\Gamma(P_1,P_2;\tau) = \lim_{T\to\infty} \frac{1}{2T} \int_{-T}^{T} \mathbf{f}(P_1, t + \tau)\mathbf{f}^*(P_2,t) \, dt \tag{1-13}$$

The function $\Gamma(P,P;\tau)$ is maximum for $\tau = 0$ [see (1-2)]:

$$|\Gamma(P,P;\tau)| \le \Gamma(P,P,0) \tag{1-14}$$

The Fourier transform of $\Gamma(P_1,P_2;\tau)$ with respect to τ defines the power spectrum

$$S(P_1,P_2;\omega) = \int_{-\infty}^{\infty} \Gamma(P_1,P_2;\tau)e^{-j\omega\tau} \, d\tau \tag{1-15}$$

From (1-12) it follows readily that

$$\Gamma(P_1,P_2;\tau) = \Gamma^*(P_2,P_1;-\tau) \tag{1-16}$$

Hence

$$S(P_1,P_2;\omega) = S^*(P_2,P_1;\omega) \tag{1-17}$$

for any process real or complex. The spectrum $S(P,P;\omega)$ is real.

We note that the average intensity of $\mathbf{f}(P,t)$ is given by

$$E\{|\mathbf{f}(P,t)|^2\} = \Gamma(P,P;0) = \frac{1}{2\pi} \int_{-\infty}^{\infty} S(P,P;\omega) \, d\omega \tag{1-18}$$

The correlation coefficient

$$\gamma(P_1,P_2;\tau) = \frac{\Gamma(P_1,P_2;\tau)}{\sqrt{\Gamma(P_1,P_1;0)\Gamma(P_2,P_2;0)}} \tag{1-19}$$

of the random variables $\mathbf{f}(P_1, t + \tau)$ and $\mathbf{f}(P_2,t)$ is called the *complex degree of coherence* of the process $\mathbf{f}(P,t)$. It is such that (Prob. 8-3)

$$|\gamma(P_1,P_2;\tau)| \leq 1 \tag{1-20}$$

Definitions We shall say that $\mathbf{f}(P,t)$ is a *spectrally pure* process if

$$\Gamma(P_1,P_2;\tau) = \Gamma(P_1,P_2)\rho(\tau) \tag{1-21}$$

Since $\rho(\tau)$ is determined within a constant, we can assume that

$$\rho(0) = 1 \tag{1-22}$$

With $s(\omega)$ the Fourier transform of $\rho(\tau)$, that is,

$$\rho(\tau) \leftrightarrow s(\omega) \tag{1-23}$$

the spectrum of a spectrally pure process is given by

$$S(P_1,P_2;\omega) = \Gamma(P_1,P_2)s(\omega) \tag{1-24}$$

The complex degree of coherence now takes the form

$$\gamma(P_1,P_2;\tau) = \frac{\Gamma(P_1,P_2)\rho(\tau)}{\sqrt{\Gamma(P_1,P_1)\Gamma(P_2,P_2)}} = \gamma(P_1,P_2)\rho(\tau) \tag{1-25}$$

If

$$\rho(\tau) = e^{-j\omega_o\tau}$$

then the process is monochromatic.

Unless otherwise stated, it will be assumed that $\mathbf{f}(P,t)$ is a spectrally pure process, as in (1-21).

Comments The monochromatic character of a process can be established by checking the form of its coherence function only for $P_1 = P_2$. If

$$\Gamma(P,P;\tau) = \Gamma(P,P)e^{-j\omega_o\tau}$$

for any P, then [see Chap. 8, (4-47)]

$$\Gamma(P_1,P_2;\tau) = \Gamma(P_1,P_2)e^{-j\omega_o\tau}$$

for any P_1, P_2.

A more general form of spectral purity results if we assume that

$$\Gamma(P_1,P_2;\tau) = \Gamma(P_1,P_2)\rho[\tau - \theta(P_1,P_2)] \tag{1-26}$$

Since $\Gamma(P,P;\tau)$ is maximum for $\tau = 0$, the quantity $\rho[-\theta(P,P)]$ must be independent of P. Denoting the function $\rho[\tau - \theta(P,P)]$ by $\rho(\tau)$, we can thus assume that $\theta(P,P) = 0$. With $s(\omega)$ as in (1-24), we conclude from (1-26) that

$$S(P_1,P_2;\omega) = \Gamma(P_1,P_2)e^{j\theta(P_1,P_2)\omega}s(\omega)$$

Hence

$$S(P,P;\omega) = \Gamma(P,P)s(\omega)$$

Thus, the spectrum (color) of a spectrally pure process is the same everywhere in space (within a constant factor).

Complete incoherence   We shall say that a process $f(P,t)$ is (completely) incoherent in a region V if

$$\gamma(P_1,P_2) = 0 \qquad \text{for } P_1 \neq P_2 \tag{1-27}$$

In this case [see also Chap. 8, (3-8)]

$$\Gamma(P_1,P_2) = q(P_1)\delta(P_1 - P_2) \tag{1-28}$$

where the expression $\delta(P_1 - P_2)$ means a point mass in the space under consideration. In three dimensions,

$$\delta(P_1 - P_2) = \delta(x_1 - x_2)\delta(y_1 - y_2)\delta(z_1 - z_2)$$

The average intensity of an incoherent field is infinite. However, for reasons given below, the function $q(P)$ is called the average intensity of $f(P,t)$ (see also page 264). Consider the integral

$$\mathbf{I}(t) = \int_V f(P,t)\, dP$$

Clearly,

$$|\mathbf{I}(t)|^2 = \iint_{VV} f(P_1,t)f^*(P_2,t)\, dP_1\, dP_2$$

Hence

$$E\{|\mathbf{I}(t)|^2\} = \iint_{VV} \Gamma(P_1,P_2)\, dP_1\, dP_2 \tag{1-29}$$

If $f(P,t)$ is incoherent, then the above yields

$$E\{|\mathbf{I}(t)|^2\} = \int_V q(P)\, dP \tag{1-30}$$

(elaborate). With P_o a point in V we conclude from the above that if the volume V is sufficiently small and $q(P)$ is continuous, then

$$E\{|\mathbf{I}(t)|^2\} \simeq Vq(P_o)$$

Complete coherence   We shall say that a process $f(P,t)$ is (completely) coherent in a region V if

$$|\gamma(P_1,P_2;0)| = |\gamma(P_1,P_2)| = 1 \tag{1-31}$$

for every P_1 and P_2 in V.   We then have [see (1-16)]

$$\Gamma(P_1,P_1)\Gamma(P_2,P_2) = |\Gamma(P_1,P_2)|^2 = \Gamma(P_1,P_2)\Gamma(P_2,P_1) \tag{1-32}$$

If $f(P,t)$ is real, then $\Gamma(P_1,P_2)$ is also real, and $\rho(-\tau) = \rho(\tau)$.   In this case,

$$\Gamma(P_1,P_2) = \Gamma(P_2,P_1)$$

It can be shown that (Prob. 10-1) if a process $f(P,t)$ is completely coherent, then a deterministic function $p(P)$ and a random signal $z(t)$ independent of P exist such that

$$f(P,t) = p(P)z(t)$$

in the sense

$$E\{|f(P,t) - p(P)z(t)|^2\} = 0$$

From the above it follows that

$$\Gamma(P_1,P_2) = p(P_1)p^*(P_2) \qquad \rho(\tau) = E\{z(t+\tau)z^*(t)\} \tag{1-33}$$

and

$$E\{|f(P_1,t) + f(P_2,t)|^2\} = |p(P_1) + p(P_2)|^2 \tag{1-34}$$

The process thus behaves like a deterministic signal with amplitude $p(P)$.

Conversely if the coherence function of a process is of the form (1-33), then the process is completely coherent.

If a field is not completely coherent or incoherent, it is called partially coherent.

Comments   Coherence is a concept related to space coordinates. Incoherence in time would mean that the random variables $f(P,t_1)$ and $f(P,t_2)$ are uncorrelated for $t_1 \neq t_2$ (white noise); however, this notion is of no interest for optical signals.

If

$$f(P,t) = f(t)$$

is independent of P, then the process $f(P,t)$ is obviously completely coherent.

The notion of complete coherence can be extended to include signals that satisfy not (1-31) but the weaker condition

$$\max_\tau |\gamma(P_1,P_2;\tau)| = 1 \tag{1-35}$$

for every P_1 and P_2. For monochromatic signals, the above is equivalent to (1-31).

Stationary processes We shall say that a process $f(P,t)$ is stationary in space if its coherence function $\Gamma(P_1,P_2)$ depends only on $P_1 - P_2$. Thus,

$$E\{f(P + Q, t + \tau)f^*(Q,t)\} = \Gamma(P)\rho(\tau) \tag{1-36}$$

Clearly, the average intensity of such a field is constant

$$E\{|f(P,t)|^2\} = \Gamma(0)$$

If the field is incoherent, then [see (1-28)]

$$\Gamma(P) = q\delta(P_1 - P_2)$$

If it is coherent, then [see (1-33)] $p(P)$ is constant and

$$\Gamma(P) = \Gamma(0) = \text{const}$$

Example 1-1 Suppose that $f(P,t)$ is a process with coherence function $\Gamma(P_1,P_2;\tau)$, and $h(P)$ is a space function (deterministic). If we form the process

$$w(P,t) = h(P)f(P,t)$$

then its coherence function is given by

$$\Gamma_w(P_1,P_2;\tau) = h(P_1)h^*(P_2)\Gamma(P_1,P_2;\tau)$$

It is easy to see that if $f(P,t)$ is coherent (incoherent), then $w(P,t)$ is also coherent (incoherent).

2. INTERFERENCE AND INTERFEROMETERS

Interference is the superposition of two or more light beams, and interferometers are instruments for forming such beams and for measuring the average intensity of the resulting superposition. We shall discuss the principle of operation of these instruments.

INTERFERENCE AT A FIXED POINT

Suppose that a uniform light beam of amplitude $f(t)$ reaches the point of observation P along two paths of respective lengths z_1 and z_2. With $v(t)$ the resulting field at P, we have

$$v(t) = a_1 f\left(t - \frac{z_1}{c}\right) + a_2 f\left(t - \frac{z_2}{c}\right) \tag{2-1}$$

where a_1 and a_2 are the attenuations along each path, and c is the velocity of light. With

$$\tau = \frac{z_1 - z_2}{c}$$

we conclude from (2-1) that if $\Gamma(\tau)$ is the coherence function of the real process $\mathbf{f}(t)$, then

$$I(\tau) = E\{|\mathbf{v}(t)|^2\} = (a_1{}^2 + a_2{}^2)\Gamma(0) + 2a_1a_2\Gamma(\tau) \tag{2-2}$$

Thus, by measuring the average intensity $I(\tau)$ of $\mathbf{v}(t)$ for various values of $z_1 - z_2$, we can determine $\Gamma(\tau)$.

The Michelson interferometer

A device for the physical realization of the above scheme is the well-known Michelson interferometer [b5], which is shown in Fig. 2-1. It consists of a light source S, a semireflecting surface G, and two mirrors M_1 and M_2. The light from S arrives at the observation point P along the paths 1 and 2, as shown. The lengths of these paths differ by

$$z_1 - z_2 = 2l$$

where l is the relative displacement of the mirror M_2. The reading of the detector equals

$$\frac{1}{2T} \int_{t-T}^{t+T} |\mathbf{v}(\xi)|^2 \, d\xi \tag{2-3}$$

and if T is sufficiently large, then it is independent of t and it equals $I(\tau)$.

In Fig. 2-2 we show

$$I(\tau) = I\left(\frac{2l}{c}\right)$$

as a function of l for a quasi-monochromatic and a monochromatic field.

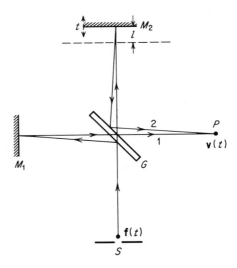

Fig. 2-1

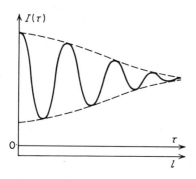

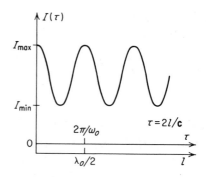

Fig. 2-2

In the latter case, $\Gamma(\tau) = \cos \omega_o\tau$; hence,

$$I(\tau) = (a_1{}^2 + a_2{}^2) + 2a_1a_2 \cos \omega_o\tau \tag{2-4}$$

and

$$\frac{I_{\max}}{I_{\min}} = \left(\frac{a_1 + a_2}{a_1 - a_2}\right)^2 \tag{2-5}$$

If

$$\lambda_o = \frac{2\pi c}{\omega_o} = 4 \times 10^{-7} \text{ m}$$

then a displacement of M_2 by a distance $l = 10^{-7}$ m causes a change of I from $I_{\max}$ to $I_{\min}$.

Variations of l of this order are produced by a piezoelectric element attached to one of the mirrors. Suppose that this element is driven by a low-frequency source $e(t) = e_1 + e_o \cos \omega_c t$, which causes a periodic displacement

$$l = l_1 + l_o \cos \omega_c t$$

of the mirror and a resulting delay

$$\frac{2l}{c} = \tau = \tau_1 + \tau_o \cos \omega_c t \tag{2-6}$$

Since τ is a function of t, the average (2-3) does not in general equal $I(\tau)$. However, if T is small compared with $1/\omega_c$, then τ can be considered as constant in the interval of integration $(t - T, t + T)$. The length $2T$ of this interval must of course be large compared with $1/\omega_o$; otherwise, the average (2-3) does not equal $I(\tau)$. Thus, if

$$\frac{1}{\omega_o} \ll T \ll \frac{1}{\omega_c}$$

and $a_1 = a_2 = 1$ in (2-1), then

$$\frac{1}{2T} \int_{t-T}^{t+T} |\mathbf{v}(\xi)|^2 \, d\xi \simeq 2[\Gamma(0) + \Gamma(\tau_1 + \tau_o \cos \omega_c t)] = I_1(t) \qquad (2\text{-}7)$$

Example 2-1 If the source is a laser beam, then the output of the detector is a curve, as in Fig. 2-3. The corresponding coherence function is a modulated wave with periodic envelope

$$\Gamma(\tau) = w(\tau) \cos \omega_o \tau \qquad w(\tau + a) = w(\tau) \qquad (2\text{-}8)$$

If the envelope $w(\tau)$ is truncated outside the interval $(0,a)$, the signal $w_o(\tau)$ results. Denoting by $W_o(\omega)$ its Fourier transform, we can easily show that the power spectrum $S(\omega)$ of $f(t)$ consists of impulses near $\pm\omega_o$, and a distance $\omega_1 = 2\pi/a$ apart; that is,

$$S(\omega) = \pi \sum_{n=-\infty}^{\infty} \beta_n[\delta(\omega - \omega_o - n\omega_1) + \delta(\omega + \omega_o - n\omega_1)] \qquad (2\text{-}9)$$

where [see Chap. 4, (2-8)] $\beta_n = W_o(n\omega_1)/a$ are the Fourier series coefficients of $w_o(\tau)$.

In Fig. 2-4 we show the average (2-7) for $\tau_o = \pi/6\omega_o$ and τ_1 such that $\cos \omega_o \tau_1 = 0$ or 1 (points 1 or 2 in the figure).

Extended light sources In the preceding analysis it was assumed that the detector records the average intensity of the field $\mathbf{v}$ at a single point and that $\mathbf{v}$ is given by (2-1). These assumptions are not, of course, exactly correct. The two beams reach the detector displaced relative to each other, and the detected signal is given by

$$\mathbf{v}(x,y,t) = \mathbf{f}\left(x, \, y, \, t - \frac{z_1}{c}\right) + \mathbf{f}\left(x - \alpha, \, y - \beta, \, t - \frac{z_2}{c}\right) \qquad (2\text{-}10)$$

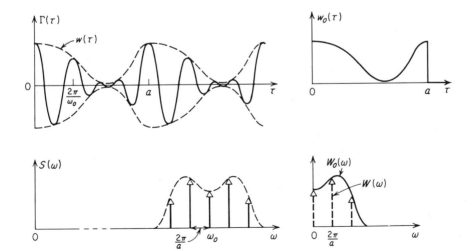

Fig. 2-3

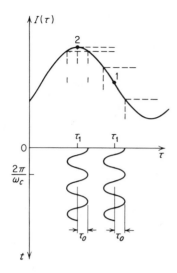

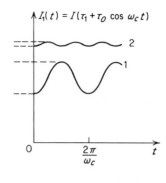

Fig. 2-4

where $\mathbf{f}(x,y,t)$ is the source beam as a function of the coordinates x and y of its cross section. The detector senses the average integral

$$I(\tau) = E\left\{\left|\frac{1}{A}\iint_A \mathbf{v}(x,y,t)\,dx\,dy\right|^2\right\} \qquad (2\text{-}11)$$

over a region A common to the beams 1 and 2 (Fig. 2-5).

We shall assume that the signal $\mathbf{f}(x,y,t)$ is stationary in space and spectrally pure:

$$E\{\mathbf{f}(x_1, y_1, t+\tau)\mathbf{f}(x_2,y_2,t)\} = \Gamma(x_1 - x_2, y_1 - y_2)\rho(\tau)$$

If the dimensions of A are small relative to the rate of variation of Γ,

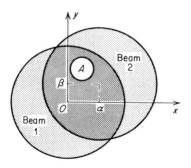

Fig. 2-5

then (2-11) yields

$$I(\tau) \simeq 2\Gamma(0,0)\rho(0) + 2\Gamma(\alpha,\beta)\rho(\tau) \qquad \tau = \frac{z_1 - z_2}{c} \qquad (2\text{-}12)$$

(elaborate). If the source is coherent, then $\Gamma(\alpha,\beta)$ is constant, and the interference pattern is independent of the displacement (α,β). If the source is incoherent, then $\Gamma(\alpha,\beta) = 0$ for $(\alpha,\beta) \neq (0,0)$. In this case, $I(\tau)$ is constant for any τ (no interference). Finally, if the source is partially coherent, then $I(\tau)$ depends on the relative displacement of the two beams. In Fig. 2-6 we show $I(\tau)$ for two values of (α,β). By varying (α,β) and observing $I(0)$, we can thus determine the coherence function $\Gamma(\alpha,\beta)$ of the light beam.

VARIABLE OBSERVATION POINT

Interference patterns can be studied by observing the field produced by two fixed sources, at several points in space. We shall discuss the principle of this method using the following simple arrangement.

Young's experiment

An opaque screen D_1 with two small openings S_1 and S_2 is illuminated by a distant source S (Fig. 2-7a). We shall evaluate the intensity of the resulting diffraction field $\mathbf{v}$ on a screen D_2 that is parallel to D_1. With $\mathbf{v}^i$ the incident field, $\mathbf{v}$ is given approximately by

$$\mathbf{v}(P,t) = \mathbf{f}_1\left(t - \frac{r_1}{c}\right) + \mathbf{f}_2\left(t - \frac{r_2}{c}\right) \qquad (2\text{-}13)$$

where

$$\mathbf{f}_1(t) = a\frac{\partial \mathbf{v}^i}{\partial t} \qquad a = \frac{A(1 + \gamma_1)}{4\pi c r_1} \qquad (2\text{-}14)$$

In the above, $\mathbf{v}^i$ is evaluated at the opening S_1, and A is the area of S_1. The function $\mathbf{f}_2(t)$ is given by a similar expression. This approximation follows from Chap. 9, (2-6a), by assuming that the dimensions of each

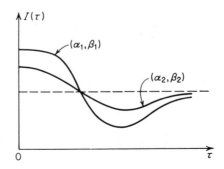

Fig. 2-6

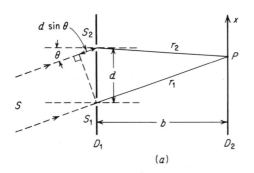

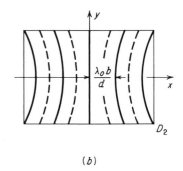

(a)   (b)

Fig. 2-7

opening are small compared with the wavelength of $\mathbf{v}^i$.   A more precise analysis for larger openings will be given in Sec. 3; however, the main features of the resulting pattern can be obtained from (2-13).

If the incident field is a uniform (coherent) plane wave, and the coefficient a in (2-14) is assumed constant, then

$$\mathbf{f}_2(t) = \mathbf{f}_1(t + t_o) \qquad t_o = \frac{d \sin \theta}{c} \tag{2-15}$$

where d is the distance between the two openings and θ is the angle of incidence.

With $\Gamma(\tau)$ the autocorrelation of $\mathbf{f}_1(t)$, we conclude from (2-13) and (2-15) that

$$E\{|\mathbf{v}(P,t)|^2\} = 2[\Gamma(0) + \Gamma(\tau + t_o)] \qquad \tau = \frac{r_1 - r_2}{c} \tag{2-16}$$

Thus, the average intensity of the diffracted field is constant on the parabolic surfaces $r_1 - r_2 + d \sin \theta = $ constant.   [This is an approximation based on the assumption that the coefficient a in (2-14) is constant.] The intersection of these surfaces with the plane D_2 gives hyperbolas of constant intensity on the observation screen (Moiré pattern).   For $\theta = 0$ (normal incidence) the intensity is maximum on the line $x = 0$ where $r_1 = r_2$.   If the incident field is quasi-monochromatic

$$\Gamma(\tau) = w(\tau) \cos \omega_o \tau$$

then $E\{|\mathbf{v}(P,t)|^2\}$ is maximum for $\tau = 2\pi n/\omega_o$, that is, along the hyperbolas (Fig. 2-7b)

$$\sqrt{\left(x + \frac{d}{2}\right)^2 + y^2 + b^2} - \sqrt{\left(x - \frac{d}{2}\right)^2 + y^2 + b^2} = \frac{2\pi n c}{\omega_o} = n \lambda_o \tag{2-17}$$

If the distance b between the planes D_1 and D_2 is large compared with d, then, near the origin of D_2,

$$r_1 - r_2 \simeq \frac{xd}{b}$$

(Fresnel approximation) and (2-17) yields the straight lines

$$x = \frac{n\lambda_o b}{d} \tag{2-18}$$

Thus a picture, recording the time average of $\mathbf{v}$ as in (2-3), will show a succession of light and dark lines (Young's fringes). The light lines are given by (2-18). The difference in intensity between light and dark fringes decreases until it becomes zero (no interference) for

$$|x| > x_o = \frac{cb\tau_o}{d}$$

where τ_o is such that $w(\tau) = 0$ for $|\tau| \geq \tau_o$.

Comment With

$$\Gamma_i(\tau) = w_i(\tau) \cos \omega_o \tau$$

the coherence function of the incident field $\mathbf{v}^i$, we conclude from (2-14) and Prob. 8-5 that

$$\Gamma(\tau) = -a^2 \frac{d^2\Gamma_i(\tau)}{d\tau^2} \tag{2-19}$$

If $\mathbf{v}^i$ is quasi-monochromatic, then $w_i(\tau)$ is slowly varying, and (2-19) yields

$$\Gamma(\tau) \simeq a^2 \omega_o^2 \Gamma_i(\tau) \tag{2-20}$$

From the above it follows that if the incident wave $\mathbf{v}^i$ is monochromatic, then for the determination of the average intensity of the diffracted field $\mathbf{v}(P,t)$, it suffices to assume that $\mathbf{f}_1(t) = a\omega_o \mathbf{v}^i$ [see Chap. 11, (6-2)].

FILTERING AND INTERFERENCE

The output

$$\mathbf{v}(t) = \int_{-\infty}^{\infty} \mathbf{f}(t - \tau)h(\tau)\, d\tau$$

of a filter can be interpreted as an interference pattern which results if an infinity of weighted values of the input $\mathbf{f}(t)$ is added. In this case,

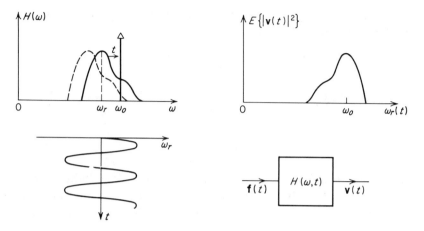

Fig. 2-8

the detector reads [see Chap. 8, (4-18)]

$$E\{|\mathbf{v}(t)|^2\} = \frac{1}{2\pi} \int_{-\infty}^{\infty} S(\omega)|H(\omega)|^2 \, d\omega \tag{2-21}$$

This average can be expressed in terms of the autocorrelation of $\mathbf{f}(t)$ [see Chap. 8, (4-11)].

If $\mathbf{f}(t)$ is monochromatic with autocorrelation

$$\Gamma(\tau) = ce^{j\omega_o \tau}$$

then (2-21) yields

$$E\{|\mathbf{v}(t)|^2\} = c|H(\omega_o)|^2 \tag{2-22}$$

To determine ω_o, we construct a time-varying filter with the property that its frequency response $H(\omega)$ moves to the right with increasing t. The position of $H(\omega)$ can thus be determined if the frequency ω_r, for which $|H(\omega)|$ is maximum, is a known function $\omega_r(t)$ of time (Fig. 2-8a). Assuming that $\omega_r(t)$ varies sufficiently slowly, we easily conclude that the detector reading $E\{|\mathbf{v}(t)|^2\}$ is a curve, as in Fig. 2-8b. Clearly, $E\{|\mathbf{v}(t)|^2\}$ is maximum at $t = t_o$ such that $\omega_r(t_o) = \omega_o$. Thus, knowing $\omega_r(t)$, we can determine ω_o.

Suppose now that

$$\Gamma(\tau) = c_1 e^{j\omega_1 \tau} + c_2 e^{j\omega_2 \tau}$$

If $\omega_1 - \omega_2$ is larger than the bandwidth $2b$ of the filter (distance between its two half-power points), then $E\{|\mathbf{v}(t)|^2\}$ has two maxima near ω_1 and ω_2. As $\omega_1 - \omega_2$ decreases, these maxima merge into one, and the frequencies ω_1, ω_2 can no longer be detected. Thus, the resolving power of the instrument is of the order of b. For a more precise statement, one should know the exact shape of $H(\omega)$ and the ratio c_1/c_2 [p2].

Comment In order to obtain a stationary pattern at the detector output, we vary $\omega_r(t)$ periodically (as in Fig. 2-8). With T_c the period of this variation, the preceding results hold if the integration interval T of the detector [see (2-3)] is such that

$$\frac{1}{\omega_o} \ll T \ll T_c \tag{2-23}$$

Fabry-Perot interferometer

A filter with time-varying characteristics can be simply realized with the arrangement shown in Fig. 2-9a. It consists of two glass plates P_1 and P_2, which are used to support a highly reflective substance coated on their inner sides [b5]. If a uniform monochromatic plane wave $e^{j\omega t}$ is normally incident upon P_1, then the transmitted wave at P_2 equals

$H(\omega)e^{j\omega t}$

Thus, the above device can be considered as a filter with system function $H(\omega)$.

We denote by r and t, respectively, the reflection and transmission coefficients of the reflective substances, and the distance between them by d. It can be easily seen that if their thickness is small and the effect of the glass plates P_1 and P_2 is neglected, then

$$H(\omega) = \frac{t^2 e^{-j\omega d/c}}{1 - r^2 e^{-j2\omega d/c}} \tag{2-24}$$

where c is the velocity of light in the medium between P_1 and P_2. This is established by setting up the proper boundary conditions, or, more

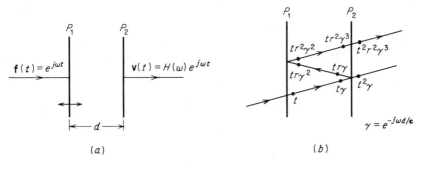

(a)   (b)

Fig. 2-9

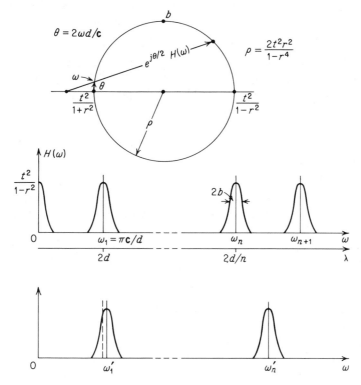

Fig. 2-10

simply, by summing the transmitted components resulting from multiple reflections (Fig. 2-9b):

$$t^2 e^{-j\omega d/c}[1 + r^2 e^{-j2\omega d/c} + \cdots + r^{2n} e^{-j2n\omega d/c} + \cdots]$$

Because of the finite thickness of the reflective substance, the parameters r and t are frequency dependent; however, for our purposes it will suffice to consider them as constants.

Clearly, $|H(\omega)|$ is periodic with period $\pi nc/d$, and its frequency dependence is affected only by r. For r close to 1, $|H(\omega)|$ takes significant values only near the resonant frequencies $\pi nc/d$ (Fig. 2-10). In this neighborhood, we have

$$e^{-j2\omega d/c} \simeq 1 - j\frac{2d}{c}(\omega - \omega_n)$$

and (2-24) yields

$$|H(\omega)|^2 \simeq \sum_{n=-\infty}^{\infty} \frac{A^2}{\alpha^2 + (\omega - \omega_n)^2} \qquad (2\text{-}25)$$

where

$$A = \frac{t^2 c}{2r^2 d} \qquad \alpha = \frac{(1 - r^2)c}{2r^2 d} \qquad \omega_n = \frac{\pi n c}{d} \tag{2-26}$$

At the resonant frequencies ω_n, the corresponding wavelength is given by

$$\lambda_n = \frac{2d}{n}$$

Thus, the Fabry-Perot interferometer acts as a bandpass filter containing an infinity of bands with centers ω_n. The absolute bandwidth of each band equals

$$2b = 2\alpha \simeq \frac{2(1 - r)c}{d} \qquad |H(\omega_n \pm b)|^2 = \frac{|H(\omega_n)|^2}{2}$$

However, the relative bandwidth

$$\frac{2b}{\omega_n} \simeq \frac{2(1 - r)}{\pi n}$$

decreases with increasing n. The inverse $\omega_n/2b$ is the Q of the cavity at the frequency ω_n. For

$$1 - r = 10^{-2} \qquad n = 10^4$$

Q is of the order of 10^6.

The frequency response $H(\omega)$ can be changed by varying either c or the distance d between the two plates. To vary c, one can inject a dielectric substance in the region between P_1 and P_2. The variation of d is effected by a piezoelectric element attached to one of the plates, as in the Michelson interferometer. We note that if d is decreased by a small quantity ϵ, and $\epsilon \ll d$, then the new resonant frequencies ω_n' are given by (Fig. 2-10)

$$\omega_n' = \frac{\pi n c}{d - \epsilon} \simeq \omega_n \left(1 + \frac{\epsilon}{d}\right) \tag{2-27}$$

and if $\epsilon = d/n$, then $\omega_n' = \omega_{n+1}$.

Suppose now that the incoming wave at P_1 is a process $\mathbf{f}(t)$ with power spectrum $S(\omega)$. If $S(\omega)$ is limited to the band (ω_n, ω_{n+1}), and it is sufficiently smooth in an interval of length $2b$, then the average intensity $E\{|\mathbf{v}(t)|^2\}$ of the output will be proportional to $S(\omega_n')$, where ω_n' is the instantaneous value of the nth resonant frequency given by (2-27). An increase of the displacement ϵ from 0 to d/n will cause an increase of ω_n' from ω_n to ω_{n+1}, and the detector will exhibit the entire spectrum $S(\omega)$ of the process $\mathbf{f}(t)$.

If $S(\omega)$ consists of discreet lines, as in Example 2-1, then the detec-

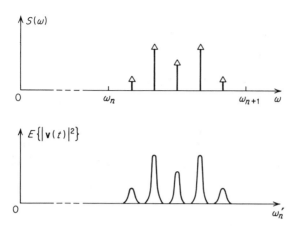

Fig. 2-11

tor will register a succession of curves (as in Fig. 2-11) which are again obtained by varying ω_n' from ω_n to ω_{n+1}. From the location and amplitude of the maxima of these curves we can determine the intensity and position of the lines of $S(\omega)$.

Suppose, finally, that $S(\omega)$ covers a broad area that overlaps with several bands of $H(\omega)$ (Fig. 2-12). For a fixed value of d, the power spectrum

$$S_v(\omega) = S(\omega)|H(\omega)|^2$$

of the output $\mathbf{v}(t)$ of the interferometer consists now of isolated bands with amplitude proportional to $S(\omega_n)$. In this case, $E\{|\mathbf{v}(t)|^2\}$ is proportional to the sum of the values of $S(\omega)$ at all resonant frequencies ω_n. It cannot, therefore, be used to evaluate directly $S(\omega_n)$. However, since each component of $S_v(\omega)$ occupies a narrow band of the spectrum, it can be determined by other methods (for example, prisms). Varying ω_n, we can thus determine the entire spectrum $S(\omega)$.

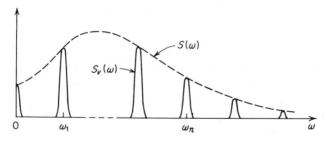

Fig. 2-12

3. PROPAGATION OF COHERENCE FUNCTIONS

Consider the wave equation

$$\nabla^2 \mathbf{v} - \frac{1}{c^2}\frac{\partial^2 \mathbf{v}}{\partial t^2} = -\mathbf{s} \tag{3-1}$$

where the source density $\mathbf{s}(P,t)$ is a stochastic process with coherence function

$$\Gamma_{ss}(P_1,P_2;t_1,t_2) = E\{\mathbf{s}(P_1,t_1)\mathbf{s}^*(P_2,t_2)\} \tag{3-2}$$

as in (1-12). The purpose of this section is to determine the coherence function Γ_{vv} of the resulting field† $\mathbf{v}(P,t)$. We find it simpler to determine first the cross-coherence function

$$\Gamma_{sv}(P_1,P_2;t_1,t_2) = E\{\mathbf{s}(P_1,t_1)\mathbf{v}^*(P_2,t_2)\} \tag{3-3}$$

between the source $\mathbf{s}$ and the field $\mathbf{v}$.

Since $\mathbf{s}$ and $\mathbf{v}$ are related by a real linear operator, it follows from the discussion of Chap. 8 that [see Chap. 8, (2-13) and (3-25)]

$$\nabla_2^2\Gamma_{sv} - \frac{1}{c^2}\frac{\partial^2 \Gamma_{sv}}{\partial t_2^2} = -\Gamma_{ss} \tag{3-4}$$

This can also be shown directly by multiplying the conjugate of (3-1), which is evaluated at (P_2,t_2) by $\mathbf{s}(P_1,t_1)$, and taking expected values. In (3-4), ∇_2 is the Laplacian with respect to the variables P_2.

Thus, the cross-coherence function between the source $\mathbf{s}(P_1,t_1)$ at the fixed point (P_1,t_1) and the resulting field $\mathbf{v}(P_2,t_2)$ at the variable point (P_2,t_2) satisfies the wave equation with source function $\Gamma_{ss}(P_1,P_2;t_1,t_2)$.

Reasoning similarly [see also Chap. 8, (2-14) and (3-27)], we find that Γ_{vv} satisfies the wave equation

$$\nabla_1^2\Gamma_{vv} - \frac{1}{c^2}\frac{\partial^2 \Gamma_{vv}}{\partial t_1^2} = -\Gamma_{sv} \tag{3-5}$$

in the variables (P_1,t_1), and with the solution Γ_{sv} of (3-4) as source function.

If $\Gamma_{ss}(P_1,P_2;\tau)$ is a function of $\tau = t_1 - t_2$, then the same is true for Γ_{sv} and Γ_{vv}. In this case, (3-4) and (3-5) yield

$$\nabla_2^2\Gamma_{sv} - \frac{1}{c^2}\frac{\partial^2 \Gamma_{sv}}{\partial \tau^2} = -\Gamma_{ss} \qquad \nabla_1^2\Gamma_{vv} - \frac{1}{c^2}\frac{\partial^2 \Gamma_{vv}}{\partial \tau^2} = -\Gamma_{sv} \tag{3-6}$$

From the above we see that the evaluation of Γ_{sv} and Γ_{vv} is reduced to the solution of the wave equation with deterministic sources, and all

† L. Mandell, "Progress in Optics," vol. 2 (ed., E. Wolf), pp. 183–248, Interscience Publishers, Inc., New York, 1963.

results of Chap. 9 hold with the proper identification of the various functions.

FREE SOURCES

Consider a point source

$$\mathbf{s} = 4\pi \mathbf{w}(t)\delta(x)\delta(y)\delta(z) \tag{3-7}$$

where $\mathbf{w}(t)$ is a stationary process with autocorrelation $R(\tau)$. As we know [see Chap. 9, (1-5)], the resulting field $\mathbf{v}(P,t)$ is given by

$$\mathbf{v}(P,t) = \frac{\mathbf{w}(t - r/\mathbf{c})}{r}$$

where r is the distance from P to the origin. Hence (Fig. 3-1)

$$\mathbf{v}(P_1, t + \tau)\mathbf{v}^*(P_2,t) = \frac{1}{r_1 r_2}\mathbf{w}\left(t + \tau - \frac{r_1}{\mathbf{c}}\right)\mathbf{w}^*\left(t - \frac{r_2}{\mathbf{c}}\right)$$

Taking expected values, we conclude that the coherence function Γ_{vv} of $\mathbf{v}$ is given by

$$\Gamma_{vv}(P_1,P_2;\tau) = \frac{1}{r_1 r_2}R\left(\tau - \frac{r_1 - r_2}{\mathbf{c}}\right) \tag{3-8}$$

Hence

$$E\{|\mathbf{v}(t)|^2\} = \frac{R(0)}{r^2} = \frac{E\{|\mathbf{w}(t)|^2\}}{r^2}$$

Furthermore [see (1-19)]

$$\gamma_{vv}(P_1,P_2;\tau) = \frac{1}{R(0)}R\left(\tau - \frac{r_1 - r_2}{\mathbf{c}}\right) \tag{3-9}$$

From the above we see that $\mathbf{v}(P,t)$ is completely coherent on the surface of a sphere centered at the point source [see (1-31)], and if we adopt definition (1-35), then $\mathbf{v}(P,t)$ is completely coherent everywhere.

The field due to two point sources $4\pi \mathbf{w}_a(t)$ and $4\pi \mathbf{w}_b(t)$, as in (3-7), is given by

$$\mathbf{v}(P,t) = \frac{\mathbf{w}_a(t - r_a/\mathbf{c})}{r_a} + \frac{\mathbf{w}_b(t - r_b/\mathbf{c})}{r_b}$$

Suppose that these sources are incoherent:

$$E\{\mathbf{w}_a(t + \tau)\mathbf{w}_b(t)\} \equiv 0$$

With $R_a(\tau)$ and $R_b(\tau)$ the autocorrelations of the signals $\mathbf{w}_a(t)$ and $\mathbf{w}_b(t)$, we conclude that

$$E\{|\mathbf{v}(P,t)|^2\} = \frac{R_a(0)}{r_a^2} + \frac{R_b(0)}{r_b^2}$$

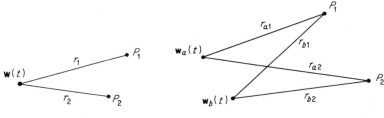

Fig. 3-1   Fig. 3-2

Thus, the average intensity of $\mathbf{v}$ equals the sum of the intensities due to each source. Its coherence function is given by

$$\Gamma(P_1,P_2;\tau) = \frac{R_a[\tau - (r_{a1} - r_{a2})/\mathbf{c}]}{r_{a1}r_{a2}} + \frac{R_b[\tau - (r_{b1} - r_{b2})/\mathbf{c}]}{r_{b1}r_{b2}}$$

where the distances are as in Fig. 3-2. If the distance between the two sources is small compared with their distance from a region V, and if the dimensions of V are also small in the same sense, then $\mathbf{v}$ is completely coherent in V because (Fraunhofer approximation)

$$r_{a1} - r_{a2} \simeq r_{b1} - r_{b2} \qquad r_{a1}r_{a2} \simeq r_{b1}r_{b2}$$

We now assume that the region V_s contains random sources with density $\mathbf{s}(P,t)$. It then follows from (3-4) and Chap. 9, (1-4), that

$$\Gamma_{sv}(P_1,P_2{}^o;t_1,t_2) = \frac{1}{4\pi} \int_{V_s} \frac{1}{r_2} \Gamma_{ss}\left(P_1,\ P_2;\ t_1,\ t_2 - \frac{r_2}{\mathbf{c}}\right) dP_2 \qquad (3\text{-}10)$$

This is the cross-coherence function between the source density $\mathbf{s}(P_1;t_1)$ at the point P_1 in V_s and the resulting field $\mathbf{v}(P_2{}^o,t_2)$ at the arbitrary point $P_2{}^o$. In the above, r_2 is the distance from $P_2{}^o$ to the point of integration P_2 (Fig. 3-3). Clearly, $\Gamma_{sv}(P_1,P_2{}^o;t_1,t_2)$ equals zero for P_1 not in V_s. Similarly, from (3-5) and Chap. 9, (1-4), we conclude that for any $P_1{}^o,\ P_2{}^o$,

$$\Gamma_{vv}(P_1{}^o,P_2{}^o;t_1,t_2) = \frac{1}{4\pi} \int_{V_s} \frac{1}{r_1} \Gamma_{sv}\left(P_1,\ P_2{}^o;\ t_1 - \frac{r_1}{\mathbf{c}},\ t_2\right) dP_1 \qquad (3\text{-}11)$$

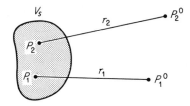

Fig. 3-3

where r_1 is the distance from P_1^o to P_1. Combining (3-10) and (3-11), we can express Γ_{vv} directly in terms of Γ_{ss}. In particular,

$$E\{|\mathbf{v}(P,t)|^2\} = \frac{1}{16\pi^2} \iint_{V_*V_*} \frac{1}{r_1 r_2} \Gamma_{ss}\left(P_1, P_2; t - \frac{r_1}{c}, t - \frac{r_2}{c}\right) dP_1\, dP_2$$

Incoherent sources

If the sources are spectrally pure and incoherent, i.e., if

$$\Gamma_{ss}(P_1,P_2;\tau) = q(P_1)\delta(P_1 - P_2)\rho(\tau)$$

then (3-10) yields

$$\Gamma_{sv}(P_1,P_2^o;\tau) = \frac{1}{4\pi r_2} q(P_1)\rho(\tau + r_2/c) \qquad r_2 = \overline{P_2^o P_1}$$

Inserting into (3-11), we find

$$\Gamma_{vv}(P_1^o,P_2^o;\tau) = \frac{1}{16\pi^2} \int_{V_*} \frac{1}{r_1 r_2} q(P_1)\rho\left(\tau + \frac{r_2 - r_1}{c}\right) dP_1$$

$$r_1 = \overline{P_1^o P_1} \quad (3\text{-}12)$$

and if $P_1^o = P_2^o = P$, then $r_1 = r_2$; hence

$$E\{|\mathbf{v}(P,t)|^2\} = \frac{\rho(0)}{16\pi^2} \int_{V_*} \frac{q(P_1)}{r_1^2} dP_1 \qquad r_1 = \overline{PP_1}$$

Thus the average intensity of the field due to incoherent sources is found by adding the intensities due to each differential element.

The Van Cittert-Zernike theorem† A special case of (3-12) is of particular interest. Suppose that a self-luminous incoherent monochromatic plane object S of average intensity $q(x,y)$ is located on the $z = 0$ plane, as in Fig. 3-4a. Its coherence function is given by

$$\Gamma_{ss}(P_1,P_2;\tau) = q(x_1,y_1)\delta(x_1 - x_2)\delta(y_1 - y_2)e^{-j\omega\tau}$$

where (x_1,y_1) and (x_2,y_2) are the coordinates of the points P_1 and P_2. Assuming that the dimensions of S are small compared with its distance from the plane $z = z_o$, we conclude from (3-12) that the coherence function of the resulting field at the points P_1^o and P_2^o on the small-angle region of this plane equals

$$\Gamma_{vv}(P_1^o,P_2^o;\tau) = \frac{e^{-j\omega\tau}}{16\pi^2 z_o^2} \iint_S q(x_1,y_1)e^{jk(r_1-r_2)}\, dx_1\, dy_1 \qquad (3\text{-}13)$$

This result can be given the following interpretation: if the point P_2^o is fixed, then Γ_{vv} is a function of P_1^o. As we see from Chap. 9,

† P. H. Van Cittert, *Physica*, vol. 1, p. 201, 1934; F. Zernike, *Physica*, vol. 5, p. 785, 1938.

(2-14), this quantity is proportional to the diffraction pattern in the plane $z = z_o$ due to the aperture function

$$q(x,y)e^{-jkr_2}e^{-j\omega t} \tag{3-14}$$

where r_2 is the distance from the fixed point P_2^o to the point (x,y) of the aperture.

We maintain that this pattern can be realized with the arrangement of Fig. 3-4b, which consists of a harmonic source s of frequency ω illuminating the aperture S, whose shape is the same as the shape of the object S in Fig. 3-4a. The aperture contains a transparency with a transmission function $q(x,y)$ and a lens L. The source is located at the point $\bar{P}_2^o$ such that its image coincides with the point P_2^o. Indeed, on the $z = 0$ plane, the amplitude of the field due to the source s is proportional to $e^{jk\bar{r}_2}$, where $\bar{r}_2$ is the distance from the source to the point (x,y). Multiplying by $q(x,y)$ and by the transmission function [Chap. 9, (5-5)] of the lens, we conclude that on the $z = 0^+$ plane, the field is proportional to

$$q(x,y)e^{jk\bar{r}_2}e^{-jk(x^2+y^2)/2f}e^{-j\omega t} \tag{3-15}$$

and since [see Chap. 9, (5-37)]

$$r_2 + \bar{r}_2 - \frac{x^2+y^2}{2f} = \overline{P_2^o\bar{P}_2^o} = \text{const}$$

(independent of x and y), the diffraction patterns due to (3-14) and (3-15) are proportional.

We note that on the surface C of a sphere centered at P_2^o, the amplitude of the field of Fig. 3-4b is proportional to $q(x,y)$.

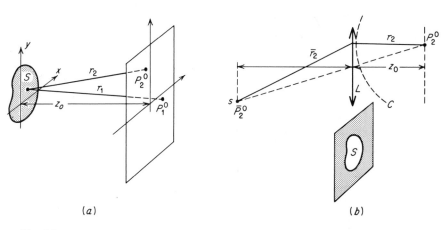

(a)   (b)

Fig. 3-4

Coherent sources

Suppose next that the sources are completely coherent, with coherence function [see (1-33)]

$$\Gamma_{ss}(P_1,P_2;\tau) = p(P_1)p^*(P_2)\rho(\tau) \qquad (3\text{-}16)$$

Since this function enters linearly in (3-10), it suffices to consider the monochromatic case

$$\rho(\tau) = e^{-j\omega\tau} \qquad \omega = kc$$

Inserting into (3-10) and (3-11), we find

$$\Gamma_{sv}(P_1,P_2{}^\circ;\tau) = e^{-j\omega\tau}p(P_1) \frac{1}{4\pi} \int_{V_\bullet} \frac{p^*(P_2)}{r_2} e^{-jkr_2} dP_2 \qquad (3\text{-}17)$$

$$\Gamma_{vv}(P_1{}^\circ,P_2{}^\circ;\tau) = e^{-j\omega\tau} \frac{1}{4\pi} \int_{V_\bullet} \frac{p(P_1)}{r_1} e^{jkr_1} dP_1 \frac{1}{4\pi} \int_{V_\bullet} \frac{p^*(P_2)}{r_2} e^{-jkr_2} dP_2$$
$$(3\text{-}18)$$

In particular,

$$E\{|\mathbf{v}(P,t)|^2\} = \left| \frac{1}{4\pi} \int_{V_\bullet} \frac{p(P_1)}{r_1} e^{jkr_1} dP_1 \right|^2 \qquad (3\text{-}19)$$

The function (3-18) is of the form (1-33). Thus the field due to coherent sources is coherent.

We also note that if the sources are deterministic and have harmonically varying density, that is,

$$s = p(P)e^{-j\omega t}$$

then the average field intensity is again given by (3-19). Completely coherent processes behave, thus, like deterministic signals.

KIRCHHOFF'S FORMULA

Consider a source-free region V_o that is bounded by the closed surface S_o. We assume that the coherence function $\Gamma(P_1,P_2;t_1,t_2)$ of a random field $\mathbf{v}$ is known for every P_1 and P_2 on S_o, and we shall determine its values $\Gamma(P_1{}^\circ,P_2{}^\circ;t_1,t_2)$ for every $P_1{}^\circ$ and $P_2{}^\circ$ in V_o. Since $\mathbf{v}$ satisfies the homogeneous wave equation, it is given by (1-3), Chap. 9. Evaluating the conjugate of this equation at $(P_2{}^\circ,t_2)$, multiplying both sides by $\mathbf{v}(P_1,t_1)$, and taking expected values, we obtain the surface integral

$$\Gamma(P_1,P_2{}^\circ;t_1,t_2)$$
$$= \frac{1}{4\pi} \int_{S_o} \left\{ \frac{\partial(1/r_2)}{\partial n} [\Gamma]_2 - \frac{1}{cr_2} \frac{\partial r_2}{\partial n} \left[\frac{\partial\Gamma}{\partial t_2} \right]_2 - \frac{1}{r_2} \left[\frac{\partial\Gamma}{\partial n} \right]_2 \right\} dS_2 \qquad (3\text{-}20)$$

where

$$[\Gamma]_2 = \Gamma\left(P_1, P_2; t_1, t_2 - \frac{r_2}{c} \right)$$

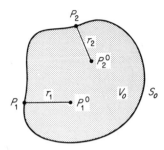

Fig. 3-5

the normal derivative $\partial/\partial n$ is with respect to the variable P_2, and (Fig. 3-5)

$$P_1, P_2 \in S_o \qquad P_2^o \in V_o \qquad r_2 = \overline{P_2 P_2^o}$$

Reasoning similarly, we conclude that for any P_1^o, P_2^o in V_o,

$$\Gamma(P_1^o, P_2^o; t_1, t_2) = \frac{1}{4\pi} \int_{S_o} \left\{ \frac{\partial(1/r_1)}{\partial n} [\Gamma]_1 - \frac{1}{cr_1} \left[\frac{\partial \Gamma}{\partial t_1} \right]_1 - \frac{1}{r_1} \left[\frac{\partial \Gamma}{\partial n} \right]_1 \right\} dS_1 \tag{3-21}$$

where

$$[\Gamma]_1 = \Gamma\left(P_1, P_2^o; t_1 - \frac{r_1}{c}, t_2\right) \qquad r_1 = \overline{P_1 P_1^o}$$

(elaborate). The integrand in (3-20) is assumed known; the integrand in (3-21) is determined from (3-20).

For monochromatic signals, the above equations reduce to (1-9), Chap. 9, with the proper changes in the various functions. The two-dimensional case can be treated similarly.

Kirchhoff's approximation

The coherence function Γ_{vv} of the diffraction field $\mathbf{v}$ due to a random plane wave $\mathbf{v}^i$ that is normally incident on a plane surface can be determined from (2-4), Chap. 9. Under the various assumptions introduced in Sec. 2, Chap. 9, this equation reduces to [see Chap. 9, (2-6a)]

$$\mathbf{v}(P^o, t) = \frac{1}{2\pi c r_o} \int_S \frac{\partial}{\partial t} \mathbf{v}^i\left(P, t - \frac{r}{c}\right) dP \tag{3-22}$$

where (Fig. 3-6)

$$P^o:(x_o, y_o, z_o) \qquad P:(x, y, 0) \qquad r_o = \overline{OP^o} \qquad r = \overline{PP^o}$$

As we know from Eq. (2-6b), Chap. 9, the above field is the same as the field due to plane sources with surface density

$$\mathring{\varrho}(x, y, t) = \frac{2}{c} \frac{\partial}{\partial t} \mathbf{v}^i(x, y, 0, t) \tag{3-23}$$

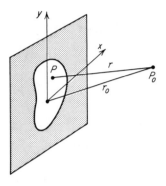

Fig. 3-6

It suffices therefore to assume that the aperture S contains a self-luminous object with density ϕ. Thus

$$\mathbf{v}(P^o,t) = \frac{1}{4\pi r_o} \int_S \phi\left(P, t - \frac{r}{c}\right) dP \tag{3-24}$$

Denoting the coherence function of the object by $\Gamma_{\varphi\varphi}(P_1,P_2;t_1,t_2)$, we conclude from (3-24), as in (3-10) and (3-11), that

$$\Gamma_{\varphi v}(P_1,P_2{}^o;t_1,t_2) = \frac{1}{4\pi r_{o2}} \int_S \Gamma_{\varphi\varphi}\left(P_1, P_2; t_1, t_2 - \frac{r_2}{c}\right) dP_2 \tag{3-25}$$

$$\Gamma_{vv}(P_1{}^o,P_2{}^o;t_1,t_2) = \frac{1}{4\pi r_{o1}} \int_S \Gamma_{\varphi v}\left(P_1, P_2{}^o; t_1 - \frac{r_1}{c}, t_2\right) dP_1 \tag{3-26}$$

The variables appearing above are shown in Fig. 3-7.

With $\Gamma_{ii}(P_1,P_2;t_1,t_2)$ the coherence function of the incoming wave on the plane $z = 0$, we see from (3-23) and Chap. 8, (3-20), that

$$\Gamma_{\varphi\varphi} = \frac{4}{c^2} \frac{\partial^2 \Gamma_{ii}}{\partial t_1\, \partial t_2} \tag{3-27}$$

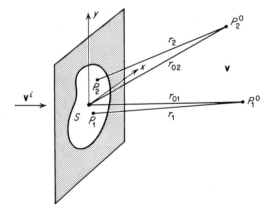

Fig. 3-7

Therefore, in order to evaluate Γ_{vv} for the diffracted field, we replace in (3-25) the function $\Gamma_{\varphi\varphi}$ by the right side of (3-27) and insert the resulting $\Gamma_{\varphi v}$ into (3-26).

Comment If the object is a self-luminous line along the x axis with line density $\mathring{\phi}(x,t)$ and coherence function $\Gamma_{\varphi\varphi}(x_1,x_2;t_1,t_2)$, then (3-25) to (3-28) still hold, provided that the integrals are one-dimensional with $dP = dx$. The resulting coherence functions $\Gamma_{\varphi v}$ and Γ_{vv} are then independent of y. The same reasoning applies for slit apertures. (See also Example 4-2.)

If the object $\mathring{\phi}$ is monochromatic

$$\Gamma_{\varphi\varphi} = \Gamma_{\varphi\varphi}(P_1,P_2)e^{-j\omega\tau} \qquad \omega = k\mathbf{c} \qquad \tau = t_1 - t_2$$

then

$$\Gamma_{\varphi v} = \Gamma_{\varphi v}(P_1,P_2{}^o)e^{-j\omega\tau} \qquad \Gamma_{vv} = \Gamma_{vv}(P_1{}^o,P_2{}^o)e^{-j\omega\tau}$$

In this case, (3-25) and (3-26) yield

$$\Gamma_{\varphi v}(P_1,P_2{}^o) = \frac{1}{4\pi r_{o2}} \int_S \Gamma_{\varphi\varphi}(P_1,P_2)e^{-jkr_2}\, dP_2 \tag{3-28}$$

$$\Gamma_{vv}(P_1{}^o,P_2{}^o) = \frac{1}{4\pi r_{o1}} \int_S \Gamma_{\varphi v}(P_1,P_2{}^o)e^{jkr_1}\, dP_1 \tag{3-29}$$

and (3-27) takes the form

$$\Gamma_{\varphi\varphi}(P_1,P_2) = -4k^2\Gamma_{ii}(P_1,P_2) \tag{3-30}$$

Transparent aperture

If a thin film with attenuation $a(P)$ and delay $\tau(P)$ is placed on the aperture S, then the field $\mathbf{v}^+$ at the right side of the film is given by [see Chap. 9, (2-2)]

$$\mathbf{v}^+(P,t) = a(P)\mathbf{v}^i[P, t - \tau(P)] \qquad P:(x,y) \tag{3-31}$$

where $\mathbf{v}^i$ is the incident wave. With Γ^+ the coherence function of this field, we conclude from the above that

$$\Gamma^+(P_1,P_2;t_1,t_2) = a(P_1)a(P_2)\Gamma_{ii}[P_1, P_2; t_1 - \tau(P_1), t_2 - \tau(P_2)] \tag{3-32}$$

for every P_1 and P_2 on S. The function Γ_{vv} of the resulting diffraction field can then be determined as in the film-free case by replacing Γ_{ii} by Γ^+.

Lenses As we know from Sec. 5, Chap. 9, a spherical lens of focal length $\mathbf{f}$ is equivalent to a transparency with delay

$$\tau(\rho) = \tau_o - \frac{\rho^2}{2\mathbf{f}\mathbf{c}} \qquad \rho = \sqrt{x^2 + y^2} \tag{3-33}$$

Neglecting the constant delay τ_o, we see from (3-32) that the coherence function Γ^+ of field $\mathbf{v}^+$ at the right side of the lens is given by

$$\Gamma^+(P_1,P_2;t_1,t_2) = \Gamma_{ii}\left(P_1,\, P_2;\, t_1 + \frac{\rho_1{}^2}{2\mathbf{f}\mathbf{c}},\, t_2 + \frac{\rho_2{}^2}{2\mathbf{f}\mathbf{c}}\right) \tag{3-34}$$

For the monochromatic case

$$\Gamma_{ii}(P_1,P_2;\tau) = \Gamma_{ii}(P_1,P_2)e^{-j\omega\tau}$$

(3-34) yields

$$\Gamma^+(P_1,P_2) = \Gamma_{ii}(P_1,P_2)e^{-jk(\rho_1{}^2-\rho_2{}^2)/2f} \tag{3-35}$$

From the above it follows that if the incoming wave $\mathbf{v}^i$ is coherent (incoherent) on the plane $z = 0$, the same is true for the field $\mathbf{v}^+$.

To conclude, we note that the integrals (3-28) and (3-29) can be simplified with the application of the various approximations introduced in Secs. 3 and 4, Chap. 9. We shall carry out the details for the Fraunhofer region (see also Prob. 11-15).

4. FRAUNHOFER DIFFRACTION

Consider a monochromatic object on the $z = 0$ plane with surface density ϕ and coherence function

$$\Gamma_{\varphi\varphi}(P_1,P_2;\tau) = \Gamma(x_1,y_1;x_2,y_2)e^{-j\omega\tau} \qquad \omega = k\mathbf{c} \tag{4-1}$$

We denote by $\bar{\Gamma}$ the two-dimensional Fourier transform of Γ with respect to the variables x_2, y_2:

$$\Gamma(x_1,y_1;x_2,y_2) \overset{x_2,y_2}{\Longleftrightarrow} \bar{\Gamma}(x_1,y_1;u_2,v_2) \tag{4-2}$$

We denote by $\bar{\bar{\Gamma}}$ the transform of $\bar{\Gamma}$ with respect to x_1, y_1:

$$\bar{\Gamma}(x_1,y_1;u_2,v_2) \overset{x_1,y_1}{\Longleftrightarrow} \bar{\bar{\Gamma}}(u_1,v_1;u_2,v_2) \tag{4-3}$$

The given object produces a field $\mathbf{v}(P_o,t)$ at a point $P_o{:}(x_o,y_o,z_o)$ specified by its distance r_o from the origin and the directional cosines $\alpha = x_o/r_o$, $\beta = y_o/r_o$. The coherence function of $\mathbf{v}$ is of the form

$$\Gamma_{vv}(P_1{}^o,P_2{}^o;\tau) = \Gamma_{vv}(\alpha_1,\beta_1;\alpha_2,\beta_2)e^{-j\omega\tau} \tag{4-4}$$

where its dependence on the distances r_{o1}, r_{o2} of the points $P_1{}^o$ and $P_2{}^o$ from the origin is omitted.

Assuming that the observation points are in the Fraunhofer region of the object, we have [see Chap. 9, (4-3)]

$$r_2 = r_{o2} - (\alpha_2 x_2 + \beta_2 y_2)$$

where r_2 is the distance from P_{2° to the point (x_2, y_2) of the object. With

$$A_1 = \frac{e^{jkr_{o1}}}{4\pi r_{o1}} \qquad A_2 = \frac{e^{jkr_{o2}}}{4\pi r_{o2}} \tag{4-5}$$

we conclude from (3-28) that

$$\Gamma_{\varphi v}(x_1, y_1; \alpha_2, \beta_2) = A_2^* \iint_S \Gamma(x_1, y_1; x_2, y_2) e^{jk(\alpha_2 x_2 + \beta_2 y_2)} \, dx_2 \, dy_2 \tag{4-6}$$

Hence

$$\Gamma_{\varphi v}(x_1, y_1; \alpha_2, \beta_2) = A_2^* \bar{\Gamma}(x_1, y_1; -k\alpha_2, -k\beta_2) \tag{4-7}$$

Reasoning similarly, we find [see (3-29)]

$$\Gamma_{vv}(\alpha_1, \beta_1; \alpha_2, \beta_2) = A_1 \iint_S \Gamma_{\varphi v}(x_1, y_1; \alpha_2, \beta_2) e^{-jk(\alpha_1 x_1 + \beta_1 y_1)} \, dx_1 \, dy_1 \tag{4-8}$$

Thus, the coherence function of the far field is given by

$$\Gamma_{vv}(\alpha_1, \beta_1; \alpha_2, \beta_2) = A_1 A_2^* \bar{\bar{\Gamma}}(k\alpha_1, k\beta_1; -k\alpha_2, -k\beta_2) \tag{4-9}$$

In particular,

$$E\{|\mathbf{v}(P, t)|^2\} = \frac{1}{(4\pi r_o)^2} \bar{\bar{\Gamma}}(k\alpha, k\beta; -k\alpha, -k\beta) \tag{4-10}$$

If the diffraction field is due not to a self-luminous object but to an incidence wave with coherence function

$$\Gamma_{ii}(x_1, y_1, z_1; x_2, y_2, z_2) e^{-j\omega\tau}$$

then the preceding results still hold, provided that $\Gamma(x_1, y_1; x_2, y_2)$ is replaced by

$$-4k^2 \Gamma_{ii}(x_1, y_1, 0; x_2, y_2, 0)$$

Incoherent objects

Suppose that the object S is completely incoherent with average intensity $q(x, y)$. We then have [see (1-28)]

$$\Gamma(x_1, y_1; x_2, y_2) = q(x_1, y_1) \delta(x_1 - x_2) \delta(y_1 - y_2) \tag{4-11}$$

Taking transforms of both sides with respect to (x_2, y_2), we obtain [see (4-2) and Chap. 4, (1-3)]

$$\bar{\Gamma}(x_1, y_1; u_2, v_2) = q(x_1, y_1) e^{-j(x_1 u_2 + y_1 v_2)} \tag{4-12}$$

With $Q(u, v)$ the Fourier transform of $q(x, y)$, i.e.,

$$q(x, y) \Leftrightarrow Q(u, v)$$

it follows from (4-12) and the shifting theorem that the function $\bar{\Gamma}$ in (4-3) is given by

$$\bar{\Gamma}(u_1,v_1;u_2,v_2) = Q(u_1 + u_2, v_1 + v_2) \tag{4-13}$$

From the above and (4-9) we conclude that

$$\Gamma_{vv}(\alpha_1,\beta_1;\alpha_2,\beta_2) = A_1 A_2^* Q[k(\alpha_1 - \alpha_2), k(\beta_1 - \beta_2)] \tag{4-14}$$

Thus on the surface of a sphere centered at the origin, the far field of an incoherent object is stationary in space. Its average intensity

$$E\{|\mathbf{v}(P,t)|^2\} = \frac{Q(0,0)}{(4\pi r_o)^2} = \frac{1}{(4\pi r_o)^2} \iint_S q(x,y)\, dx\, dy \tag{4-15}$$

is constant.

Coherent objects

We next assume that the object is completely coherent, with coherence function [see (1-33)]

$$\Gamma(x_1,y_1;x_2,y_2) = p(x_1,y_1)p^*(x_2,y_2) \tag{4-16}$$

If $P(u,v)$ is the transform of $p(x,y)$, i.e.,

$$p(x,y) \Leftrightarrow P(u,v) \qquad \text{then} \qquad p^*(x,y) \Leftrightarrow P^*(-u,-v) \tag{4-17}$$

Hence

$$\Gamma = p(x_1,y_1)P^*(-u_2, -v_2) \qquad \bar{\Gamma} = P(u_1,v_1)P^*(-u_2,-v_2) \tag{4-18}$$

From the above and (4-9) it follows that

$$\Gamma_{vv}(\alpha_1,\beta_1;\alpha_2,\beta_2) = A_1 A_2^* P(k\alpha_1,k\beta_1)P^*(k\alpha_2,k\beta_2) \tag{4-19}$$

and

$$E\{|\mathbf{v}(P,t)|^2\} = \left| \frac{P(k\alpha,k\beta)}{4\pi r_o} \right|^2 \tag{4-20}$$

We again note that if the object is deterministic with amplitude $p(x,y)$, then the coherence function of the resulting far field is given by (4-19).

Stationary objects

Suppose finally that the object is stationary in space with coherence function [see (1-36)]

$$\Gamma(x_1,y_1;x_2,y_2) = w(x_1 - x_2, y_1 - y_2) \tag{4-21}$$

Denoting the transform of $w(x,y)$ by $W(u,v)$, i.e.,

$$w(x,y) \Leftrightarrow W(u,v)$$

we conclude that

$$\bar{\Gamma} = e^{-j(x_1 u_2 + y_1 v_2)} W(-u_2, -v_2)$$
$$\bar{\bar{\Gamma}} = 4\pi^2 \delta(u_1 + u_2) \delta(v_1 + v_2) W(-u_2, -v_2)$$

(4-22)

and (4-9) yields

$$\Gamma_{vv}(\alpha_1, \beta_1; \alpha_2, \beta_2) = 4\pi^2 A_1 A_2^* \delta[k(\alpha_1 - \alpha_2)] \delta[k(\beta_1 - \beta_2)] W(k\alpha_2, k\beta_2)$$

(4-23)

The above shows that the far field of a stationary object is completely incoherent on the surface of a sphere. This is, of course, only an approximation and is based on the assumption that (4-21) holds everywhere on the $z = 0$ plane. For objects of finite size, it is not true.

Example 4-1 We shall determine the coherence function of the far field of a circular object.

a. Suppose first that the object is completely incoherent with constant average intensity

$$q(x,y) = \begin{cases} 1 & \sqrt{x^2 + y^2} < a \\ 0 & \text{otherwise} \end{cases}$$

(4-24)

We then have [see Chap. 3, (4-31)]

$$q(x,y) \Leftrightarrow 2\pi a \frac{J_1(a\sqrt{u^2 + v^2})}{\sqrt{u^2 + v^2}}$$

and for $r_{o1} = r_{o2} = r$, (4-14) yields

$$\Gamma_{vv}(\alpha_1, \beta_1; \alpha_2, \beta_2) = \frac{a J_1(ka\sqrt{(\alpha_1 - \alpha_2)^2 + (\beta_1 - \beta_2)^2})}{8\pi k r^2 \sqrt{(\alpha_1 - \alpha_2)^2 + (\beta_1 - \beta_2)^2}}$$

(4-25)

b. If the object is completely coherent with $p(x,y)$, as in (4-24), then (4-19) yields

$$\Gamma_{vv}(\alpha_1, \beta_1; \alpha_2, \beta_2) = \frac{a^2 J_1(ka\sqrt{\alpha_1^2 + \beta_1^2}) J_1(ka\sqrt{\alpha_2^2 + \beta_2^2})}{4k^2 r^2 \sqrt{\alpha_1^2 + \beta_1^2} \sqrt{\alpha_2^2 + \beta_2^2}}$$

(4-26)

Example 4-2 (Line sources) Consider a monochromatic line source on the segment $(-a,a)$ of the x axis (Fig. 4-1) with line density $\phi(x,t)$ and coherence function

$$E\{\phi(x_1, t + \tau)\phi^*(x_2, t)\} = \Gamma(x_1, x_2)e^{-j\omega\tau}$$

Since the resulting field is independent of y, we obtain, from (3-28) and (3-29),

$$\Gamma_{\varphi v}(x_1; \alpha_2) = \frac{1}{4\pi r_{o2}} \int_{-a}^{a} \Gamma(x_1, x_2)e^{-jkr_2} \, dx_2$$
$$\Gamma_{vv}(\alpha_1; \alpha_2) = \frac{1}{4\pi r_{o1}} \int_{-a}^{a} \Gamma_{\varphi v}(x_1; \alpha_2)e^{jkr_1} \, dx_1$$

(4-27)

In the Fraunhofer region, the above yield

$$\Gamma_{\varphi v}(x_1;\alpha_2) = A_2^* \int_{-a}^{a} \Gamma(x_1,x_2)e^{jk\alpha_2 x_2}\,dx_2$$

$$\Gamma_{vv}(\alpha_1;\alpha_2) = A_1 \int_{-a}^{a} \Gamma_{\varphi v}(x_1;\alpha_2)e^{-jk\alpha_1 x_1}\,dx_1 \tag{4-28}$$

With

$$\Gamma(x_1,x_2) \overset{x_2}{\leftrightarrow} \overline{\Gamma}(x_1,u_2) \overset{x_1}{\leftrightarrow} \overline{\overline{\Gamma}}(u_1,u_2)$$

we conclude that

$$\Gamma_{\varphi v}(x_1,\alpha_2) = A_2^*\overline{\Gamma}(x_1,-k\alpha_2) \qquad \Gamma_{vv}(\alpha_1,\alpha_2) = A_1 A_2^* \overline{\overline{\Gamma}}(k\alpha_1,-k\alpha_2) \tag{4-29}$$

If the object is completely incoherent

$$\Gamma(x_1,x_2) = q(x_1)\delta(x_1 - x_2) \qquad q(x) \leftrightarrow Q(u)$$

then (4-28) yields

$$\Gamma_{vv}(\alpha_1,\alpha_2) = A_1 A_2^* Q[k(\alpha_1 - \alpha_2)] \tag{4-30}$$

As a special case, we assume that $q(x) = q = $ constant for $|x| < a$. We then have

$$Q(u) = \frac{2q \sin au}{u}$$

Hence

$$\Gamma_{vv}(\alpha_1,\alpha_2) = 2q A_1 A_2^* \frac{\sin ak(\alpha_1 - \alpha_2)}{k(\alpha_1 - \alpha_2)}$$

Comments

1. As we see from (4-9), the coherence function $\Gamma_{vv}(P_1^o,P_2^o)$ is proportional to the transform $\overline{\overline{\Gamma}}$ on the surface of a sphere centered at the origin. With

$$r_{oi} = z_o + \frac{\rho_i^2}{2z_o} \qquad \rho_i = \sqrt{x_{oi}^2 + y_{oi}^2}$$

we conclude that on the plane $z = z_o$, Γ_{vv} is proportional to

$$e^{jk(\rho_1^2 - \rho_2^2)/2z_o}\overline{\overline{\Gamma}}\left(\frac{kx_{o1}}{z_o}, \frac{ky_{o1}}{z_o}; -\frac{kx_{o2}}{z_o}, -\frac{ky_{o2}}{z_o}\right) \tag{4-31}$$

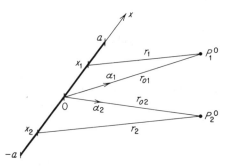

Fig. 4-1

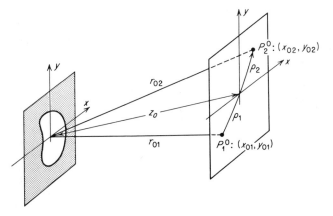

Fig. 4-2

where (Fig. 4-2)

$$P_1{}^o:(x_{o1}, y_{o1}, z_o) \qquad P_2{}^o:(x_{o2}, y_{o2}, z_o)$$

2. If an object is coherent, with coherence function

$$p(x_1, y_1) p^*(x_2, y_2)$$

as in (4-16), then $\Gamma_{vv}(P_1{}^o, P_2{}^o)$ takes significant values only if both points $P_1{}^o$ and $P_2{}^o$ are in a small cone determined by the "duration" of the Fourier transform $P(u, v)$ of $p(x, y)$. If, however, the object is completely incoherent with average intensity $q(x, y)$, then Γ_{vv} takes significant values when the *difference* of the directional cosines of the points $P_1{}^o$ and $P_2{}^o$ is small. In the latter case, an arbitrary point in space is surrounded by a coherent region specified by the duration of $Q(u, v)$, and all information about the object is contained in this region. One might, thus, say that a coherent object is visible only in a small region; an incoherent object is visible everywhere.

Example 4-3 (Young's experiment) An opaque screen D_1 with two circular openings S_1 and S_2 is illuminated by an extended monochromatic random source S, as in Fig. 4-3. We shall determine the intensity of the far field **v** on a screen D_2 that is parallel to D_1.

If the radius a of the circles S_1 and S_2 is sufficiently small, then the incident wave can be considered as completely coherent on S_1 or S_2. With

$$\Gamma_{ii}(P_1, P_2) = \text{const} \qquad \text{for } P_1 \in S_1, P_2 \in S_2$$

we conclude that, within a factor, the coherence function of the equivalent sources at the screen is given by [see (3-30)]

$$-4k^2 \Gamma_{ii}(P_1, P_2) = \Gamma(P_1, P_2) = \begin{cases} 1 & P_1, P_2 \in S_1 \quad \text{or} \quad P_1, P_2 \in S_2 \\ \gamma & P_1 \in S_1, P_2 \in S_2 \\ \gamma^* & P_1 \in S_2, P_2 \in S_1 \end{cases}$$

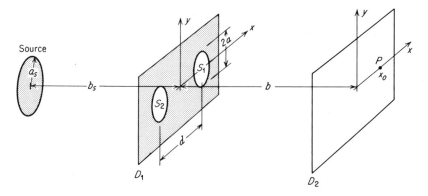

Fig. 4-3

where $P_1:(x_1,y_1)$, $P_2:(x_2,y_2)$.   With

$$Y(u,v) = 2\pi a \frac{J_1(a\sqrt{u^2+v^2})}{\sqrt{u^2+v^2}}$$

the Fourier transform of a circle, we have

$$\bar{\Gamma}(x_1,y_1;u_2,v_2) = \begin{cases} Y(u_2,v_2)(e^{-ju_2d/2} + \gamma e^{ju_2d/2}) & (x_1,y_1) \in S_1 \\ Y(u_2,v_2)(e^{ju_2d/2} + \gamma^* e^{-ju_2d/2}) & (x_1,y_1) \in S_2 \end{cases}$$

Hence

$$\bar{\Gamma} = 2Y(u_1,v_1)Y(u_2,v_2)\left[\cos\frac{(u_1+u_2)d}{2} + \mathrm{Re}\ \gamma e^{-j(u_1-u_2)d/2}\right]$$

Inserting into (4-10), we thus conclude that along the x axis of the observation screen $D_2(\beta = 0)$ the intensity of the diffracted field is given by

$$E\{|\mathbf{v}(P,t)|^2\} = \frac{1}{2}\left[\frac{J_1(ak\alpha)}{kb\alpha}\right]^2(1 + \mathrm{Re}\ \gamma e^{-jk\alpha d}) \tag{4-32}$$

where b is the distance between the two screens, and $\alpha = x_0/b$.

If the light source S is an incoherent disc of radius a_s that is a distance b_s from D_1, then (see Example 4-1)

$$\gamma = 2\frac{J_1(ka_sd/b_s)}{ka_sd/b_s}$$

Generalization   We now assume that the screen D_1 contains n openings of the same shape such that S_i is obtained by a translation of the region S_o as in Fig. 4-4.   If S_o is of sufficiently small dimensions, then

$$\Gamma(P_i,P_m) = \gamma_{im} \qquad \text{for } P_i \in S_i,\ P_m \in S_m$$

With

$$Y(u,v) = \iint\limits_{S_o} e^{-j(ux+vy)}\,dx\,dy$$

it is easy to show that

$$\bar{\Gamma}(x_1, y_1; u_2, v_2) = Y(u_2, v_2) \sum_{m=1}^{n} \gamma_{im} e^{-j(u_2 d_m + v_2 e_m)} \qquad (x_1, y_1) \in S_i$$

Hence

$$\bar{\bar{\Gamma}}(u_1, v_1; u_2, v_2) = Y(u_1, v_1) Y(u_2, v_2) \sum_{i,m=1}^{n} \gamma_{im} e^{-j(u_1 d_i + v_1 e_i + u_2 d_m + v_2 e_m)}$$

and (4-10) yields

$$E\{|\mathbf{v}(P,t)|^2\} = \left| \frac{Y(k\alpha, k\beta)}{4\pi r_o} \right|^2 \sum_{i,m=1}^{n} \gamma_{im} e^{-jk[\alpha(d_i - d_m) + \beta(e_i - e_m)]}$$

The above quantity is, of course, real because $\gamma_{im} = \gamma_{mi}^*$.

Polychromatic signals

Consider finally a spectrally pure object with coherence function

$$\Gamma_{\varphi\varphi} = \Gamma(x_1, y_1; x_2, y_2) \rho(\tau)$$

With $s(\omega)$ the Fourier transform of $\rho(\tau)$ and $\bar{\bar{\Gamma}}$ as in (4-3), we conclude from

$$\rho(\tau) = \frac{1}{2\pi} \int_{-\infty}^{\infty} s(-\omega) e^{-j\omega\tau} \, d\omega$$

and the linearity of Fourier transforms, that for $r_{o1} = r_{o2} = r_o$ [see (4-9)]

$$\Gamma_{vv}(\alpha_1, \beta_1; \alpha_2, \beta_2; \tau)$$
$$= \frac{1}{32\pi^3 r_o^2} \int_{-\infty}^{\infty} \bar{\bar{\Gamma}}\left(\frac{\omega\alpha_1}{c}, \frac{\omega\beta_1}{c}; -\frac{\omega\alpha_2}{c}, -\frac{\omega\beta_2}{c} \right) s(-\omega) e^{-j\omega\tau} \, d\omega$$

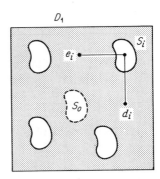

Fig. 4-4

PROBLEMS

10-1. Show that if a process $f(P,t)$ is completely coherent, then we can find a deterministic function $p(P)$ and a random signal $z(t)$ independent of P such that

$$f(P,t) = p(P)z(t)$$

in the sense

$$E\{|f(P,t) - p(P)z(t)|^2\} = 0$$

Hint: With P_o a fixed point, choose

$$z(t) = \frac{f(P_o,t)}{\Gamma(P_o,P_o)} \qquad p(P) = \Gamma(P,P_o)$$

10-2. Show that if a self-luminous plane object S is incoherent with coherence function $q(x_1,y_1)\delta(x_1 - x_2)\delta(y_1 - y_2)\rho(\tau)$, then the average intensity of the resulting far field, which is distance r from S, is given by

$$E\{|g|^2\} = \frac{-4\rho''(0)}{(4\pi rc)^2} \iint\limits_{S} q(x,y) \, dx \, dy$$

10-3. (a) Show that if the aperture function $f(P)$ is completely coherent, then the near zone and the Fraunhofer cone are the same as for the deterministic case.

(b) If $f(P)$ is partially coherent with

$$\Gamma(P_1,P_2) = 0 \qquad \text{for } \overline{P_1P_2} > \delta$$

then the near zone is reduced to the interval $(0,\delta^2/4\lambda)$, and the angle of the Fraunhofer cone equals λ/δ (Fig. P10-3).

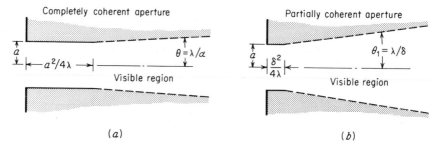

Fig. P10-3

10-4. A circular aperture of radius a is illuminated by a plane wave whose amplitude is a random signal $\phi(t)$, coherence function is $\Gamma(\tau)$, and power spectrum is $S(\omega)$. Show that the average intensity of the resulting far field g is given by

$$E\{|g|^2\} = \frac{B}{2\pi} \int_{-\infty}^{\infty} J_1^2 \left(\frac{a\rho_o}{cr_o}\omega\right) S(\omega) \, d\omega \qquad B = \left[\frac{a(1 + \gamma_o)}{2\rho_o}\right]^2$$

Hint: Use Prob. 9-8 and Chap. 8, (4-18).

Special case: If

$$\Gamma(\tau) = A_1 e^{i\omega_1\tau} + A_2 e^{i\omega_2\tau}$$

then

$$E\{|\mathbf{g}|^2\} = B\left[\left|A_1J_1\left(\frac{a\rho_o}{cr_o}\omega_1\right)\right|^2 + \left|A_2J_1\left(\frac{a\rho_o}{cr_o}\omega_2\right)\right|^2\right]$$

10-5. Consider a monochromatic source with coherence function [see (4-1)]

$$\Gamma(x_1,y_1;x_2,y_2) = \begin{cases} w(x_1 - x_2, y_1 - y_2) & (x_1,y_1) \text{ and } (x_2,y_2) \text{ in } R \\ 0 & \text{otherwise} \end{cases}$$

(stationary in R). We assume that $w(x,y) = 0$ for $|x| > a$ or $|y| > a$. Show that if a is small compared with the dimensions of R, then the coherence function of the far field $\mathbf{v}$ [see (4-9)] is given by

$$\Gamma_{vv} = A_1 A_2^* P_R[k(\alpha_1 - \alpha_2),\ k(\beta_1 - \beta_2)]W(k\alpha_2, k\beta_2)$$

and its intensity is given by

$$E\{|\mathbf{v}|^2\} = \frac{R_o}{(4\pi r_o)^2} W(k\alpha, k\beta)$$

where R_o is the area of R, $W(u,v)$ is the transform of $w(x,y)$, and

$$P_R(u,v) = \iint\limits_R e^{-j(ux+vy)}\, dx\, dy$$

11
APPLICATIONS

In the last two chapters we dealt with general properties of optical fields. We now discuss various applications, stressing the system interpretation of image formation. In these examples, we avoid detailed description of special topics, and use mainly earlier results.

1. HOLOGRAPHY†

Consider an object f located in the region $z < 0$ of the space and illuminated by a light source S. We shall assume that the source is harmonic, i.e., that its time dependence is of the form

$$e^{-j\omega t}$$

However, all our conclusions will also hold if the source is a completely coherent monochromatic process.

† D. Gabor, *Nature*, May, 1948; *Proc. Roy. Soc. (London)*, Ser. A, vol. 197, 1949, p. 454; *Proc. Phys. Soc.*, vol. 64, sec. B, 1951, p. 449.

It is known that† if the diffracted field $g(x,y,z)$ generated by the object f is given everywhere on the plane $z = 0$, then it is uniquely determined in the region $z > 0$. If, therefore, we can somehow record the function

$$g(x,y,0) = D(x,y) \tag{1-1}$$

on a photographic plate and then reconstruct $g(x,y,0)$ by illuminating the plate with a plane wave, then the reconstructed field $g_r(x,y,z)$ will equal $g(x,y,z)$. Hence, an observer looking at the plate will see the object f. This is the principle of holography [s6].‡

We denote by $T(x,y)$ the transmission function of the developed plate (hologram). In general, $T(x,y)$ is a nonlinear function of the *intensity* of the incident field. However, if the variation of $g(x,y,0)$ is not too great, then this function can be approximated by a straight line. Omitting then, as we shall often do, a proportionality factor, we assume that

$$T(x,y) = |g(x,y,0)|^2 = |D(x,y)|^2 \tag{1-2}$$

We have thus a record not of the field g but of its intensity $|g|^2$. Therefore the effect due to the original object cannot be recreated because the phase of g is lost. As we shall presently see, this difficulty can be overcome if the plate is illuminated not only by the object, but also directly by the source.

FORMATION OF THE HOLOGRAM

Consider the arrangement of Fig. 1-1a, which consists of the source S, the object f (transparent or solid), and the hologram plate h. We denote by $U(x,y)$ the field reaching the plate directly from the source, and denote by $D(x,y)$ the field coming from the object f. The direct field U is usually much larger than the diffracted field D:

$$|U(x,y)| \gg |D(x,y)| \tag{1-3}$$

However, in the following analysis, no use will be made of this condition.

With $g(x,y,z)$ the total field, we thus have

$$g(x,y,0) = U(x,y) + D(x,y) \tag{1-4}$$

Inserting into (1-2), we conclude that the transmission function $T(x,y)$

---

† If $g(x,y,z)$ is determined from Kirchhoff's formula [Chap. 9, (1-9)], then the boundary value of its normal derivative is also needed. However, the functions g and $\partial g / \partial n$ are not independent. It can be shown that if g is known, then $\partial g / \partial n$ is uniquely determined.

‡ E. N. Leith and J. Upatnieks, *J. Opt. Soc. Am.*, vol. 52, 1962, p. 1123; and L. J. Cutrona, E. N. Leith, C. J. Palermo, and L. J. Porcello, *IRE Trans. Inform. Theory*, vol. 6, 1960, pp. 386–400.

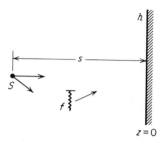 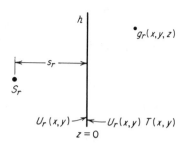

Fig. 1-1

of the hologram is now given by

$$T(x,y) = |U + D|^2 = |U|^2 + U^*D + UD^* + |D|^2 \tag{1-5}$$

This expression contains the term D, that is, the magnitude *and phase* of the diffracted field. Therefore, all information about the object available to an observer in the region $z > 0$ is stored on the plate, provided that the term D can be separated from the other terms in (1-5).

RECONSTRUCTION OF THE OBJECT

We now illuminate the developed plate by a source S_r (Fig. 1-1b), creating thus a new field $g_r(x,y,z)$. If the field due to this source equals $U_r(x,y)$ at $z = 0^-$ then at $z = 0^+$ it is given by

$$g_r(x,y,0^+) = U_r(x,y)T(x,y) \tag{1-6}$$

Inserting (1-5) into the above, we conclude that on the $z = 0^+$ plane, the reconstructed field consists of the following four terms:

Source: $V_s = U_r|U|^2$

Object: $V_o = U_r U^* D$

Conjugate object: $V_c = U_r U D^*$ $\qquad$ (1-7)

Ambiguity term: $V_a = U_r|D|^2$

The meaning of these terms will be discussed presently.

We shall assume that S and S_r are point sources on the z axis at distances s and s_r, respectively, from the hologram. Other arrangements are often used to separate the direct beam from the diffracted field, or the object from the conjugate object; however, they lead essentially to similar conclusions. The effect of extended sources is considered in Prob. 11-3.

Introducing the Fresnel approximation for the field of a point source, we thus have

$$U(x,y) = Ae^{jk\rho^2/2s} \qquad U_r(x,y) = A_re^{jk\rho^2/2s_r} \qquad \rho = \sqrt{x^2 + y^2}$$

$$(1\text{-}8)$$

The constants A and A_r will be assumed real.

Source

From (1-7) and (1-8) it follows that the source term V_s is given by

$$V_s(x,y) = A_rA^2e^{jk\rho^2/2s_r} \qquad (1\text{-}9)$$

This is the field due to a point source at S_r (Fig. 1-2a).

Object

The second and most important term V_o takes the form

$$V_o(x,y) = A_rAe^{j(k\rho^2/2)(1/s_r-1/s)}D(x,y) \qquad (1\text{-}10)$$

To interpret the above, we note that if the hologram is replaced by a lens L_1 of focal length f_1 such that

$$\frac{1}{f_1} = \frac{1}{s} - \frac{1}{s_r} \qquad (1\text{-}11)$$

then on the $z = 0^+$ plane the field coming from the object f will be proportional to $V_o(x,y)$ because the transmission function of the lens equals the exponential term in (1-10). Hence, in the reconstruction process,

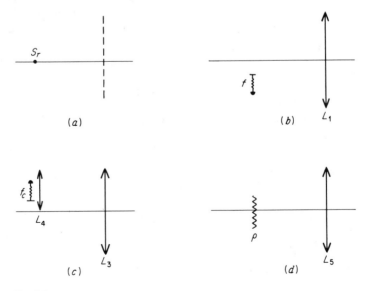

(a)

(b) L_1

(c) L_3 L_4

(d) L_5

Fig. 1-2

the term $V_o(x,y)$ creates the same effect as the object f seen through the lens L_1 (Fig. 1-2b).

If $s_r = s$, that is, if the reconstruction source S_r is placed in the position of the original source S, then the lens effect is eliminated.

We note that although the hologram is a plane surface, an observer moving about in the region $z > 0$ can "see" the sides of the object f.

Scaling Suppose now that the hologram is scaled down by a factor α; a new hologram h_α results with transmission function

$$T_\alpha(x,y) = T(\alpha x, \alpha y) \tag{1-12}$$

As we shall presently show, in order to recover the original object f without distortion, we must illuminate the reduced hologram h_α with a source S_α of frequency

$$\omega_\alpha = \alpha\omega \tag{1-13}$$

In the reconstruction of $T_\alpha(x,y)$ with the source S_α, the object term takes the form

$$U_\alpha(x,y)U^*(\alpha x, \alpha y)D(\alpha x, \alpha y) = A_\alpha A e^{j\alpha k\rho^2/2s\alpha}e^{-jk\alpha^2\rho^2/2s}D(\alpha x, \alpha y) \tag{1-14}$$

where s_α is the distance of the source S_α from the hologram, and

$$U_\alpha(x,y) = A_\alpha e^{j\alpha k\rho^2/2s\alpha}$$

is the field due to this source. This expression equals the function $D(\alpha x, \alpha y)$ multiplied by the transmission function of a lens L_2 of focal length $\mathbf{f}_2$ given by

$$\frac{1}{\mathbf{f}_2} = \frac{\alpha}{s} - \frac{1}{s_\alpha} \tag{1-15}$$

To complete the interpretation of (1-14), it remains to determine an object f_α of frequency $\alpha\omega$ such that its field on the $z = 0$ plane equals $D(\alpha x, \alpha y)$. For this purpose we shall need the following property of optical fields:

Theorem If the source distribution (volume density)

$$s(x,y,z)e^{-j\omega t}$$

produces the field

$$g(x,y,z)e^{-j\omega t}$$

then the source distribution

$$\alpha^2 s(\alpha x, \alpha y, \alpha z)e^{-j\alpha\omega t}$$

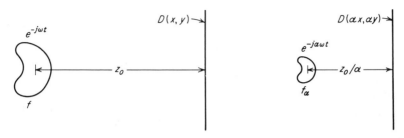

Fig. 1-3

will produce the field

$$g(\alpha x, \alpha y, \alpha z)e^{-j\alpha\omega t}$$

In other words, an optical field is not changed if the space coordinates and the wavelength of the sources are reduced by the same factor. The scaling must, of course, include all diffracting objects (boundary conditions). This theorem follows readily from the wave equation (see Prob. 11-1).

From the above we conclude that if all the dimensions of the arrangement of Fig. 1-3 are reduced by a factor α and the frequency of the source is multiplied by α, then the diffracted field coming from the new object f_α will equal $D(\alpha x, \alpha y)$ (within a factor). Hence, in the reconstruction process, the observer sees the reduced object brought closer to the hologram and observed through the lens L_2. If $s_\alpha = s/\alpha$, then the lens effect is eliminated.

Distortion   If the reconstruction frequency equals $\beta\omega$, and β is different from the scaling factor α, then the above no longer holds. To examine the nature of the term V_o, we write the transmission function $T(\alpha x, \alpha y)$ of the reduced hologram in the form

$$T(\alpha x, \alpha y) = T(\gamma\beta x, \gamma\beta y) \qquad \gamma = \frac{\alpha}{\beta}$$

Using the preceding results, we conclude that it suffices to examine the effect of replacing $T(x,y)$ by $T(\gamma x, \gamma y)$, keeping the frequency constant.

Our problem now is to find an object such that if it is illuminated by a source of frequency ω, it produces the field $D(\gamma x, \gamma y)$ on the plane $z = 0$.

We shall assume first that f is a two-dimensional object on the plane $z = -z_o$ (Fig. 1-4), and that it generates the field [see Chap. 9, (3-49)]

$$D(x,y) = \iint_S f(\xi,\eta)e^{jk\frac{(\xi-x)^2+(\eta-y)^2}{2z_o}} \, d\xi \, d\eta$$

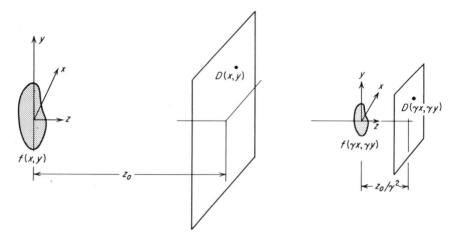

Fig. 1-4

With

$$\xi = \gamma\xi_1 \qquad \eta = \gamma\eta_1 \qquad z_o = \gamma^2 z_1$$

the above yields

$$D(\gamma x,\gamma y) = \gamma^2 \iint\limits_{S_1} f(\gamma\xi_1,\gamma\eta_1)e^{jk\frac{(\xi_1-x)^2+(\eta_1-y)^2}{2z_1}} \, d\xi_1 \, d\eta_1$$

Hence, if the object $f(\gamma x,\gamma y)$ (scaling down of the original object by the factor γ) is placed at a distance z_o/γ^2 from the $z = 0$ plane, it will generate the field $D(\gamma x,\gamma y)$.

It can be shown that (Prob. 11-4) in the three-dimensional case, the reconstruction of $f(x,y,z)$ yields approximately the object $f(\gamma x,\gamma y,\gamma^2 z)$ at a distance z_o/γ^2 from the hologram. In other words, the x and y dimensions are scaled by the factor γ and the z dimension by the factor γ^2. For example, a sphere appears as an ellipsoid.

Conjugate object

The term V_c in (1-7) is given by

$$V_c(x,y) = A_r A e^{j(k\rho^2/2)(1/s+1/s_r)} D^*(x,y) \tag{1-16}$$

To interpret it we shall assume for simplicity that the object f is two-dimensional.

Fraunhofer region We maintain that the effect of the term V_c in the $z > 0$ region is a field produced by the conjugate object (Fig. 1-2c)

$$f_c(x,y) = f^*(-x,-y) \tag{1-17}$$

and a lens L_3 of focal length $\mathbf{f_3}$ given by

$$\frac{1}{\mathbf{f_3}} = \frac{2}{z_o} - \frac{1}{s} - \frac{1}{s_r} \tag{1-18}$$

The lens is on the $z = 0$ plane, and the conjugate object is on the same plane as the object f, which is a distance z_o from the hologram.

We note that if

$$s_r > \frac{z_o}{1 - z_o/s}$$

then the lens L_3 forms a *real* image of the conjugate object f_c. This image is in the $z > 0$ region, and is a distance z_1 from the hologram, where [see Chap. 9, (5-16)]

$$\frac{1}{z_o} + \frac{1}{z_1} = \frac{1}{\mathbf{f_3}}$$

With (1-18), the above yields

$$\frac{1}{z_1} = \frac{1}{z_o} - \frac{1}{s} - \frac{1}{s_r} \tag{1-19}$$

If $s = s_r = \infty$, that is, if both sources are plane waves, then $z_1 = z_o$.

Proof With $F(u,v)$ the Fourier transform of $f(x,y)$, we have [see Chap. 9, (4-8)]

$$D(x,y) = e^{jk\rho^2/2z_o}F\left(\frac{kx}{z_o}, \frac{ky}{z_o}\right) \tag{1-20}$$

The Fourier transform $F_c(u,v)$ of $f_c(x,y)$ equals $F^*(u,v)$. Hence the field $D_c(x,y)$ on the $z = 0$ plane due to the conjugate object $f_c(x,y)$ is given by

$$D_c(x,y) = e^{jk\rho^2/2z_o}F^*\left(\frac{kx}{z_o}, \frac{ky}{z_o}\right) \tag{1-21}$$

From (1-16), (1-20), and (1-21) we conclude that

$$V_c(x,y) = A_r A e^{j(k\rho^2/2)(1/s+1/s_r)}e^{-jk\rho^2/z_o}D_c(x,y) \tag{1-22}$$

and our assertion follows.

Fresnel region If the hologram is in the Fresnel region of the object, then (1-20) still holds, provided that $F(u,v)$ is replaced by the Fourier transform $F_\sigma(u,v)$ of the function [see Chap. 9, (3-7a)]

$$f(x,y)e^{jk\rho^2/2z_o}$$

In this case, $F_\sigma^*(u,v)$ is the transform of

$$f^*(-x,-y)e^{-jk\rho^2/2z_o} = f_c(x,y)e^{-jk\rho^2/z_o}e^{jk\rho^2/2z_o}$$

Therefore, the term $D_c(x,y)$ must be interpreted as the field due to the object

$$f_c(x,y)e^{-jk\rho^2/z_o} \tag{1-23}$$

(elaborate). This object is realized by a lens L_4 (Fig. 1-2c) of focal length

$$\mathbf{f}_4 = \frac{z_o}{2}$$

next to $f_c(x,y)$. Thus, the effect of the term V_c is the conjugate object $f_c(x,y)$ seen through the lenses L_3 and L_4. Its real image is again on the $z = z_1$ plane, where z_1 is given by (1-19).

Ambiguity term

The last term in (1-7) is given by

$$V_a(x,y) = A_r e^{jk\rho^2/2s_r}|D(x,y)|^2 \tag{1-24}$$

If $A \gg |D(x,y)|$, that is, if the direct light from the source is much stronger than the diffracted light, then the term V_a is negligible compared with V_o or V_c. However, we shall determine its effect.

Fraunhofer region   The inverse Fourier transform of $|F(u,v)|^2$ equals the function [see Chap. 3, (2-12)]

$$\rho(x,y) = \iint\limits_S f(x + \xi, y + \eta)f^*(\xi,\eta)\, d\xi\, d\eta \tag{1-25}$$

If this function is placed on the plane of the original object f, then the resulting field $R(x,y)$ in the $z = 0$ plane will be given by

$$R(x,y) = e^{jk\rho^2/2z_o}\left|F\left(\frac{kx}{z_o}, \frac{ky}{z_o}\right)\right|^2 = e^{jk\rho^2/2z_o}|D(x,y)|^2$$

Hence,

$$V_a(x,y) = A_r e^{jk(\rho^2/2)(1/s_r - 1/z_o)}R(x,y) \tag{1-26}$$

From the above it follows that the term V_a yields the object $\rho(x,y)$ as seen through a lens L_5 of focal length $\mathbf{f}_5$ given by

$$\frac{1}{\mathbf{f}_5} = \frac{1}{z_o} - \frac{1}{s_r} \tag{1-27}$$

Fresnel region   If the hologram is in the Fresnel region of the object, then the same conclusions hold, provided that $\rho(x,y)$ is replaced by the "ambiguity function"

$$\chi(x,y) = \iint\limits_S f(x + \xi, y + \eta)f^*(\xi,\eta)e^{jk(x\xi+y\eta)/z_o}\, d\xi\, d\eta \tag{1-28}$$

introduced in Example 2-4, Chap. 3 (see Prob. 11-2).

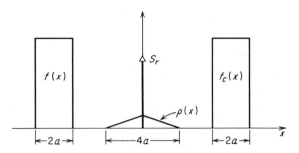

Fig. 1-5

Summary In the reconstruction process, the observer sees the following four objects: the source S_r; the object f through a lens L_1; the conjugate object f_c through lenses L_3 and L_4; and the ambiguity function through lens L_5.

Example 1-1 Suppose that the object f is a slit of width $2a$ (Fig. 1-5) and that both sources are uniform plane waves. In this case, the four terms generated by the hologram are the functions shown in Fig. 1-5. The conjugate object f_c is also a slit of width $2a$, and is uniformly illuminated. The ambiguity term ρ is a slit of width $4a$ and is illuminated by a wave whose amplitude decreases linearly away from the center of the slit.

2. OPTICAL SYSTEMS

In this section we give a system interpretation to the diffraction field and to the role of lenses. The material is related to the analysis of Chap. 6, Sec. 4. We consider only one-dimensional objects and lenses.

We showed in Chap. 9 that the field due to a plane object is proportional to the field from an aperture, and, in the Fresnel region, it is given by Chap. 9, (3-7). Omitting a proportionality factor and the dependence of $g(x,z_o)$ on z_o, we can write this fundamental relationship in the form

$$g(x) = \int_{-b}^{b} f(\xi) e^{jk(x-\xi)^2/2z_o} \, d\xi \tag{2-1}$$

Since $f(x) = 0$ for $|x| > b$, the above is a convolution integral

$$g(x) = f(x) * e^{j\alpha x^2} \qquad \alpha = \frac{k}{2z_o} \tag{2-2}$$

In other words, the field $g(x)$ on a plane $z = z_o$ in the Fresnel region of an object $f(x)$ can be considered as the output of a linear system with input $f(x)$ and impulse response (Fig. 2-1)

$$e^{j\alpha x^2} \qquad \alpha = \frac{k}{2z_o} = \frac{\pi}{\lambda z_o}$$

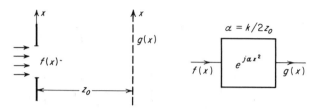

Fig. 2-1

The corresponding system function is given by [see Chap. 3, (1-31)]

$$e^{-ju^2/4\alpha} = e^{-jz_o\lambda u^2/4\pi}$$

This result greatly simplifies the analysis of optical systems.

Change of planes Suppose that on the plane P_o the diffracted field equals $g_o(x)$ and that the plane P_1 is at a distance z_1 from P_o (Fig. 2-2). Since

$$e^{-j(z_o+z_1)\lambda u^2/4\pi} = e^{-jz_o\lambda u^2/4\pi}e^{-jz_1\lambda u^2/4\pi}$$

it follows that the field $g_1(x)$ on the plane P_1 can be considered as the output of a system with input $g_o(x)$ and system function $e^{-jz_1\lambda u^2/4\pi}$. In other words, $g_1(x)$ is the diffraction field of the object $g_o(x)$. This observation can be used to determine the effect of defocusing in an optical system whose field on the image plane is known.

Lens

A lens of focal length **f** is equivalent to a transparency with transmission function

$$T(x) = e^{-j\beta x^2} \qquad \beta = \frac{k}{2\mathbf{f}} \tag{2-3}$$

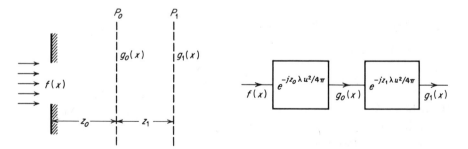

Fig. 2-2

This is true, of course, only in the region $|x| < a$ of the lens. Ignoring, at first, the fact that a is finite, we conclude that if the incident field is $r(x)$, then the field on a plane tangent just to the right of the lens will equal

$$a(x) = r(x)e^{-j\beta x^2} \tag{2-4}$$

The propagated field can be determined from (2-1), where now the function $f(x)$ equals $a(x)$. Hence, the field $g(x)$ on a plane P_o, a distance z_o from the lens (Fig. 2-3), is given by

$$g(x) = [r(x)e^{-j\beta x^2}] * e^{j\gamma x^2} \qquad \gamma = \frac{k}{2z_o} \tag{2-5}$$

Thus, to determine the diffracted field $g(x)$ on the plane P_o we multiply $r(x)$ by the (linear FM) signal $e^{-j\beta x^2}$ and use the product as the input to a system with impulse response $e^{j\gamma x^2}$.

On the focal plane $z_o = \mathbf{f}$ we have $\beta = \gamma$, and (2-5) yields

$$g(x) = \int_{-\infty}^{\infty} r(\xi)e^{-j\beta\xi^2}e^{j\beta(x-\xi^2)}\, d\xi = e^{j\beta x^2}\int_{-\infty}^{\infty} r(\xi)e^{-j2\beta x\xi}\, d\xi$$

With $R(u)$ the Fourier transform of $r(x)$, the above yields

$$g(x) = e^{j\beta x^2}R(2\beta x) \qquad \beta = \frac{k}{2\mathbf{f}} \tag{2-6}$$

The intensity $|g(x)|^2$ of the diffracted field on the focal plane of a lens is thus proportional to the energy spectrum $|R(2\beta x)|^2$ of the incoming wave [see also Chap. 6, (4-6)].

We shall now account for the finite size of the lens. The field in

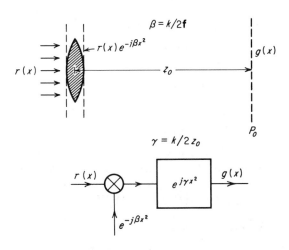

Fig. 2-3

the region $z > 0$ is given by Kirchhoff's integral over the entire $z = 0$ plane. In the region $|x| < a$, the field equals the function (2-4), but in the region $|x| > a$ it equals the incident field $r(x)$. The integration over the latter region yields the field due to the incoming wave with the lens replaced by an opaque screen. Therefore, in the region of interest (near the axis of the lens) it can be ignored.

From the preceding reasoning it follows that a lens of size $2a$ is equivalent to a transparency

$$T_a(x) = e^{-j\beta x^2} p_a(x) \qquad p_a(x) = \begin{cases} 1 & |x| < a \\ 0 & |x| > a \end{cases} \qquad (2\text{-}7)$$

Hence (2-5) and (2-6) still hold, provided that $r(x)$ is replaced by the product $r(x)p_a(x)$.

FOCAL PLANE FIELD AS FOURIER TRANSFORM

Consider a perfect lens L, that is, a lens whose transmission function is given by (2-3) for every x (in the region of interest). In the following we shall show that the amplitude $g(x)$ of the field on the right focal plane P_r of the lens (Fig. 2-4a) equals the Fourier transform of the amplitude $f(x)$ of the field on the plane P_s to its left, multiplied by a phase factor depending on the distance z_s from P_s to L. Specifically, we shall prove that

$$g(x) = \sqrt{\frac{\pi}{\alpha}} \, e^{j\pi/4} e^{j\beta x^2(1-\beta/\alpha)} F(2\beta x) \qquad (2\text{-}8)$$

where

$$f(x) \leftrightarrow F(u) \qquad \alpha = \frac{k}{2z_s} \qquad \beta = \frac{k}{2f} \qquad (2\text{-}9)$$

Clearly, (2-6) is a special case of (2-8).

Proof On the plane P^- tangent to L at its left, the field is given by [see (2-2)]

$$r(x) = f(x) * e^{j\alpha x^2} \qquad (2\text{-}10)$$

On the plane P^+ tangent to L at its right, the field equals [see (2-4)]

$$[f(x) * e^{j\alpha x^2}] * e^{-j\beta x^2}$$

Finally, the field $g(x)$ on the focal plane P_r is obtained by convolving the above with $e^{j\beta x^2}$. Hence, to prove (2-8), it suffices to show that

$$g(x) = \{[f(x) * e^{j\alpha x^2}]e^{-j\beta x^2}\} * e^{j\beta x^2} = \sqrt{\frac{\pi}{\alpha}} \, e^{j\pi/4} e^{j\beta x^2(1-\beta/\alpha)} F(2\beta x) \qquad (2\text{-}11)$$

We first note that

$$\int_{-\infty}^{\infty} f(\xi) e^{j\alpha(x-\xi)^2} \, d\xi = e^{j\alpha x^2} \int_{-\infty}^{\infty} f(\xi) e^{j\alpha \xi^2} e^{-j2\alpha x\xi} \, d\xi = e^{j\alpha x^2} F_1(2\alpha x)$$

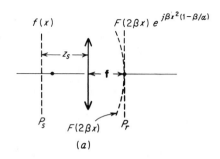

(a)

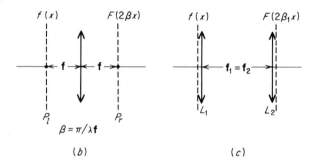

(b)   (c)

Fig. 2-4

where

$$f(x)e^{j\alpha x^2} \leftrightarrow F_1(u) \tag{2-12}$$

Hence,

$$g(x) = \int_{-\infty}^{\infty} e^{j(\alpha-\beta)\xi^2} F_1(2\alpha\xi) e^{j\beta(x-\xi)^2} \, d\xi = e^{j\beta x^2} \int_{-\infty}^{\infty} e^{j\alpha\xi^2} F_1(2\alpha\xi) e^{-j2\beta x\xi} \, d\xi$$

and, with $2\alpha\xi = u$,

$$g(x) = \frac{1}{2\alpha} e^{j\beta x^2} \int_{-\infty}^{\infty} e^{ju^2/4\alpha} F_1(u) e^{-j\beta xu/\alpha} \, du \tag{2-13}$$

Since

$$\sqrt{\frac{\alpha}{\pi}} e^{j\pi/4} e^{-j\alpha x^2} \leftrightarrow e^{ju^2/4\alpha} \tag{2-14}$$

it follows from the convolution theorem that [see (2-12)]

$$\frac{1}{2\pi} \int_{-\infty}^{\infty} e^{ju^2/4\alpha} F_1(u) e^{juy} \, du = \sqrt{\frac{\alpha}{\pi}} e^{j\pi/4} \int_{-\infty}^{\infty} f(\xi) e^{j\alpha\xi^2} e^{-j\alpha(y-\xi)^2} \, d\xi$$

$$= \sqrt{\frac{\alpha}{\pi}} e^{j\pi/4} e^{-j\alpha y^2} \int_{-\infty}^{\infty} f(\xi) e^{-j2\alpha y\xi} \, d\xi = \sqrt{\frac{\alpha}{\pi}} e^{j\pi/4} e^{-j\alpha y^2} F(-2\alpha y)$$

From the above and (2-13) we conclude, with $y = -\beta x/\alpha$, that

$$g(x) = e^{j\pi/4} \sqrt{\frac{\pi}{\alpha}} e^{j\beta x^2} e^{-j\beta^2 x^2/\alpha} F(2\beta x) \tag{2-15}$$

and (2-8) results.

We note that on the surface of the cylinder C of radius

$$r = \frac{\mathbf{f}^2}{z_s - \mathbf{f}} \tag{2-16}$$

the phase term in (2-8) is eliminated [see Chap. 9, (4-19)].

Focal planes

If $z_s = \mathbf{f}$, then $\alpha = \beta$. Introducing the factor that was omitted in (2-2) [see Chap. 9, (3-7)], we conclude that

$$g(x) = AF\left(\frac{2\pi x}{\lambda \mathbf{f}}\right) \qquad A = \frac{1}{\sqrt{\lambda \mathbf{f}}} e^{-j(2k\mathbf{f}+\pi/4)} \tag{2-17}$$

Thus *the amplitude of the field $g(x)$ on the right focal plane P_r of a lens is proportional to the Fourier transform of the amplitude $f(x)$ of the field on the left focal plane P_l (Fig. 2-4b).*

Dual optical systems†

Taking transforms of both sides of (2-2) and using the pair

$$e^{j\alpha x^2} \longleftrightarrow e^{-ju^2/4\alpha}$$

(within a factor), we conclude that

$$G(u) = F(u)e^{-ju^2/4\alpha}$$

In the u space, the term

$$e^{-ju^2/4\alpha}$$

can be considered as the transmission function of a lens of focal length

$$\mathbf{f}_u = 2\alpha k = \frac{4\pi^2}{\lambda^2 z_o}$$

Hence, if $f(x)$ and $g(x)$ are the fields in two planes that are a distance z_o apart, then their transforms $F(u)$ and $G(u)$ are the fields to the left and right of a lens of focal length $\mathbf{f}_u$ (Fig. 2-5a).

Reasoning similarly, we conclude from (2-4) that

$$A(u) = R(u) * e^{ju^2/4\beta}$$

Hence, if $r(x)$ and $a(x)$ are the fields to the left and right of a lens of

† A. Papoulis, *J. Opt. Soc. Am.*, vol. 58, no. 5, May, 1968, pp. 653–654.

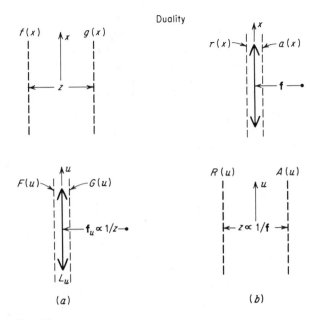

Fig. 2-5

focal length $\mathbf{f}$, then $R(u)$ and $A(u)$ are the fields in two planes that are a distance $4\pi^2/\lambda^2\mathbf{f}$ apart.

The preceding discussion leads to the following dualism: Consider the system S of Fig. 2-6a. Replacing each region of free space between two planes P_i and P_{i+1} that are a distance z_i apart by a lens of focal length $4\pi^2/\lambda^2z_i$ and each lens L_i of focal length $\mathbf{f}_i$ by two planes that are a distance $4\pi^2/\lambda^2\mathbf{f}_i$ apart, we obtain the system S_u of Fig. 2-6b (dual of S). If the

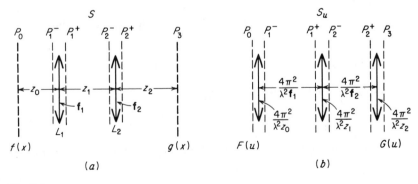

Fig. 2-6

input to S is a signal $f(x)$, and the input to S_u is the Fourier transform $F(u)$ of $f(x)$, then the field on each plane of S_u is the Fourier transform of the field on the corresponding plane of S.

This dualism is illustrated in Fig. 2-4. The output of Fig. 2-4b is the Fourier transform of its input (omitting sealing factors). Hence, the output of its dual system (Fig. 2-4c) is also the Fourier transform of the input (elaborate).

The preceding results can be readily extended to random fields (Prob. 11-16) and to spherical lenses (Prob. 11-8).

IMAGE FORMATION

Consider a lens L with transmission function $T_a(x)$ as in (2-7) and an object $f(x)$ distance z_s from L. We shall determine the image $g(x)$ of $f(x)$ on its image plane P_o, where (Fig. 2-7a)

$$\frac{1}{z_o} + \frac{1}{z_s} = \frac{1}{\mathbf{f}} \tag{2-18}$$

The field on the planes P^- and P^+ is given by $r(x)$ and $r(x)T_a(x)$, respectively [see (2-7)]; hence,

$$g(x) = \{[f(x) * e^{-j\alpha x^2}]e^{-j\beta x^2}p_a(x)\} * e^{j\gamma x^2} \tag{2-19}$$

where

$$\alpha = \frac{k}{2z_s} \qquad \beta = \frac{k}{2\mathbf{f}} \qquad \gamma = \frac{k}{2z_o} \tag{2-20}$$

In Fig. 2-7b we give the system interpretation of (2-19). Condition (2-18) is equivalent to

$$\alpha + \gamma = \beta \tag{2-21}$$

To evaluate (2-19), we assume first that

$$p_a(x) \equiv 1$$

that is, we ignore the fact that the lens is of finite size. This assumption is satisfactory if the function

$$f(x) * e^{j\alpha x^2}$$

is negligible for $|x| > a$. In this case, (2-19) yields

$$g(x) = \frac{\pi}{\alpha} e^{j\gamma\beta x^2/\alpha} f\left(-\frac{\gamma x}{\alpha}\right) \tag{2-22}$$

as we see from Chap. 6, (4-17). Ignoring the factor π/α, we have

$$g(x) = e^{jkz_s x^2/z_o \mathbf{f}} f\left(-\frac{z_s x}{z_o}\right) \tag{2-23}$$

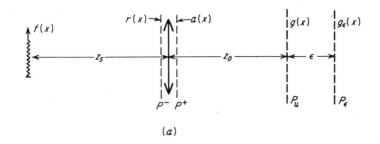

(a)

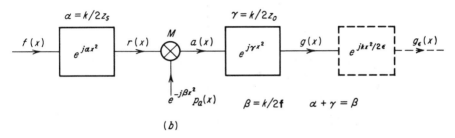

(b)

Fig. 2-7

as in Chap. 9, (5-23). Thus, the image equals the object $f(x)$ magnified by the factor $-z_0/z_s$. The term

$$w(x) = e^{jkz_s x^2/z_0 \mathfrak{f}} \tag{2-24}$$

introduces a phase distortion. If the size of the object $f(x)$ is $2b$

$$f(x) = 0 \qquad \text{for } |x| > b$$

and

$$2\pi b^2 z_0 \ll \lambda z_s \mathfrak{f} \tag{2-25}$$

then

$$e^{jkz_s x^2/z_0 \mathfrak{f}} \simeq 1 \qquad \text{for } \left| \frac{z_s x}{z_0} \right| < b$$

and (2-23) yields

$$g(x) \simeq f\left(-\frac{z_s x}{z_0} \right) \tag{2-26}$$

We shall now take into account the effect of the term $p_a(x)$ in (2-19). With

$$f_2(x) = [f(x)e^{j\alpha x^2}] * \frac{\sin 2\alpha a x}{\pi x} \tag{2-27}$$

it follows from Chap. 6, (4-28) and (4-24), that

$$g(x) = \frac{\pi}{\alpha} e^{j\gamma x^2} f_2\left(-\frac{\gamma x}{\alpha} \right) \tag{2-28}$$

If $\alpha a^2 \gg \pi^2$, that is, if

$$a^2 \gg \pi \lambda z_s$$

then [see Chap. 6, (4-31)]

$$f_2(x) = \left[f(x) * \frac{\sin 2\alpha a x}{\pi x} \right] e^{j\alpha x^2}$$

and (2-28) yields

$$g(x) = \frac{\pi}{\alpha} e^{j\gamma\beta x^2/\alpha} \varphi \left(-\frac{\gamma x}{\alpha} \right) \tag{2-29}$$

where

$$\varphi(x) = f(x) * \frac{\sin 2\alpha a x}{\pi x} \tag{2-30}$$

From the above it follows that if

$$a^2 \gg \pi \lambda z_s \qquad \text{and} \qquad \pi b^2 z_o \ll \lambda z_s f \tag{2-31}$$

then

$$g(x) \simeq \varphi \left(-\frac{z_s x}{z_o} \right) \tag{2-32}$$

Shift invariance

Our optical arrangement is equivalent to the system of Fig. 2-7b. Because of the presence of the multiplier M, this system is not shift-invariant, i.e., the image of $f(x - x_o)$ is not $g(x - x_o)$. However, if (2-31) holds, then $g(x)$ is given by (2-32) or the equivalent

$$g(x) = f\left(-\frac{z_s x}{z_o} \right) * h(x) \qquad h(x) \propto \frac{\sin (kax/z_o)}{x} \tag{2-33}$$

If, therefore, the unit of the x axis in the object plane equals $-z_o/z_s$, then the system is shift-invariant with input $f(x)$, impulse response $h(x)$, and system function

$$H(u) = \begin{cases} 1 & |u| < \dfrac{ka}{z_o} \\ 0 & |u| > \dfrac{ka}{z_o} \end{cases}$$

Comment We note that the response to $f(x - x_o)$ equals $g(x - x_o)$ only if (2-25) holds for the shifted object, i.e., only if

$$2\pi(b \pm x_o)^2 z_o \ll \lambda z_s f$$

Defocusing

We shall now determine the field $g_\epsilon(x)$ on a plane P_ϵ that is a distance ϵ from the image plane P_o. As we noted earlier, $g_\epsilon(x)$ is the diffraction field of an object equal to the image plane field $g(x)$ (change of planes). Hence [see (2-2)],

$$g_\epsilon(x) = g(x) * e^{jkx^2/2\epsilon}$$

Using the approximation (2-33), we conclude that $g_\epsilon(x)$ is the output of a system with input $f(x)$ and impulse response

$$h_\epsilon(x) \propto \frac{\sin (kax/z_o)}{x} * e^{jkx^2/2\epsilon} \tag{2-34}$$

If $|\epsilon|$ is sufficiently small, then the term $e^{jkx^2/2\epsilon}$ can be considered as an impulse, as in the near-zone approximation, Chap. 9, (3-12); hence,

$$h_\epsilon(x) \propto \frac{\sin (kax/z_o)}{x} \qquad |\epsilon| \ll \frac{\lambda z_o^2}{a^2}$$

If the defocusing is due to the fact that the object $f(x)$ is moved to a plane that is a distance δ from its original position, then (2-34) still holds provided that

$$\epsilon = \frac{\delta z_o^2}{z_s^2}$$

The defocusing is now negligible for

$$|\delta| \ll \frac{\lambda z_s^2}{a^2}$$

Defining, somewhat arbitrarily, the "depth of field" by $d = \lambda z_s^2/5a^2$, we see that if

$$\lambda = 5 \times 10^{-7} \qquad z_s = 6 \qquad a = 3 \times 10^{-3}$$

then

$$d = 0.4$$

RANDOM SIGNALS

As we see from (2-29), the image of the object $f(x)$ (properly scaled) is given by

$$g(x) = [f(x) * h(x)]w(x) \tag{2-35}$$

where

$$h(x) = \frac{\sin (kax/z_o)}{x} \qquad w(x) = e^{jz_s x^2/z_o f}$$

Suppose now that the object is a monochromatic random signal

$f(x,t)$ with coherence function

$$\Gamma_{ff}(x_1,x_2)e^{-j\omega\tau}$$

From the discussion of Chap. 8, Sec. 2, it follows that the cross-coherence function $\Gamma_{fg}(x_1,x_2)$ between the object $f(x,t)$ and its image $g(x,t)$ is the image of the object $\Gamma_{ff}(x_1,x_2)$ considered as a function of x_2 (see page 261). From the above and (2-29) it follows that

$$\Gamma_{fg}(x_1,x_2) = [\Gamma_{ff}(x_1,x_2) * h(x_2)]w^*(x_2) \tag{2-36}$$

where x_1 is a point in the object plane and x_2 is a point in the image plane, and the convolution is with respect to x_2.

Similarly, the coherence function of the image $g(x,t)$ is given by

$$\Gamma_{gg}(x_1,x_2) = [\Gamma_{fg}(x_1,x_2) * h(x_1)]w(x_1) \tag{2-37}$$

If the object is completely incoherent,

$$\Gamma_{ff}(x_1,x_2) = q(x_1)\delta(x_1 - x_2) \tag{2-38}$$

then (2-36) and (2-37) yield

$$\Gamma_{fg}(x_1,x_2) = q(x_1)h(x_2 - x_1)w^*(x_2) \tag{2-39}$$

$$\Gamma_{gg}(x_1,x_2) = \{[q(x_1)h(x_2 - x_1)] * h(x_1)\}w(x_1)w^*(x_2) \tag{2-40}$$

From the above it follows that the average intensity of the image $g(x,t)$ is given by

$$E\{|g(x,t)|^2\} = \int_{-\infty}^{\infty} q(x - \xi)|h(\xi)|^2 \, d\xi = q(x) * |h(x)|^2 \tag{2-41}$$

We note that if $q(x)$ is the average intensity of the actual object (before scaling), then the function $q(x)$ in (2-38) should be replaced by

$$\frac{z_o}{z_s} q\left(-\frac{z_s x}{z_o}\right)$$

If the object is completely coherent, then

$$\Gamma_{ff}(x_1,x_2) = p(x_1)p^*(x_2)$$

In this case,

$$E\{|g(x,t)|^2\} = |p(x) * h(x)|^2 \tag{2-42}$$

This follows readily from (2-36) and (2-37).

Lens size The quality of the image improves with increasing a because $h(x)$ approaches an impulse. If a is sufficiently large, then (2-42) equals $|p(x)|^2$. Since the area of $h(x)$ is independent of a, a further increase of the lens size will have no effect on the image of a coherent object. However, the intensity of the image of an incoherent object will increase because the area of $|h(x)|^2$ is proportional to a. This point is illustrated in the next example.

Example 2-1   We shall determine the image of a uniformly illuminated object of width $2b$ (Fig. 2-8a). With the necessary scaling, the size of the object equals $2b_1$, where

$$b_1 = \frac{z_o b}{z_s}$$

Hence, for the coherent case,

$$p(x) = \begin{cases} 1 & |x| < b_1 \\ 0 & |x| > b_1 \end{cases}$$

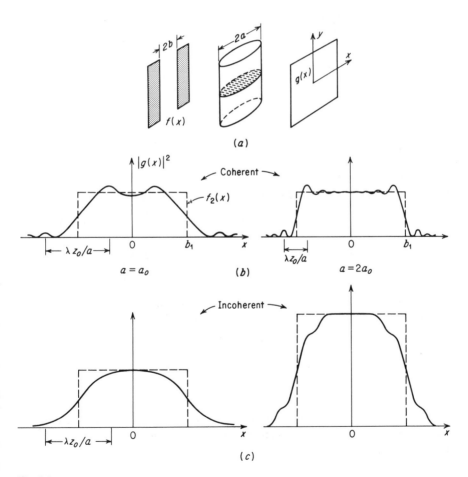

Fig. 2-8

and (2-42) yields

$$E\{|\mathbf{g}(x,t)|^2\} = \left| \int_{x-b_1}^{x+b_1} \frac{\sin (ka\xi/z_o)}{k\xi/z_o} \, d\xi \right|^2$$

$$= \frac{z_o^2}{k^2} \left| Si \left[\frac{ka(x+b_1)}{z_o} \right] - Si \left[\frac{ka(x-b_1)}{z_o} \right] \right| \quad (2\text{-}43)$$

where

$$Si(x) = \int_0^x \frac{\sin y}{y} \, dy$$

is the *sine integral*.

In Fig. 2-8b we show the average intensity of $\mathbf{g}(x,t)$ for $a = a_o$ and $a = 2a_o$. We note that as a increases, the transition from light to dark sharpens, but the intensity of the light region remains unchanged. Furthermore, since the sign of the integrand in (2-43) alternates, the transition is not monotone, but it consists of a succession of dark and bright bands. The "gray" region is of the order of $\lambda z_o/2a$.

For the incoherent case,

$$q(x) = \begin{cases} 1 & |x| < b_1 \\ 0 & |x| > b_1 \end{cases}$$

and (2-41) yields the quantity

$$E\{|\mathbf{g}(x,t)|^2\} = \int_{x-b_1}^{x+b_1} \frac{\sin^2 (ka\xi/z_o)}{(ka\xi/z_o)^2} \, d\xi = \frac{z_o a}{k} \int_{ka(x-b_1)/z_o}^{ka(x+b_1)/z_o} (\sin^2 y/y^2) \, dy$$

shown in Fig. 2-8c for $a = a_o$ and $a = 2a_o$. Since the integrand is positive, the transition from light to dark is now monotone. Furthermore, an increase in a results not only in sharper edges, but also in a brighter image.

3. LIGHT CONCENTRATION AND FRESNEL ZONE PLATES

In this section we examine the concentration of light as it passes through a lens, and we show that a similar effect can be attained if the lens is replaced by an aperture consisting of rings suitably spaced [j1].

LIGHT CONCENTRATION

Consider a uniform plane wave normally incident on a circular aperture of radius a (Fig. 3-1). As we know [see Chap. 9, (3-52)], the resulting field $g(0,z_o)$ along the z axis is given by

$$g(0,z_o) = \frac{2\pi B}{\lambda z_o} \int_0^a \rho e^{jk\rho^2/2z_o} \, d\rho \quad (3\text{-}1)$$

where the intensity $|B|^2$ of the coefficient B equals the intensity of the incoming wave. If a lens of focal length $\mathbf{f}$ is placed in front of the aperture, then $g(0,z_o)$ is again given by (3-1), provided that the integrand is replaced by the function

$$\rho e^{jk\rho^2/2z_o} e^{-jk\rho^2/2\mathbf{f}} \quad (3\text{-}2)$$

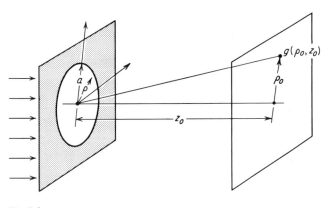

Fig. 3-1

For $z_o = f$ we thus obtain

$$g(0,f) = \frac{2\pi B}{\lambda f} \int_0^a \rho \, d\rho = \frac{\pi a^2 B}{\lambda f} \qquad (3\text{-}3)$$

Hence, on its focal point, a spherical lens concentrates the intensity of the incoming wave by a factor

$$A = \left(\frac{\pi a^2}{\lambda f}\right)^2 \qquad (3\text{-}4)$$

Example 3-1   If

$$a = 8 \times 10^{-3} \text{ m} \qquad f = 4a \qquad \lambda = 6.28 \times 10^{-7} \text{ m}$$

then

$$A = 10^8$$

Cylindrical lenses

Suppose now that the aperture is a vertical strip of width $2a$. In this case, the resulting field is given by [see Chap. 9, (3-7a)]

$$g(0,z_o) = \frac{C}{\sqrt{\lambda z_o}} \int_{-a}^a e^{jk x^2/2z_o} \, dx \qquad (3\text{-}5)$$

where again $|C|^2$ equals the intensity of the incoming wave. Therefore, if a cylindrical lens of focal length $f = z_o$ is placed in front of the aperture, then

$$g(0,f) = \frac{2aC}{\sqrt{\lambda z_o}} \qquad (3\text{-}6)$$

This holds, of course, along the entire line $x = 0$, $z_o = f$. Hence, on its focal point (line), a cylindrical lens concentrates the intensity of the incoming wave by a factor

$$A = \frac{4a^2}{\lambda f} \tag{3-7}$$

Zone plates

In the preceding analysis, the role of the lens was to introduce the factor $e^{-jk\rho^2/2f}$, canceling the term

$$e^{jk\rho^2/2z_o} = \cos(k\rho^2/2z_o) + j\sin(k\rho^2/2z_o)$$

in the integral (3-1). A similar result can be attained if the negative parts of $\cos(k\rho^2/2z_o)$ or $\sin(k\rho^2/2z_o)$ are canceled by suitably coated apertures. For this purpose, we form a plate with transmission function (Fig. 3-2)

$$T(\rho) = U\left(\cos\frac{\rho^2}{2\sigma^2}\right) \qquad U(x) = \begin{cases} 1 & x \geq 0 \\ 0 & x < 0 \end{cases} \tag{3-8}$$

where σ is a parameter that is characteristic of the plate. This function is realized with n transparent rings in the intervals

$$s_{2i} \leq \rho \leq s_{2i+1}$$

where

$$s_o = 0 \qquad s_i = \sigma\sqrt{\pi(2i-1)} \qquad i = 1, 2, \ldots, n \tag{3-9}$$

alternating with n opaque rings in the intervals $s_{2i-1} < \rho < s_{2i}$. The radius a of the last transparent ring equals s_n:

$$a = s_n = \sigma\sqrt{\pi(2n-1)} \tag{3-10}$$

We define the *focal length* $\mathbf{f}_p$ of the plate by

$$\mathbf{f}_p = k\sigma^2 = 2\pi\sigma^2/\lambda \tag{3-11}$$

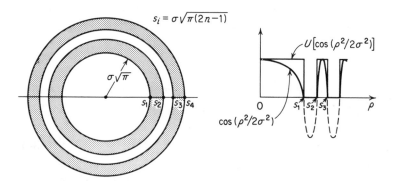

Fig. 3-2

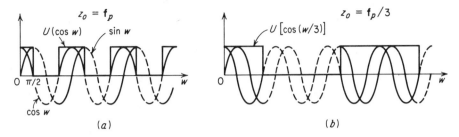

Fig. 3-3

and we maintain that if n is large, then at the focal point $z_o = \mathbf{f}_p$ the plate concentrates the intensity of the incoming wave by the factor

$$A_p = n^2 + 1 \simeq \left(\frac{a^2}{\lambda \mathbf{f}_p}\right)^2 \tag{3-12}$$

Proof Inserting the factor (3-8) into (3-1), we have

$$g(0,z_o) = \frac{2\pi B}{\lambda z_o} \int_0^a \rho e^{jk\rho^2/2z_o} U[\cos(\rho^2/2\sigma^2)] \, d\rho$$

$$= B \int_0^{ka^2/2z_o} e^{jw} U[\cos(wz_o/\mathbf{f}_p)] \, dw \tag{3-13}$$

If $z_o = \mathbf{f}_p$, then $ka^2/2z_o = \pi(n - \frac{1}{2})$, and the above yields (Fig. 3-3a)

$$g(0,\mathbf{f}_p) = B(j + n) \tag{3-14}$$

from which (3-12) follows.

If the plate is illuminated not by a plane wave but by a point source, then $g(0,z_o)$ is obtained by replacing the integrand in (3-1) by

$$e^{jk\rho^2/2z_s} e^{jk\rho^2/2z_o} U\left(\cos\frac{\rho^2}{2\sigma^2}\right)$$

Hence, the preceding results hold, provided that z_o is such that

$$\frac{1}{z_s} + \frac{1}{z_o} = \frac{1}{\mathbf{f}_p}$$

as in the case of a lens.   Thus, under the preceding special conditions, a zone plate is equivalent to a transparency with transmission function

$$\frac{1}{\pi} e^{-j\rho^2/2\sigma^2} \qquad \rho \le a \tag{3-15}$$

i.e., to a lens with radius a, focal length $k\sigma^2$, and attenuation $1/\pi$.

Comments

1. The diffraction field (3-13) plotted as a function of z_o (Fig. 3-4) has

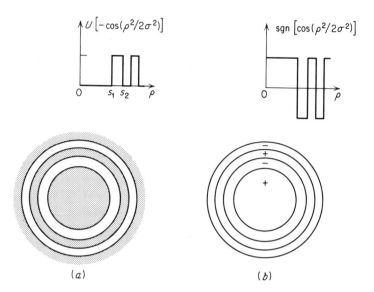

(a)   (b)

Fig. 3-4

secondary maxima at the points $z_o = \mathbf{f}_p/(2i+1)$:

$$\left| g\left(0, \frac{\mathbf{f}_p}{2i+1}\right)\right| = \frac{|g(0,\mathbf{f}_p)|}{2i+1} \qquad i = 0, 1, \ldots \qquad (3\text{-}16)$$

Indeed, for $i = 1$ we have (Fig. 3-3b)

$$g\left(0, \frac{\mathbf{f}_p}{3}\right) = B\left(j - \frac{n}{3}\right)$$

and (3-16) follows for large n [see (3-14)]. Reasoning similarly, we can justify (3-16) for any i.

2. Unlike a lens, the focal distance $\mathbf{f}_p$ of a plate depends on the wavelength λ.

If the incoming wave v^i is monochromatic, then the diffracted field g is large near $z_o = \mathbf{f}_p = 2\pi\sigma^2/\lambda$. However, if the spectrum of v^i occupies the band (ω_1,ω_2), then g is large along the portion $(\omega_1\sigma^2/\mathbf{c},\omega_2\sigma^2/\mathbf{c})$ of the z axis. A zone plate focuses, thus, a polychromatic plane wave into a linear segment whose length is proportional to the bandwidth of this wave.

3. If the transparent and opaque parts of the plate are interchanged, a plate with transmission function

$$T(\rho) = U\left(-\cos\frac{\rho^2}{2\sigma^2}\right) \qquad \rho \leq s_{n-1}$$

results. Since (Fig. 3-4a)

$$g(0,\mathbf{f}_p) = -B(n-1)$$

the corresponding concentration factor A_p is essentially the same as in (3-12).

The concentration can be doubled if the opaque part of the plate is replaced by a dielectric substance which reverses the sign of the incoming wave. We now have

$$T'(\rho) = \operatorname{sgn}\left(\cos\frac{\rho^2}{2\sigma^2}\right) \qquad \text{where} \qquad \operatorname{sgn} x = \begin{cases} 1 & x > 0 \\ -1 & x < 0 \end{cases}$$

(Fig. 3-4b) and

$$g(0,\mathbf{f}_p) = B(j + 2n - 1)$$

Similar results can be obtained with the sine plates

$$U\left(\pm \sin\frac{\rho^2}{2\sigma^2}\right) \qquad \text{or} \qquad \operatorname{sgn}\left(\sin\frac{\rho^2}{2\sigma^2}\right)$$

One-dimensional plates

The one-dimensional form of (3-8) is a plate with transmission function

$$T(x) = U\left(\cos\frac{x^2}{2\sigma^2}\right) \qquad |x| \le a \tag{3-17}$$

realized by vertical strips, as in Fig. 3-5. Inserting into (3-5) and using the evenness of the integrand, we conclude that the resulting field at $z_o = \mathbf{f}_p = k\sigma^2$ is given by

$$g(0,\mathbf{f}_p) = \frac{2C}{\sqrt{\lambda \mathbf{f}_p}} \int_0^a U\left(\cos\frac{x^2}{2\sigma^2}\right) e^{jx^2/2\sigma^2}\, dx \tag{3-18}$$

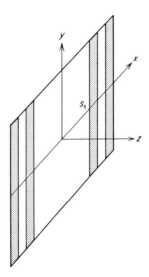

Fig. 3-5

because $k/2z_o = 1/2\sigma^2$. With $x/\sigma\sqrt{2} = y$ the above yields [see (3-10)]

$$g(0,\mathbf{f}_p) = \frac{2C}{\sqrt{\pi}} \int_0^{\sqrt{\pi(n-1/2)}} U(\cos y^2)e^{jy^2}\, dy \tag{3-19}$$

This quantity can be given a graphical interpretation in terms of the Cornu spiral, i.e., the plot of the Fresnel integral (Fig. 1-4, Chap. 3):

$$\sqrt{\frac{2}{\pi}} \int_0^x e^{jy^2}\, dy$$

For this purpose, we show in Fig. 3-6a a portion of the spiral of length $\sqrt{2n-1}$, and in Fig. 3-6b we add vectorially the segments of increasing real part (solid lines). It is easy to see that (3-19) equals $\sqrt{2}\,C$ times the complex number representing the end point P of the resulting curve Γ. Since each portion of Γ (with the exception of the first two or three segments) is approximately a semicircle, it follows that the real part of P equals $1/\pi$ times the length $\sqrt{2n-1}$ of the spiral. The imaginary part equals about $\frac{1}{2}$; hence, for n sufficiently large,

$$g(0,\mathbf{f}_p) \simeq \frac{\sqrt{2}\,C}{\pi} \sqrt{2n-1} = \frac{2Ba}{\pi\sqrt{\lambda\mathbf{f}_p}}$$

Thus, at its focal point (line) the plate concentrates the intensity of the incoming wave by a factor

$$A_p = \frac{4a^2}{\pi^2\lambda\mathbf{f}_p} = \frac{4n-2}{\pi^2} \tag{3-20}$$

That is, it acts as a cylindrical lens with transmission function

$$\frac{1}{\pi}\, e^{-jx^2/2\sigma^2}$$

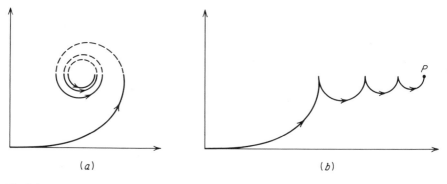

(a)   (b)

Fig. 3-6

Image formation   The equivalence between a plate and a lens holds not only for uniform incidence and for the field at the focal point, but also for more general conditions.   We shall consider only the one-dimensional case. If the incident wave on the plate equals $f(x)$, the resulting field is given by [see Chap. 9, (3-7a)]

$$g(x_o, z_o) = \frac{1}{\sqrt{\lambda z_o}} \int_{-a}^{a} f(x) e^{-jkxx_o/z_o} U\left(\cos \frac{x^2}{2\sigma^2}\right) e^{jkx^2/2z_o}\, dx \qquad (3\text{-}21)$$

Suppose that the term

$$f(x) e^{-jkxx_o/f_p} \qquad (3\text{-}22)$$

is sufficiently smooth in any interval of length $s_{2i+2} - s_{2i}$.   Then, for $z_o = f_p$, (3-21) yields

$$g(x_o, f_p) = \frac{1}{\pi \sqrt{\lambda f_p}} \int_{-a}^{a} f(x) e^{-jxx_o/f_p}\, dx \qquad (3\text{-}23)$$

(elaborate).   Hence, except for the factor $1/\pi$, $g(x_o, f_p)$ is the same as the field due to a lens [see Chap. 9, (5-10)].

We note that the integral in (3-23) equals $F(kx_o/f_p)$ where $F(u)$ is the Fourier transform of $f(x)$.   As we know (uncertainty principle), this function takes significant values for $|u| < \pi/a$.   Therefore, the field g is negligible if $kx_o/f_p > \pi/a$.   Thus, in the region of interest,

$$\frac{k|xx_o|}{f_p} < \frac{\pi|x|}{a}$$

Limiting x_o to this region, we conclude that as x increases by $s_{2i+2} - s_{2i}$, the exponent in (3-22) will increase by a quantity that is small compared to one.   Hence, the second factor in (3-22) satisfies the requirement of smoothness.   For the validity of (3-23), it suffices therefore to assume that $f(x)$ is nearly constant in each zone of the plate.

4. FILTERING

As we have noted, if the input to an optical system is a harmonic object $f(x,y)$, then the Fourier transform $G(u,v)$ of its image $g(x,y)$, properly scaled, equals (approximately) the field at the exit pupil of the system. In particular, if the object is a point at the origin, then $G(u,v)$ equals the transform $H(u,v)$ of the spread function $h(x,y)$.   This property of optical systems can be used to improve the image by inserting a film (filter) with a suitable transmission function $T(u,v)$ in the plane of the exit pupil.†
The resulting spread function $h_1(x,y)$ is then the inverse of the product

$$H_1(u,v) = H(u,v) T(u,v) \qquad (4\text{-}1)$$

† H. H. Hopkins, *Proc. Phys. Soc.*, vol. 79, 1962, pp. 889–919.

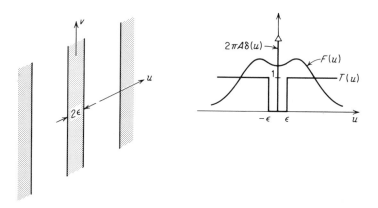

Fig. 4-1

If, therefore, $T(u,v)$ is such that

$$T(u,v) = \frac{1}{H(u,v)} \tag{4-2}$$

then $H_1(u,v) = 1$, and the system is perfect. This condition cannot, of course, be met because H equals zero outside the region of the pupil. However, as we shall presently show, the concept of spatial filtering has important applications.† The analysis will be carried out mostly in one dimension.

CONTRAST IMPROVEMENT

Suppose that the input is of the form

$$A + f(x)$$

where $f(x)$ is the object of interest, and A is a uniform background which we wish to eliminate. The transform of the input is

$$2\pi A \delta(u) + F(u)$$

Thus, the background appears only at the center of the exit pupil; therefore, it can be eliminated if the center portion of the output lens is covered with a dark substance (Fig. 4-1). With

$$T(u) = \begin{cases} 0 & |u| < \epsilon \\ 1 & |u| > \epsilon \end{cases} \tag{4-3}$$

as the transmission function of this substance, it follows from (4-1) that if $F(u)$ does not contain an impulse at the origin and if ϵ is sufficiently

† A. Vanderlugt, *IEEE Trans. Inform. Theory*, vol. 10, no. 139, 1964.

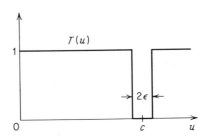

Fig. 4-2

small, then the transform $G(u)$ of the image $g(x)$ is given by

$$G(u) = H(u)T(u)[2\pi A\delta(u) + F(u)] \simeq H(u)F(u) \tag{4-4}$$

The component A is, thus, eliminated.

Comment If the object is a film of extent $2b$, then the background equals zero for $|x| > b$; hence, its transform is not an impulse, but the function

$$\frac{2A \sin bu}{u}$$

This function cannot be entirely eliminated, but it can be made negligible if its first lobe is obscured, that is, if $\epsilon > \pi/b$.

Elimination of periodic noise

The above scheme can be modified to eliminate an undesirable periodic component added to the object. If the noise equals $\cos cx$, then its transform is $\pi\delta(u - c) + \pi\delta(u + c)$; hence, the filter must be such that (Fig. 4-2)

$$T(u) = \begin{cases} 0 & |u \pm c| < \epsilon \\ 1 & \text{otherwise} \end{cases}$$

If the noise is periodic with period $2\pi/c$, then its spectrum consists of impulses at $u = \pm nc$. Assuming that $F(u)$ is zero for $|u| > c$, we con-

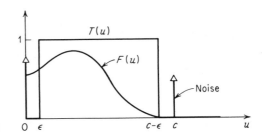

Fig. 4-3

clude that the noise is eliminated if $T(u)$ is a bandpass filter passing only the frequencies from ϵ to $c - \epsilon$ (Fig. 4-3).

PHASE CONTRAST METHOD†

Consider a "phase object," i.e., an object of the form

$$f(x) = e^{j\alpha\varphi(x)} \tag{4-5}$$

This object cannot be seen because the eye or any other sensing device responds to its intensity:

$$|f(x)|^2 = 1$$

It will be shown that the object can be made visible if the filter

$$T(u) = \begin{cases} j & |u| < \epsilon \\ 1 & |u| > \epsilon \end{cases} \tag{4-6}$$

is inserted in the exit pupil of the sensing instrument (microscope), i.e., if the center of its pupil is covered with a suitable dielectric material. We shall assume for simplicity that the instrument is perfect, i.e., that $H(u) = 1$.

If α is sufficiently small, then

$$f(x) \simeq 1 + j\alpha\varphi(x) \tag{4-7}$$

Hence

$$F(u) = 2\pi\delta(u) + j\alpha\Phi(u)$$

where $\Phi(u)$ is the transform of $\varphi(x)$. The field to the right of the filter (4-6) equals

$$G(u) = F(u)T(u) \simeq 2\pi j\delta(u) + j\alpha\Phi(u) \tag{4-8}$$

because the effect of the filter on $\Phi(u)$ is negligible [see also (4-4)]. Hence, the resulting image $g(x)$ is given by

$$g(x) = [1 + \alpha\varphi(x)]j$$

We now have

$$|g(x)|^2 \simeq 1 + 2\alpha\varphi(x) \tag{4-9}$$

Contrast improvement

As we see from (4-9), if α is small, then the term of interest $\alpha\varphi(x)$ is negligible compared with the background 1. This situation can be improved if the filter introduces not only a phase delay but also a strong attenu-

† F. Zernike, *Z. Tech. Physik.*, vol. 16, 1935, p. 454; *Physik. Z.*, vol. 36, 1935, p. 848; *Physica*, vol. 19, 1942, pp. 686, 974.

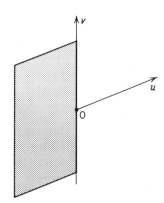

Fig. 4-4

ation.† Assuming then that its transmission equals

$$T_1(u) = \begin{cases} jt & |u| < \epsilon \\ 1 & |u| > \epsilon \end{cases} \tag{4-10}$$

where t is a constant less than one, we have

$$G(u) = F(u)T_1(u) \simeq 2\pi jt\delta(u) + j\alpha\Phi(u)$$

Hence,

$$g(x) = [t + \alpha\varphi(x)]j$$

The background is thus reduced.

HILBERT TRANSFORMS

In the following, we give an optical interpretation to the Hilbert transform and use the related notions (single-side band) to reduce the distortion of an optical system due to the finite size of its exit pupil.

Suppose that the input to a perfect optical system is a *real* object $f(x)$. If a mask is inserted in the exit pupil that obstructs the region $u < 0$ (Fig. 4-4), then the transform $G(u)$ of the resulting image $g(x)$ is given by

$$G(u) = \begin{cases} F(u) & u \geq 0 \\ 0 & u < 0 \end{cases} \tag{4-11}$$

With $\hat{f}(x)$ the Hilbert transform of $f(x)$ and $z(x)$ the analytic signal associated with $f(x)$, it follows from the discussion of Chap. 3, Sec. 3, that

$$g(x) = \tfrac{1}{2}[f(x) + j\hat{f}(x)] = \tfrac{1}{2}z(x) \tag{4-12}$$

† M. Françon, Le contraste de phase en optique et en microscopie, *Rev. Opt.*, Paris, 1950.

Single-side band transmission

If an object $f(x)$ is the input to an ideal system, then its image $g(x)$ is such that (Fig. 4-5a)

$$G(u) = \begin{cases} F(u) & |u| < a \\ 0 & |u| > a \end{cases} \qquad g(x) = f(x) * \frac{\sin ax}{x} \qquad (4\text{-}13)$$

where a is the radius of the exit lens. As a increases, $g(x)$ tends to $f(x)$; the quality of the image is thus limited by the size of a. Using (4-12), we shall show that if $f(x)$ is real, then the same image $g(x)$ can be obtained with a lens of radius $a/2$.

For this purpose, we add a strong background to the object $f(x)$, that is, we use as input the function

$$A + f(x)$$

The resulting field at the exit plane equals

$$2\pi A \delta(u) + F(u)$$

If, therefore, the output lens is of radius $a/2$, and it is placed off center so as to transmit the portion $(-\epsilon, a - \epsilon)$ of the u axis, then the transform $G_1(u)$ of the resulting image $g_1(x)$ will be such that (Fig. 4-5b)

$$G_1(u) = \begin{cases} 2\pi A \delta(u) + G(u) & u \geq 0 \\ 0 & u \leq 0 \end{cases} \qquad (4\text{-}14)$$

With $\hat{g}(x)$ the Hilbert transform of $g(x)$, it thus follows that

$$g_1(x) = A + \tfrac{1}{2}[g(x) + j\hat{g}(x)]$$

If A is sufficiently large, then

$$|g_1(x)|^2 = |A + \tfrac{1}{2}g(x)|^2 + \tfrac{1}{4}|\hat{g}(x)|^2 \simeq A^2 + Ag(x) \qquad (4\text{-}15)$$

In the above, $g(x)$ is the image obtained with a lens of radius a.

MOVEMENT EFFECT AND IMAGE RESTORATION

Suppose that the image of an object is $g(x,y)$. If, during the exposure, the film (or the object) moves, then a new image $g_m(x,y)$ results. In the following, we evaluate g_m and we discuss means for canceling the effect of motion by suitable filtering.†

We assume that the time dependence of the source is of the form

$$\varphi(t)e^{-j\omega t} \qquad (4\text{-}16)$$

where $\varphi(t)$ is a slowly varying signal so that harmonic analysis can be applied.

† A. Lohmann, "Communications and Information Theory Aspects of Modern Optics" (ed. L. O'Neill), pp. 51–90, General Electric Corporation, 1962.

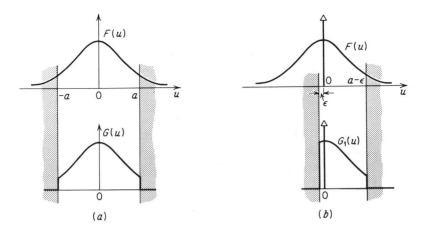

Fig. 4-5

If the motion is a translation in the xy plane, then it is specified by the trajectory

$$x = x(t) \qquad y = y(t) \qquad x(0) = 0,\, y(0) = 0 \tag{4-17}$$

Rectilinear motion

We shall assume that the film moves along the x axis with uniform velocity s:

$$x(t) = st \qquad y(t) = 0$$

Suppose first that

$$\varphi(t) = \begin{cases} 1 & |t| \le T/2 \\ 0 & |t| > T/2 \end{cases}$$

Interpreting $g_m(x,y)$ as the integral of the field at the point (x,y) of the moving plane during the exposure, we have

$$g_m(x,y) = A \int_{-a}^{a} g(x - \xi,\, y)\, d\xi \qquad A = \frac{1}{s} \qquad a = \frac{sT}{2} \tag{4-18}$$

Hence, $g_m(x,y)$ can be considered as the output of a system M with input $g(x,y)$ and point spread

$$h_m(x,y) = A\, p_a(x)\, \delta(y) \tag{4-19}$$

This is a line singularity as in Fig. 4-6. The corresponding system function is given by (see Example 1-3, Chap. 4)

$$H_m(u,v) = A\, \frac{\sin au}{u} \tag{4-20}$$

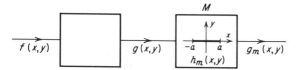

Fig. 4-6

Thus if the original system is connected in cascade with M (Fig. 4-6), the resulting still image will equal $g_m(x,y)$.

From the above it follows that the effect of the motion can be eliminated with a filter having as transmission function the inverse $u/\sin au$ of $H_m(u,v)$. Such a function can, of course, be realized only approximately.

If the restoring filter is a "differentiator"

$$T(u,v) = u$$

then

$$H_m(u,v)T(u,v) = A \sin au = \frac{A}{2j}\left(e^{jau} - e^{-jau}\right)$$

Hence, the corrected image is

$$\frac{Aj}{2}\left[g(x - a, y) - g(x + a, y)\right]$$

Thus, a filter with linearly increasing transmission recovers the original image g but it adds to it a "ghost" at a distance $2a$ from g.

Suppose next that the signal $\varphi(t)$ in (4-16) is an arbitrary function with Fourier transform $\Phi(\omega)$. In this case, the point spread of the equivalent system is given by

$$h_m(x,y) = \frac{1}{s}\,\varphi\left(\frac{x}{s}\right)\delta(y)$$

and its system function is given by

$$H_m(u,v) = \Phi(su)$$

Thus, the filter transmission must now equal the inverse of $\Phi(su)$.

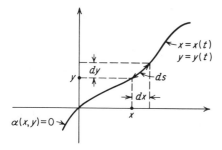

Fig. 4-7

If $\varphi(t) = \cos \omega_o t$, then

$$\Phi(\omega) = \pi\delta(\omega - \omega_o) + \pi\delta(\omega + \omega_o)$$
$$H_m(u,v) = \pi\delta(su - \omega_o) + \pi\delta(su + \omega_o)$$

With $G_m(u,v)$ the transform of $g_m(x,y)$, it follows from the above that [see Chap. 2, (2-3) and (2-8)]

$$G_m(u,v) = G(u,v)H_m(u,v) = \frac{\pi}{s} G\left(\frac{\omega_o}{s}, v\right) \delta\left(u - \frac{\omega_o}{s}\right)$$
$$+ \frac{\pi}{s} G\left(-\frac{\omega_o}{s}, v\right) \delta\left(u - \frac{\omega_o}{s}\right)$$

Hence, the distorted image is of the form

$$g_m(x,y) = Cr(y) \cos\left(\frac{\omega_o}{s} x + \theta\right)$$

(elaborate). This is true, of course, only if the exposure time T is large compared with $1/\omega_o$.

Arbitrary motion

We now comment briefly on the general case. During the motion of the film, its origin traces a curve

$$\alpha(x,y) = 0$$

which is obtained by eliminating the parameter t in (4-17). The point spread $h_m(x,y)$ of the equivalent system is a line along this curve, with line density

$$\lambda(x,y) = \frac{\varphi(t)}{\sqrt{(\dot{x})^2 + (\dot{y})^2}} \qquad (4\text{-}21)$$

where x and y are related to t by (4-17). The above results from the fact that in the time interval $(t, t + dt)$, the origin traces the segment (Fig. 4-7)

$$ds = dt \sqrt{(\dot{x})^2 + (\dot{y})^2}$$

and the corresponding light flux equals $\varphi(t)\, dt$. Introducing the notation of Chap. 2, Sec. 2, we can show that

$$h_m(x,y) = \frac{\alpha_y}{\dot{x}} \delta[\alpha(x,y)]$$

This follows from (4-21) and Chap. 2, (2-19) (elaborate).

OBJECT RECONSTRUCTION FROM DIFFRACTION-LIMITED IMAGE

Consider an ideal (low-pass) system (Fig. 4-8):

$$H(u) = p_a(u) \qquad h(x) = \frac{\sin ax}{\pi x} \qquad (4\text{-}22)$$

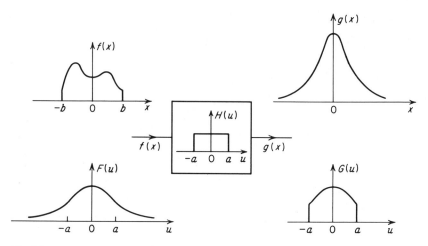

Fig. 4-8

Since

$$G(u) = \begin{cases} F(u) & |u| \le a \\ 0 & |u| > a \end{cases} \tag{4-23}$$

the input $f(x)$ cannot, in general, be reconstructed from its image $g(x)$ because all components of $F(u)$ above $|u| = a$ are lost. However, if $f(x)$ is of finite extent

$$f(x) = 0 \quad \text{for } |x| > b \tag{4-24}$$

then it can be recovered in terms of its response

$$g(x) = \int_{-b}^{b} f(\xi) \frac{\sin a(x - \xi)}{\pi(x - \xi)} d\xi \tag{4-25}$$

The above follows from the fact that the transform $F(u)$ of a signal of finite extent is an analytic function of u (see Chap. 3, Sec. 3). Therefore, if it is known in the interval $(-a,a)$ (or any other interval), it can be determined, at least in principle, for every u. In the following, we discuss a direct method for recovering $f(x)$ from $g(x)$.

Prolate spheroidal functions

For this purpose, we shall use the functions $\varphi_n(x)$ introduced in Chap. 6, Sec. 5.† These functions satisfy the integral equation

$$\int_{-b}^{b} \varphi_n(\xi) \frac{\sin a(x - \xi)}{\pi(x - \xi)} d\xi = \lambda_n \varphi_n(x) \qquad n = 0, 1, \ldots \tag{4-26}$$

† C. W. Barnes, *J. Opt. Soc. Am.*, vol. 56, May, 1966, pp. 573–578.

where the constants λ_n are the corresponding eigenvalues. They have the following properties.

If the signal

$$\varphi_{bn}(x) = \begin{cases} \varphi_n(x) & |x| \le b \\ 0 & |x| > b \end{cases} \tag{4-27}$$

which results when $\varphi_n(x)$ is truncated above $|x| = b$, is used as input to the system (4-22), then the resulting output equals $\lambda_n \varphi_n(x)$ (Fig. 4-9). This is an immediate consequence of (4-25) and (4-26).

The functions $\varphi_n(x)$ are orthogonal in the intervals $(-\infty, \infty)$ *and* $(-b, b)$ (see Prob. 11-17).

$$\int_{-\infty}^{\infty} \varphi_n(x)\varphi_m(x)\,dx = \begin{cases} 1 & n = m \\ 0 & n \ne m \end{cases}$$

$$\int_{-b}^{b} \varphi_n(x)\varphi_m(x)\,dx = \begin{cases} \lambda_n & n = m \\ 0 & n \ne m \end{cases} \tag{4-28}$$

They form a complete set in the above intervals. By this we mean that any function $g(x)$, band-limited as in (4-23), can be written as a series

$$g(x) = \sum_{n=0}^{\infty} c_n \varphi_n(x) \tag{4-29}$$

and a function $f(x)$ of limited extent, as in (4-24), can be written as a series

$$f(x) = \sum_{n=0}^{\infty} d_n \varphi_{bn}(x) \tag{4-30}$$

The coefficients c_n and d_n are given by

$$c_n = \int_{-\infty}^{\infty} g(x)\varphi_n(x)\,dx \qquad d_n = \frac{1}{\lambda_n} \int_{-b}^{b} f(x)\varphi_n(x)\,dx \tag{4-31}$$

respectively, as we see from (4-28).

We are now ready to solve our problem. If the unknown input $f(x)$

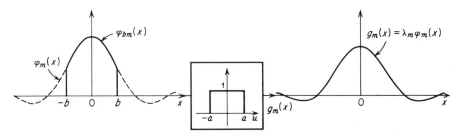

Fig. 4-9

is expanded into a series, as in (4-30), then the output will equal

$$g(x) = \sum_{n=0}^{\infty} \lambda_n d_n \varphi_n(x) \tag{4-32}$$

because the response to $\varphi_{bn}(x)$ is $\lambda_n \varphi_n(x)$. From (4-29) and (4-32) it follows that

$$d_n = \frac{c_n}{\lambda_n} \tag{4-33}$$

Thus, the constants d_n can be found from (4-33) where c_n are the coefficients of the expansion of the known function $g(x)$.

5. APODIZATION†

We are given an optical system with point spread h. By a proper scaling, we can assume that the radius of the exit pupil equals one and that the field H at the exit pupil equals the Fourier transform of h.

If the system is ideal (diffraction-limited), then

$$h(r) = \frac{2J_1(r)}{r} \qquad r = \sqrt{x^2 + y^2} \tag{5-1}$$

for a spherical lens with circular aperture, and

$$h(x) = \frac{\sin x}{x} \tag{5-2}$$

for a spherical lens with slit aperture or for a cylindrical lens.

The object of this section is to modify H (for example, by coating the lens) so as to improve the system performance. Since the image of an object is obtained by convolving its amplitude with $h(x)$ for coherent signals or its intensity with $|h(x)|^2$ for incoherent signals [see (2-30) and (2-31)], it is desirable for a satisfactory performance to choose H so as to reduce the spread of h. However, since $H(u)$ must be such that

$$H(u) = 0 \qquad \text{for } |u| > 1 \tag{5-3}$$

it follows from the uncertainty principle that $h(x)$ cannot be made arbitrarily narrow. Our problem then is to define a suitable performance criterion depending on the applications and to choose $H(u)$ so as to meet this criterion subject to the constraint (5-3).

We shall carry out the analysis mostly for the one-dimensional case,

† P. Jacquinot and Mme. B. Roizen-Dossier, Apodization, "Progress in Optics" (ed. E. Wolf), vol. III, John Wiley & Sons, Inc., New York, 1964; G. Toraldo di Francia, *Suppl. Nuovo Cimento*, vol. 9, 1952, p. 426.

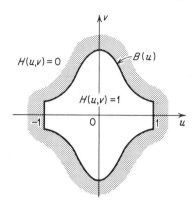

Fig. 5-1

stating briefly the corresponding conclusions for circularly symmetrical spread functions. The results can also be used for the following special case of two-dimensional apertures: Suppose that the system function $H(u,v)$ of an ideal system is modified not by a film but by the introduction of a diaphragm of proper shape. If

$$v = B(u)$$

is the equation of the boundary of this diaphragm (Fig. 5-1), then $H(u,v) = 1$ in the unmasked region $|u| \leq 1$, $|v| \leq B(u)$, and equals zero elsewhere. With $b(x)$ the inverse of $B(u)$, it follows from Chap. 3, (4-29), that the point spread $h(x,y)$ of the resulting system is such that

$$h(x,0) = b(x) \tag{5-4}$$

Thus, for the apodization of the response along the x axis, it suffices to solve the one-dimensional problem and use the optimum solution $H(u)$ as the boundary $B(u)$ of the exit pupil.

In the apodization problem, the following parameters are of interest.

1. The total energy of $h(x)$:

$$E = \int_{-\infty}^{\infty} |h(x)|^2 \, dx \tag{5-5}$$

2. The energy ratio in a specified interval $(-b,b)$:

$$\alpha(b) = \frac{1}{E} \int_{-b}^{b} |h(x)|^2 \, dx \tag{5-6}$$

3. The radius of gyration σ of $|h(x)|^2$:

$$\sigma^2 = \frac{1}{E} \int_{-\infty}^{\infty} x^2 |h(x)|^2 \, dx \tag{5-7}$$

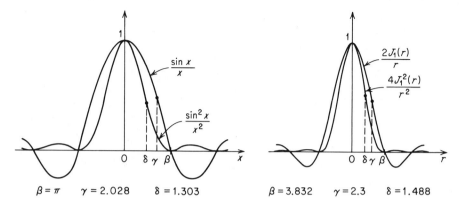

$$\beta = \pi \qquad \gamma = 2.028 \qquad \delta = 1.303 \qquad\qquad \beta = 3.832 \qquad \gamma = 2.3 \qquad \delta = 1.488$$

Fig. 5-2

4. The asymptotic form of $h(x)$:

$$h(x) \sim \frac{A}{x^n} \qquad \text{for } x \to \infty \tag{5-8}$$

5. The first zero of $h(x)$:

$$h(\beta) = 0 \qquad h(x) \neq 0 \qquad \text{for } |x| < \beta \tag{5-9}$$

6. The first point of inflexion of the curves $h(x)$ and $|h(x)|^2$:

$$\frac{d^2 h(x)}{dx^2} \bigg|_{x=\gamma} = 0 \qquad \frac{d^2 |h(x)|^2}{dx^2} \bigg|_{x=\delta} = 0 \tag{5-10}$$

7. The value $h(0)$ of $h(x)$ at the origin.

It is easy to show that for the response $\sin x / x$ of an ideal system with slit aperture (Fig. 5-2)

$$\beta = \pi \qquad \gamma = 2.082 \qquad \delta = 1.303 \tag{5-11}$$

and for the circular response $2J_1(r)/r$

$$\beta = 3.832 \qquad \gamma = 2.3000 \qquad \delta = 1.488 \tag{5-12}$$

MAXIMUM ENCLOSED ENERGY

As we have shown in Chap. 6, Sec. 5, the function $h(x)$ that maximizes the energy ratio (5-6), subject to the constraint (5-3), equals the eigenfunction $\varphi_0(x)$ of the integral equation

$$\int_{-1}^{1} \varphi(\xi) \frac{\sin (x - \xi)}{\pi (x - \xi)} \, d\xi = \lambda \varphi(x) \tag{5-13}$$

which corresponds to the maximum eigenvalue λ_o, and the resulting maximum energy ratio $\alpha_o(b)$ equals λ_o.

For the circular case, (5-13) takes the form of Chap. 6, (5-42).

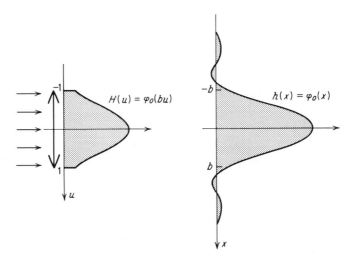

Fig. 5-3

If $b \ll 1$, then the optimum functions $\varphi_o(x)$ and $\varphi_o(r)$ tend to the responses (5-2) and (5-1) of the ideal system. [See Chap. 6, (5-5) and (5-40).]

The Fourier transform of $\varphi_o(x)$ equals $\varphi_o(bu)$ for $|u| < 1$, and it is zero for $|u| > 1$ [see Chap. 6, (5-15)]; hence, if the filter

$$H(u) = \varphi_o(bu) \tag{5-14}$$

is inserted in the output of an ideal system, the resulting point spread will equal the optimum function $\varphi_o(x)$ (Fig. 5-3).

Experimental determination of $\varphi_o(x)$

In Fig. 5-4 we show n ideal (low-pass) systems in cascade. The input $f_{i+1}(x)$ to the $i + 1$ system is related to the output $g_i(x)$ of the preceding

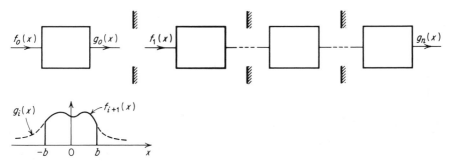

Fig. 5-4

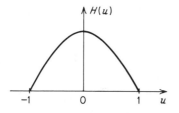
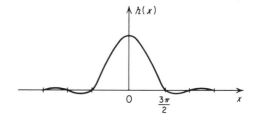

Fig. 5-5

system by

$$f_{i+1}(x) = \begin{cases} g_i(x) & |x| \le b \\ 0 & |x| > b \end{cases}$$

Thus $f_{i+1}(x)$ is obtained by masking the portion $|x| > b$ of $g_i(x)$. The input $f_o(x)$ is arbitrary. We maintain that as n increases, the output $g_n(x)$ tends to the optimum function $\varphi_o(x)$.

Indeed, expanding $f_1(x)$ into a series, as in (4-30), we have

$$f_1(x) = \sum_{r=0}^{\infty} a_r \varphi_r(x) \qquad |x| \le b$$

Hence [see (4-32)],

$$g_n(x) = \sum_{r=0}^{\infty} a_r \lambda_r{}^n \varphi_r(x) \tag{5-15}$$

Since

$$\lambda_o > \lambda_1 > \cdots > \lambda_n > \cdots$$

it follows from (5-15) that $g_n(x)$ tends to the first nonzero term in (5-15). If the function $f_1(x)$ is such that $a_o \ne 0$, then the limit is $a_o \lambda_o{}^n \varphi_o(x)$.

MINIMUM RADIUS OF GYRATION

We know from Chap. 6, (3-21), that the radius of gyration σ, defined in (5-7), must be such that

$$\sigma \ge \frac{\pi}{2} \tag{5-16}$$

and that the equality holds only if [see Chap. 6, (3-22)]

$$H(u) = A \cos \frac{\pi u}{2} \qquad |u| \le 1 \tag{5-17}$$

The corresponding spread function is given by (Fig. 5-5)

$$h(x) = \frac{\sin (x - \pi/2)}{x - \pi/2} + \frac{\sin (x + \pi/2)}{x + \pi/2} = \frac{\pi \cos x}{(\pi/2)^2 - x^2} \tag{5-18}$$

This function equals the amplitude of the image of two equal coherent sources, distance π apart.

ASYMPTOTIC APODIZATION

Consider two point sources located at the points $x = x_1$ and $x = x_2$ of the x axis of the object plane. If the sources are coherent and their respective amplitudes are p_1 and p_2, then the intensity of their image equals

$$I_c(x) = |p_1 h(x - x_1) + p_2 h(x - x_2)|^2 \tag{5-19}$$

If they are incoherent, then the intensity of their image equals

$$I_i(x) = q_1 |h(x - x_1)|^2 + q_2 |h(x - x_2)|^2 \tag{5-20}$$

The above relationships also hold for the circular case, provided that I is observed along the x axis.

We shall be concerned here with the problem of selecting $h(x)$ so as to facilitate the detection of these points from the observation of the total illuminance $I(x)$. Suppose first that $q_1 \gg q_2$. The weak point can then be detected only if its distance $|x_1 - x_2|$ from the bright point is large compared with the "duration" of $h(x)$.

In this case, the quantity of interest is the behavior of $h(x)$ for large x, and the problem is to find a system function $H(u)$ such that its inverse $h(x)$ tends to zero rapidly with $x \to \infty$. This problem was treated in Chap. 7, Secs. 2 and 4.

It was shown that if the function $H(u)$ and its first $n - 1$ derivatives equal zero at the end points ± 1 of the exit pupil, i.e.,

$$H^{(r)}(\pm 1) = 0 \qquad r = 0, 1, \ldots, n - 1 \tag{5-21}$$

then

$$h(x) \sim \frac{B}{x^{n+1}} \qquad \text{for } x \to \infty \tag{5-22}$$

provided that these derivatives do not contain any singularities in the interval $(-1, +1)$.

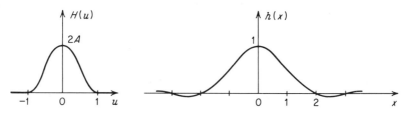

Fig. 5-6

Thus, in order to obtain a rapidly attenuating spread $h(x)$, we must choose for transmission function $H(u)$ a curve having a high order of tangency with the x axis at the points ± 1.

The function $H(u)$ in (5-17) is zero for $u = \pm 1$, and its inverse (5-18) tends to zero as $1/x^2$, in agreement with (5-22). For faster attenuation, we form the "raised cosine" (Fig. 5-6)

$$H(u) = A(1 + \cos \pi u) \qquad |u| \leq 1 \qquad (5\text{-}23)$$

This function and its derivative vanish for $u = \pm 1$; hence, the corresponding spread

$$h(x) = \frac{\sin x}{x} + \frac{1}{2}\left[\frac{\sin (x + \pi)}{x + \pi} + \frac{\sin (x - \pi)}{x - \pi}\right] = \frac{\sin \pi x}{x(\pi^2 - x^2)}$$

$$(5\text{-}24)$$

tends to zero as $1/x^3$.

An example of a highly attenuated spread is obtained from the pair [see Chap. 3, (1-19)]

$$\frac{J_n(x)}{x^n} \leftrightarrow \begin{cases} A(1 - u^2)^{n-\frac{1}{2}} & |u| \leq 1 \\ 0 & |u| \geq 1 \end{cases} \qquad (5\text{-}25)$$

RESOLUTION

Suppose now that the object consists of two points such that the ratio q_1/q_2 of their intensities is of the order of one. In this case, their separability depends on the behavior of $h(x)$ "near" the origin. By the resolving power of an optical system we shall mean the smallest distance d below which two such points cannot be distinguished. This power is, of course, a function of the ratio q_1/q_2; therefore, any criterion based on the assumption that $q_1 = q_2$ must be interpreted loosely.

Rayleigh criterion[†] A common measure of the resolving power of a system is the value β of the first zero of $h(x)$:

$$h(\beta) = 0$$

If $x_1 - x_2 = \beta$, then for $x = x_1$ the response $h(x - x_1)$ of the first point attains its maximum value $h(0)$, and the response $h(x - x_2)$ of the second point equals zero.

In Fig. 5-7 we show the illuminance

$$I_i(x) = |h(x - \eta)|^2 + |h(x + \eta)|^2 \qquad (5\text{-}26)$$

of the image of two equal ($q_1 = q_2 = 1$) incoherent sources for an ideal system with $h(x) = \sin x/x$.

[†] Lord Rayleigh, *Phil. Mag.*, vol. 11, 1881, p. 214.

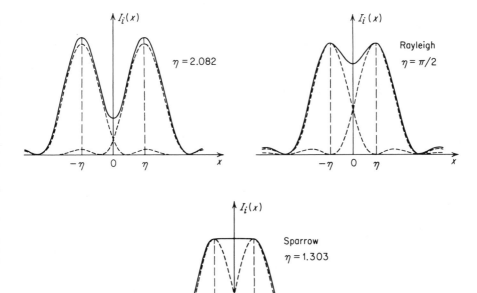

Fig. 5-7

Clearly, the function $I_i(x)$ depends on the distance 2η between these points. It is plotted for the following three values of 2η

$$2\eta = 2\gamma = 4.164 \qquad 2\eta = \beta = \pi \qquad 2\eta = 2\delta = 2.606$$

Sparrow criterion For $\eta = \beta/2$, the curve $I_i(x)$ has two distinct maxima away from the origin. As η decreases, the two maxima come closer, and the ratio $I_{i,\max}/I_i(0)$ decreases until, for some $\eta = \eta_i$, it equals one. We then have

$$\frac{d^2 I_i(x)}{dx^2}\bigg|_{x=0} = 0 \qquad \eta = \eta_i \tag{5-27}$$

Thus, for $\eta > \eta_i$, $I_i(0)$ is minimum; for $\eta = \eta_i$, the curve $I_i(x)$ is flat at the origin; for $\eta < \eta_i$, $I_i(0)$ is maximum.

The value η_i of η for which (5-27) holds defines the resolution of the optical system in the Sparrow sense. If we assume that $h(x)$ is even (i.e.,

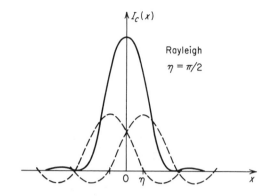

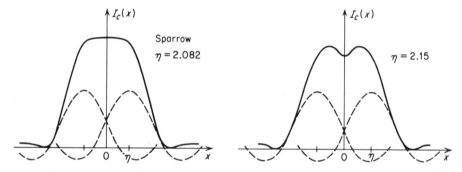

Fig. 5-8

that the system function is real), then (5-27) is equivalent to

$$\frac{d^2|h(x)|^2}{dx^2}\bigg|_{x=\eta_i} = 0 \tag{5-28}$$

as it is easy to show (Prob. 11-20). In other words, the constant η_i equals the point of inflexion δ of the *intensity* $|h(x)|^2$.

Suppose now that the object consists of two coherent points. In this case, the intensity of their image is given by

$$I_c(x) = |h(x - \eta) + h(x + \eta)|^2 \tag{5-29}$$

$(p_1 = p_2 = 1)$. This function is shown in Fig. 5-8 for $h(x) = \sin x/x$ and

$$\eta = \frac{\beta}{2} = \frac{\pi}{2} \qquad \eta = \gamma = 2.082 \qquad \eta = 2.15$$

At the Rayleigh point $\eta = \pi/2$, $I_c(x)$ no longer has two maxima.

The resolution in the Sparrow sense is now the value η_c of η such that

$$\frac{d^2 I_c(x)}{dx^2}\bigg|_{x=0} = 0 \qquad \eta = \eta_c \tag{5-30}$$

It is easy to show again that (5-30) is equivalent to

$$\frac{d^2 h(x)}{dx^2}\bigg|_{x=\eta_c} = 0 \tag{5-31}$$

Thus, η_c equals the point of inflexion γ of the *amplitude* $h(x)$. For the ideal system, $2\eta_c = 4.6$ is larger than $\beta = \pi$.

Improvement of resolving power

In the following, we shall discuss methods for decreasing the parameters β, γ, and δ of a system by suitable filtering.

Zero reduction   The first zero β of an ideal system equals π. This constant can be simply reduced by covering the center of the exit pupil with an opaque screen S (Fig. 5-9a). If the radius of S equals e, then the resulting transmission function is

$$H(u) = \begin{cases} 1 & e \le |u| \le 1 \\ 0 & \text{otherwise} \end{cases} \tag{5-32}$$

and the corresponding spread

$$h(x) = \frac{\sin x}{x} - \frac{\sin ex}{x}$$

The zero of this function decreases from π to $\pi/2$ as e increases from 0 to 1.

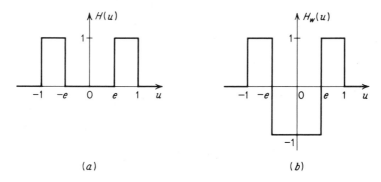

(a)   (b)

Fig. 5-9

Wilkins screen A further decrease is possible if the screen S is replaced by a film with transmission $T = -1$. We now have (Fig. 5-9b)

$$H_w(u) = \begin{cases} 1 & e \leq |u| \leq 1 \\ -1 & |u| < e \end{cases} \qquad h_w(x) = \frac{\sin x}{x} - 2\frac{\sin ex}{x} \qquad (5\text{-}33)$$

Given any number β between 0 and π, we can choose e such that $h_w(\beta) = 0$.

Comment The Wilkins screen is optimum in the following sense.†
Given a system whose transmission is an arbitrary function $H(u)$ real or complex and a number β, we introduce a filter $T(u)$ at the exit pupil such that the resulting spread $h_w(x)$, that is, the inverse of the product $H(u)T(u)$, is zero for $x = \beta$:

$$h_w(\beta) = 0$$

We wish to select $T(u)$ so as to maximize

$$h_w(0) = \frac{1}{2\pi} \int_{-1}^{1} H(u)T(u)\,du$$

subject to the constraint

$$|T(u)| \leq 1$$

It can be shown that (Prob. 11-19) the optimum $T(u)$ must be such that

$$H(u)T(u) = \begin{cases} |H(u)| & e \leq |u| \leq 1 \\ -|H(u)| & |u| \leq e \end{cases} \qquad (5\text{-}34)$$

The constant e is determined from

$$2\pi h_w(\beta) = 0 = \int_0^e |H(u)| \cos \beta u\,du - \int_e^1 |H(u)| \cos \beta u\,du$$

Luneberg optimization Consider the class C of all functions band-limited as in (5-3), and of total energy E. In this class we seek an optimum $h_o(x)$ such that its value $h_o(0)$ at the origin is maximum, subject to the condition

$$h_o(\beta) = 0$$

where β is a given number [14].
This problem is solved at the end of Chap. 6, Sec. 1. We have shown in Chap. 6, (1-51), that the optimum $h_o(x)$ is given by

$$h_o(x) = \frac{\sin x}{x} - \epsilon \left[\frac{\sin (x - \beta)}{x - \beta} + \frac{\sin (x + \beta)}{x + \beta} \right] \qquad (5\text{-}35)$$

† J. E. Wilkins, Jr., *J. Opt. Soc. Am.*, vol. 53, no. 4, 1963, pp. 420–424.

where

$$\epsilon = \frac{\sin \beta / \beta}{1 + \sin 2\beta / 2\beta}$$

The corresponding system function is

$$H_o(u) = 1 - 2\epsilon \cos \beta u \qquad |u| \leq 1$$

as we see from (5-35).

For the equivalent circular problem we find† (Prob. 11-21)

$$H_o(w) = 1 - \epsilon J_o(\beta w) \qquad w \leq 1$$

The inverse $h_o(r)$ of $H_o(w)$ is obtained from Chap. 5, (1-20) and (1-23).

Comment If the condition $h(\beta) = 0$ is removed, then $|h(0)|$ is maximum for $h(x) = \sin x / x$ [see Chap. 6, (1-14)].

Reduction of Sparrow limit For the coherent case, the Luneberg optimization takes the following form. In the above class C, we seek again an optimum $h_o(x)$ which maximizes $h_o(0)$, subject to the constraint

$$h_o''(\gamma) = 0$$

where again, γ is a given constant.

In this case, the optimum is given by

$$h_o(x) = s(x) - \epsilon[s''(x - \gamma) + s''(x + \gamma)] \tag{5-36}$$

where [see Chap. 6, (1-54)]

$$s(x) = \frac{\sin x}{x} \qquad \text{and} \qquad \epsilon = \frac{s''(\gamma)}{0.2 + s^{(4)}(2\gamma)}$$

From (5-36) and the theorems of Fourier transforms it follows that

$$H_o(u) = 1 + 2\epsilon x^2 \cos \gamma x$$

For the equivalent circular problem we find‡

$$H_o(w) = 1 + w^2 J_o(\gamma w)$$

The incoherent case can be treated similarly.

SUPERRESOLUTION

If the behavior of $h(x)$ outside a specified interval $(-b,b)$ is of no interest, then its shape within this interval can be made arbitrary. We can choose, for example, a narrow curve $f(x)$, as in Fig. 5-10. By extending

---

† R. Barakat, *J. Opt. Soc. Am.*, vol. 52, no. 4, 1962, pp. 264–275; *J. Opt. Soc. Am.*, vol. 52, no. 4, 1962, pp. 276–284.

‡ R. Barakat and E. Levin, *J. Opt. Soc. Am.*, vol. 53, no. 2, 1963, pp. 274–282.

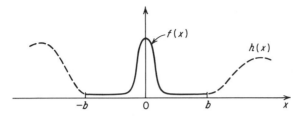

Fig. 5-10

suitably its definition outside the interval $(-b,b)$, we can obtain a signal $h(x)$ with band-limited transform, as in (5-3). This is done as follows. We expand $f(x)$ into a series of prolate functions as in (4-30):

$$f(x) = \sum_{n=0}^{\infty} a_n \varphi_n(x)$$

The above sum equals $f(x)$ for $|x| \leq b$; however, it defines a function $h(x)$ for every x. Since the transform of $\varphi_n(x)$ is zero for $|u| > 1$, the function $h(x)$ satisfies the constraint (5-3).

The disadvantage of this method is the fact that, depending on the nature of $f(x)$, only a small part of the energy of $h(x)$ is in the interval of interest $(-b,b)$.

6. STELLAR INTERFEROMETER

Consider a random field $\mathbf{v}(P,t)$ and its values

$$\mathbf{f}_1(t) = \mathbf{v}(P_1,t) \qquad \mathbf{f}_2(t) = \mathbf{v}(P_2,t) \tag{6-1}$$

at the points P_1 and P_2. The cross-correlation (coherence) function $\Gamma_{12}(\tau)$ of the signals $\mathbf{f}_1(t)$ and $\mathbf{f}_2(t)$ can be determined with the arrange-

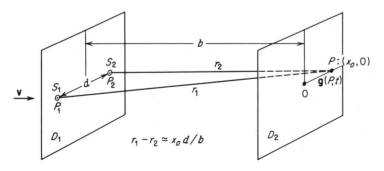

Fig. 6-1

ment of Fig. 6-1 (Young's experiment), which consists of a screen D_1 with two small openings S_1 and S_2 at the points P_1 and P_2. For the purposes of this analysis it will suffice to assume that the resulting diffracted field $\mathbf{g}(P,t)$ is given by

$$\mathbf{g}(P,t) = \mathbf{f}_1\left(t - \frac{r_1}{c}\right) + \mathbf{f}_2\left(t - \frac{r_2}{c}\right) \tag{6-2}$$

where r_1 and r_2 are the distances from P_1 and P_2 to the point of observation P (see Comment, page 377). From the above it follows that the average intensity I of $\mathbf{g}$ is given by

$$I(\tau) = E\{|\mathbf{g}(P,t)|^2\} = \Gamma_{11}(0) + \Gamma_{22}(0) + 2\,\mathrm{Re}\,\Gamma_{12}(\tau) \tag{6-3}$$

where $\Gamma_{11}(0)$ and $\Gamma_{22}(0)$ is the average intensity of $\mathbf{f}_1(t)$ and $\mathbf{f}_2(t)$, respectively, and $\tau = (r_1 - r_2)/c$. If the point $P:(x_o,0)$ is on the x axis of the plane D_2, which is a distance b from D_1, and the line P_1P_2 is parallel to this axis, then

$$\tau = \frac{r_1 - r_2}{c} \simeq \frac{x_o d}{bc} \qquad x_o,\, d \ll b$$

Suppose now that the field $\mathbf{v}$ is monochromatic with constant intensity B. In this case,

$$\Gamma_{12}(\tau) = Ae^{j\varphi}e^{-j\omega\tau} \qquad \Gamma_{11}(0) = \Gamma_{22}(0) = B \tag{6-4}$$

and (6-3) yields the expression

$$I(\tau) = 2B + 2A\cos(\omega\tau - \varphi) \tag{6-5}$$

which is shown in Fig. 6-2 as a function of τ. Thus, by observing the average intensity of $\mathbf{g}$ along the x axis of the plane D_2, we can determine the sine curve (6-5) and, hence, the constants A and φ.

MEASUREMENT OF ANGULAR SEPARATION OF TWO STARS

Suppose now that the field $\mathbf{v}$ is due to two distant monochromatic sources located on the lines L_1 and L_2 which form the incident plane P_i. We

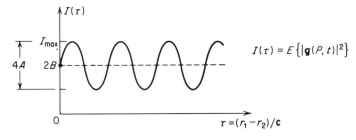

Fig. 6-2

wish to measure the angle θ_o of these lines [b5]. If the sources are sufficiently far, then the field $\mathbf{v}$ is the sum of two plane waves propagating along the directions L_1 and L_2, and on the $z = 0$ plane it is given by

$$\mathbf{v} = \mathbf{n}_1 e^{jk(u_1x+v_1y)} + \mathbf{n}_2 e^{jk(u_2x+v_2y)} \tag{6-6}$$

where u_1, v_1 and u_2, v_2 are the xy directional cosines of these two directions (Fig. 6-3).

We shall assume that the two waves are incoherent with respective intensities q_1 and q_2, that is, that

$$E\{\mathbf{n}_1\mathbf{n}_2^*\} = 0 \qquad E\{|\mathbf{n}_1|^2\} = q_1 \qquad E\{|\mathbf{n}_2|^2\} = q_2 \tag{6-7}$$

With

$$P_1:(x,y) \qquad P_2:(0,0)$$

as two points on the $z = 0$ plane, it follows from (6-6) and (6-7) that

$$E\{|\mathbf{v}(P_1,t)|^2\} = \Gamma_{11}(0) = q_1 + q_2 = E\{|\mathbf{v}(P_2,t)|^2 \tag{6-8}$$

and

$$E\{\mathbf{v}(P_1, t + \tau)\mathbf{v}^*(P_2,t)\} = \Gamma_{12}(\tau) = [q_1 e^{jk(u_1x+v_1y)} + q_2 e^{jk(u_2x+v_2y)}]e^{-j\omega\tau} \tag{6-9}$$

Inserting Young's screen on the $z = 0$ plane, we obtain a diffracted field $\mathbf{g}$ whose average intensity $I(\tau)$ is given by (6-5). The parameters of this curve are functions of the coordinates (x,y) of the point P_1. As we see from (6-4) and (6-9)

$$A(x,y)e^{j\varphi(x,y)} = q_1 e^{jk(u_1x+v_1y)} + q_2 e^{jk(u_2x+v_2y)} \qquad B = q_1 + q_2 \tag{6-10}$$

Hence, if $I(\tau)$ is measured for various values of x and y, then, in principle, all constants in (6-10) can be evaluated. This approach will be used to determine the size of an extended object. For our problem, the following scheme leads to a more precise measurement of the angle θ_o.

From (6-5) it follows that the maximum value I_{max} of $I(\tau)$ is given by

$$I_{max} = 2(A + B)$$

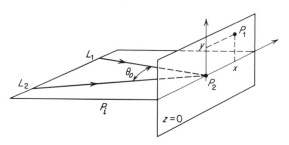

Fig. 6-3

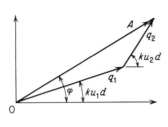

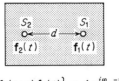

$$E\{f_1(t+\tau)\,f_2(t)\} = A\,e^{j\varphi}e^{-j\omega\tau}$$

Fig. 6-4

In this expression, $B = q_1 + q_2$ is constant, and A is the length of the sum of the vectors

$$q_1 e^{jk(u_1x+v_1y)} \qquad \text{and} \qquad q_2 e^{jk(u_2x+v_2y)}$$

shown in Fig. 6-4.

Suppose first that the plane of incidence P_i is known. Assuming that it is parallel to the xz plane, we conclude from (6-10), with $v_1 = v_2 = 0$, that

$$A = |q_1 e^{jku_1x} + q_2 e^{jku_2x}| = |q_1 e^{jk(u_1-u_2)x} + q_2| \tag{6-11}$$

In the above, $x = d$ is the distance between the openings S_1 and S_2 of the screen. If d is such that $k(u_1 - u_2)d \ll 1$, then

$$A \simeq q_1 + q_2 \qquad I_{\max} \simeq 4(q_1 + q_2)$$

As d increases, A decreases, and when d reaches the value d_o such that

$$k(u_1 - u_2)d_o = \pi \tag{6-12}$$

then

$$A = q_1 - q_2 \qquad I_{\max} = 4q_1$$

(We assumed that $q_1 > q_2$.) If θ_o is small, then $\theta_o = u_1 - u_2$, and (6-12) yields

$$\theta_o = \frac{\lambda}{2d_o} \tag{6-13}$$

Thus, to determine θ_o, we increase the distance d between the openings S_1 and S_2 of the screen D_1 until the maximum intensity $I_{\max}$ of the resulting diffracted field is minimum (Fig. 6-5).

If the plane P_i is not known, then we start with a fixed d, and observe $I_{\max}$ by rotating the screen. If d is sufficiently small (less than d_o), then $I_{\max}$ is minimum when the line S_1S_2 is parallel to the incident plane. Having thus determined the orientation of P_i, we proceed as above.

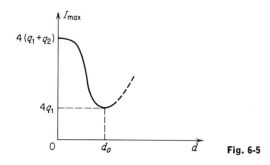

Fig. 6-5

SIZE AND INTENSITY DISTRIBUTION OF DISTANT OBJECTS

We shall now assume that the field $\mathbf{v}$ on the $z = 0$ plane is of the form

$$\mathbf{v}(x,y) = \iint_R \mathbf{n}(u,v)e^{-jk(ux+vy)} \, du \, dv \tag{6-14}$$

The above can be interpreted as a superposition of plane waves of amplitude $\mathbf{n}(u,v) \, du \, dv$ coming from every direction (u,v) in the angular region R.

Such a field results, for example, if the observer is located in the Fraunhofer region of an object $\mathbf{f}(\xi,\eta)$.   As we see from Chap. 9, (4-6), the corresponding field is given by

$$\mathbf{v}(x,y) = \iint_S \mathbf{f}(\xi,\eta)e^{-jk(x\xi+y\eta)/z_o} \, d\xi \, d\eta \tag{6-15}$$

and with $\xi = z_o u$, $\eta = z_o v$, and

$$\mathbf{n}(u,v) = z_o^2 \mathbf{f}(z_o u, z_o v) \tag{6-16}$$

(6-14) follows.   The region R is the angular cone from the observer to the surface S.

Conversely, any field of the form (6-14) can be interpreted as resulting from a distant plane object, as defined by (6-16).

It is easy to see that (6-6) is a special case of (6-14).

It should be pointed out that in deriving (6-14), we assumed that the object is harmonic in time.   However, the consequences of (6-14), specifically the expression (6-18) for the coherence function of the field $\mathbf{v}$, are also valid if the object is monochromatic [see Chap. 10, (4-14)].

We shall assume that the component waves in (6-14) are completely incoherent with average intensity $q(u,v)$, that is, that the coherence function of the process $\mathbf{n}(x,y)$ is of the form

$$\Gamma_{nn}(u_1,v_1;u_2,v_2) = q(u_1,v_1)\delta(u_1 - u_2)\delta(v_1 - v_2) \tag{6-17}$$

Our problem now is to find the function $q(u,v)$.

The integral in (6-14) is of the form of Chap. 8, (6-36). Hence, with $Q(\alpha,\beta)$ the Fourier transform of $q(u,v)$, i.e.,

$$q(u,v) \Leftrightarrow Q(\alpha,\beta)$$

it follows from Chap. 8, (6-39), that the coherence function of the field $\mathbf{v}$ is given by [see also Chap. 10, (4-14)]

$$\Gamma_{vv}(x_1,y_1;x_2,y_2) = Q[k(x_1 - x_2),k(y_1 - y_2)] \tag{6-18}$$

Thus, $\mathbf{v}$ is stationary, with average intensity $Q(0,0)$, and [see (6-9)]

$$\Gamma_{11}(0) = \Gamma_{22}(0) = Q(0) \qquad \Gamma_{12}(\tau) = Q(kx,ky)e^{-j\omega\tau} \tag{6-19}$$

Hence, with

$$Q(kx,ky) = A(x,y)e^{j\varphi(x,y)}$$

the diffracted field (6-5) yields

$$I(\tau) = 2Q(0,0) + 2A(x,y) \cos [\omega\tau - \varphi(x,y)] \tag{6-20}$$

To determine $A(x,y)$ and $\varphi(x,y)$, it suffices, therefore, to plot $I(\tau)$ for various values of x and y, that is, for various locations of the opening S_1. The unknown intensity $q(u,v)$ is then computed from the inversion formula

$$q(u,v) = \int\!\!\!\int_{-\infty}^{\infty} Q(\alpha,\beta)e^{j(\alpha u+\beta v)} \, d\alpha \, d\beta$$

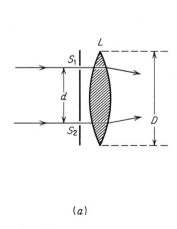

(a)

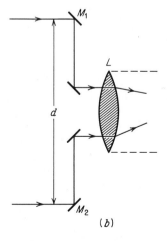

(b)

Fig. 6-6

Comments If the radius of the region R equals δ, then the transform $Q(\alpha,\beta)$ takes significant values in a square whose size is of the order of π/δ. Hence, the distance d between the openings of the interferometer must take values from zero to λ/δ at least.

In the measurement of celestial bodies the diffracted pattern $I(\tau)$ is observed through a telescope, as in Fig. 6-6a. In this arrangement, d cannot exceed the diameter D of the telescope; therefore, only objects whose angular size exceeds λ/D can be measured. However, it is possible to observe smaller objects if the light enters the openings S_1 and S_2 through the mirror arrangement of Fig. 6-6b (Michelson stellar interferometer). In this case, the interfering signals $\mathbf{f}_1(t)$ and $\mathbf{f}_2(t)$ are the values of $\mathbf{v}(P,t)$ at the locations of the mirrors M_1 and M_2, and d equals the distance between these mirrors.

PROBLEMS

11-1. Show that if

$$\nabla^2 f + k^2 f = -s(x,y,z) \qquad \nabla^2 g + \alpha^2 g = -s_1(x,y,z)$$

and

$$s_1(x,y,z) = \alpha^2 s(\alpha x, \alpha y, \alpha z)$$

then

$$g(x,y,z) = f(\alpha x, \alpha y, \alpha z)$$

11-2. With

$$D(x) = f(x) * e^{j\alpha x^2} \qquad \chi(x) = \int_{-\infty}^{\infty} f(x + \xi)f^*(\xi)e^{j2\alpha x \xi}\, d\xi$$

show that

$$D^*(x) = \{[f^*(-x)e^{-j2\alpha x^2}] * e^{j\alpha x^2}\}e^{-j2\alpha x^2}$$

$$|D(x)|^2 = [\chi(x) * e^{j\alpha x^2}]e^{-j\alpha x^2}$$

11-3. (a) In the formation of the Fraunhofer hologram $T(x,y)$ of an object $f(x,y)$, S is a point source. Show that if in the reconstruction of $f(x,y)$, S_r is a circular source of radius a, then the object term $v_o(x,y)$ is no longer $f(x,y)$, but it equals the convolution of $f(x,y)$ with the disk $p_a(r)$.

(b) If S and S_r are circles of radius a, then $v_o(x,y)$ equals the convolution of $f(x,y)$ with the function

$$\left(2\,\cos^{-1}\frac{r}{2a} - \frac{r}{a}\sqrt{1 - \frac{r^2}{4a^2}}\right)p_{2a}(r)$$

Hint: The term $D(x,y)$ in (1-10) is multiplied by: (a) $J_1(ar)/r$; and (b) $J_1^2(ar)/r^2$ [see also Chap. 5, (1-26)].

11-4. Consider the integrals

$$D(x,y) = \int_V f(\xi,\eta,\zeta)e^{jkr}\, d\xi\, d\eta\, d\zeta$$

$$D_1(x,y) = \int_{V_1} f_1(\xi,\eta,\zeta)e^{jkr_1}\, d\xi\, d\eta\, d\zeta$$

where $r = \sqrt{(x - \xi)^2 + (y - \eta)^2 + \zeta^2}$. Assuming that $|\zeta| \gg |x - \xi|$ and $|y - \eta|$ for every (ξ, η, ζ) in V, show that if

$$f_1(x,y,z) = \gamma^3 f(\gamma x, \gamma y, \gamma^2 z) e^{jk(1-\gamma^2)z}$$

and if V_1, r_1 are similarly related to V, r, then $D_1(x,y) = D(x,y)$.

11-5. The optical arrangement of Fig. P11-5 consists of two perfect cylindrical lenses L_1 and L_2 a distance $f_1 + f_2$ apart, with focal lengths f_1 and f_2. Show that if the amplitude of the field on the left focal plane P_l of L_1 equals $\varphi(x)$, then the amplitude $g(x)$ of the field on the right focal plane P_r of L_2 is given by

$$g(x) = A\varphi\left(-\frac{f_1 x}{f_2}\right) \qquad \text{where} \qquad |A| = \sqrt{f_1/f_2}$$

(no phase distortion). Derive a similar result for two-dimensional signals and spherical lenses.

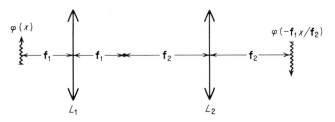

Fig. P11-5

11-6. In an optical system, the image of a point object M of amplitude $e^{j\omega t}$ equals $\omega h(\omega r) e^{j\omega t}$ (point spread).

(a) Show that if the amplitude of M is a random signal $z(t)$ with power spectrum $S(\omega)$, then the power spectrum of its image $g(r,t)$ equals $\omega^2 h^2(\omega r) S(\omega)$.

(b) With

$$h(r) \stackrel{h}{\leftrightarrow} \bar{h}(w) \qquad \text{and} \qquad \bar{s}(u) = \int_{-\infty}^{\infty} \bar{h}(\sqrt{u^2 + v^2})\, dv$$

show that

$$g(r,t) = \frac{-j}{2\pi r^2} z(t) * \bar{s}'\left(\frac{t}{r}\right)$$

Apply the above to an ideal system with $h(r) = J_1(ar)/r$.

11-7. With

$$M_n = \int_0^{\infty} r^n h(r)\, dr \qquad m_n = \int_{-\infty}^{\infty} x^n s(x)\, dx$$

as the moments of the point spread $h(r)$ and the line spread $s(x)$ of an optical system, show that

$$m_n = 2\pi M_{2n+1} \frac{(2n)!}{(n!)^2 a^{2n}}$$

Hint: Use Chap. 5, (2-4).

11-8. (a) Show that if the field on the plane $z = z_1$ equals $f(x,y)$, then the field $g(x,y)$ on the plane $z = z_1 + z_o$ is the output of a system with input $f(x,y)$ and point spread

$$A e^{jk(x^2+y^2)/2z_o}$$

(b) Show that, if the field on the left focal plane of a lens equals $f(x,y)$, then the field on the right focal plane is proportional to the Fourier transform $F(u,v)$ of $f(x,y)$:

$$g(x,y) = j\lambda \mathrm{f} A^2 F\left(\frac{kx}{\mathrm{f}}, \frac{ky}{\mathrm{f}}\right)$$

11-9. The point spread of an ideal optical system equals $aJ_1(ar)/r$. Show that the image $g(r)$ of the object $f(r) = \delta(r - b)$ (ring of radius b) is given by

$$g(r) = 2\pi ab \frac{bJ_1(ab)J_o(ar) - rJ_o(ab)J_1(ar)}{b^2 - r^2}$$

and that $g(r)$ is maximum for $r = b$ [see Chap. 6, (2-14)].

11-10. Consider a one-dimensional system with spread $h(x)$ and system function $H(u)$. We assume that $H(u) = 0$ for $|x| > a$, that is, that the size of the exit pupil equals $2a$.

(a) Show that the image $g(x)$ of an object $f(x)$ is given by

$$g(x) = \sum_{n=-\infty}^{\infty} B_n \frac{\sin (ax - n\pi)}{ax - n\pi} \quad \text{where} \quad B_n = \int_{-\infty}^{\infty} f(\xi) h\left(\frac{n\pi}{a} - \xi\right) d\xi$$

Hint: $g(x)$ is band-limited and $g(n\pi/a) = B_n$.

(b) The input $\mathbf{f}(x)$ is a random object with coherence function $\Gamma(x_1,x_2)$. With $\Gamma_{gg}(x_1,x_2)$ the coherence function of the resulting image $\mathbf{g}(x)$, show that the Fourier transform of $\Gamma_{gg}(x_1,x_2)$ is zero outside the square $|x_1| < a$, $|x_2| < a$.

(c) Show that

$$\Gamma_{gg}(x_1,x_2) = \sum_{m,n=-\infty}^{\infty} \frac{\sin (ax_1 - m\pi)}{ax_1 - m\pi} B_{mn} \frac{\sin (ax_2 - n\pi)}{ax_2 - n\pi}$$

where

$$B_{mn} = \iint_{-\infty}^{\infty} h\left(\frac{m\pi}{a} - \xi_1\right) \Gamma(\xi_1,\xi_2) h^*\left(\frac{n\pi}{a} - \xi_2\right) d\xi_1 \, d\xi_2$$

The elements B_{mn} form the so-called *illumination matrix*.†

Hint: Use (b) Chap. 8, (3-6) and Chap. 4, (3-36).

11-11. (a) The input to a system with system function $H(u,v)$ is an incoherent object with intensity

$$q(x,y) = e^{j(u_o x + v_o y)}$$

Show that the intensity of its image equals

$$E\{|\mathbf{g}(x,y)|^2\} = A e^{(u_o x + v_o y)} \quad \text{where}$$

$$A = \frac{1}{4\pi^2} \iint_{-\infty}^{\infty} H(u + u_o, v + v_o) H^*(u,v) \, du \, dv$$

† E. O'Neill, "Introduction to Statistical Optics," Addison-Wesley Press, Inc., Cambridge, Mass., 1963.

Hint: If

$$h(x,y) \Leftrightarrow H(u,v)$$

then

$$|h(x,y)|^2 \Leftrightarrow H_1(u,v) = \frac{1}{4\pi^2} H(u,v) ** H^*(-u,-v)$$

(b) If the object is periodic, that is,

$$q(x,y) = \sum_{m,n=-\infty}^{\infty} A_{mn} e^{j(mu_o x + nv_o y)}$$

then

$$E\{|g(x,y)|^2\} = \sum_{m,n=-\infty}^{\infty} A_{mn} H_1(mu_o, nv_o) e^{j(mu_o x + nv_o y)}$$

11-12. The system function of an ideal optical system equals $p_a(w)$, where a is the radius of the exit pupil (Fig. P11-12). Show that if the input is an incoherent object with intensity $q(x,y)$, then the intensity of its image $g(x,y)$ is obtained by passing $q(x,y)$ through a system with system function (see Example 1-6, Chap. 2)

$$H_i(w) = \begin{cases} (2\theta - \sin 2\theta)a^2 & |w| < 2a \\ 0 & |w| > 2a \end{cases} \qquad \cos \theta = \frac{w}{2a}$$

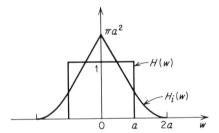

Fig. P11-12

11-13. (a) The point spread of an optical system is $h(r)$. Show that if an incoherent line object of unit intensity is located on the y axis, then the intensity $I_i(x)$ of its image is given by

$$I_i(x) = \int_{-\infty}^{\infty} |h(r)|^2 \, dy \qquad r = \sqrt{x^2 + y^2}$$

(b) With

$$E(r) = 2\pi \int_r^{\infty} \rho |h(\rho)|^2 \, d\rho$$

the energy of $h(r)$ outside a circle of radius r, show that

$$E(r) = \int_{-\infty}^{\infty} I_i(\sqrt{r^2 + y^2}) \, dy$$

Hint: Use Chap. 2, (3-52).

11-14. Two point sources $\mathbf{m}_1$ and $\mathbf{m}_2$, such that

$$E\{|\mathbf{m}_1|^2\} = Q_1 \qquad E\{|\mathbf{m}_2|^2\} = Q_2 \qquad E\{\mathbf{m}_1\mathbf{m}_2^*\} = \Gamma$$

(partially coherent), are placed on the x axis of an optical system at $x = \eta$ and $x = -\eta$. Show that the intensity of the resulting image $g(x,0)$ along the x axis is given by

$$E\{|\mathbf{g}|^2\} = Q_1|h(x - \eta)|^2 + Q_2|h(x + \eta)|^2 + 2 \operatorname{Re} \Gamma h(x - \eta)h^*(x + \eta)$$

where $h(r)$ is the point spread of the system.

11-15. (Fresnel field of partially coherent sources) (a) A random monochromatic object with coherence function $\Gamma(x_1,x_2)$ is placed on the $z = 0$ plane. Show that the coherence function of the resulting field $\mathbf{v}$ on the $z = z_o$ plane is given by (within a factor)

$$\Gamma_{vv}(x_1,x_2) = [\Gamma(x_1,x_2) * e^{-j\alpha x_2{}^2}] * e^{j\alpha x_1{}^2} \qquad \alpha = \frac{k}{2z_o}$$

where the first convolution is in x_2 and the second is in x_1 [see Chap. 10, (3-29)].

(b) Show that if the object is incoherent with

$$\Gamma(x_1,x_2) = q(x_1)\delta(x_1 - x_2) \qquad \text{and} \qquad q(x) \leftrightarrow Q(u)$$

then

$$\Gamma_{vt}(x_1,x_2) = e^{j\alpha(x_1{}^2 - x_2{}^2)}Q[2\alpha(x_1 - x_2)]$$

11-16. (a) A random monochromatic object with coherence function $\Gamma(x_1,x_2)$ is placed on the left focal plane of a lens (Fig. 2-4, Chap. 11). Show that the coherence function of the field $\mathbf{g}$ on the right focal plane is given by

$$\Gamma_{gg}(x_1,x_2) = \frac{\pi}{\beta} \bar{\Gamma}(2\beta x_1, -2\beta x_2)$$

where

$$\Gamma(x_1,x_2) \leftrightarrow \bar{\bar{\Gamma}}(u_1,u_2) \qquad \beta = \frac{k}{2f}$$

(b) Show that if

$$\Gamma(x_1,x_2) = q(x_1)\delta(x_1 - x_2) \qquad q(x) \leftrightarrow Q(u)$$

then

$$\Gamma_{gg}(x_1,x_2) = \frac{\pi}{\beta} Q[2\beta(x_1 - x_2)]$$

11-17. Show that if

$$\int_{-b}^{b} \varphi_n(\xi) \frac{\sin a(x - \xi)}{\pi(x - \xi)} d\xi = \lambda_n\varphi_n(x)$$

then

$$\int_{-\infty}^{\infty} \varphi_n(x)\varphi_m(x) \, dx = \begin{cases} 1 & n = m \\ 0 & n \neq m \end{cases} \qquad \int_{-b}^{b} \varphi_n(x)\varphi_m(x) \, dx = \begin{cases} \lambda_n & n = m \\ 0 & n \neq m \end{cases}$$

11-18.† (Resolution of periodic objects) The exit pupil of an optical system is a circle of radius a_0; that is, $H(u,v) = 0$ for $u^2 + v^2 > a_0{}^2$. The input is a periodic object

† R. K. Luneburg, "Mathematical Theory of Optics," University of California Press, Berkeley, California, 1964.

(Fig. P11-18)

$$q(x + m\bar{x}, y + n\bar{y}) = q(x,y)$$

(a) Show that if the object is incoherent and

$$\bar{x} < \frac{\pi}{a_0} \qquad \bar{y} < \frac{\pi}{a_0}$$

then

$$E\{|g|^2\} = \text{const}$$

In physical coordinates, the input is $f(-z_s x/z_o)$, and $a_0 = ka/z_o$ [see (2-23)]. Hence if

$$\frac{\bar{x}}{z_s} < \frac{\lambda}{2a} \qquad \frac{\bar{y}}{z_s} < \frac{\lambda}{2a}$$

then the image has constant intensity; i.e., no detail of the object is visible.

(b) If the object is coherent, then it is invisible for

$$\frac{\bar{x}}{z_s} < \frac{\lambda}{a} \qquad \frac{\bar{y}}{z_s} < \frac{\lambda}{a}$$

Thus, if an object is coherent (incoherent), details smaller than $\lambda z_s/a(\lambda z_s/2a)$ are not visible.

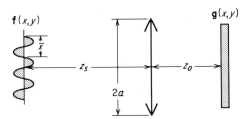

Invisible object

Incoherent : $\dfrac{\bar{x}}{z_s} < \dfrac{\lambda}{2a}$

Coherent : $\dfrac{\bar{x}}{z_s} < \dfrac{\lambda}{a}$

Fig. P11-18

11-19. (Wilkins screen) Given a function

$$H(u) = A(u)e^{-i\varphi(u)}$$

and a constant β, we form the integral

$$w(x) = \int_{-1}^{1} H(u)T(u)e^{iux}\,du$$

Find $T(u)$ such that it maximizes $|w(0)|$ subject to the constraints $|T(u)| \leq 1$, $w(\beta) = 0$.

Answer:

$$T(u) = \begin{cases} -e^{i\varphi(u)} & |u| < e \\ e^{i\varphi(u)} & e \leq |u| \leq 1 \end{cases}$$

where e is such that (Fig. P11-19)

$$\int_0^e A(u) \cos \beta u \, du = \int_e^1 A(u) \cos \beta u \, du$$

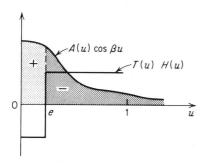

Fig. P11-19

11-20. The function $h(x)$ is real and even. With

$$I_c(x) = [h(x - \gamma) + h(x + \gamma)]^2 \qquad I_i(x) = h^2(x - \delta) + h^2(x + \delta)$$

show that if

$$\frac{d^2 h(\gamma)}{dx^2} = 0 \qquad \frac{d^2 h^2(\delta)}{dx^2} = 0$$

then

$$\frac{d^2 I_c(0)}{dx^2} = 0 \qquad \frac{d^2 I_i(0)}{dx^2} = 0$$

11-21.† Given E and β, we consider the family of functions $h(r)$ of energy E, such that $h(\beta) = 0$. We further assume that the Hankel transform $\bar{h}(w)$ of $h(r)$ is zero for $w > 1$. Thus

$$h(\beta) = \int_0^1 w\bar{h}(w)J_o(\beta w) \, dw = 0 \qquad E = 2\pi \int_0^1 \bar{h}^2(w) \, dw$$

Show that if $h(r)$ is such that $|h(0)|$ is maximum, then

$$\bar{h}(w) = \begin{cases} A[1 - \epsilon J_o(\beta w)] & w < 0 \\ 0 & w > 0 \end{cases} \qquad \epsilon = \frac{2J_1(\beta)}{\beta[J_o^2(\beta) + J_1^2(\beta)]}$$

Hint: Apply Schwarz inequality to

$$h(0) = \int_0^1 w\bar{h}(w)[1 - \epsilon J_o(\beta w)] \, dw$$

and note that if ϵ is as above, then [see Chap. 5, (5-23)] $h(\beta) = 0$.

† R. Barakat, Solution of Luneberg Apodization Problems, *J. Opt. Soc. Am.*, vol. 52, no. 3, 1962, p. 264.

REFERENCES

The following books are references for the chapters indicated by boldface numbers in parentheses.

[a1] Arsac, J.: "Fourier Transforms and the Theory of Distributions" (trans. from the French), Prentice-Hall, Inc., Englewood Cliffs, N.J., 1966. (**2, 3, 4**)

[b1] Baker, B. B., and E. T. Copson: "The Mathematical Theory of Huygens' Principle," Clarendon Press, Oxford, 1950. (**9**)

[b2] Bennett, A., H. Jupnik, H. Osterberg, and O. W. Richards: "Phase Microscopy," John Wiley & Sons, Inc., New York, 1952. (**11**)

[b3] Beran, M., and G. Parrent: "Theory of Partial Coherence," Prentice-Hall, Inc., Englewood Cliffs, N.J., 1964. (**10**)

[b4] Bochner, S.: "Lectures on Fourier Integrals," Princeton University Press, Princeton, N.J., 1959. (**3**)

[b5] Born, M., and E. Wolf: "Principles of Optics," Pergamon Press, 1959. (**1, 9, 10, 11**)

[b6] Bracewell, R. N.: "The Fourier Transform and Its Applications," McGraw-Hill Book Company, 1965. (**3**)

[c1] Colombo, S.: "Les transformations de Mellin et de Hankel," Centre National de la Recherche Scientifique, Paris, 1959. (**5**)

[c2] Cook, C. E., and M. Bernfeld: "Radar Signals," Academic Press Inc., New York, 1967. (**6**)

[d1] Doetsch, G.: "Theorie und Anwendung der Laplace-transformation," Dover Publications, Inc., New York, 1943. (**3, 7**)

[d2] Duffieux, P. M.: "L'intégrale de Fourier et ses applications à l'optique," Faculté des Sciences de Besançon, 1947. (**1, 3, 9**)

[e1] Erde'lyi, A.: "Asymptotic Expansions," Dover Publications, Inc., New York, 1956. (**7**)

[e2] ———: "Operational Calculus and Generalized Functions," Holt, Rinehart and Winston, Inc., New York, 1962. (**2, 3**)

[g1] Goodman, J. W.: "Introduction to Fourier Optics," McGraw-Hill Book Company, New York, 1968.

[j1] Jenkins, F. A., and H. E. White: "Fundamentals of Optics," McGraw-Hill Book Company, 1957. (**9**)

[j2] Jennison, R. C.: "Fourier Transforms and Convolution for the Experimentalist," Pergamon Press, New York, 1960. (**2, 3**)

[l1] Lanczos, C.: "Discourse on Fourier Series," Hafner Publishing Company, Inc., New York, 1966. (**4**)·

[l2] Lee, Y. W.: "Statistical Theory of Communications," John Wiley & Sons, Inc., New York, 1960. (**8**)

[l3] Lighthill, M. J.: "An Introduction to Fourier Analysis and Generalized Functions," Cambridge University Press, London, 1969. (**2**)

[l4] Luneberg, R. K.: "Mathematical Theory of Optics," University of California Press, Berkeley, California, 1964. (**11**)

[m1] Mertz, L.: "Transformations in Optics," John Wiley & Sons, Inc., New York, 1965. (**9**)

[m2] Middleton, D.: "An Introduction to Statistical Communication Theory," McGraw-Hill Book Company, New York, 1960. **(8)**

[m3] Mikusinski, J.: "Operational Calculus," Pergamon Press, 1959. **(2)**

[o1] O'Neill, E. L.: "Introduction to Statistical Optics," Addison-Wesley Publishing Company, Inc., 1963. **(1, 2, 9, 11)**

[p1] Papoulis, A.: "Probability, Random Variables, and Stochastic Processes," McGraw-Hill Book Company, 1965. **(8)**

[p2] ———: "The Fourier Integral and Its Applications," McGraw-Hill Book Company, 1962. **(2, 3, 4, 6)**

[p3] Parzen, E.: "Stochastic Processes," Holden-Day, Inc., San Francisco, 1962. **(8)**

[p4] Petiau, G.: "La théorie des fonctions de Bessel," Centre National de la Recherche Scientifique, 1955. **(5)**

[p5] Poli, L., and P. Delerue: "Calcul Symbolique à deux variables et ses applications," Gauthier-Villars, Paris, 1954. **(2, 4)**

[s1] Schwartz, M.: "Information Transmission, Modulation, and Noise," McGraw-Hill Book Company, New York, 1959. **(3)**

[s2] Silver, S.: "Microwave Antenna Theory and Design," McGraw-Hill Book Company, New York, 1949. **(7)**

[s3] Slater C., and N. H. Frank: "Introduction to Theoretical Physics," McGraw-Hill Book Company, New York, 1933. **(9)**

[s4] Sneddon, I. N.: "Fourier Transforms," McGraw-Hill Book Company, New York, 1951. **(3, 4, 5)**

[s5] Stratton, J. A.: "Electromagnetic Theory," McGraw-Hill Book Company, New York, 1941. **(9)**

[s6] Stroke, G. W.: "An Introduction to Coherent Optics and Holography," Academic Press, Inc., New York, 1966. **(11)**

[t1] Titchmarsh, E. C.: "Introduction to the Theory of Fourier Integrals," Oxford University Press, Oxford, 1937. **(3)**

[u1] Uspensky, J. V.: "Introduction to Mathematical Probability," McGraw-Hill Book Company, New York, 1937. **(3)**

[w1] Watson, G. N.: "A Treatise on the Theory of Bessel Functions," 2d ed., Cambridge University Press, London, 1966. **(5)**

[w2] Widder, D. V.: "The Laplace Transform," Princeton University Press, Princeton, N.J., 1941. **(3, 7)**

[w3] Woodward, P. M.: "Probability and Information Theory," McGraw-Hill Book Company, New York, 1953. **(3)**

[z1] Zadeh, L., and C. A. Desoer: "Linear System Theory: The State Space Approach," McGraw-Hill Book Company, New York, 1964. **(2)**

[z2] Zemanian, A. H.: "Distribution Theory and Transform Analysis: An Introduction to Generalized Functions with Applications," McGraw-Hill Book Company, New York, 1965. **(2)**

INDEX